GEOGRAPHY
AND
CARTOGRAPHY
a reference handbook

GEOGRAPHY
AND
CARTOGRAPHY
a reference handbook

THIRD EDITION REVISED AND ENLARGED

C B MURIEL LOCK

BA PhD FRGS

CLIVE BINGLEY
LONDON

LINNET BOOKS
HAMDEN · CONN

In tribute to all those whose courage,
endurance and initiative have enabled men to
come to terms, albeit still limited, with
the physical world around them

Publishing history
GEOGRAPHY: A REFERENCE HANDBOOK FIRST PUBLISHED 1968
REPRINTED WITH MINOR CORRECTIONS 1969
SECOND EDITION REVISED AND ENLARGED FIRST PUBLISHED 1972

MODERN MAPS & ATLASES FIRST PUBLISHED 1969

THIS COMBINED AND REVISED EDITION OF BOTH WORKS
FIRST PUBLISHED 1976 BY CLIVE BINGLEY LTD
16 PEMBRIDGE ROAD LONDON W11
SIMULTANEOUSLY PUBLISHED IN THE USA BY LINNET BOOKS
AN IMPRINT OF THE SHOE STRING PRESS INC
995 SHERMAN AVENUE HAMDEN CONNECTICUT 06514
PHOTOSET PRINTED AND BOUND IN THE UK
BY REDWOOD BURN LTD TROWBRIDGE AND ESHER
COPYRIGHT © C B MURIEL LOCK 1976
ALL RIGHTS RESERVED

CLIVE BINGLEY ISBN: 0–85157–217–0
LINNET BOOKS ISBN: 0–208–01522–1

Library of Congress Cataloging in Publication Data

Lock, Clara Beatrice Muriel, 1914–
    Geography and cartography.
    Combined and rev. ed. of Geography: a reference handbook,
first published in 1968, and of Modern maps and atlases, first
published in 1969.
    Includes index.
    1. Geography—Dictionaries.   2. Cartography.
I. Title.
G63.L6 1976   910'.3   76–8273
ISBN 0–208–01522–1

FOREWORD

This handbook had its origin in the belief that a quick reference book covering some of the main focal points of geographical study would be useful to both geographers and librarians. It has not been the intention to maintain a balanced coverage either regionally or thematically (this the author hopes to attempt in a future publication), but to draw attention to the outstanding scholars whose achievements have helped to shape the modern concept of geographical studies and to some of the organisations and sources of the greatest continuing significance within the framework of world geography.

Selection of entries is international in scope, with a British bias. Terms are not included, as there are now several excellent dictionaries of geographical terms, but some notes are offered on abstracts, cartobibliography, cataloguing, classification, globes and guides. Biographical entries, which do not include living geographers, are concerned with academic and bibliographical achievements rather than with personal details. Titles of works in foreign languages have been given in the original when these are considered readily recognisable by English-speaking readers, otherwise in the most familiar form.

CBML

FOREWORD TO THE SECOND EDITION

The success of the first edition of this handbook has made a new edition desirable, at the same time enabling a wider concept to be carried out. While keeping the basic entries of the first edition (revised as necessary), representing a body of material which should be known to all practising geographers and relevant specialist librarians, the scope now covers a number of works of essential value to scholars concentrating on the geography of particular regions or systematic studies. Among the new entries is an extended one on national bibliographies of interest to geographers. New publications emphasise the establishment of current trends in geographical thought—the qualitative and quantitative approaches, expansion of facsimile publication, renewed emphasis on field work, environmental studies and conservation, also a revived preoccupation with the value and potentialities of maps, the care of maps and map collections and the use of automation in their preparation.

Several outstanding geographers have died since the first edition appeared; I would again stress the policy behind the inclusion of biographical entries, as stated in the foreword to the first edition; one or two reviewers failed to take note and regretted the omission of some names whose owners were still very much alive!

Inclusion of all the items herein can be justified; it is in the area of omissions that differences of opinion are bound to arise. Suggestions for future editions will be welcomed. Two fundamental works only have been included from the fast-growing literature on the Moon. Factual data to be found in *Orbis Geographicus* has not been duplicated—for instance, 'Chairs and institutions of university geography' or 'Hydrographic departments'. Selection of key documents is now being made increasingly acute by the greater numbers of reports issued in mimeographed form, having limited circulation, and by the publication of geographic research in non-geographic journals.

Comments in the entries are not to be considered as comparable with reviews or full bibliographical descriptions; the intention is to point out why the works are important, naming the significant features; these may be the presentation of new ideas or factual knowledge, the summary of otherwise scattered material, notes on the development of some aspect of geography, or a work in some way unique.

CBML

FOREWORD TO THE THIRD EDITION

A third edition of *Geography: a reference handbook* being called for at the same time as a second edition of *Modern maps and atlases*, my publisher has kindly concurred with the idea that a further enlarged edition of the Handbook should be prepared containing additional extended articles and including some of the updated cartographical material that would otherwise appear in a revised *Modern maps . . .*, as it seems unlikely that I shall have the opportunity of undertaking a complete revision of the latter. A larger number of references has been appended to many of the entries, demonstrating the variety of aspects of the subject concerned.

Readers are advised to make full use of the index for locating individual requirements.

CBML

LIST OF EXTENDED ENTRIES

Atlases
Audio-visual aids
Bibliographies, national
Classification
Education in geography and cartography
Globes
Map librarianship
Maps (brief historical outline)

1 'About Sweden 1700–1963: *a bibliographical outline'*, compiled by Bure Holmbäck and others, was published by The Swedish Institute, Stockholm. About five thousand titles have been systematically divided among a number of subject fields, including special sections on Geography and Maps; the former *Books in English on Sweden*, by Nils Afzelins, 1951, has been incorporated. Arrangement within the sections is alphabetical by author or title.

2 'Abr-Nahrain: *an annual published by the Department of Middle Eastern Studies'*, University of Melbourne, 1959–60–, usually contains in each issue at least one article of interest to geographers. The chief editor is J Bowman. In volume I, for example, appeared 'Aspects of Phoenician settlement in the West Mediterranean', by W Culican; and in volume X, 1970–1971, issued on the occasion of the 28th International Congress of Orientalists held in Canberra in January 1971, is 'Asian studies in Australia, 1970', by R R C de Crespigny, and 'The traders of the pearl . . .', by B E Collers. There are plates and figures in the text.

3 Abstracts: the central abstracting service is *Geo Abstracts (qv)*. Two main groups of other abstracting services should also be scanned for relevant articles: (a) those covering a wider field, such as *GeoScience abstracts; Historical abstracts; Economic abstracts; Tropical abstracts;* and (b) those dealing with specific fields of interest to individual geographers, of which examples are *African abstracts; Copper abstracts (see* Copper Development Association); *Forestry abstracts; Meteorological abstracts and bibliography; Rubber abstracts; Zinc abstracts (see* Zinc Development Association); *Aluminium abstracts (see* Aluminium Federation); *Industrial diamond abstracts (see* Industrial Diamond Information Bureau). Some of the leading geographical periodicals including abstracts are *Annales de géographie (qv); Erde (qv); Geographical journal of the Hungarian Academy of Sciences; Referativnyi zhurnal geografiya (qv); Soviet geography (qv); Revue Canadienne de géographie (qv); Revue de géographie de Lyon; Journal of the Società Geografica Italiana; Cartography (qv); Geografisch tijdschrift; Geographical bulletin,* Department of Mines and Technical Surveys (*see* Canada, Department of Mines and Technical Surveys); *L'information géographique (qv); Nigerian geographical journal; Polar record (qv)*. Other relevant abstracting services may be identified in the *Index bibliographicus*, in *Abstracting services in science, technology, medicine, agriculture,* *social sciences and humanities* (FID) and in *Ulrich's periodicals directory*.

4 Academy of Sciences, USSR, the highest Soviet institute of learning, counting among its members the most outstanding Soviet scientists and scholars, was founded in St Petersburg in 1724; it has been known as the Russian Academy of Sciences, the St Petersburg Academy of Sciences and, until 1917, the Imperial Academy of Sciences. In 1917, the original name was resumed, until, in 1925, it was finally renamed as above. The headquarters has been in Moscow since 1934. The academy co-ordinates the work of scientific organisations and institutes of higher learning and establishes and maintains contacts with scientific institutions abroad; it is a member of more than forty international bodies. High level conferences, meetings, discussions and research projects are sponsored. Each subject department has its own branches, in addition to the Scientific Research Institute on Sakhalin Island and the Institute of Physics in Krasnoyarsk. The branches study the local natural resources and economy. Publications include seventy learned journals and numerous scientific papers. In addition to the All Union Academy of Sciences, the constituent republics have their own academies, also numerous academies in specialised fields, such as agriculture.

5 'Acta cartographica' (Theatrum Orbis Terrarum) is the title given to a series of unabridged reprints of monographs and studies of a cartographical-historical nature, drawn from some fifty of the foremost European and American historical and geographical journals since 1800. This century was chosen for first consideration because of the relative scarcity of the material. Three volumes have been published each year from 1967, each having its own table of contents; an annual index is published. The annual indexes are being cumulated in a separate general index of authors and subjects. The project has an international advisory board, being composed at the outset of W Bonacker, Y de Dainville, C Koeman, W W Ristow and R A Skelton. Leaflets giving the contents of each volume are available from the publishers. 'The contents of volumes I–XV', 1967–1972, was compiled and edited by Dr Werner Horn.

6 'Acta geographica', the title of a publication of the Department of Geography, University of Stellenbosch, 1967–, is mostly, though not entirely, concerned with Africa. All articles are in Afrikaans, with no summaries in other languages; edited by Professor A Nel and produced irregularly.

7 'Acta historiae Neerlandica', published annually since 1966 by Brill of Leiden, is a periodical intended to make more widely known the progress of historical work in the Netherlands. From the articles selected, reprinted in English, French or German, one or two in each volume are of interest to specialist geographers, for example, 'The balance of trade of the Netherlands in the middle of the sixteenth century', 'Village and hamlet in a sandy region of the Netherlands in the middle of the eighteenth century'. Tables, graphs and sketch-maps are included.

8 Admiralty: *Geographical handbooks* series (*qv*).

9 'The Admiralty chart: *British naval hydrography in the nineteenth century'*, by G S Ritchie, Rear Admiral, Hydrographer of the Navy (Hollis and Carter, 1967), has become one of the central works on its subject, illustrated with a few photographs and maps. The statements in the introduction—'I hope I have presented a broad picture of the progress of British Hydrography throughout the nineteenth century, accompanied by detailed sketches here and there to show something of the men, the ships in which they sailed, and the conditions under which they worked in the ever changing theatres of hydrographic interest dictated by politics, war, and, above all, trade . . .', and 'I trust that I have shown that throughout the nineteenth century the naval surveyors were alert to every aspect of the physical properties of the sea and the floor beneath, and that these properties were observed, measured and recorded to limits imposed only by the instruments and equipment available to them . . .'—summarise the theme of the book. The charting of waters in all parts of the world is chronicled, under the successive Hydrographers of the Navy, Alexander Dalrymple, Thomas Hurd, Sir William E Parry, Sir Francis Beaufort, John Washington, Sir George H Richards, Sir Frederick J O Evans and Sir William J L Wharton.

Refer also

H C Anderson: 'User requirements for modern nautical charts', *Surveying and Mapping*, June 1970.

Vice-Admiral Sir Archibald Day: *The Admiralty Hydrographic Service 1795–1919* (HMSO, 1968).

S Fawcett: 'Problems on the maintenance of Admiralty charts', ICA Technical Symposium, Edinburgh, 1964.

G A Magee: 'The Admiralty chart: trends in content and design', *The cartographic journal*, June 1968.

C H Martin: 'Present and future trends in the maintenance of nautical charts', *Canadian cartography*, 1964.

L N Pascoe: 'Some problems on charts', *The cartographic journal*, June 1968.

G S Ritchie: 'Developments in British hydrography since the days of Captain Cook', *Journal of the Royal Society of Arts*, April 1970.

'Surveyors of the oceans', *The geographical magazine*, October 1969.

See also under Charts

10 'Advanced practical geography', by Arthur Guest (Heinemann Educational Books, 1968), is based on the study of eight maps—'The Sussex Weald and South Downs', 'Dovedale', 'Crackington Haven', 'The Cairngorms', 'The upper Neath and Taff Basins', 'Alluvial valleys', 'Settlement and population' and 'Climatic data'. At each stage, there are worked examples and a wide variety of exercises based on the maps and photographs. Special sections on the diagrammatic representation of statistical material and on climate and weather maps are also included. The geomorphological features shown on the regional maps are analysed and explained, correlating these features with the methods of portraying them cartographically and by diagrams.

11 'Advances in environmental sciences and technology', edited by James N Pitts, University of California, and Robert L Metcalf, University of Illinois (Wiley, 1970–), aims to help delineate and present solutions to the many environmental problems created by modern technology. The publishers state that the series of papers are designed not to be emotive but to present facts, both chemical and statistical, which surround the problems.

12 'Aerial surveys and integrated studies', the proceedings of the Toulouse Conference, September 1964, under the joint sponsorship of Unesco, the National Centre for Scientific Research and the University of Toulouse (Unesco, in English and French, 1968), contains reviews of research concerning the applications of aerial photograph interpretation to the investigation of natural resources, major surveys and sample surveys, other surveys of an integrated nature and, finally, a discussion on survey principles.

Refer also

J Tricart *et al.*: *Introduction à l'utilisation des photographies aériennes en géographie, géologie, écologie* . . . (Paris: Société d'Edition d'Enseignement Supérieur, 1970).

John Wright: 'Air photographs for small expeditions', *The geographical journal*, June 1973.

13 'Afghanistan', a quarterly, has been published since 1946 at Kabul, in separate English and French editions, later, in a single edition, each issue containing some articles in French, some in English. Contributions are from local scholars or public officials.

Refer also

Afghanistan: development in brief (London Information Bureau, Royal Afghan Embassy, 1958); a well illustrated review of recent developments, followed by brief sections on geography, history, culture and people.

Afghanistan at a glance (Kabul: Government Printing House, 1957) presents a general description of the country.

Afghanistan present and past (Kabul: Government Printing House, 1958), a general survey.

M L Clifford: *The land and the people of Afghanistan* (Washington, DC: Lippincott, 1962).

W K Frazer-Tytler: *Afghanistan*, revised by M C Gillett (OUP, 1967, third edition of the classic work first published in 1950).

J Humlum *et al.*: *Le géographie de l'Afghanistan: étude d'un pays aride* (Gyldendal, 1959).

M B Watkins: *Afghanistan* (Van Nostrand, 1963).

Douglas S Way: *Terrain analysis: a guide to site selection using aerial photographic interpretation* (Wiley, 1973).

14 'Africa: maps and statistics', complete in twelve volumes by the Africa Institute, Pretoria, 1962–, contains in each part a statistical text, in English and Afrikaans, and a bibliography relating to the whole of Africa, grouped under the following subject headings: Population, Vital and medical aspects, Cultural and educational aspects, Transport and communication, Energy resources, production and consumption, Agriculture and forestry, Pastoral and marine products, Mining, industry and labour, Manufacturing industries, Commerce and finance, Economy, Technical and scientific development in Africa. The text is illustrated with maps, tables and figures.

15 'Africa on maps dating from the 12th to the 18th century' was edited by Egon Klemp for the Deutsche Staatsbibliothek, Berlin (Edition Leipzig, 1969; available in the United Kingdom from Sweet and Maxwell). The maps are intended to present 'a selection of the more important maps of the continent' in reproduction. Some medieval world maps, such as the Hereford and Catalan, are also included. A set of notes and brief bibliographies accompany the maps.

16 'Africa research bulletin', a cumulative monthly booklist having detachable pages, contains summaries of news from African countries; a systematic reference work, issued by Africa Research Limited, London and Exeter, England, 1964–
  Refer also
  African research and documentation, Journal of the African Studies Association of the United Kingdom and the Standing Commission on Library Materials on Africa, Centre of West African Studies, University of Birmingham.

17 'Africa south of the Sahara', by A T Grove (OUP, 1967 Second ed., 1970), covers physical environment, vegetation, soils, fauna, pests and disease, the people, traditional trading, farming and fishing, followed by sections on African prehistory and the development of each country. The Indian Ocean islands are included, the Malagasy Republic, Mauritius, Réunion, the Comores and the Seychelles. The text is illustrated and there is a bibliography.
  There are many guides to the vast literature on Africa. *Refer*, for example, *Africa south of the Sahara: a select and annotated bibliography* 1964–1968, *comp* K M Glazier (Stanford, Hoover Institution Press, 1969).
  See also the following entries, entries cited in the Index, also
  Printed catalogues of African collections, eg *Library catalogue of the School of Oriental and African Studies*, University of London (G K Hall, 28 volumes, 1963).
  The General Reference and Bibliography Division of the Library of Congress has issued several bibliographies of documents relating to the whole or parts of Africa.
  Africa south of the Sahara, one of the Europa annual reference books, contains surveys of all the countries south of the Sahara Desert.

R Mansell Prothero, *ed.: People and land in Africa south of the Sahara: readings in social geography* (OUP, 1972).

18 'African bibliography' of current publications, originally published quarterly in *Africa*, journal of the International African Institute, has from 1971 appeared as a quarterly separate publication entitled *International African bibliography*. Books, articles, conference and other papers are included.

Refer also

Sanford H Bederman: *A bibliographic aid to the study of the geography of Africa* . . . (Bureau of Business and Economic Research, Georgia State University, second edition, 1972).

Mary Jane Gibson, *comp: Portuguese Africa: a guide to official publications* (Library of Congress, 1967)

J W Witherall, *comp: French-speaking West Africa: a guide to official publications* (Library of Congress, 1967).

19 'African heritage: *studies in African culture, history and anthropology'* is the general title of a series of foundation documents edited by Weston La Barre for reproduction by the Johnson Reprint Corporation, which together present a picture of the development of African life against the varied landscapes of this vast country. *The present state of the Empire of Morocco*, for example, written by Louis Sauer de Chavanne and published in English in London in two volumes, 1788, describes the climate, soil, cities, ports, animals and products.

20 'African notes', in printed form from 1970, beginning then with volume six, number one, is a semi-annual issued by the Institute of African Studies, University of Ibadan in January and July. It aims to serve primarily as a forum for contributions for people who are professionally involved with the study of traditional culture.

21 African studies centres are located, among others, at the School of Oriental and African Studies, University of London, which issues a *Bulletin*; Institute of Commonwealth Studies, University of Oxford; the Centre of African Studies, University of Edinburgh; African Studies Unit, University of Leeds, which publishes the *Leeds African studies bulletin;* Centre of West African Studies, University of Birmingham; African Studies Centre, University of Cambridge; School of African and Asian Studies, University of Sussex; African Studies

Centre, Boston University; African Studies Centre, University of Chicago; African Studies Centre, University of California; Centre of African Studies, University of Warsaw, its chief publication being the *African bulletin*. Special collections, in addition to those in Africa itself, include the Africa Collection, Hoover Institution, Stanford University; the Africa Department, Northwestern University, where a joint acquisition list of Africana is issued, the contribution of nineteen libraries in Evanston, Illinois, and others in the United States, Canada and the United Kingdom; the African Department, University of Yale; the Scandinavian Institute of African Studies, University of Uppsala and the African Institute at the University of Geneva, with its publication *Génève-Afrique*. Important work is carried out by the Committee for the Comparative Study of New Nations, University of Chicago; the Programme of East African Studies, Syracuse University; the Committee on African Studies in Canada, University of Alberta. In 1966, the Rhodes-Livingstone Institute became part of the University of Zambia. All previous publications were wound up and new series were promoted by the re-named Institute for Social Research, University of Zambia.

Refer also

Directory of Afro-American resources (Bowker, 1971), which lists 2,108 organisations and institutions with 5,365 collections of primary and secondary source materials.

R L Collison, *comp: The SCOLMA directory of libraries and special collections on Africa* (Crosby Lockwood, second edition, 1967).

Peter Duignan, *ed: A guide to research and reference works on sub-Saharan Africa* (Stanford, California: Hoover Institution, Stanford University, 1972).

C Struik (Pty) Ltd, of Cape Town, specialise in Africana, particularly the Africana Collectanea series of reprints.

22 'An African survey, revised 1956: *a study of problems arising in Africa South of the Sahara*', by Lord Hailey, was originally published in November 1938, reprinted in 1939 as essentially a new and more comprehensive work and issued again in 1957 by the Oxford University Press for the Royal Institute of International Affairs. Besides 'The physical background', 'Meteorology and climatology', 'Survey and mapping' and 'Geographical research and study', other sections of particular interest to geographers include 'The African peoples', 'Population records', 'The land', 'Agriculture and animal

16

husbandry', 'Forests', 'Water supply and irrigation', 'Soil conservation', 'Economic development in Africa', 'Projects of economic development', 'Minerals and mines', 'transport and communications' and 'The organization of research'. Folded maps in the text illustrate leading topics.

An address by Sir Frederick Pedlar, "Lord Hailey: his contribution to Africa', was printed in the *Journal* of the Royal Society of Arts . . ., July 1970.

Refer also

N Barbour, *ed. A survey of north-west Africa* (OUP, second edition, 1962).

R Battistini: *L'Afrique Australe et Madagascar* (Paris: PUF, 1967).

R J Harrison Church: *Some geographical aspects of West African development* (Bell, 1966).

Pierre Gourou: *L'Afrique* (Paris: Hachette, 1970)

W A Hance: *African economic development* (New York: Praeger, 1967).

B W Hodder and D R Harris, *ed: Africa in transition* (Methuen, 1967).

B S Hoyle and D Hilling, *ed: Seaports and developments in tropical Africa* (Macmillan, 1972).

A M Kamarck: *The economics of African development* (Pall Mall, 1967; New York: Praeger, revised edition, 1971).

G H T Kimble: *Tropical Africa* (New York: Twentieth Century Fund, 1960, two volumes; abridged edition, Doubleday, 1962, *Anchor books* series).

R G Krishna: *Economic co-operation in Africa: retrospect and prospect*; based on the International Seminar on Economic Co-operation in Africa held at University College, Nairobi, 1965 (OUP, 1967).

Robert A Lystad, *ed: The African world: a survey of social research* (Pall Mall Press for the African Studies Association, 1965).

Peter J M McEwan and Robert B Sutcliffe, *ed: The Study of Africa* (Methuen, 1965).

H O N Oboli and R J Harrison Church: *An outline geography of West Africa* (Harrap, fourth edition, 1965).

'The planned development of scientific research in Africa', Malcolm S Adiseshiah, *in Impact*, 1964, no 3, also published separately by Unesco.

A review of the natural resources of the African continent (Unesco, 1963).

P Robson and D A Lury, *ed: The economics of Africa* (Allen and Unwin, 1969).

H J Spiro: *Patterns of African development: five comparisons* (Prentice-Hall, 1967).

L D Stamp: *Africa: a study in tropical development* (Wiley, second edition, 1964).

Tectonics of Africa (Unesco, 1971).

Gordon Wolstenholme and Maeve O'Connor, *ed: Man and Africa*: a CIBA Foundation Symposium jointly with the Haile Selassie I Prize Trust under the patronage of His Imperial Majesty Haile Selassie I Emperor of Ethiopia (Churchill, 1965).

E B Worthington: *Science in Africa: a review of scientific research relating to tropical and southern Africa* (OUP for the Committee of the African Research Survey under the auspices of The Royal Institute of International Affairs, 1958).

23 'Africana catalogues', issued by the Africana Center, International University Bookseller Inc, New York, from January 1967–, are designed not only as sales catalogues but as bibliographic guides to publications on Africa. Information is given on books and pamphlets and on serial publications produced in the United States and elsewhere by research institutions and associations concerned.

Refer also

The *Africana catalog* of the Ibadan University Library, reproduced in two volumes by G K Hall, 1972.

Africa south of the Sahara: Index to periodical literature, 1900–1970, four volume reproduction of the card catalogue maintained by the African section of the General Reference and Bibliography Section, Library of Congress (G K Hall, 1971).

24 'Afrika Kartenwerk' is an ambitious West German project, of which the four representative 1:1M sheets of Tunisia, Nigeria, East Africa and Mozambique-Transvaal were selected for display at the 21st Geographical Congress of the International Cartographic Association. For each individual area, eighteen thematic maps have been prepared to show a wide range of environmental phenomena as well as various aspects of human activity. In addition, larger scale maps, at 1:50,000 or 1:10,000, have been produced of selected subareas, each set accompanied by a descriptive memoir.

25 'Afrikaforum' (or *Internationales Afrikaforum*), the most comprehensive German-language periodical concerned with African affairs, is published ten times a year, the issues for July/August and September/October being double numbers, by the Weltform Verlag Gmbh, Munich. Articles, commentary, news items, short reports and a 'Market studies' feature giving the latest information on African industry, are prepared in close collaboration with the *Africa research bulletin* editors, of London and Exeter (*qv*), the *Bulletin de l'Afrique Noire*, Paris and *Problèmes Africains*, Brussels. From time to time, information on an individual industry is presented in the form of a detailed portrait or an intensive analysis of some particular aspect. Also published by the Weltforum Verlag Gmbh is *Africa studies*, monographs in English and German from the Ifo Institute for Economic Research, Munich.

Refer also Africana notes and queries.

26 Agostini, Giovanni de (1863–1941), founder of the Istituto Geografico De Agostini (*qv*), was an outstanding cartographer, who exerted great influence on Italian cartography. His most widely known single achievement is probably the *Grande atlante geografico* (*qv*).

27 'An agricultural atlas of Scotland' was begun in 1966 with the help of grants from the Carnegie Trust, the Leverhulme Trust and the University of Edinburgh; the information portrayed therein was intended for use by both geographers and all those concerned with agricultural administration and advisory work. The maps are monochrome at scales appropriate to a quarto page; most of them were based on the June 1965 parish summaries, which offered the latest overall data available. Seven main categories of data are considered; physical features, economic characteristics, land uses, crops, livestock, types of farming and crofting. In the preparation of distribution maps, an atlas autocode programme, later named Camap, was devised for use with a KDF9 computer and the maps were drawn by a line printer.

Refer also

    'An agricultural atlas of Scotland', by J T Coppock, *The cartographic journal*, June 1969, which includes sample sheets.

    An agricultural atlas of Scotland, compiled by H J Wood (Gill, 1931).

28 'Agricultural development in Nigeria 1965–1980', a report prepared at the Nigerian government's request by FAO, has resulted in an important analytical study considering the food requirements of the rapidly growing population, the raw materials necessary for the expansion of the country's interests, the exports needed to pay for imports of capital goods and the means of livelihood for the additional working population that must find employment in agriculture by 1980. The text, divided into four parts, deals with 'The policy framework', 'Policies and programmes for development of agricultural production', 'Organizational and institutional aspects' and 'Appendices and annex tables', accompanied by the essential maps and charts; an important document, not only for students of Nigerian geography, but also for those concerned with similar problems in other parts of the world.

29 Agricultural Economics Research Institute, University of Oxford, founded in 1913, provides facilities for research and for various forms of undergraduate and post-graduate teaching. Occasional talks are given to farmers. The field of interest covers the economics of agricultural production, financial accounts and enterprise costing, land economics, marketing studies, agricultural income, statistical studies, rural social organisation, international trade, the world markets and the demand for food, agricultural legislation, administration and economic intelligence. *The farm economist*, published three times a year, contains articles on current research work by members of the Institute and some outside contributors; the quarterly *Digest of agricultural economics* includes summaries of all important publications on agricultural economics which have appeared in Britain during the previous quarter, together with selected studies from overseas having application to Great Britain. *A record of agricultural policy*, by agreement with the Farm Economics Branch, Cambridge University, who formerly published it, is issued by the Institute biennially. Other publications include: Colin Clark: *The economics of irrigation in dry climates;* K E Hunt and K R Clark: *The state of British agriculture, 1959–1960; a comprehensive collection of statistics*; and, by the same two authors, *Poultry and eggs in Britain, 1961–62.*

30 'An agricultural geography of Great Britain', by J T Coppock (Bell, 1971), in the *Advanced economic geographies* series, traces the variations in agricultural activity under the following headings: 'The changing context of British farming', 'Land and weather', 'Farm and fields', 'Men and machines', 'Markets and marketing', 'Land and livestock', 'Dairying', 'Beef cattle', 'Sheep and lambs', 'Pigs and poultry', 'Crops', Horticulture', 'The pattern of farming', with a number of small distribution maps in the text and end of chapter references.

Refer also

A R H Baker and R A Butlin, *ed: Studies of field systems in the British Isles* (CUP, 1973).

H C Darby: *The medieval Fenland* (Newton Abbot: David and Charles, second edition, 1974).

P J Perry: *British farming in the Great Depression 1870–1914: an historical geography* (Newton Abbott: David and Charles, 1973).

31 **'Agricultural geography symposium:** *a report on the proceedings'* of the symposium held at Liverpool and Nottingham in 1964 as part of the programme of the 20th International Geographical Congress, was edited by E S Simpson, Department of Geography, University of Liverpool (Research paper no 3).

Refer also

Colin Clark: *The economics of subsistence agriculture* (Macmillan, fourth edition, 1970).

Colin Clark and Margaret Haswell: *The economics of subsistence agriculture* (Macmillan, fourth edition, 1972).

A C de Vries and B C P H van Baak: *Drainage of agricultural land: a bibliography* (Wageningen: International Institute of Land Reclamation and Improvement, 1966).

Pierre George: *Précis de géographie rurale* (Paris: PUF, 1963).

H F Gregor: *Geography of agriculture: themes of research* (Prentice-Hall, 1970).

David Grigg: *The harsh lands: a study in agricultural development* (Macmillan; New York: St Martin's Press; Dublin: Gill and Macmillan, 1970).

R B Morgan and R J C Munton: *Agricultural geography* (Methuen, 1971).

Clifton R Wharton, *jr, ed: Subsistence agriculture and economic development* (Cass, 1970).

32 **'Agricultural meteorology'** is the title given to the Proceedings of the World Meteorological Organization Seminar held at the Melbourne Bureau of Meteorology in 1966 (WMO, 1968, in two volumes). Mainly of interest to countries in South East Asia and the South West Pacific, this was the third WMO seminar to deal with agricultural meteorology, the two previous meetings having taken place in Venezuela, 1960, and in the United Arab Republic, 1964.

33 'Agricultural research in tropical Africa', by St G C Cooper, FAO Regional Adviser, and others, is a searching analysis of contemporary African research into agricultural problems (East African Literature Bureau, 1970). Problems investigated include 'The diversity of Africa', 'Research organization, aspects and defects', 'The regionalization of research', 'The rice dilemma', 'Wheat in the African economy', 'Research and food production', 'The protein issue', 'The fertilizer perspective', 'The financing of agricultural research' and 'The manpower resources, its amount and distribution', followed by an evaluation of the special cases of individual countries.

34 'Agricultural typology and land use mapping' was the subject of a symposium organised by the Commission for Agricultural Typology of the International Geographical Union held in New Delhi, 1968; the following papers and discussions, together with the proceedings of the symposium, were published in a special issue of *Geographia Polonica*—'Land use and types of farming', 'The land of Hungary and types of its utilization', 'Farming systems of the world', 'A conceptual model of four types of world agriculture', 'A new approach to the study of changes in cropland use: a case study of Uttar Pradesh, India', 'Land use studies as a basis for agricultural typology of East-Central Europe'.

The IGU Commission on Agricultural Typology was established in 1964; its work is based on various forms of contribution and/or active participation in the Commission activities by geographers and agricultural economists. Close contacts are maintained with FAO.

Refer also

I Ya Yurovskiy: 'Large-scale agricultural mapping', *Geodesy and Aerophotography*, 1967.

35 'Agroclimatological methods', Proceedings of the symposium held at Reading in 1966, was published in English and French (Unesco, 1968). The symposium reviewed the problems of agroclimatology on macro- or micro-scales, the published text including graphs and illustrations, and was complementary to the Unesco symposium held in Copenhagen, 1965, which dealt with ecosystems, involving research on a micro scale.

36 'Aguilar nuevo atlas de España' (Madrid, 1961) consists of four main sections, all subdivided as necessary: 'General geography', 'Historical geography', 'Regional geography' and 'Provincial geography'. The work is a fine production and an excellent introduction to the geography of Spain, with text in Spanish, illustrated with black and white photographs, statistical diagrams, graphs and charts and including a bibliography; the cartography shows a bold use of colour, especially in the relief representation by contours and layer colouring.

37 'Aids to geographical research: *bibliographies, periodicals, atlases, gazetteers and other reference books'*, compiled by John Kirtland Wright and Elizabeth T Platt (American Geographical Society, first edition, with sub-title 'Bibliographies and periodicals', by J K Wright, 1923; second edition with E T Platt, completely revised, Columbia University Press for the American Geographical Society, 1947; Research series, no 22), remained for many years the only comprehensive English language attempt to cover the subject objectively, that is, from other than the teaching aspect. The detailed annotations are particularly helpful. 'This book is intended to be of help to anyone who has occasion to make a serious study of geography' begins the Introduction. Grouped in three main parts—'General aids', 'Topical aids', 'Regional aids and general geographical periodicals'—each is subdivided as necessary. An appendix gives as an explanatory note a 'Classified index of American professional geographers, libraries of geographical utility and institutions engaged in geographical research' and there is a substantial index.

38 Akademiya Nauk SSSR, the Institute of Geography of the Academy of Sciences, is the major research body for geographical studies in the USSR. Work is carried out on a vast scale and with practical application. More than three hundred geographers work in ten divisions: physical geography; geomorphology; climatology and hydrology; biogeography; glaciology; cartography; economic geography of the USSR; geography of people's democracies; geography of capitalist countries; history of geography. One of the most important functions is the investigation of research problems posed by the government. The organisation of field expeditions is also important, often in conjunction with the universities and with other institutes of the academy. A vast publishing programme, including the results of the field research, comprises much of the most valuable achievements of Soviet geography. *Izvestiya, seriya geograficheskaya,* 1951—bi-monthly, has the contents page in English and is illustrated with fine maps, photographs and charts. The book reviewing section is detailed and authoritative. The second great geographical journal of the institute is the *Referativnyi zhurnal geografiya* (*qv*).

39 'Alaska', by Bern Keating (National Geographic Society, 1969; second edition, 1971), is notable for its fine coloured photographs; there is a tinted relief map at the beginning of each section and a National Geographic Society Cartographic Division map in the front cover. The text, divided by the headings 'The great land', 'Where fiords and forest meet', 'Metropolis in the making' (Anchorage), 'Westward to tomorrow', 'Between the great ranges', 'Adventure in the Arctic', 'The Arctic coast and Eskimos' and 'The frontier beyond', concludes with a list of *National geographic magazine* articles on Alaska.

    Refer also

       Eric Hultén: *Flora of Alaska and neighboring territories: a manual of the vascular plants* (Stanford UP, 1968).

       George W Ryers: *Alaska in transition: the southwest region* (Johns Hopkins Press for the Arctic Institute of North America and Resources for the Future, Inc., 1960).

40 'The Aldine university atlas' (Aldine Publishing Company, 1969) is a version of Philip's *Library atlas* prepared for the American market; detailed maps of the British Isles are replaced by thematic maps of the States and Southern Canada and statistical information on the nations of the world takes the place of some of the meteorological graphs.

41 Al-Idrisi (*c* 1099–1154), one of the best known of the great Arab school of geographers, travelled in north Africa and in Asia Minor, before settling in Sicily, where, on the order of King Roger II, he compiled a description of the world, based on a synthesis of contemporary knowledge, and a world map. He divided the world into seven latitudinal climates or zones between the equator and the north pole, each zone being sub-divided into ten parts by lines at right-angles to those of the latitudes. In the best known of the two editions of his work, there are seventy maps, each representing one of the parts. The Mediterranean coastline is shown in particular detail. The earliest known translation was published in Rome, 1619, based on an incomplete abridgement of the work.

A complete edition, prepared by an editorial committee formed by The Italian Institute for the Middle and Far East, the University Oriental Institute at Naples and the Institute of Oriental Studies of the University of Palermo, began publication by Brill of Leiden in 1970, in eight fascicules, 1–7 containing the seven 'climes', the eighth, the maps, in Arabic, with translation and introduction, commentary, glossary and indices.

> *Refer also*
> al-Idrisi: *Description de l'Afrique et de l'Espagne: Texte arabe*, published for the first time, from *ms* at Paris and at Oxford, by R Dozy and M J de Goeje, with a translation, notes, a glossary, from the 1866 edition (1968).

42 All-Union Geographical Society of the USSR, the most important organisation for co-ordinating the country's research in geographical subjects, was founded in Leningrad in 1845. The Society now comprises twenty-four main branches, eighty-four minor branches and sixteen sub-branches; membership numbers some ten thousand, composed entirely of professional geographers. The Leningrad branch remains the headquarters, with a membership of over a thousand; here is located a fine library holding more than three hundred thousand volumes, a great map collection and archives, including the private collections and manuscripts of many eminent Russian geographers of the past. Other important branches are the Moscow, Ukrainian and Georgian. A number of sections are devoted to individual aspects of geography. A vast number of scientific conferences and expeditions is organised; in addition, the quinquennial congresses of the Society, begun in Leningrad in 1947, have been of the utmost significance. The main part of the publishing programme comes within the responsibility of the Academy of Sciences and the State Publishing House of Geographical Literature; this includes journals, reports of research and scholarly monographs on all aspects of geography, especially physical, regional and economic. *Izvestiya vsesoyuznogo geograficheskogo obschchestva* is the journal of the main society; *Voprosy geografii* that of the Moscow branch, both of which are included in the translation policy of *Soviet* *geography . . . (qv).*

43 Almagià, Roberto (1884–1962) was a scholar of international repute, who exerted a unique influence on geographical studies through his academic work and publications. His interests, reflected in the geography departments of the universities of Padua and Rome, ranged from geology and oceanography to the history of geographical science, especially cartography, and the whole field of human geography. He became president of the Società di Studi Geografici, Florence, president of the Italian National Committee for Geography and a vice-president of the International Geographical Union. Among the best known of his publications are *L'Italia*, in two volumes, 1959; *Il mondo attuale*, in two volumes, 1953; *I primi esploratori dell'America*, 1937. His *Monumenta cartographica vaticana*, in four volumes, 1944–55, was prepared while he was working in the Apostolic Library during the second world war. As co-editor of the *Rivista geografica Italiana*, he helped to make this one of the great geographical periodicals.

44 Aluminium Federation, London, formerly the Aluminium Development Association, is one of the many examples of special organisations producing source material of central interest to economic geographers. The publication programme includes information bulletins, brochures, technical memoranda and other papers, and the *Research reports* series; regular contributions are made to the quarterly *The aluminium courier* and to *Aluminium abstracts*, produced fortnightly by the Centre International de Développement de l'Aluminium. The library contains upwards of two thousand books, besides a vast collection of pamphlets, patents and periodicals. An information department and technical advisory service are maintained.

45 'Amazonia', a new periodical devoted to the limnological landscape ecology of Amazonia, established close scientific collaboration between the Instituto Nacional de Pesquisas de Amazonía in Manáus, Brazil, and the Hydro-biologische Anstalt der Max-Planck-Gesellschaft zur Fönderung der Wissenschaften in Plön (Federal Republic of Germany), published by the Kommissions-Verlag Walter G Mühlau, Kiel, from 1965.

46 'The American city: an urban geography', by Raymond E

26

Murphy (McGraw-Hill, 1966), presents a systematic analysis of many aspects of urban geography. The text outlines classifications and comparisons of cities as unit areas and analyses the patterns of the interiors of cities. Source material is mentioned for further study of past, present and future urban geographical research.

47 American Geographical Society of New York, founded in 1852 by a group of businessmen to advance the science of geography by discussion, publication and lectures, to establish in the chief city of the United States a place where accurate information on every part of the globe could be obtained and to encourage exploration and research, has developed into one of the greatest influences on world geography. Its history is best traced in the file of *The geographical review (qv)* and in the anniversary volume by J K Wright, *Geography in the making: the American Geographical Society, 1851–1951* (The Society, 1952). A *Newsletter*, issued four times a year, includes notes on projects in progress; *Focus (qv)* and *Soviet geography . . . (qv)* are two more of the Society's periodical publications and the total vast publishing programme includes research monographs, maps and atlases. For many years, the Society has promoted studies relating to questions of wide public interest; for example, pioneer settlement, polar exploration and conservation of resources. Current research includes studies on perception of the environment, on glacier fluctuations and on the automation of cartographic generalisation. The *Serial atlas of the marine environment (qv)* and *Antarctic map folio series (qv)* present in continuing map form results of interdisciplinary research in the physical sciences. Books and monographs appear at intervals in the *Research* series, *Special publications, Studies in urban geography* and other series. The various departments are always engaged in research, especially the Cartographic Department, which makes maps for all kinds of purposes. The continuing grant from the World Data Survey A, Glaciology, was withdrawn at the end of 1969 and arrangements were made shortly after to transfer the collection of maps, photographs and reports to the Water Resources Division of the US Geological Survey at Tacoma, Washington. G K Hall published *Index to maps in books and periodicals*, prepared by the Department, in ten volumes, 1967.

The Society's library is one of the largest geographical collections in the world, including monographs, pamphlets, periodicals, photographs, atlases and maps. Since 1923, a research catalogue has been maintained, arranged by a scheme of classification specially devised to serve geographical research; the catalogue contains references to monographs, periodical articles, government documents and maps, both separately published and those included in books and periodicals. In 1962, G K Hall reproduced the catalogue in fifteen volumes, which are available as a complete set or in eight individual sections. Ten-yearly supplements are being made available in printed, cumulative form; the Regional Sections of the Supplement 1962–1971 are already available in two volumes from G K Hall. From the research catalogue has developed the bibliographical tool, *Current geographical publications (qv)*.

Refer also

Lynn S Mullins: 'American Geographical Society Research Catalogue', *Focus on Indiana Libraries*, Winter 1972.

48 'American history atlas', compiled by Martin Gilbert, with cartography by Arthur Banks (Weidenfeld and Nicolson, 1968), is a short but informative visual guide to American history. 112 monochrome maps show relevant facts by symbols or by 'window' notes.

49 'The American Neptune', quarterly journal of maritime history, is published by the Peabody Museum of Salem, Massachusetts. Articles are frequently of special interest, such as 'Early steam navigation in China', a main theme in 1966. Book reviews are included and there is a pictorial supplement, an inset section of photographs and other illustrations, in addition to those in the text.

50 Amtmann, Bernard, Inc, Montreal, antiquarian booksellers, specialise in very useful catalogues, including out of print and rare books, scientific books and periodicals, arranged alphabetically by author or by title in the absence of a known author, each entry bearing a running number for ordering purposes. Each catalogue deals with one region, with emphasis on Canada, the Arctic and the Antarctic, but also with other areas, such as 'Pacific North-west', which was in three parts, or 'Voyages and travels'. Many of the catalogues have interesting reprints of title pages on the front cover.

51 'The analysis of geographical data', by W H Theakstone and C Harrison (Heinemann Educational Books, 1970), provides an interesting text on the statistical analysis of the many kinds of data handled by geographers, broadly concerned with spatial distribution. Figures and diagrams are included, also a glossary of symbols and a glossary of terms.

52 'The ancient explorers', by M Cary and E H Warmington (Methuen, 1929; revised edition, Pelican Books, 1963), a classic saga of exploration, begins with a discussion of the objects of the ancient explorers and the materials and equipment available to them. The following chapters deal with the opening up of the first known parts of the world, with a final chapter summing up the results of ancient explorations. There are fifteen maps in the text and extensive notes.

53 'Animals and maps', by Wilma George (Secker and Warburg, 1969), sets out to show the knowledge early cartographers possessed of the distribution of animals in the continents and that the 'monsters' depicted were not always merely mythical or pictorial. The Preface, by Dr Helen Wallis, traces the outline of cartographic progress, both in man's ideas about his physical environment and in mapping techniques; and in the author's Introduction are mentioned some examples of the 'long tradition' of regarding animal symbols on maps as 'utterly pictorial'. The main text is divided regionally, following a chapter concerning the 'Ancient world and the Middle Ages'—'Neotropical region', 'Nearctic region', 'Palearctic region', 'Oriental region', 'Ethiopian region', 'Australian region' and 'World maps'. Many reproductions and figures are included throughout the text and a list of references is appended.
Refer also
   Wilma George: *Animal geography* (Heinemann, 1962).

54 'Annales de géographie', founded by Paul Vidal de la Blache and Marcel Dubois in 1891, soon became and has remained one of the foremost of the scholarly geographical journals devoted to the development and principles of the subject, its aim being 'to reason, to link, to interpret'. In 1941, it joined with the *Bulletin* of the Société de Géographie de Paris under the title *Annales de géographie et bulletin de la Société de Géographie*. In the six issues each year, the articles maintain the highest standard of original scholarship or synthesis; the summaries of contemporary knowledge of the continents in the early numbers are of special interest. The notes and reports of projects are invaluable, as are the numerous maps; 'Books received' has been a feature since 1933, statistics sections since 1937; the importance given to bibliographical work was early shown in the inclusion of the annual bibliographies, which subsequently developed into the independent *Bibliographie géographique internationale* (*qv*). Annual and ten-yearly indexes are prepared.

55 '**Annotated bibliography of Afghanistan**', compiled by Donald N Wilber (New Haven: Human Relations Area Files Press, third edition, 1968), contains general sources of information and reference books, in broad subject groupings, including geography and history, each section having a brief introduction; the entries, frequently annotated, are numbered and there is a name index.

56 '**Annotated bibliography of Burma**', prepared by the Burma Research Project at New York University, was edited by Frank N Trager and others (New Haven: Human Relations Area Files Press, 1956). Included are bibliographies, books, pamphlets and other separates (these merely listed); periodicals; government publications; general works, geographical and historical monographs. The entries are numbered for reference and many are briefly annotated.

57 '**An annotated world list of selected current geographical serials in English**: *with an appendix of major periodicals in various languages regularly providing English summaries of articles, or periodicals partly in English and partly in other languages*' is a useful pamphlet, compiled by Chauncy D Harris (Department of Geography, University of Chicago, 1960), now o.p. A second edition also went quickly out of print and an expanded and revised third edition, 1971, *Research paper* no 137, entitled *Annotated world list of selected current geographical serials in English, French and German, including serials in other languages with supplementary use of English or other international languages*, covers 316 serials from sixty-four countries, the selection having been made on the basis of the quality of geographical material, frequency, regularity and longevity of publication, citations in international bibliographies and availability in major libraries.

See also the author's *International list of geographical serials*.

58 '**Annual summary of information on natural disasters**', 1970–, continues the work of a series of publications by the Union Internationale de Secours which came to an end in 1966. Of the four sections: *Earthquakes* is compiled by Professor J P Rothé; *Tsunanis*, compiled from information supplied to Unesco by the Tsunanis

Warning Centre in Honolulu; *Storm surges*, from information supplied by the Tidal Institute, University of Liverpool; and *Volcanic eruptions*, from information given by the Vulcanological Society of Japan and by Dr Latter of the Institute of Geological Sciences, Edinburgh.

Refer also

F M Bullard: *Volcanoes in history, in theory, in eruption* (University of Texas Press, 1962, reprinted 1968).

59 'Antarctic', the quarterly news bulletin of the New Zealand Antarctic Society, 1956–; book reviews are included.

There is also the *Antarctic record* issued by the Ministry of Education, Tokyo; and the *Information bulletin* of the Soviet Antarctic Expedition, in addition to the following major reference works on the Antarctic.

60 'Antarctic bibliography', prepared at the Library of Congress, under the editorship of George A Doumani, sponsored by the Office of Antarctic Programs, National Science Foundation, Washington DC (Washington DC, Superintendent of Documents, 1965–), originated in the bibliographic card service of Antarctic abstracts compiled and disseminated by the Cold Regions Bibliography section of the Library of Congress, Science and Technology Division, 1963–. All topics relevant to the region south of latitude 60 degrees south and the sub-Antarctic islands were included, the first volume covering mainly 1962–1964. Since 1963, polar libraries and interested scientists, both within and outside the United States, have availed themselves of the service, entries being printed on four by five inch cards. The first two thousand entries have been published by the Office of Antarctic Programs. Entries represent the publications of some thirty countries, in thirteen languages, with emphasis on the USA, arrangement being by subject groupings, with author, subject and grantee indexes.

There is also the bibliography bearing the same title, compiled by John Riscoe, sponsored by the US Navy Department, Bureau of Aeronautics (Washington, DC; Government Printing Office, 1951), which includes maps.

61 'Antarctic ecology', in two volumes, edited by M W Holdgate, of the Nature Conservancy, London, is a major reference work (Academic Press, 1970), dealing comprehensively with the Antarctic and offering comparisons with the Arctic regions. The text represents the papers from the second symposium of the Biological Working Group of the Scientific Committee on Antarctic Research, the first volume dealing with past environments and biotas, marine plankton and its pelagic consumers, marine benthos, seals and seabirds; the second with freshwater systems in the Antarctic and the Arctic, terrestrial soils, vegetation and fauna, concluding with a review of conservation.

62 'Antarctic journal of the United States', 1966–, is issued bimonthly by the Office of Antarctic Programs of the National Science Foundation and the United States Naval Support Force, Antarctica, of the Department of Defense, jointly, to provide a forum for the exchange of information on the Antarctic.
>   *Refer also*
>   Kenneth J Bertrand: *Americans in Antarctica, 1775–1948* (American Geographical Society, 1972).

63 The 'Antarctic map folio' series, begun by the American Geographical Society in 1964, sponsored by the National Science Foundation, is planned to comprise about twenty folios, each containing several sheets of maps and text on a specialised subject within the whole, under the general editorship of V C Bushnell. The aim is to summarise existing knowledge of the Antarctic continent and adjacent waters. Two particularly interesting recent folios to appear were no 12 and no 13, published in August 1970: The first, 'Geologic maps of Antarctica', is the work of Campbell Craddock and twenty-four other contributors, comprising two groups of maps, regional maps of bedrock geology at 1:1M scale, and continental maps of fossil sites, tectonics and additional features at a smaller scale. The second, 'Circumpolar characteristics of Antarctic waters . . . .', by A L Gordon and R D Goldberg, covers all the waters surrounding the continent as far north as 40 degrees south.

64 'Antarctic research: a review of British scientific achievement in Antarctica', edited by Sir Raymond Priestley and others, covers the period 1944 to the end of 1963 (Butterworth, 1964), with illustrations, diagrams, bibliographies and maps in a separate folder. Leading authorities have contributed twenty-one informative articles on various aspects, presented in non-technical language.

65 'Antarctica', edited by Trevor Hatherton (Methuen, 1965) and published with the co-operation of the New Zealand Antarctic Society, surveys the present state of knowledge of the continent. The twenty-one scholars involved have together made a comprehensive coverage, arranged under four main headings: 'The nations in Antarctica', which includes a summary of mapping; 'The southern ocean'; 'The Antarctic continent' and 'The south Polar atmosphere'. The work has been accepted as a standard treatise, which has been translated into Russian and Spanish. There are numerous magnificent photographs throughout the text, also sketchmaps and diagrams where useful, and a folded 'Map of the Antarctic region' fits into a back cover pocket. Two appendices set out 'The Antarctic Treaty' and 'National stations in Antarctica since 1957'. There is also a bibliography.

Refer also, from the vast existing literature

The '*Antarctic research*' series (American Geophysical Union).

Roald Amundsen: *The South Pole: an account of the Norwegian Antarctic Expedition in the "Fram" 1910–1912* (Translated from the Norwegian by A G Chater, Murray, two volumes, 1912).

ANARE: 'Australian National Antarctic Research Expeditions'.

A Cailleux: *L'Antarctique* (Paris: PUF, 1967).

C M Clapperton: 'Antarctic links with the Andes', *The geographical magazine*, November 1971.

Frank Debenham: *Antarctica: the story of a continent* (Jenkins, 1959).

Sir Vivian Fuchs and Sir E Hillary: *The crossing of Antarctica, the Commonwealth Trans-Antarctic Expedition, 1955–1958* (Cassell, 1958).

D M Goodall: *The seventh continent* (Royston: Priory Press, 1969).

H G R King: *The Antarctic* (Blandford Press, 1969).

Louis O Quam and Horace D Porter, *ed: Research in the Antarctic* (American Association for the Advancement of Science, 1971).

L B Quatermain: *New Zealand and the Antarctic* (Wellington: Shearer, 1971).

66 'Antique maps and their cartographers', by Raymond Lister (Bell,

1970), begins with a study of map-making among primitive peoples, tracing its development to the eighteenth century; following chapters are devoted to the achievements of individual countries—the Low Countries, France, Great Britain, Scandinavia and Russia, Africa, Asia, America and Australasia, accompanied by numerous black and white reproductions, end of chapter bibliographies and a 'General bibliography'. Maps are described in the manner expected of a life-long lover and collector of early maps; seldom is any linkage attempted with contemporary techniques or with geographical developments. The work, eminently readable, is general in approach; nor does it take into account some more recent specific publications, such as the *Atlantes Neerlandici . . . (qv)*.

Refer also

Douglas Gohm: *Antique maps of Europe, the Americas, West Indies, Australasia, Africa, the Orient* (Octopus Books, 1972).

R A Skelton: *Maps—a historical survey of their study and collecting* (University of Chicago Pr., 1972).

Richard van de Gohm: *Antique maps for the collector* (Bartholomew, 1972).

67 'Arcano del mare', the first marine atlas, produced by Sir Robert Dudley in three volumes, 1646–47. The charts, drawn on the Mercator projection and finely engraved by Antonio Francesco Lucini in Florence, marked a great advance on those in previous works. A second, corrected edition, was issued in 1661.

68 'Arctic', quarterly journal of the Arctic Institute of North America, 1948–, contains papers summarising original research, notes and reviews, with at least one erudite article of central interest.

69 'Arctic and Alpine research', issued quarterly, was initiated in 1969 by the Institute of Arctic and Alpine Research, University of Colorado, 'to provide a vehicle for scientists, at the international level, with a special interest in Arctic and Alpine environments, to give emphasis to INSTAAR development and to assist in the experiment of environmental teaching being undertaken within the Institute'. The high latitude and mountainous areas of the world and related topics of the Pleistocene era form the central theme.

70 'The Arctic basin', in a revised edition by J E Sater (Arctic Institute of North America, 1969), originated with a report from the Institute prepared in 1960 for the US Army to provide an account of the environmental factors relevant to operations in the Arctic. Much material was added and the revised edition comprises a comprehensive general account of the physical features, the history of exploration and the nature of human settlement in the area.

Refer also

Wally Herbert: 'The first surface crossing of the Arctic Ocean', *The geographical journal*, December 1970.

E A Macdonald: *Polar operations* (US Naval Institute, 1969).

Robert E Peary. *The North Pole* (Hodder and Stoughton, 1910).

R J Price and D E Sugden: *Polar geomorphology* (Institute of British Geographers for the British Geomorphological Research Group, 1972).

J E Sater *et al: Arctic environment and resources* (Arctic Institute of North America, 1971).

71 'The Arctic bibliography', edited by Marie Tremaine for the Arctic Institute of North America, 1953– (McGill-Queen's University Press), contains abstracts and index entries in Russian, English, Scandinavian, German and other languages, as appropriate. Coverage of geophysical studies has increased through the years, as more detailed research has been made possible, with the expansion of transportation. The publication is recognised as the standard, unified research tool for the area; entries are numbered and the location of each document is noted with full bibliographical description, annotated as necessary. Preliminary work had been begun under an Office of Naval Research contract with the Arctic Institute of North America, with the support of the Department of the Army, the Department of the Navy and the Department of the Air Force, under the supervision of a directing committee. The developed project, from 1953, was prepared in co-operation with the Department of Defense under the direction of the Arctic Institute.

Refer also

Charles W Hartman and Robert F Carlson: *Bibliography of Arctic water resources* (University of Alaska, 1970).

72 Arctic Institute of North America was established after the second world war to encourage scientific research into Arctic conditions and to act as a repository for information, with emphasis on the North American Arctic; activities have since been extended to include the Antarctic. The main centre is in Montreal, with a large section also in Washington. Publications include reports and special studies; *Arctic* (*qv*) and *The Arctic bibliography* (*qv*) are of international importance. A library was established at McGill University in 1949, moving subsequently to new premises. Holdings include some six thousand books, more than twenty thousand pamphlets, several hundred reports on research projects, periodicals, photographs and more than five thousand maps. A unique reference service, operated since 1959, enables the library to handle research and information projects on a cost plus basis; indexes, abstracts and bibliographies are compiled, also translations by request, and accessions lists are issued.

73 'Area', the house journal of the Institute of British Geographers, 1969–, when a new periodical was considered desirable in addition to the institute's *Newsletter*, aims to encourage free and impartial discussion of ideas and techniques, 'to probe, to report and to examine the implications of work being done in these expanding fields of study'. *Area* appears four times a year; the first issue, of fifty-six pages, showed the variety of content, being full of information and comment on 'Computer graphics', a 'General report of the Edinburgh British Honduras-Yucatan Expedition', 'Social science research in geography', 'Centre for Environmental Studies' (*qv*), 'Research at the Countryside Commission', 'Metrication in the *Transactions*', 'The Institute of Agricultural History at the University of Reading' and several reports of conferences and symposia. A few sketchmaps usually illustrate the text.

74 'La Argentina: suma de geografia', under the direction of Francisco de Aparicio, Horacio A Difrieri and others, is a superb publication in nine volumes on all aspects of geography and cartography (Buenos Aires: Ediciones Peuser, 1958–1963). Maps were contributed by Hildebrando O Boccio and the aerial photography was the work of the Instituto Fotopográfico Argentino, the Instituto Geográfico Militar and the Ministerio de Marina. The text is in Spanish, but the folding maps, photographic reproductions, diagrams and the superb aerial photographs facilitate understanding. Included is a detailed description of the *Atlas aerofotográfico*.

75 'Arid lands: a geographical appraisal', edited for Unesco/

Methuen by E S Hills, 1966, was planned to present a broadly based conspectus of the vast area of dry country in the world. The book deals with all aspects of the problem of aridity, ranging from water supply, use and management, through industrialisation and social life in the arid zones.

Refer also

X de Planhol and P Rognon: *Les zones tropicales arides et subtropicales* (Paris: Colin, 1970).

H E Dregne: *Arid lands in transition* (American Association for the Advancement of Science, 1970).

Patricia Paylore, *comp: Seventy-five years of arid lands research at the University of Arizona a selective bibliography of arid lands research 1891–1965* (Office of Arid Lands Research, University of Arizona, 1966)

76 '**Arid lands in perspective:** *including AAAS papers on water importation into arid lands,* edited by William G McGinnies and Bram J Goldman (American Association for the Advancement of Science and the University of Arizona Press, 1969), is one of the contributions to the Unesco project, Arid Zone Research, illustrated and including maps, diagrams and bibliographies. The first section contains nineteen papers on a wide range of topics; a second group, on physical geography, comprises studies of quantitative analysis of desert topography and the classification of arid land soils. There are a number of regional studies. There are two bibliographical papers: one by Andrew Warren on desert dunes, the other by Patricia Paylore on the sources for arid lands research. A final section comprises twelve papers and comments deriving from a symposium on water importation into arid lands, sponsored by the AAAS, held in Dallas, Texas, in December 1968.

Refer also

J L Gardner and L E Myers, *ed: Water supplies for arid regions* (University of Arizona, 1967).

K W Glennie: *Desert sedimentary environments* (Amsterdam: Elsevier Publishing Co., 1970).

W G McGinnies *et al*, ed: *Food, fiber and the arid lands* (University of Arizona, 1971).

Martin Simons: *Deserts: the problem of water in arid lands* (OUP, 1967, 1968).

J J Tricart and A Cailleux: *Le modèle des régions sèches* (Paris: Société d'Edition d'Enseignement Supérieur, 1969).

77 '**Arid land research institutions:** *a world directory*', by Patricia Paylore (University of Arizona Press, 1967), formed part of an inventory of geographical research on desert environments being conducted by the Institute of Arid Lands Research of the University of Arizona. The project as a whole seeks to determine in detail what topics are being or have been investigated relating to the world's deserts and what remains to be done. Subsequently, a compendium will be issued based on a comprehensive critical review of the published literature, augmented by consultations with leading scientific specialists. Topics to be covered are physical features, flora and fauna, weather and climate, coastal deserts and regional types. The work above-mentioned is the first directory of arid zone institutions to appear since the Unesco *Directory of institutions engaged in arid zone research,* 1953. Since that time, the rate of research in this field has increased considerably and the number of entries in the present publication is more than double those listed by Unesco—more than two hundred organisations in thirty-nine countries. Arrangement is by countries and each entry is annotated with notes on the scope and type of work in the organisation concerned. A first supplement appeared in 1968, prepared also by Patricia Paylore (Natick: Earth Sciences Laboratory, United States Army Natick Laboratories, 1968), which included yet more institutions and updated the existing entries as necessary.

78 Arnold, Edward, (Publishers) Limited, London, have a special interest in books on geography, mainly devoted to the more scientific aspects of the subject and having a bias towards the educational. A catalogue, *Geography*, published at intervals, lists all titles designed for sixth form level and above. Recent titles of particular interest include David Harvey: *Explanation in geography* (*qv*); Peter Haggett and Richard J Chorley: *Network analysis in geography* (*qv*); a new edition of F J Monkhouse: *A dictionary of geography* (*qv*); and the series *Progress in geography* (*qv*).

79 'The art of navigation in England in Elizabethan and early Stuart times', by David W Waters (Hollis and Carter, 1958), a thorough and scholarly work, considers 'The development of the art of navigation in Europe in the fifteenth and early sixteenth centuries'; and 'The English contribution'; followed by thirty-three appendices on specific topics integral to the subject. The text is illustrated by many plates, reproductions and diagrams and there is a bibliography. *Compare* similar works by E G R Taylor (*qv*).

80 '**The Asia bulletin:** *a monthly review from Asia Publishing House*' frequently includes books, documents and reports of interest to the geographer—for example, P L Mehra: *The Younghusband Expedition,* 1968—or on economic conditions, the methodology of economic research and on trade and industry in India and other Asia countries.

Refer also

A T Embree *et al, comp: Asia: a guide to basic books* (New York: Asia Society, 1966) and a supplement, a guide to paperbacks on Asia, compiled by J H Bailey and others.

Peter L A Gosling: *Maps, atlases and gazetteers for Asian studies: a critical guide* (University of the State of New York, 1965).

C A Fisher: *Modern Asian studies* (CUP for the School of Oriental and African Studies, University of London, 1967).

R T Shand, *ed: Agricultural development in Asia* (Allen and Unwin, 1970).

81 Asia, East by South: a cultural geography, by J E Spencer and William L Thomas (Wiley, second edition, 1971), concerned with cultural geography in its widest interpretation, aims to make a contribution to a more complete understanding of the Orient; 'Chapters have been rationalised to accord with the regional political concepts of the Orient as they existed at the time of the revision.' The three parts, 'Systematic geography', 'The regional expression of culture' and 'For use in reference' are each subdivided. Areally, India, Pakistan, Ceylon, Southeast Asia, the Irrawaddy Valley and Burma, Thailand, Cambodia, Vietnam, Malaysia, Indonesia, the Philippines, China, Korea and Japan are covered. Photographs, graphs, diagrams and sketchmaps abound throughout the text. In the third part, statistical abstracts are given for 'Estimates of populations, densities and mortality rates, as of 1970'; 'Estimates of significant agricultural crop acreages and animal populations'; 'Selected social indicators'; and 'Selected economic indicators'. A section, 'Bibliographical suggestions', arranged in accordance with the chapters in the text, includes articles as well as monographs in the English language, followed by a subject and placename index.

Refer also

Iain Buchanan: *Singapore in Southeast Asia: an economic and political appraisal* (Bell, 1972).

Albert Kolb: *East Asia: China, Japan, Korea, Vietnam: the geography of a cultural region* (Methuen, translated by C A M Sym, 1971).

Alice Taylor, *ed: Southeast Asia* (Newton Abbot: David and Charles, in co-operation with the American Geographical Society, *Focus* series, 1972).

82 '**Asian survey:** *a monthly review of contemporary Asian affairs*' has been published from 1960 by the Institute of International Studies, University of California at Berkeley. The Institute, established in 1955, carries on organised research in comparative and international affairs, provides facilities for research for individual scholars and serves as an administrative agency which assists in promoting new research interests among the faculty. The journal reflects these aims in major articles, shorter notes and comments. The first three volumes of the journal have been reprinted by Kraus.

83 Asia's lands and peoples: *a geography of one-third the earth and two-thirds its people*', by George B Cressey (New York: McGraw-Hill, 1944; third edition, revised 1963), follows a regional treatment after general opening comments—'China', 'Japan and Korea', 'Soviet Union', 'Southwestern Asia', 'India and Pakistan', 'Southeastern Asia', subdivided as necessary. Photographs, maps and diagrams abound throughout the text and there is a substantial section of 'Suggested readings' limited to the more readily accessible literature.

Refer also

Crossroads: land and life in Southwest Asia, by the same author (Syracuse University; Lippincott, 1960; Feffer and Simons International University Editions).

E H G Dobby: *Monsoon Asia* (ULP, third edition, revised, 1966).

Jacques Dupois: *L'Asia méridionale* (Paris: PUF, 1969).

D J Dwyer, *ed: The city as a centre of change in Asia* (Hong Kong University Pr.; OUP, 1972).

W G East and O H K Spate, *ed: The changing map of Asia: a political geography* (Methuen, fifth edition, 1971).

Norton Ginsburg, *ed: The pattern of Asia* (Prentice-Hall; Constable, 1958).

E S Kirby: *Economic development in East Asia* (New York:

Praeger; Allen and Unwin, 1967).

Owen and Eleanor Lattimore: *Silks, spices and empire: Asia seen through the eyes of its discoverers* (New York: Delacorte Pr., 1968).

84 Associated Publishers, Amsterdam, an independent publishing company, was founded in the Spring of 1967 by a group of Dutch reprint publishers— A Asher and Company; John Benjamins N V Scientific Periodical Trade; E J Bonset; S Emmering; De Graaf, publisher, Nieuwkoop; Gerard Th. Van Heusden, publisher and bookseller; B M Israël N V; Fritz Knuf, publisher, Hilversum; Meridian Publishing Company; Editions Rodopi N V; P Schippers N V (B R Grüner); and Theatrum Orbis Terrarum Limited (*qv*), all, with the two noted exceptions, at Amsterdam, having the aim of working in closer mutual co-operation. Each specialises in one or more fields. Reference works, maps, atlases and periodicals of permanent value have been reproduced and catalogues have been issued representing the output of an individual publisher or of the new group.

85 The Association française pour l'études des eaux (AFEE) collects, classifies, selects and analyses all documents, published or unpublished, French and foreign, dealing with water from the scientific, technical, economic or legal points of view. The Association has drawn up a *Thesaurus national de l'eau*, 1971. In a monthly bulletin, *Information eaux* (formerly *Eaux et industries*), documents that have been analysed are listed serially, with annotations.

86 Association of American Geographers, the organisation for professional geographers, was founded in 1904. The annual conferences, the opportunities for publication and the awards offered have proved a great stimulus to academic work. A quarterly journal, *Annals*, has been issued since 1911, carrying abstracts, bibliographies, statistics and reviews. A recent innovation has been the issue of special volumes of the *Annals* in which symposia beyond the normal scope of the journal may appear. After amalgamation with the Society of Professional Geographers, a bi-monthly journal, *Professional geographer*, was issued, 1949– and in 1961 a new journal, the *Southeastern geographer*, was launched by the south-east division of the Association. In 1971, the *Historical geography* newsletter began publication and, in collaboration with the National Academy of Sciences, National Research Council, the Association issued

States and trends of geography in the United States 1957–1960: a Report prepared for the Commission on Geography, Pan American Institute of Geography and History.

87 Association of Geography Teachers of Ireland was founded in 1962 with the aim of giving every Irish child a sound knowledge and understanding of geography. Constant efforts have been made to improve syllabuses, teaching methods and textbooks. The Association's journal, *Geographical viewpoint*, has been issued since 1964, annually, five issues constituting a volume; lectures, discussions and field meetings are arranged and travelling exhibitions prepared.

88 'The astronomical and mathematical foundations of geography', by Charles H Cotter (Hollis and Carter, 1966), a small introductory work setting out the fundamentals of this basic aspect of geography, reviews the development of such studies, proceeding to clarify 'Ideas on the size and shape of the earth', 'The sphere and the ellipsoid', 'The triangle', 'Problems of sailing on the earth', 'The earth's orbit', 'The earth's rotation and problems of finding latitude and longitude', 'The elements of surveying' and 'Map projections'. Line drawings accompany the text and there is a selected list for further reading.
Compare similar works by E G R Taylor (*qv*)

89 Athens Center of Ekistics, Athens Technological Institute, Graduate School of Ekistics, has organised an annual international seminar on 'Ekistics and the future of human settlements' from 1965. The aim is to provide an opportunity for interdisciplinary exchange and discussions on growth and change within the subject. The Centre consists of five divisions: Research, Education, International programmes, a documentation unit and Administration. Library facilities are available. The pioneer of the study, ekistics, was Dr C A Doxiadis, expert on development planning, whose book: *Ekistics: an introduction to the science of human settlements*, gave impetus and precision to this emerging aspect of population study. *Ekistics*, the monthly periodical issued by the Centre, includes original articles as well as abstracts from relevant articles in other journals, each issue being devoted to a particular aspect; also *Ekistics index*, monthly, consists of a list of cross-referenced articles selected from some six hundred periodicals from fifty countries; annually, a selection of

Scientific reports is produced and there is the monthly ATO-ACE Newsletter, which is circulated gratis.

90 'Atlante internazionale della Consociazione Turistica', a comprehensive reference atlas, was originally conceived by Luigi V Bertarelli, carried out with the collaboration of Olinto Marinelli and Pietro Corbellini and presented to the tenth Italian Geographical Congress in 1927. Between 1927 and 1938, five editions were published, the 1938 edition being particularly carefully revised. The edition of 1955–1956 was issued in serial instalments, directed by Manlio Castiglioni, to mark the sixtieth anniversary of the Club's foundation and the eighth edition was edited by Sandro Toniolo, 1964–1968. The work, in two volumes, is an atlas totalling more than 170 plates and a gazetteer-index of about 250,000 entries. The plates, with many large-scale insets, were each drawn and engraved by hand and printed by the most modern lithographic techniques. Relief is by hachuring and hill shading, with frequent spot heights. A brief summary of the source material is shown on the back of each plate, and useful notes, glossaries and diagrams are included. The atlas has been used as the base for other world atlases, notably for the *Gyldendals verdens-atlas*, Copenhagen, 1951.

   Refer

   Sandro Toniolo: 'The new edition of the "Atlante Internazionale" issued by the Touring Club Italiano', *International Yearbook of Cartography*, 1970.

91 'Atlantes Neerlandici: *bibliography of terrestrial, maritime and celestial atlases and pilot books, published in the Netherlands up to 1880*', compiled and edited by Dr Ir C Koeman, in three volumes (Amsterdam: Theatrum Orbis Terrarum Limited, 1967–), under the authority of the Committee for the Bibliography of early Dutch atlases, is in five volumes. 'Maps, like paintings and prints, belong to the characteristic manifestations of seventeenth century Dutch culture' states the key theme. Each entry contains a complete bibliographical description, including any distinguishing characteristic, of editions and issues of atlases published in the Netherlands and by Dutch cartographers elsewhere, arranged in alphabetical order of cartographers. Volume I comprises 'Van der Aa to Blaeu; II, Blussé-Mercator'; III Mercator–; these being land atlases and town books. The fourth volume deals with sea atlases, pilot guides and celestial atlases.

Biographies of the outstanding publishers and map-makers, chronological lists, personal, publishers', cartographers' and geographical names indexes and, in the fifth volume, a cumulative index complete the work, which is generously illustrated with reproductions. A useful point is the indication of location of copies.

Refer also

    G R Crone: 'Seventeenth century Dutch charts of the East Indies', *The geographical journal*, November–December, 1943.

92 'Atlas', the journal of Dublin University Geographical Society, is not confined in scope to articles on Ireland. Features include 'Society news' and a modest review section. There are usually sketch-maps in the text.

93 'Atlas aérien' is an exciting and valuable experiment by Gallimard, in five volumes: 1, Alps, Rhône, Provence, Corse, 1955; 2, Bretagne, Loire, Sologne et Berry, Entre Loire et Gironde, 1956; 3, Pyrénées, Languedoc, Aquitaine, Massif Central, 1958; 4, Paris et la vallée de la Seine, Ile-de-France, Beauce et Brie, Normandie, de la Picardie à la Flandre, 1962; 5, Alsace, Lorraine, Morvan et Bourgogne, Jura, 1964.

94 'Atlas Antarktiki', a loose-leaf atlas with a cover-to-cover English translation, edited by Dr U G Bakaev and others (Glavnoe Upravlenie Geodezii i Kartografii, 1966), consists of 225 plates carrying more than three hundred maps, charts, diagrams and comprehensive legend. The outline runs as follows: Historical matter; General aspects; Aeronomy and Physics of the Earth; Geology and Topography; Climate; Waters of the Pacific Ocean. Seven regions are distinguished, of which the maps are in a separate portfolio. Layer colouring is used to portray relief and the colouring systems throughout are very fine.

95 'Atlas botanic', compiled by Professor Lucia Popovici and Professor Dr Constanta Moruzi (Bucharest: Didactic and Pedagogic Publishing House), is in four main sections: Plant evolution, Plant morphology and physiology, Plant systematics and Geobotanics, Nature protection and curiosities from the plant world. 181 coloured tables accompany an explanatory text and all the plates are printed in six to eight colour offset. A classification of plants is included, also explanations of some botanic terms, an alphabetical index and bibliographical references.

96 'Atlas Československovenské Socialistiché Republiky', edited by Antonin Gotz (Prague: Československa Akademie Vedústrědni Sprava Geodézie a Kartografie, 1966), consisting of fifty-eight map sheets and a gazetteer, is a beautiful example of a national atlas. The length of Czechoslovakia east-west suggested two-page spreads, on which the whole country could be shown at 1:1M. Much detail is included and the judicious selection of symbols and colouring makes the detail effective. When desirable, for comparison, as with crop production, sixteen maps at 1:4M are shown on the double page. All the usual aspects are covered, with, in addition, a survey of housing conditions, equipment, floor space, electricity consumption, etc.

Refer also

J Demek *et al*: *Geography of Czechoslovakia* (Prague: Academia, Publishing House of the Czechoslovak Academy of Sciences, 1971).

Dobroslau Líbal: *The towns and cities of Czechoslovakia* (Prague: translated by Joy Turner, Artia, 1970).

97 'Atlas de Belgique': plans for the national atlas were begun by the Comité National de Géographie as early as 1937, but the work was necessarily delayed. The first loose-leaf sheets, at a standard scale of 1:500,000, were issued in 1954. The Atlas covers all aspects of the geography of Belgium, incorporating the latest available data from government and other authorities; sketchmaps and diagrams add to the elucidation of the information included and commentaries in French and Flemish accompany each sheet.

Note that the maps of the *Atlas du Survey National*, begun by the Administration de l'Urbanisme, Ministère des Travaux Publique in 1964, supplement those of the national atlas. Several hundred of these maps, dealing with a wide range of subjects, are available for reference in the offices of the Administration in Brussels. The maps are excellently produced and brief texts provide explanatory comment for each.

98 'Atlas de Colombia', edited by Eduardo Acevedo Latorre, of the Sociedad Geográfico de Colombia (República de Colombia, Instituto Geográfico Agustín Codassi, Bogotá, Academia Colombiana de Historia, 1967), is a glorious production, having the aim of 'compiling more or less all cartographic works about geographical aspects

. . . to summarize the present status of geographical investigations in the country'. As indicated, therefore, this is not an original atlas; most of the plates have appeared elsewhere, a large number being from the four-volume *Atlas de Economía Colombiana* (Banco de la Repúblico, Bogotá, 1959–1964), also edited by Acevedo Latorre. Much of the work is intended for the general public rather than the research-minded geographer; but for geographers particularly there are three special sections: on historical cartography, including some fine reproductions; a section on natural environments and one on economic and demographic aspects. 1964 census material was not included and this is a pity, for there were great changes in population after 1951. The colour printing is of a very high quality and the production has throughout a multitude of illustrations, extra maps and diagrams. There are an excellent section of drawings of products shown alongside statistics relating to them, a dictionary of astronomical, geodetic and physical terms relating to the world as a whole, an introduction and a bibliography. The final section contains hypsometric maps of the individual states and plans of their capitals, with a special section on Bogotá. Based on this atlas is the *Atlas escolar de Colombia*, of which a first edition was for limited circulation only, a revised definitive edition being planned for distribution to secondary schools.

99 'Atlas de France', one of the most interesting of the national atlases, was first published 1934–1945, with a second edition, 1953–1959, in loose-leaf form, by the Comité National de Géographie, printed by the Service Géographique de l'Armée. Some plates in the second edition were reprinted from the first, but by more modern methods; the new plates show types of agriculture, livestock distribution, electrical energy and density of railway traffic. Population data were based on the 1946 figures. Field work was of very high quality and the whole production demonstrates the best of French cartography. Interesting new techniques included the use of proportional spheres to denote urban centres; and useful plans of medieval towns were included. Scales range between 1:1,250,000 and 1:8M.

Refer also

Atlas industriel de la France (La Documentation Française, 1959–60).

Atlas historique et culturel de la France (Amsterdam: Elsevier, 1957).

Atlas historique de la France contemporaine 1800–1965 (P A

46

Bouju *et al*, 1966).

A J B Tussler and A J L Alden: *A map book of France* (Macmillan, 1968).

100 'Atlas de la France de l'est', an excellent example of a regional atlas, was prepared by l'Association pour l'Atlas de la France de l'Est and edited by La Librairie Istra, Strasbourg, 1959 (Les Editions Berger-Levrault, Nancy, 1960). Seventy loose-leaf maps, accompanied by explanatory notes in a binder, give a more detailed treatment of the region than was possible in the national atlas. In the introduction by Professor Henri Baulig, the unity of the region from the population aspect is brought out; its frontier position and its independence of spirit are stressed.

Refer also

Atlas de la France rurale, edited by Jean Duplex (Colin, 1968).

M F Reitel: *Les régions de la France de l'Est et leur environment géographique* (Paris: PUF, 1966).

101 'Atlas de Moçambique' (Empresa Moderna, Lourenço Marques, 1962), in Portuguese, consists of folded sheets of regional maps and single sheets of thematic maps and diagrams. River systems are excellently shown in blue, with other physical features indicated by signs, as, for example, marshy country, and spot heights are given. Settlements are clearly marked, also communications and the discovery and exploration of the country are special themes treated.

102 'Atlas de Paris et de la région Parisienne', edited by Jacqueline Beaujeu-Garnier and Jean Bastié (L'Association Universitaire de Recherches Géographiques et Cartographiques—Édition Berger-Levrault, 1967), is one of the most interesting in a long line of regional atlases of France. Governmental ministries have contributed to its preparation, also organisations such as the Centre National de la Recherche Scientifique, the Institut National de la Statistique et d'Etudes Economiques and the Institut de Géographie of the Université de Paris. The governments of the District and the City of Paris and of the Department of the Seine subsidised the atlas financially and also provided substantial research assistance. The completed work comprises some 350 major maps, 961 pages of explanatory text, which complements and elaborates on the maps, making the whole a geographical study of the first order. Innumerable smaller maps and charts and statistical information are inserted throughout and there are bibliographical references at the end of each section. Particularly interesting is the examination of population patterns and the relationship of Paris to the rest of France, with an emphasis on economic factors.

Refere also
  Atlas des nappes aquiferes de la région Parisienne, 1970.

103 'Atlas de Schweiz', the national atlas of Switzerland, is in continuous publication at Berne, by Eidgenössische Landestopographie, 1965–. The atlas, edited by Professor Imhof, with the co-operation of numerous authorities, is being produced in the highest standard of Swiss cartography, using the large-scale maps of Switzerland recently completed; explanatory notes and statistical tables accompany each map.

104 'Atlas de Venezuela', published by the Republica de Venezuela Ministerio de Obras Publicas, Direccion de Cartografia Nacional, 1969, is a beautiful production, finely planned on the basis of historical cartography, current cartography, Caracas and Federal maps, thematic maps dealing with physical features, population, economy, communications, town plans; minor maps, sketchmaps, diagrams, photographs and statistics are placed throughout the work, with explanatory notes. Aerial photographs highlight the variety of relief. Included is a summary of the progress of mapping in Venezuela, accompanied by delicately reproduced early maps, for example, the Blaeu map of 1635. The use of colour is bold and imaginative, particularly in the town plans and every kind of skill has been brought to the whole production. There is a bibliography.

105 'Atlas der Deutscher Agrarlandschaft', prepared jointly by the university departments of geography and the Deutsche Forschungsgemeinschaft, was published by Franz Steiner Verlag, Weisbaden, 1962–1965. The atlas is in five sections: the first examines specific topics covering the whole extent of the Federal Republic; the second provides an analysis of the relationship between physical factors and agriculture; the third concerns agriculture round the great urban centres; the fourth shows social and economic influences on land use and, finally, a selection of the topics considered is shown mapped on larger scales. The cartography, carried out by the Institut für Landeskunde, is superb, and the text concise and clear—the whole work demonstrating the best of German scholarship and the erudite results that can be achieved by co-operation between academic geographers backed by official resources.

Refer also

Robert E Dickinson: *Germany: a general and regional geography* (Methuen, second edition, 1961).

Alan Mayhew: *Rural settlement and farming in Germany* (Batsford, 1973).

106 'Atlas der Donauländer' (Atlas of the Danubian countries), in loose-leaf elephant folio format, edited by Josef Breu, was published from 1970 as the sheets were completed by the Österreichisches Ost- und Südosteuropa-Institut. The sheets are folded and, in some cases, statistics and notes are printed on the reverse. The area covered includes Albania, Austria, Bulgaria, Czechoslovakia, Hungary, Poland, Rumania, parts of the Soviet Union and Yugoslavia. Physical features, demography, economic aspects, communications and traffic are among the topics given prominence, on which full-page notes in German, English, French and Russian are interspersed among the map sheets.

107 'Atlas der Portugal' was begun in 1941, under the direction of Aristides de Amorim Girão. A second edition, compiled during 1958–1959 to commemorate the fifth centenary of the death of Prince Henry the Navigator, is a most comprehensive and carefully planned atlas and a fine example of cartography (Coimbra, Instituto de Estudos Geográficos, Faculdade de Letras, 1960). About forty maps, at scales ranging from 1:1,500,000 to 1:5M., include geology, drainage, climate, agriculture, population, industries and trade, communications and dialects as their main topics. One section deals with Portuguese overseas provinces. Each plate is accompanied by an explanatory text in Portuguese and English.

108 'Atlas du Luxembourg' (Ministère de l'Education Nationale, 1970) begins with two prefaces, one in French by J Dupong, Minister of National Education and, in English, by Professor K C Edwards, of the University of Nottingham, Department of Geography, whose department co-operated in the preparation of the atlas. Within the six main sections—Historical aspects, Physical conditions, Administrative divisions, Demography, Economic activities and Social services—the maps are numbered to allow for new insertions. Facing each map are listed the sources used and, in some cases, descriptive comments. Some of the maps are monochrome, some in two or more colours, as considered suitable.

109 'Atlas du Maroc', prepared by the Comité National de Géographie du Maroc (Rabat: Institut Scientifique Chérifien, 1968–), is still in progress. When complete, the atlas is planned to consist of eleven sections and fifty-four sub-sections, covering all aspects of the physical and human geography of the country. The maps so far produced are detailed and attractive; they, together with the accompanying text, have already added greatly to knowledge of the Moroccan economy.

110 'Atlas for anthropology', compiled by Robert F Spencer and Eldon Johnson (Dubuque, Iowa: William Brown, 1960), provides a useful collection of folded maps in black and white, held within a spiral binding; they deal with cultural and tribal groups and language families of the world, with sections devoted to the Old World and to the New World and the racial distribution of mankind.

111 'Atlas général Larousse' was published in 1959 and distributed in Great Britain by Harrap. Seventy-two full or double plate maps are printed in six colours, in addition to many in two colours. City plans are included, also statistical tables, commentaries and a name gazetteer of some fifty-five thousand entries. Historical maps comprise fifty-five pages and thirty articles by eminent historians are a valuable feature.

112 'Atlas général Vidal-Lablache', first produced in 1894, with further issues in 1909, 1918, 1922, 1933, 1938 and 1951, is a fine example of French geography and cartography, under the direction of Paul Vidal de la Blache and Emmanuel de Martonne. The 1951 edition (Paris: Armand Colin) carries an increased number of maps in two parts, 'cartes historiques' and 'cartes géographiques', with an index gazetteer of thirty-one pages.

113 'The atlas geografic Republica Socialista România' was published by the Editura Didactica si Pedagogica, Bucharest; 109 maps, edited by Dr Victor Tufescu, present information on modern Rumania. Geology, relief forms, hydrography, climate, agriculture, industry, mining, population, communications and international trade are all covered either on double-page spreads at 1:1,750,000 or

50

single pages at 1:2,500,000, with a number of regional maps on larger scales. Diagrams and sketch maps are included as necessary, for example, to illustrate the air links between towns; most of the country is depicted also on small-scale regional maps at 1:4M.

114 'Atlas historique (Atlas Belfram): *Provence, Comtat, Orange, Nice, Monaco'*, compiled by E Baratier and others (Paris: Colin, 1969), numbers more than three hundred maps, plans of towns and buildings and textual commentary. Patron of the new atlas was President Pompidou and contributions were selected from among archaeologists, prehistorians, economists, sociologists, geographers and philologians, working under the direction of R H Bautier, of the Ecole des Chartes. Introductory maps present an outline of the geological, physiographic and archaeological background and a number of specialist studies enhance the reference value of the work. Also included are a biographical repertory and topographical dictionary.

115 'Atlas internationale Larousse', a useful reference atlas, in a second edition, 1957, contains nearly seventy folding maps, with accompanying text in French, English and Spanish.

116 'Atlas mira': an outstanding event in the development of Soviet cartography was the publication of the *Great Soviet world atlas*, 1937–40, on which a specially organised research committee had worked. The atlas was integrated in character, containing political, historical, topographical and special-purpose maps. On the outbreak of war in 1939, the two volumes so far available were withdrawn. A new atlas, edited by A N Baranov and others, was issued in its place, published in 1954 by the Chief Directorate of Geodesy and Cartography, Moscow. The USSR is covered comprehensively and other countries are well represented. The emphasis is on relief maps, plus general political and communications maps. Economic maps are not included; these may be found in the world atlas designed for school use, the *Geograficheskii atlas*, 1954. Maps of areas outside Russia are arranged by continents; each section includes general maps of politico-administrative divisions, communications and physical features, followed by detailed regional maps. Nearly all major towns and areas of particular interest have been given inset maps. The index comprises more than two hundred thousand entries. In 1962 and 1967 the State Publishing House for Geodesy and Cartography, in connection with the Ministry for Geology and

Natural Resources of the USSR, brought out new editions of the great atlas, with additional economic maps, those showing natural resources and power being especially valuable. The section covering the USSR forms, in effect, a national atlas. A medium-sized *Atlas mira*, edited by S I Shurova and others, was published in Moscow, 1959; and a small *Atlas mira*, in a third edition, 1958, is a handy atlas of political maps on smaller scales, edited by I M Itenberg and others. A pocket edition of the great atlas is available also, and still another *Atlas mira* is a military atlas, published in Moscow, 1958.

Refer also

George Kish: *Economic atlas of the Soviet Union* (University of Michigan Pr., second edition, 1971).

V I Sukhov: 'Soviet cartography and the course of its evolution', *Geodesy and Aerophotography*, 1967.

117 'Atlas nacional de Cuba' (Academia de Ciencias de Cuba, Havana, 1970), the first national atlas of Cuba, published in Spanish and Russian, comprises sections of maps and text and a summary of 'geographical data', based mainly on figures for 1965–1969; it was prepared as a homage to the 'glorious revolution . . .'. In traditional groupings, the base maps were made by the Cuban Institute of Geodesy and Cartography and cartography, colour and printing were done at the Geodesy and Cartographic Bureau attached to the Council of Ministers of the Soviet Union.

118 'Atlas nacional de España', prepared at the Instituto Geográfico y Catastral, Madrid, 1965, is in loose-leaf form, provided with a box container. Topographic and thematic maps are large and very fine, the subject matter being detailed, yet clearly visible, due particularly to the judicious choice of several type faces, of symbols and colouring. Accompanying the atlas are two bound volumes, an index of placenames and an excellent review of the geography of Spain, entitled 'Reseña geográfica'; the latter following a general introduction, is divided into main sections: Orography, Coastal Regions, Frontiers, Hydrography, Natural regions, and Spanish Territories in North Africa. Each of these sections includes many subdivisions, the subject content being linked with the relevant map sheets.

119 'Atlas narodov mira' (Atlas of the peoples of the world), edited by S I Bruk and V S Apenchénko (Moscow: Glavnoye Upravleniye

Geodezii i Kartografii Gosudarstvennogo Geologicheskogo Komiteta SSSR and Institut Etnografii im N N Miklukho-Maklaya Akademii Nauk SSSR, 1964), shows the distribution of ethnic groups throughout the world magnificently presented on 106 coloured sheets. A series of world maps portrays the distribution of states, density of population, the ethnic groups, languages and races of mankind, followed by ninety-seven regional maps showing in detail the contrasts between the density and distribution of population between countries or parts of countries. The Soviet Union is given particular attention, but there is an adequate treatment of the rest of the world. An English translation of the table of contents and the legends on the plates has been issued in a separate volume by the Telberg Book Corporation of New York. The colours and symbols on the maps were carefully considered to suggest relationships; description of the methods and much of the information had been previously published by the Institute of Ethnology. Statistical tables show details of 910 ethnic groups, as of 1961, arranged by continents and countries, also data on ethnic structure in each country of the world. An alphabetical index of 1,600 peoples gives the English equivalents of Russian names and the documentation of the whole work is excellent. Reference should be made also to [Numbers and distribution of the peoples of the world], also edited by S I Bruk, 1962, including maps, bibliographies, more detailed statistical tables and textual material, arranged as in the atlas; 1959, or the nearest year to it, has been taken as the base—for example, for India, the censuses of 1931 and 1951 were used.

120 'Atlas of African prehistory', compiled by Professor J Desmond Clark (University of Chicago Pr., 1967), consisting of twelve maps and thirty-eight overlays, was prepared for use with 'Background to evolution in Africa', a collection of papers edited by W W Bishop and Professor Clark. An international committee appointed in 1963 by the Pan-African Congress on pre-history and quaternary studies assisted in the project. The environment in which prehistoric man lived provided the central theme. Five maps at the scale of 1:20M. present topography, geology, soils, mean annual rainfall and the chief types of vegetation, based on the Bartholomew 1:10M. Centre Géologique Internationale de l'Afrique, 1964, and R W J Jeay's vegetation map of Southern Africa, 1958, with reference also to the vegetation map of the area north of the Sahara in the Oxford regional atlas. Six maps, on hypothetical rainfall and vegetation zones were compiled by Karl W Butzer. For use with these base maps the transparent overlays include information on faunal distribution, the distribution of man in the earlier middle and later Pleistocene, the distribution of trypanosomiasis and malaria and the distribution of artifacts from different periods, of prehistoric paintings and engravings.

121 **'Atlas of Alberta',** compiled by the Department of Geography, University of Alberta, was edited by T A Drinkwater and others (University of Alberta Press and University of Toronto Press, 1969), one of several atlases of the Canadian provinces recently published or in preparation. In many ways, the overall plan follows the conventional regional form and it is a true atlas also in the sense that it includes no text apart from the preface. Relief and geology, climate, water, vegetation, soil and wild life are followed by history and population, land use, agriculture, forestry, minerals, power, manufacturing and service industries, including transport and communications. There is an obvious concentration on the analysis of settlement patterns, emphasising the fact that in Alberta large areas have a small and scattered population. Double page maps are at the 1:2M scale, those on single pages are at 1:3,300,000 and there are many smaller scale maps. Production of the atlas is very fine and the symbols and colour ranges have been carefully selected.

122 **'An atlas of Anglesey',** edited by Melville Richards (Llangefni: The Anglesey Community Council, 1972), consists of 160 pages of comprehensive analysis, an excellent example of a regional atlas. Full-page regional and thematic maps are followed by descriptive text, with some photographs.

123 **'Atlas Antarktiki',** a loose-leaf atlas with a cover-to-cover English translation, edited by Dr U G Bakaev and others (Glavnoe Upravlenie Geodezii i Kartografii, 1966), consists of 225 plates carrying more than three hundred maps, charts, diagrams and comprehensive legend. The outline runs as follows: Historical matter; General aspects; Aeronomy and Physics of the Earth; Geology and Topography; Climate; Waters of the Pacific Ocean. Seven regions are distinguished, of which the maps are in a separate portfolio. Layer colouring is used to portray relief and the colouring systems throughout are very fine.

124 'Atlas of the Arab world and the Middle East' was published by Macmillan in 1960. The maps, prepared by Djambata, Amsterdam, cover physical features, political data, climate and natural regions, town plans and settlement types. North Africa is included, Libya, Egypt, Sahara region of the UAR, the Nile region, the Sudan, Near East, Syria, Northern region of the UAR and Lebanon, the Jordan region, with a separate map of Jerusalem at 1:22,500, the coastal zone of Lebanon and the region of Syria, Iraq, the Arabian Peninsula, Iran and Turkey. Endpapers depict 'The spread of Islam in the early twentieth century: refugee camps in the Near East' and 'Middle East oil concessions and the world of Islam in the Middle Ages'. There is a useful introduction and text, with photographs, throughout the work. The maps are not too cluttered with detail; the river systems and irrigation projects being especially well executed.

Refer also

Atlas of the Middle East (Tel Aviv: 'Yavneh' Publishing House, 1964).

Social, economic and political studies of the Middle East, edited C A O Van Nieuwenhuijze, published from 1971 by Brill of Leiden.

Michael Adams, *ed: The Middle East: a handbook* (Blond, 1971).

N J G Pounds and K C Kingsbury: *An atlas of Middle Eastern affairs* (Methuen, 1964, 1966).

125 'Atlas of Australian resources', the first comprehensive atlas of Australia, was prepared by the Department of Natural Development, Canberra, Commonwealth Government of Australia, and edited by Dr Konrad Frenzel (Angus and Robertson, first series 1952–1960). Thirty plates, with accompanying text, were issued as loose sheets, mounted or unmounted, and with a binder or box container, as required. The base map was on a polyconic projection, scale 1:6M. The sheets cover structure, geology, physical features, drainage and climate; land use and agricultural production; transport, all aspects of population, industries and manufactures; a special feature being a chart of 'Major developmental projects'. Commentary by a specialist accompanies each large map, illustrated by informative diagrams and special maps. In 1961, work began on a second series, planned for continuous revision, replacing the original thirty map sheets. Projections were changed as necessary and drawing and reproduction techniques improved where possible. The reverse of some sheets was used for additional maps and lists of references; a special booklet accompanies each map sheet.

126 'An atlas of Australian soils' was published by the Melbourne University Press in association with the Soils Division of the Commonwealth Scientific and Industrial Organization. Planned in ten sheets, the first sheets to appear were those for the Port Augusta-Adelaide-Hamilton area, 1960; the Melbourne-Tasmania area, 1962; Canberra-Sydney-Bourke-Armidale, 1966. Handbooks compiled by K H Northcote accompany each sheet; the maps are based upon his scheme of classification of Australian soils, using a system of primary profile forms, subdivisions, subsections and classes. The complete atlas was exhibited at the Ninth International Congress of Soil Science at Adelaide, 1968.

Refer also

K H Northcote: 'A factual key for the recognition of Australian soils' (CSIRO Divisional Report, 1960, second edition, 1965).

C G Stephen: 'The soil landscapes of Australia' (CSIRO, Soil publication, no 18, 1961).

127 'Atlas of birds in Britain' has been prepared by the British Trust for Ornithology, 1968–1972. The fieldwork for the atlas was carried out by voluntary observers who, since 1968, have been plotting on a ten km National Grid square basis, as was done in the case of the *Atlas of the British flora* (*qv*).

128 'The atlas of Britain and Northern Ireland' (Oxford: Clarendon Press, 1963) was a publication of the greatest cartographical interest. In the words of the publishers, the atlas is 'a statement, on a general basis, of modern Britain's resources, physical, economic and industrial—a complete and ordered portrait of this country from the rocks beneath to the industry above'. Historical geography is not included. Data are taken from the 1951 census, from 1955 agricultural and fisheries figures, with 1948–57 averages, and from 1954–56 figures for the majority of the industrial maps; the latest information possible has been incorporated where this is particularly vital, as with atomic energy and air traffic. A fold-out section at the back gives details of authorities and sources. While preserving the traditional form, an original approach is revealed, both in the four-fold overall design and in the treatment and colouring of individual maps. The standard scale adopted was 1:2M, which allows the whole area to be shown on one page; this is also the scale of the very useful 'transparent reference overlay'. The 1:1M scale and the 1:500,000 were used for successively greater detail. The larger-scale maps and the overlay are marked with the national grid, which is used also in the gazeteer. Imagination is one keynote of the atlas, revealed in the choice of subjects—for example, the map of coastal relief—and in the variety of cartographic techniques and use of colour. Another key-note is the practical approach throughout, the constant invitation to purposive use, shown, for example, in the placing of pairs of maps for comparative study on facing pages, the additional information on the map sheets both in word and diagrammatic form, the notes at the end and the evocative use of symbols.

129 'Atlas of the British flora', edited by F H Perring and M Walters (Nelson for the Botanical Society of the British Isles, 1962), consists of black and white distribution maps portraying 1,700 flowering plants and ferns; included also are twelve transparent overlays concerned with climate, topography and geology. The text begins with an introductory history of the mapping of plant distribution, followed by an outline of the method used in preparing the maps for this work and the interpretation of the maps.

130 'Atlas of Canada' (1906, 1915) was, in its third edition, undertaken by the Geographical Branch of the Department of Mines and Technical Surveys in 1959 (dated 1957), a superb achievement covering all aspects, with special emphasis on economic factors—'an outline of the physical background and the economic development of the nation at mid-century' (Foreward). Particularly useful is the series of urban land use maps, linked with the World Land Use Survey of the International Geographical Union. The original atlas of Canada, 1906, was published by the Department of the Interior of the Canadian Government, revised and enlarged in 1915. The first printing of a fourth edition is in the form of folios of loose maps intended for inclusion in a box binder. Explanatory text clarifies the more complex topics.

Refer also
Ice atlas of Arctic Canada, compiled by Charles Swithinbank (Canada Defence Research Board, 1960).
L J O'Brien, *ed: Canadian cartography, 1962. Proceedings* of

the Symposium on Cartography, held at the Canadian Institute of Surveying, February 1962.

131 'Atlas of Central Europe' (Kartographisches Institut Bertelsmann, second edition, 1962; Murray, 1963) had the aim of promoting the cause of European unity. It covers Germany, the Low Countries, Switzerland and Austria, stressing the distribution of major features of production, industry, population and communications. Twenty pages in full colour, on a basic scale of 1:1M., include some physical and other maps not found in other British or American publications. The second edition was greatly modernised, though the background colours are still perhaps rather heavy. Names throughout have not been translated. There is an index of more than thirty-seven thousand entries.

Refer also

The atlas *Östliches Mitteleuropa* (Bielefeld: Velhagen and Klasing, 1959–).

132 'Atlas of Denmark' is a particularly excellent example of co-operation in the production of a national atlas, by geographers associated with the University Geographical Laboratory, a number of firms and individuals, the Royal Danish Geographical Society, the Carlsberg Foundation and the Danish Government. Edited by Niels Nielsen, in five volumes, 1949–, the atlas includes information on historical evolution and occupational changes, together with detailed treatment of the ten sections into which the country has been divided and accompanying text in Danish and English. Air photography has been used to great effect.

Refer also

W M Gertsen: 'Danish topographic mapping', *The cartographic journal,* December 1970, which is illustrated by reproductions of map excerpts.

133 'Atlas of diseases', produced in sheets, 1950–, by the American Geographical Society, under the direction of Dr Jacques M May, was issued with the quarterly *Geographical review,* in which there appeared descriptions supplementary to the annotations on the map sheets themselves. The maps include world distribution of major diseases such as cholera, leprosy, and two studies of human starvation: 'Sources of selected foods' and 'Diets and deficiency diseases'. With each map are bibliographies and references; in addition, Dr May's three-volume work, *Studies in medical geography*, 1958, 1961, should be used in conjunction with the maps. The maps portraying studies of poliomyelitis and cholera data and of the distribution of malaria and yellow fever all demonstrate different fields of research in which progress has been encouraged by the application of techniques demonstrated here. The First Report of the Commission on Medical Geography (Ecology of Health and Disease) of the International Geographical Union was presented to the seventeenth International Geographical Congress, 1952, by Jacques M May; in it, he considers the study of diseases and the progress of their correlation with the physical environment. He discusses the presentation of such data on maps, mentions the Society's *Atlas of diseases* and future research in the field.

Refer also

René Dubos: *Man, medicine and environment* (New York: Praeger, 1968).

N D McGlashan, *ed: Medical geography: techniques and field studies* (Methuen, 1972; university paperback, 1974).

R P Misra: *Medical geography of India* (New Delhi: National Book Trust, India, 1970).

L D Stamp: *The geography of life and death; some aspects of medical geography*, 1964.

Studies in medical geography, which have been published regularly from 1958 by the American Geographical Society.

134 'The atlas of the earth', edited by T Loftas (Mitchell Beazley with George Philip, 1972), comprises an encyclopaedic collection of maps, illustrations, diagrams and legends, grouped within the headings 'The good earth', 'The earth in space', 'Life', 'Resources' and 'Man'. The map section, 'World atlas', was taken from Philip's *University atlas*, the individual maps being on larger scales and having added a short feature showing 'National Parks'.

Refer also

Ronald Tank, *ed: Focus on environmental geology: a collection of case histories and readings from original sources* (OUP, 1973).

135 'Atlas of Edinburgh', published by the Edinburgh Branch of the Geographical Association, 1965, comprises thirty-nine pages of maps, text and illustrations in a paper cover, with a spiral binding;

the material was provided by members of the Branch, mainly by teachers of geography in Edinburgh schools, organised and introduced by Professor J Wreford Watson, including a brief outline of 'The rise and growth of Edinburgh'. All aspects of physical features and climate, land use, social and statistical data are incorporated and the maps are interspersed with annotated photographs, graphs, diagrams and drawings.

136 'An atlas of Ethiopia', in a revised edition, was prepared by Mesfin Wolde-Mariam and the Department of Geography, Haile Selassie I University (Addis Ababa: Ministry of Education, 1970). A preliminary atlas was issued in 1962. In the second edition, new statistical information was added by the Central Statistics Office of the Ethiopian Government and by the UN Economic Commission for Africa. Most of the information is presented cartographically, on some sixty maps, the remainder by tables and diagrams; the maps are monochrome and included are some aerial photographs. No gazetteer was incorporated.

137 'An atlas of European affairs' (Methuen, 1964), with text by Norman J G Pounds and maps by Robert C Kingsbury, is built around the theme of the continuing importance of Europe in world affairs. Monochrome sketch-maps and facing text deal with many aspects of European politics and economics, population, language and religious groups, individual countries and the then great coordinating bodies such as the European Community, OECD and NATO, the Coal and Steel Community and the European Economic Community. It is a useful reference work, but hardly an atlas.

138 'Atlas of European birds', compiled by K H Voous (Nelson, 1960), originally published earlier in the year as *Atlas van de Europese vogels* by Elsevier of Amsterdam, was translated by Professor Voous into English. For each species of bird native to Europe there is a map showing its breeding range, not only within the continent but extralimitally also. The fine collection of 355 photographs covers the essential features of the bird and each bird is also described, giving factual information of habitat, characteristics, nesting and migration, all from a geographical point of view.

139 'Atlas of European cities' (Hammond, 1967), a handy personal guide for the business or pleasure traveller, is small in format; the black and white or blue and white street plans have basic information printed on the opposite pages, with spaces left for notes.

140 'Atlas of European history', edited by E W Fox and H S Deighton (OUP, 1969), contains two types of maps. The first is concerned with topography, expressed by layer colouring and shading, as it has formed the basis for the location of historical settlements and other developments. These maps have purposely been kept as clear of detail as possible, so that only the really important names can be quickly assimilated and remain in the mind's eye. Secondly, there are the historical thematic maps, either inset with the physical maps or as separate sheets. Good colour arrangements in the land areas set off the grey sea and allow details to stand out well, such as the changing political condition of Europe, shown in bold black. The editor states—'The first requirement for this Atlas, then, was that it should provide information . . . as simply and clearly as possible'. There are several interesting innovations; for example, the double page of 'The great explorations' and 'Renaissance Italy'.

Refer also

J F Horrabin: *An atlas of European history from the second to the twentieth century* (Gollancz, 1935).

C T Smith: *An historical geography of Western Europe before 1800* (Longmans, 1967).

141 'Atlas of evolution', compiled by Sir Gavin de Beer (Nelson, 1964), consists of 202 pages of concise text including many line diagrams, photographs and drawings, in which the bold use of colour makes an immediate visual impact. The quality of the map content could be improved, but the printing, done in Holland, is very fine; there is a bibliography and an adequate index.

142 'Atlas of Finland', first published by the Geographical Society of Finland in 1899, was issued 'to assist the people of Finland to know themselves and their country'. A second edition appeared in 1911 and the third, 1925–28, comprised two volumes, thirty-eight plates of maps and a volume of text. The fourth edition, compiled by the Geographical Society and the Institute of Geography of the University of Helsinki under the direction of Leo Aario, was completed in 1960, the cartographic work and reproduction of the plates being done by the General Survey Office. The atlas contains 445 maps and diagrams, on scales ranging from 1:1M to 1:9M, mostly on double-page sheets; comparison of the maps is facilitated, as groups of related maps are shown together. The atlas is a splendid example of a national atlas, covering all aspects of the nature and economy of the country and, from the first, has been of special interest as a survey of a northern country in detail and at such uniformly high standard. The meterological section, for example, includes frost data and the section on forests and water power is of great practical value. Population density and analysis are particularly well treated, as are agriculture and industry. Throughout, the atlas gives an indefinable impression of enthusiasm and pride of country. Experimental symbols have been used with effect. There is a foldout 'Communes' map, with inset 'Administrative provinces, 1960', which can be kept open while consulting other sheets. The notes in the 1960 edition are briefer than those for former editions; in this edition, all references to matters not presented in the atlas itself have been omitted, since the publication of *Suomen Maantieteen Käsikirj*—Handbook of Finnish Geography, 1936 and 1951, there has been no need for such copious texts. *Explanatory notes*, a separate volume published in 1962, is in English. Legends and marginal information on the map sheets are in Finnish, Swedish and English and there are detailed contents pages. The Preface was translated into English by Richard Ojakangas and others.

Refer also

Fennia, 1889– and *Suomi*, 1952 (a general geography of Finland), both published by the Geographical Society of Finland.

Hikka Aaltonen: *Books in English on Finland* (Turku University Library, 1964).

Hillar Kallas and Sylvie Nickels, *ed: Finland: creation and construction* (Allen and Unwin, 1969).

Raye R Platt, *ed: Finland and its geography: an American Geographical Society handbook* (New York: Duell, Sloan and Pearce; Little, Brown, 1955).

143 The 'Atlas of Florida', by Erwin Raisz and associates with text by John R Dunkle (Gainsville, 1964), was prepared in the Department of Geography of the University of Florida. It contains 57 pages of colourful information and three supplementary pages of statistics. An enterprising range of methods is used to present this State, 1845–, which has had the fastest growing population of any in the Union; time charts, bar graphs, divided circles and flow diagrams complement quantitative and non-quantitative maps, accompanied by notes of past events and present scenes; a popular atlas, significant of the current trend to reproduce local characteristics geographically.

144 'Atlas of Germany', see *Die Bundersrepublik Deutschland in Karten* and *Deutscher Planungsatlas.*

145 'Atlas of glaciers in South Norway', prepared by G Ostrem and T Ziegler (Oslo: Hydrologisk Avdeling, 1969), is available from the Hydrological Division, Norwegian Water Resources and Electricity Board, Oslo. The work, compiled as a result of a glacier inventory carried out in accordance with a resolution of the International Hydrological Decade, contains maps of each drainage basin, showing the glacier outline and existing water gauges. A description is given of the various areas, together with photographs of typical glacier types. Text is in Norwegian and English.
Refer also
    W V Lewis, *ed: Investigations on Norwegian cirque glaciers* (Royal Geographical Society, 1960, *Research* series, no 4).

146 'Atlas of the Great Barrier Reef', compiled by W G H Maxwell (Elsevier, 1969), is mainly a geological appreciation of the Australian Great Barrier Reef province, illustrated with maps, photographs and figures—a book, rather than an atlas proper. Following an introductory chapter, chapters II and III provide short and conventional reviews of the morphology and structure of the South West Pacific, which are amply supported by maps and cross-sections, together with a summary of the tectonic framework and evolution of eastern Queensland and its continental shelf. Chapter IV presents a series of detailed maps and cross-sections showing the tectonic evolution of the continental shelf and continental islands. There follows a long chapter VI on the morphology and distribution of reefs, with maps, cross-sections, aerial and underwater photographs and the final chapter summarises the results of extensive fieldwork and data analysis, accompanied by a group of maps covering the one thousand miles of Queensland's broad continental shelf.

147 'Atlas of Greece', loose-leaf, in Greek, English and French, includes maps of the Departments of Greece at 1:200,000, adapted to the data of the population census of 1961 (Athens: National Statistical Service of Greece, 1965). The maps, on folded plates, were originally prepared to serve the needs of the Population-Housing and Agriculture-Livestock Census of 1961; the NSSG, however, considered that they could be of multiple use for the conduct of the new statistical surveys planned for the future and could also be made the framework for sample selection. Features especially well marked include roads—'carriage', national, municipal and communual—, railways, hydrographic networks and settlements. Ground relief is shown by altitude curves (per 200 m) and auxiliary curves (per 100m), with the corresponding shading emphasising the more important planimetric details. There is a separately published *Directory*.

> *Refer also*
> *Economic and social atlas of Greece* (Athens: Centre of Economic Research, Social Sciences Centre, 1964).
> P – Y Péchoux and M Sivignon: *Les Balkans* (Paris: PUF, 1971).
> E G Woods: *The Baltic region: a study in physical and human geography* (Methuen, 1932)—a classic.

148 'Atlas of the history of geographical discoveries and explorations', edited by K B Martova and others (Moscow, 1959), prepared under the direction of an editorial committee, of which the Chairman was K A Salichtchev. Ninety-two pages of maps are especially valuable for coverage of Russian exploration.

149 'The atlas of Indonesian resources' (Djakarta: The National Atlas Agency) began publication in 1963 with an initial group of thirty sheets, which appeared during the course of the next three years.

> *Refer also*
> G J Missen: *Viewpoint on Indonesia: a geographical study* (Nelson, 1972).

150 'Atlas of Islamic history', compiled by Harry W Hazard, with maps executed by H Lester Cooke, jr, and J McA Smiley (Princeton University Press, 1954, third edition, in the *Oriental studies* series, volume 12), is intended, from the first appearance of the work in 1951, for students, businessmen, government officials and all concerned with Near and Middle East affairs. It assembles material otherwise scattered and the historical analyses in the third edition are brought up to date to 1953. The Islamic world from Morocco to Iran is the area considered in the main part of the work, from the seventh century—the first Islamic century—to the twentieth century, the thirteenth Islamic century, with notes on Moslem sea power, the Moslem calendar, the Crusades and the Ottoman Empire. A final section deals with Islam in the Middle and Far East, with India, Central Asia, South-eastern Asia and Indonesia. Each map is faced by explanatory text; there are conversion tables and an index.

151 'Atlas of Israel', the national atlas, published in a second (English language) edition, 1970, was designed to combine and present in concise form a vast amount of information about every aspect of the country. The contents span the whole range of the history of the Holy Land from pre-historic times to the present. An official work of the State of Israel, prepared by the Survey and Elsevier Publishing Company, Amsterdam, it is the most reliable, accurate and comprehensive work on Israel yet produced, the result of co-operation by a large team of eminent scientists, economists and historians from the Hebrew University at Jerusalem, working in concert with the staff of the Department of Surveys and other Israeli government institutions. The first (Hebrew) edition was published sheet by sheet between 1956 and 1964 by the Department of Surveys, Ministry of Labour (Survey of Israel) and the Bialik Institute of the Jewish Agency. Sub-titles were in English. In compiling the maps for the English edition, coverage was extended in many cases to include the entire area under Israeli administration since 1967; it includes Judea and Samaria, as well as the Gaza Plain and the Golan Heights. Production was given the most intensive consideration. The 120 gram paper was manufactured in the Hadera Paper Mill, the inks were specially made in Haifa and the colours mixed at the Reproduction Department of the Survey of Israel. The double-page sheets are grouped as follows: Cartography, Geomorphology, Geology, Climate, Hydrology, Botany, Zoology, Land Utilization, History, Population, Settlements, Agriculture, Industry and trade, Communications, Services, such as cultural features and tourism. Each section is sub-divided and each introduced by concise, informative text. A number of the historical maps have never appeared before. One of these is a half-page map of Palestine as it was under the Arabs, 640–1099, another that of Palestine under the Mamluks, 1291–1516 and a third of the period 1516–1900. The spread of Christianity is clearly recorded and there are maps showing archaeological excavation sites, by period. The Preface outlines the approach to the atlas, transliteration of place-names, a short pronunciation guide and a description of the early maps, especially of *The Medeba map,* with reproductions, including 'Map of the Palestine Exploration Fund' and 'British maps of the early twentieth century', each with a bibliography.

Refer also

F J Shulman: *American and British doctoral dissertations on Israel and Palestine in modern times* (Ann Arbor: Xerox University Microfilms, 1973).

152 'Atlas of Japan: physical, economic and social', edited by Ryvjiro Ishida (Tokyo: International Society for Educational Information, 1970), was a joint government-academic work, undertaken in conjunction with the compilation of basic reference works about Japan in the major languages. The sixty-four pages of maps are accompanied by a textual commentary in English, French and Spanish. Population data was taken from the 1960 Census; otherwise, the information is more up to date.

Note that two other excellent atlases on Japan are wholly in Japanese and not easily available in Britain: *Nippon Keizai Chizu* (economic), edited by K Aki and others and *Nippon Rekishi Chizu* (historical), edited by T Nishioka and S Hattori.

153 'Atlas of London and the London region' was prepared by Emrys Jones and D J Sinclair at the London School of Economics and Political Science (Pergamon Press, 1968). The total of seventy maps fit into a container. Work on the atlas had been in progress by a team of experts during the previous seven years, beginning with a programme of research into socio-economic topics, supported by the Anthropological and Geographical Research Division of the School. In the earliest stages, further financial assistance was given by the Frederick Soddy Trust. In 1965, a grant from the Department of Economic Affairs made actual production practical and this was later backed by an additional grant from the Greater London Council. The maps in the atlas are at various decimal scales, showing a series of areas from Central London to the whole of south-east England. The statistical units at which the demographic and economic data are mapped vary according to the scales. The choice of topics was governed in part by the funds available. All the maps are on DD standard sheets, so that they can be stored flat, once folded. Printing is on one side of the sheet only and each map is accompanied by a brief text panel and explanatory key. Two sections, one on physical background and the other showing historical background, preface the main body of the atlas, which deals with aspects of population distribution, density, housing standards, land utilisation, industry, employment and transport. Such sources as the 1961 Census, the 1966 Sample Census and the London Traffic Survey were used, in addition to newly gathered data. A base map is printed in pale grey; in all the other maps, colouring is bold and, probably, controversial.

Refer also

North London geographer, journal of the Geography Department of the Polytechnic of North London

Claude Chaline: *La metropole Londonienne: croissance et planification urbaine* (Paris: Colin, 1973).

J T Coppock and H C Prince, *ed: Greater London* (Faber, 1964).

David Donnison and David Eversley, *ed: London: urban patterns, problems and policies*. A study sponsored by the Centre for Environmental Studies (Heinemann, 1973).

Note that atlases of individual towns and cities within their region have been on the increase during the past two or three decades. Further examples include *An atlas of Durham City*, edited by H Bowen-Jones at the Department of Geography, Durham College in the University of Durham, 1960; *An atlas of Harrogate*, prepared by J A Patmore and others at the Liverpool University Department of Geography (Corporation of Harrogate, 1963); *A Gloucestershire and Bristol atlas* (Bristol and Gloucestershire Archaeological Society, 1961). *See also Atlas of Edinburgh.*

154 '**Atlas of meteorology:** *a series of over four hundred maps . . . ,*' compiled by J G Bartholomew and A J Herbertson and edited by Alexander Buchan, was issued under the patronage of the Royal Geographical Society (Bartholomew, 1899) as volume III of Bartholomew's *Physical atlas*. Still basically useful and evocative of ideas, its information must now be supplemented by reference to, for example, the US Navy *Marine climatic atlas of the world,* in four volumes, 1955–1958; the *Climatological atlas of the world,* by H Walter and H Lieth, published in a binder by G Fischer, Jena, as the first part of a three-volume work; and the *World map of climatology,* by H E Landsberg and others, edited by E Rodenwaldt and H Jusatz (Springer-Verlag, 1963; second edition 1965).

Refer also

R G Barry and A H Perry: *Synoptic climatology* (Methuen, 1973).

John Lockwood: *World climatology: an environmental approach* (Arnold, 1974).

155 'Atlas of Mexico', compiled by Michael E Bonine and others (University of Texas, Bureau of Business Research, 1970), aims to provide a cross-section of Mexican economic and social development in the mid-1960s. In progressive groupings are treated the chief physical features of the country, the nature of its life, population, agriculture and land use, transport, trade, commerce and industry. An appendix includes statistical tables and diagrams and a bibliography of sources. The maps are clear, on two scales, the physical features being drawn on the larger and the social and economic data on the smaller.

Refer also

Bibliografía industrial de México

David Barkin and Timothy King: *Regional economic development: the River Basin approach in Mexico* (CUP, 1970).

Ezio Faccioli: 'Soil dynamics research in Mexico', *Nature and resources* . . . , July–October, 1973.

Timothy King: *Mexico: industrialization and trade policies since 1940* (OUP for the Development Centre of the Organization for Economic Co-operation and Development, 1970).

Clark W Reynolds: *The Mexican economy: twentieth-century structure and growth* (Yale University Pr., 1970).

156 'Atlas of Minnesota resources and settlement', compiled by John R Borchert and Donald P Yaeger (St Paul: Minnesota State Planning Agency, 1968, revised 1969), was intended to be 'a working document . . . produced relatively quickly and inexpensively' and, as such, provides a useful example of such a working tool. The concept began as a product of a seminar on Population Estimates and Projections for State Planning, sponsored by the Minnesota State Planning Agency and held at the University of Minnesota Department of Geography during 1967–68. The work comprises 262 pages of maps, some in colour, the rest in black and white, and three maps in a pocket, with brief textual comment.

157 'Atlas of New Zealand geography', compiled by G J R Linge and

R M Frazer (A and H Reed, Wellington, 1966), contains sixty-one black and white maps and thirty pages of text. The arrangement of topics treated runs from geology and surface relief, climate and soils, agriculture and land use to population and industry; a series of topographic maps illustrates particular regions and there are special land use and industrial maps of Auckland. Many insets and diagrams are included and each map is explained by a page of text and bibliographies, including articles from journals.

158 **'An atlas of North American affairs',** compiled by D K Adams and H B Rodgers (Methuen paperback, 1969), is a handy reference volume featuring topics of current interest, such as the problem of 'Megalopolis', as well as traditional subjects—climate, population, etc. All the maps are monochrome, varying in scale with the subject, some having insets. The Canadian part of the continent is not comprehensively covered and Alaska is confined to an inset. A recurrent theme is the transformation of the economies of both Canada and the United States by large-scale industrialisation.

    Refer also

    W P Cumming *et al: The discovery of North America* (Elek, 1971).

    L M Hacker, *comp: Major documents in American economic history* (Princeton, New Jersey: Van Nostrand, 1961, two volumes).

    N J G Pounds: *North America* (Murray, third, revised edition, 1971).

    J Wreford Watson: *North America: its countries and regions* (Longmans, 1963; second edition, 1968).

159 **'Atlas of physical, economic and social resources of the Lower Mekong Basin'** (New York: United Nations, 1968) was prepared under the direction of the United States Agency for International Development, Bureau for East Asia, by the Engineer Agency for Resources Inventories and the Tennessee Valley Authority for the Committee for Co-ordination of Investigations of the Lower Mekong Basin, the United Nations Economic Commission for Asia and the Far East. Areas covered are Cambodia, Laos, the Republic of Viet-Nam and Thailand. This unique collection of maps provides an inventory, in cartographic and narrative form, of the natural and man-made resources within the drainage basin of the Mekong. The finished product represents years of cumulative effort by many organisations and individuals in the fields of mapping, aerial photography and geography. Individual maps will be periodically reviewed and a companion bibliography is in process of preparation.

160 'An atlas of population change 1951–66—*the Yorkshire and Humberside Planning Region*', compiled by D G Symes and E G Thomas, with R R Dean (Hull University, Department of Geography, Miscellaneous series, no 8, 1968), presents a successful example of contemporary work in population mapping. Here are seventeen folded maps portraying the demographic analysis of the 1961 Census statistics compared with population changes during 1951–1961. The mapping symbols of three maps are the now familiar proportional spheres; the rest of the maps are compiled on an experimental system of choropleth mapping. There is some explanatory text. Local authority boundary lines are printed on a transparent overlay.

161 'Atlas of the Prairie Provinces', published by OUP, Canada, 1971, is the first large-scale atlas to emphasise the basic unity of the central western part of North America; the maps cover all major aspects of the physical, ethnic and economic geography of the prairies, including also a climatological table for selected areas and details of the populations and principal economies of the Indian communities in the three provinces.

162 'Atlas of Saskatchewan' edited by J Howard Richards (University of Saskatchewan, 1969), provides a wealth of information put together by a number of specialists, with K I Fung as cartographic editor. The statistical maps are interesting for the mathematical techniques used in their compilation. Text is included on each aspect treated and the whole atlas is most attractive and carefully documented.

163 'Atlas of social and economic regions of Europe' has been in process of preparation by the Soziographisches Institut an der Universität Frankfurt am Main, under the direction of Ludwig Neundörfer (Verlag August Lutzeyer, Baden-Baden, 1964–), under the aegis of the Council of Europe and with the assistance of the government of the Federal Republic of Germany and the Deutsche Forschungsgemeinschaft. Intended as a basis for the social and economic planning of Europe in the second half of the twen-

70

tieth century, the work is being issued in instalments, in separate folders, each containing a hundred maps, accompanied by texts and keys in German, English and French, detailed gazetteers and lists of statistical sources.

Refer also

T G Jordan: *The European culture area: a systematic geography* (Harper and Row, 1973).

164 'Atlas of South-East Asia', with introduction by D G E Hall (Macmillan: St Martin's Press, 1964) and maps by Djambatan, Amsterdam, consists of sixty-four pages of maps portraying the physical characteristics and the political and land-use conditions applying in the Philippines, Indonesia, Singapore, Malaya, Thailand, Indochina and Burma. Scales range from 1:25,000 for the town plans to 1:40M for general and distribution maps. Historical maps have been used as endpapers. Photographs accompany the explanatory text.

Refer also

P P Courtenay: *A geography of trade and development in Malaya* (Bell, 1972).

Lim Chong-Yah: *Economic development of modern Malaya* (OUP, 1967).

165 'Atlas of Tanzania', compiled, published and printed by the Surveys and Mapping Division, Ministry of Lands, Settlement and Water Development, Dar-es-Salaam, 1967, replaces the *Atlas of Tanzania* of 1957. The aim of the later work is stated in the Foreword—'not as a luxury or an academic publication . . .' but to present 'Tanzania's human and natural resources for use in development planning'. The maps are printed in many colours on high quality paper; there are some omissions compared with the previous atlas and some new material has been added, such as the maps of potential land use and fisheries. Explanatory notes face the maps and it would be helpful to refer to some of the *Research papers* and *Notes* issued by the Bureau of Resource Assessment and Land Use Planning at the University College, Dar-es-Salaam, also to the reports of the second Five Year Development Plan, 1969–74.

Refer also

L Berry, *ed: Tanzania in maps* (ULP, 1971).

John Hutton, *ed: Urban challenge in East Africa* (Nairobi: East African Publishing House, 1972).

W T W Morgan, *ed: East Africa: its peoples and resources* (OUP, second edition, 1972).

166 'Atlas of the Union of South Africa', prepared by A M and W J Talbot in collaboration with the Trigonometry Survey Office and under the aegis of the National Committee for Social Research (Government Printer, 1960), is in English and Afrikaans. This is a comprehensive atlas, covering numerous aspects of South Africa; maps show relief, geology, mining, soils, vegetation, climate, water resources, agriculture, industries, population, occupations, transportation and trade. The introductory texts are valuable, illustrated by sketchmaps, tables and diagrams.

It may be helpful to refer also to the smaller *Road atlas and touring guide of Southern Africa,* published by the Automobile Association of South Africa. In addition to the detailed maps, diagrammatic maps are included of the entrances and exits of more than two hundred towns.

167 'Atlas of the United States': *see 'National atlas of the United States'.*

168 'Atlas of the universe', compiled by Patrick Moore (Mitchell Beazley with George Philip, 1970), includes such information on the history of scientific thought and discovery, on physics and astrophysics, celestial mechanics, chemistry, geology and technology as will help in the understanding of the universe in which the earth is but one planet. Maps are accompanied by photographs, graphs and diagrams, grouped in five sections. 'Observation and exploration of space'; 'An atlas of the earth from space'; 'The Moon'; 'The solar system'; and 'The stars'. Each section includes explanatory text, illustrations and captions. A foreword was contributed by Sir Bernard Lovell.

169 'Atlas of Western Europe', compiled by Jean Dollfus and an advisory committee drawn from several European universities, has been issued in English by Murray and in French, German, Italian and Dutch by the Istituto Geografico de Agostini, Novara. The atlas has been constructed with the Common Market in mind. Paul-Henri Spaak has contributed a preface. Twenty-four colour maps and three in monochrome, accompanied by illustrations, depict the relief and climate, geological and mineral deposits, aspects of demography, land use, communications and industries, followed by an index of principal place-names and their equivalents. The monochrome maps are of 'Administrative divisions', 'European Community-Council of Europe-NATO' and 'Europe and Africa'.

Compare

170 'Atlas of central Europe', taken from the latest reprint of the *Bertelsmann world atlas* and made available in Britain by Murray, 1963. At the standard scale 1:1M., basic topographic data are presented in greater detail than in most atlases; new trends in geographical teaching and thinking have been kept in mind and some map sheets use a 'sampling' method in depth, rather than attempting an overall more superficial coverage. There is a comprehensive index of more than thirty-seven thousand entries.

171 'Atlas of the world commodities, production, trade and consumption: *an economic-geographical survey'*, by Olof Jonasson and Bo Carlsund (Göteborg: Akademiforlaget/Gumperts . . .; Scandinavian University Books, 1961, for the Göteburg Graduate School of Economics, where Olof Jonasson is Professor), contains maps of the staple goods in world trade, with major emphasis on animal and vegetable raw materials, also minerals, coal and petroleum. The section on international sea-borne shipping is most useful. The maps are diagrammatic, in black and white, accompanied by brief text and statistics.

172 'An atlas of world history', compiled by S de Vries and others (Nelson, 1965), comprises sixty-four maps, each designed to clarify one topic, in black and white and with textual commentary. There are useful plans and a section 'Battlefields of antiquity'.

173 'Atlas of world physical features', compiled by R E Snead (Wiley, 1972), was based on texts by Strahler and Thornbury on physical geography and geomorphology and it aims to complement these standard works by portraying the distribution of a wide variety of landforms. The Atlas is in eight sections, each with a short explanatory text, totalling 103 maps. References in each section and at the end note source material and give suggestions for further study. Particularly interesting are the maps showing climatic parameters followed by maps of morpho-climatic regions, types of weathering and variation in erosion rates.

174 'Atlas of the world's resources', issued by the Department of Geography, University of Maryland, in three volumes (Prentice-Hall, 1952–1954), with notes and accompanying texts, under the chief editorship of William van Royen, consists of: I The agricultural resources of the world; II The mineral resources of the world; III Forest and fishery resources of the world.

Refer also

John A Dawson and John C Doornkamp, *ed: Evaluating the human environment: essays in applied geography* (Arnold, 1973).

Brian J Skinner: *Earth resources* (Prentice-Hall, 1969).

175 'Atlas Östliches Mitteleuropa' was prepared by T Kraus, E Meynen, H Mortensen and H Schlenger (Velhagen and Klasing, 1959). It is a superb, loose-leaf production, very well documented, containing clear maps, the product of fine cartography and a judicious use of colour. The regional maps, at the scale 1:300,000, are in a pocket at the end and a set of aerial photographs complements the maps.

176 'Atlas över Sverige', a magnificent atlas giving a clear picture of the country's natural and cultural geography, population and economy, trade and port traffic, was first prepared in 1900, with a new edition, published in sheets, 1953– by Svenska Sällskapet för Antropologi och Geografi, Stockholm (Kartografiska Institutet, General-Stabens Litografiska Anstallt, Stockholm). Text is in Swedish, with English summaries, map titles and legends.

177 'Atlas Porrua de la Republica Mexicana' was prepared in collaboration with Professor Jorge Hernandes Millares and Professor Alejandro Carillo Escribano (Editorial Porrua, S A, Mexico, 1966) Included are physical maps, general and historical monographs concerning the federal states and black and white plans of the main settlements. Vital statistics are usefully gathered together and there are some fine photographs and an explanatory text.

Refer also

Claude Bataillon: *Les régions géographiques au Mexique* (Paris: Institut des Hautes Études de L'Amérique Latine, 1967).

J L Tamayo: *Geografía moderna de México* (Mexico: Editorial Patriad, 1960).

178 'Atlas van Nederland' is a fine example of the work of the Topographic Service, Delft, which is responsible for the production ('sGravenhage: Government Printing and Publishing Office, 1963–). Work began in 1963, following planning by the Ministry of Education, the Royal Netherlands Geographical Society and the Society for Economic and Social Geography, the complete atlas containing 109 sheets, loose-leaf in a sturdy binder. Most sheets carry Dutch and English explanatory texts, sometimes illustrated with diagrams. The sheets, as issued, represented all sections of the atlas, beginning with a sheet demonstrating the history of cartographic techniques in the Netherlands by sixteen fragments of printed maps from the sixteenth century to the present, compiled by Dr C Koeman. Contemporary social and economic conditions are meticulously mapped, with special inset maps and diagrams as required. The treatment of soils is particularly outstanding. The clear colouring throughout is striking and aesthetically pleasing, both in all the thematic maps and in the relief map, 'The Netherlands and surrounding countries' on 1:500,000, in which eight layer colours are used, with contouring, to show land relief, and five colours to show sea depths and tidal flats. Great skill has been shown in the selection and placing of names to avoid over-crowding.

179 Atlases Two outstanding periods of atlas production may be distinguished, the last thirty years or so of the sixteenth century and our own times. Collections of maps began to appear some years before the name 'atlas' was applied to them. Some of these have been retrospectively called atlases, notably the collection called the *Lafreri Atlas*. Antonio Lafreri, an engraver and map-seller in Rome, engraved, about the year 1570, an elaborate title-page for this collection and, among the figures represented was that of Atlas, this being the first occasion known on which this symbol was used. Rumold Mercator caused the term 'atlas' to be universally adopted for map-collections by using the Atlas figure as the centrepiece of the title page of his 1595 collection, *Atlas sive Cosmographicae Meditationes de Fabrica mundi et Fabricati figura*. The conception of an atlas thereafter was of a collection of maps brought together with some unifying characteristic and such an unadorned collection is still referred to as being in the 'classical' tradition of atlas design.

The *Theatrum Orbis Terrarum* of Abraham Ortelius, 1570, is usually thought to be the first collection of maps gathered together by a scholarly method. Some thirty editions were published before

1598, besides an English edition in 1606 and a final Latin edition in 1612. Gerhard Mercator advanced still further in the scholarly approach to atlas design and his concept of the complete *Geographia*, of which only a small part was finished before his death, bridges the centuries towards contemporary regional and national atlases. In 1595, Rumold Mercator brought out the great folio volume, abovementioned, which embodies his father's genius. Three more great names soon became known in atlas production, that of Jodocus Hondius, who purchased the plates of Mercator's *Atlas* in 1604, of Jan Jansson and of the Blaeus, father and son. From the house of Blaeu came especially outstanding achievements, all enlarging on previous work, including the *Atlantis Appendix*, 1630; *Appendix Theatri A. Ortelii et Atlantis G. Mercatoris*, 1631; *Novus Atlas*, 1634; *Theatrum Orbis Terrarum, sive Atlas Novus*, 1635; and the *Atlas Maior sive Cosmographia Blaviana*. Following the lead of the Dutch cartographers, map publishers in France and Germany produced many atlases before the end of the century. In Italy, the great V M Coronelli, Cosmographer to the Republic of Venice, is remembered chiefly for his globes and his *Atlante Veneto* in twelve volumes, 1697. By the beginning of the nineteenth century, the atlas as we know it was in existence, gradually improving both in accuracy and in cartographic presentation.

The editions of Stieler's *Hand-Atlas*, from 1817 on, have demonstrated these developments very effectively. Gradually, new concepts emerged, such as the *Physikalischer Atlas* of Heinrich Berghaus, 1848, but it has been left to the present generation of atlas publishers to apply the term to a great variety of productions. Contemporary atlases frequently include illustrations, explanatory text and additional inset maps, tables and diagrams; many are in effect graphic encyclopaedias of geographical knowledge. They are expected to have an adequate index, using references to latitude and longitude and/or to a locational grid or map references. The need for accurate planning in agriculture, industry and development projects of all kinds and the increasing use of mapping as a technique in dealing with a wide variety of problems in physical and human geography and in administration, combined with recent cartographic innovations, have resulted in an all but overwhelming array of efficient, evocative and exciting new atlases during the past few decades.

Pre-eminent among large world atlases, especially for British libraries, is the Mid-Century Edition of *The Times atlas of the world*, compiled by the House of Bartholomew for The Times Publishing

Company, in five volumes, completed in 1960. The chief of the Soviet world atlases, issued in 1954 by the Chief Directorate of Geodesy and Cartography, Moscow, took the place of the pre-war *Bolshoy Sovetskiy Atlas Mira*, of which the two volumes completed by 1939 were withdrawn on the outbreak of war. The new Atlas covers the USSR comprehensively, but other countries are also well represented. The State Publishing House for Geodesy and Cartography in connection with the Ministry for Geology and Natural Resources of the USSR brought out a new edition in 1962. A great variety of atlases is produced by the Istituto Geografico de Agostini in Novara, the best known perhaps being the *Grande Atlante Geografico* in its fifth edition. The *Atlante Internazionale della Consociazione Turistica* is another great Italian world atlas, issued in a ninth edition, 1955–56, to mark the sixtieth anniversary of the Club's foundation. All these atlases reflect both geographic and cartographic scholarship.

Medium sized and small world atlases are produced by several well-known cartographic publishers. The Oxford atlases, prepared by the Cartographic Department of the Clarendon Press, are in a class by themselves, incorporating original research and interesting experiments in the use of projections. The largest in the Bartholomew range of world atlases is *The citizen's atlas of the world*; others include the *Advanced atlas of modern geography*, the *Edinburgh world atlas of modern geography, The comparative atlas of physical and political geography* and *The Columbus atlas*. Influential German atlases include *Der Grosse Bertelsmann Weltatlas, Der Grosse Brockhaus atlas* and *Stieler's atlas of modern geography*. The *National Geographic atlas of the world*, the McGraw-Hill *International atlas*, the *Encyclopaedia Britannica world atlas*, the *Atlas international Larousse*, the *Atlas général Vidal-Lablache*, the *Faber atlas, Goode's world atlas*—all contain useful features, while Philip, Stanford, Cassell and Collins have produced many reliable library and school atlases in recent years. With the perfection of relief model maps, it was only a question of time before the first Relief Form Atlas was produced. An atlas published by the Institut Géographique Nationale, based on photographs taken in surveys of France and French territories overseas was issued also in an English edition in 1956. Another early example of this type of map form was Harrap's *3-D junior atlas*, edited by Professor Frank Debenham, particularly useful in the study of landforms.

The making of national and regional atlases is a cartographical task of high priority in all developed or developing countries; these atlases are made for the purpose of supplying detailed information about the physical and socio-economic conditions of the given country or region and are serving both scientific and practical purposes. They may serve also as base-maps for further planning studies and for compilation of schemes intended for regional organisation. The IGU Commission on National Atlases was established in 1956; the development of recommendations concerning the subject matters of national atlases and the thematic maps symbols was considered as the Commission's principal objective. The establishment of such a Commission in itself reflected the new demands being made on cartography, which resulted in the creation of complex atlases. The compilation of national atlases intended for general information is as a rule controlled by high-level scientific institutes; examples are the *Atlas de Belgique, The national atlas of the United States of America, National atlas of Hungary*. The 1:625,000 sheets of the National Planning series of Great Britain are component parts of the national atlas; the publication of the so-called 'national' *Atlas of Britain and Northern Ireland* (Oxford: Clarendon Press, 1963) was not only a cartographic event of the greatest interest but the culmination of more than twenty years of discussion and negotiation for the production of a truly British national atlas.

A feature of modern atlas development has been the increasing number of special atlases, each in its subject presenting encyclopaedic information in map and graphic form. Outstanding examples are the *Atlas of diseases*, 1950, and the *Welt-Seuchen atlas*, 1952, the *Moon atlas*, 1961, the *Mercantile Marine atlas*, the *Morskoy atlas*, the *Atlas of economic development* (University of Chicago, 1961), the *Atlas of economic geography* (Meiklejohn, new edition, 1955), the *Oxford Economic Atlas* series and the *Atlas of world history* (Rand McNally, 1957). Special regional atlases range from the *Ice atlas of the northern hemisphere* to the *Atlas de la France vinicole* and the *Atlas Schweizerischen Volkskunde*.

> (The historical aspect of this entry has been largely based on the article 'Atlases' contributed to the *Encyclopaedia of librarianship*, third edition, 1966)
>
> For references to individual items, *consult* the Index.

180 'Atmosphere, weather and climate', by R G Barry and R J Chorley (Methuen, 1968), aims to bring together the latest ideas on synoptic and dynamic climatology in a concise text, generously illustrated with sketchmaps and diagrams of all kinds. The first three chapters deal with the nature of the atmosphere, continuing with a discussion on the air masses and the processes which lead to the development of frontal and other depressions and concluding with a brief consideration of the modifications of climate produced by urban and forest environments and of the inherent variability of climate with time. Appendix I presents a summary of the major schemes of climatic classification for reference purposes and Appendix II sets out 'Nomograms of height, length and temperature'. There is a short bibliography.

181 'Atmospheric tides, thermal and gravitational', by Sydney Chapman and Richard S Lindzen (Dordrecht-Holland: D Reidel Publicity Company, 1970), summarises the latest known facts and theorises on the travelling waves and daily oscillations caused by the sun's heat and the moon's attraction acting on the rotating earth's atmosphere, beginning with a historical introduction. Data, methods of data analysis and the mathematical methods for solving the theoretical equations are all discussed.

182 Audio-visual materials Geography is of all subjects particularly suited to illustration by all kinds of audio-visual material. Such material is now produced by a wide variety of organisations—those devoted entirely to audio-visual publishing on a commercial scale, those issuing it as an educational service, either free or at small charges, or in conjunction with conventional book production. Included are films, slides, collections of reference material issued for class use, generally kept together in some specially designed folder, and all kinds of wall charts or illustrations suitable for use on epidiascope or tape. In its fullest development, the correlated audio-visual aid is one in which an audio element—a record or tape—is designed to be used in conjunction with a filmstrip or other visual element; in some cases, the record or tape contains an audible electronic 'ping', which signals when to advance the frame of the filmstrip, while, in others, the teacher's notes indicate how the components are to be employed together.

Items in this form of publishing quickly go out of print or are replaced by new series; *the examples cited in this entry do, however, give an idea of the kind of material potentially available.*

Geographical teaching at all levels requires generous accommodation and provision of equipment—for the housing and display of selected documentary material, wall maps, large and small scale topographical maps and a selection of thematic maps and, ideally, space and opportunity for making models—such as erosion action or volcanoes—, for the study of weather and demonstration of, for example, farming or industrial commodities. A number of schools possess a 'geographical laboratory'. The illustrations and slides loan collections held by public libraries have through the years been increasingly used in school teaching, especially with the improvement in projectors and epidiascopes. The Association of Special Libraries and Information Bureaux (Aslib) has an Audio-Visual Group and a Film Libraries Group; a national catalogue is available, also a manual of techniques, information on storage and control and on the standardisation and usage of terminology.

The National Organisation for Audio-Visual Aids evolved over the years in response to the needs of educationists. Sections include The National Committee for Audio-Visual Aids in Education, the Educational Foundation for Visual Aids and the National Audio-Visual Aids Centre, which maintains a reference library of audio-visual publications. *Visual education*, the monthly magazine, lists additions to the film library; the July issue each year comprises the *Visual education yearbook*. The EFVA National Catalogue gives details of films and filmstrips made by all organisations preparing material specifically for teaching purposes, thus providing a comprehensive source of information. All the material described is available from the Foundation Film Library, the national library of educational films, at Weybridge, Surrey. Each of the eight parts of the Catalogue deals with a separate group of subjects and, in addition, a catalogue of wall charts, containing charts from all sources, with details of size and price and the addresses of suppliers, is available. Supplementary catalogues and lists, also information leaflets, are prepared as necessary and a special information service, called *Veniss*, is a co-ordinating feature.

The British Universities Film Council is concerned with co-ordinating work with audio-visual material, exploiting possibilities, making sources known and establishing a centralised unit to help surmount any difficulties of cost and availability; conferences are a main part of the programme.

The famous Rank Film Library, Rank Audio Visual Limited, Brentford, Middlesex, is probably the largest 16mm film distribution organisation in Europe for educational and industrial films. Founded in 1933 and known as the 'Gebescope' Library until 1946, it was part of the equipment sales organisation. Expansion of

80

activities was rapid after the second world war and the library now maintains separate industrial films and technical services departments. The education department, set up in 1933 to promote the use and understanding of film as a visual aid, is responsible for the preparation and selection of films, filmstrips, slides and 8 mm film loops for educational purposes and for advice on their use, also for the teaching notes supplied with all films and filmstrips. These latter are written by subject experts and many of them are considered to be models of their kind. The greatest changes through the years may be observed in the films provided for geography teaching and the presentation of background knowledge. Sample studies and the 'current affairs' approach enable more purposeful studies, with the aim of linking geographical factors with past and present life throughout the world. Such are *Gibraltar: gateway to the Mediterranean; Hong Kong: cross-roads of the Orient; The fishing grounds of the world; The growth of London* and *London today; Factories, mines and waterways.* One film in particular serves to demonstrate the power of this medium to awaken enthusiasm and broaden the perception of interests waiting to be explored: *The map and the ground* aims to encourage geographical field work in schools, ranging from the work of nine-year-olds to the in-service training of teachers. In Part I, primary school children are making measurements of rainfall, temperature, wind direction and strength and a field study excursion is shown in progress, with subsequent follow-up classwork. In Part II, a fourth year secondary school class is observing geology, farming and natural vegetation; a river study is included, followed by a final synthesis of the day's work; lastly, teachers are shown engaged in a parish study at Ewell. Another example will suffice to indicate the full-scale treatment of a specific topic, *Rivers at work: an introduction to fluvial processes*, prepared by M J Clark and W J Allen. The film, which runs for twenty minutes, provides a 'process-form' approach to the study of fluvial landscapes, devised to be shown in short sections and with repetition as desired. The accompanying handbook is clearly and concisely composed and a bibliography covers all available systematic textbooks, giving specific references for the further explanation of points raised in the film. *Film news* is the news sheet of the Rank Film Library and comprehensive, illustrated catalogues are prepared each year, while individual brochures and leaflets are circulated concerning special projects, during the course of each year.

The Central Film Library and its affiliated libraries in Glasgow and Cardiff distribute a wide variety of material, some on hire, others on free loan, both coloured and black and white, for which a catalogue is available. The Scottish Central Film Library is the most extensive of the activities of the Scottish Film Council. Begun in 1939, it is in four main sections: a basic stock of educational films, including all Educational Films of Scotland productions, Central Office of Information Films, a duplicate set of British Film Institute Library classics and films deposited by sponsoring organisations.

Aerofilms and Aero Pictorial Limited, London, maintains a unique collection of aerial photographs, mainly oblique, some vertical. More than three hundred thousand photographs illustrate geological and topographical features, soil, mining and quarrying, forestry, industry, communications, settlements of all kinds and places of historic interest. Some of these have been collected and published in the *Aerofilms book of aerial photographs*, a book of 320 pages containing over five hundred illustrations, which has replaced the index to the library. Sets of oblique aerial photographs are issued, each containing a number of letterpress prints, in a strong manilla envelope.

Aerial photographs of England and Wales are available from the Ministry concerned with Housing and Local Government—at present also the Ministry of the Environment—on double or single weight glossy paper. There is no search fee for orders, but a minimum charge is imposed. A typical example of the increasing overseas organisations offering aerial photograph services is the National Air Photo Library, Surveys and Mapping Branch, Department of Energy, Mines and Resources, Ottawa. The Library files hold more than three million oblique, vertical and trimetrogon photographs, which together provide an aerial view of the whole of Canada.

Common Ground (1951) Limited, London, publishes only 35 mm filmstrips, some in black and white, some in colour, designed essentially as aids in learning. Advisers and authors include outstanding educationists in Britain and abroad in a great variety of subjects and teaching notes form an integral part of all the standard filmstrips. The range of films is graded—infants, five to seven years; primary, seven to eleven years; modern secondary, eleven to fifteen; grammar, twelve to eighteen; technical, sixteen plus. An annual catalogue, illustrated by a number of coloured plates, lists published works available at the beginning of the year. Recent new sections have dealt with vocational training, comprising materials to assist in the implementation of the Industrial Training Act and in line with the contemporary emphasis on practical preparation in school for work in the world; and 'overhead transparencies', which are provided with a plastic universal mount, enabling the order of overlays to be changed easily, as desired. The transparencies are produced on Melinex sheet, a stable and tear-resistant material, and the image is on the reverse side of the sheet, so that the teacher's additions and annotations can be made without damaging the transparency; they are supplied in a stiff envelope, designed to assist filing, and teaching notes are provided where appropriate. Much used titles include 'California', 'The Lakes peninsula of Ontario', 'The coastline of England', many current topics set in Asia and Africa, 'Morocco', 'North and Central Wales' and 'The weather map'. Specific topics are of use in conjunction with local studies; examples are 'How pottery is made', by the Hon. Josiah Wedgwood, and a series 'London markets'. A splendid new addition to the 'Geography is colour' series has been *Puerto Rio*, by A Coleman and W G V Balchin, consisting of 35 frames, plus the title and location map frame; as usual, the series is accompanied by an excellent explanatory booklet, giving also a selection of books and articles for further reading. A complete catalogue of Common Ground filmstrips is available on request.

Visual Publications (VP) of London issues a particularly useful major series of filmstrips, *The earth and man*. The earth's physical features, climate and ecology are linked to man's response in the human geography sub-series, *The earth today*, which has recently been developed further with the introduction of the Visual Publications' new integrated media kits; these kits combine filmstrips with 'follow-up' material—photographs, maps and diagrams—with notes. *The origins of the earth* and *The earth without man* were prepared by Ruth Way; *Physical geography—Elements of climate*, by G H Dury. Other physical geography sets deal with features such as rocks, minerals and rivers. Further series concern individual regions of the world, such as *Canada: a nation built on trade* and *The Persian Gulf*. A set of six strips covers *Britain in the twentieth-century environment: its origin and growth* series. Still more recent series include *Know the land*, by May B Hyde and J Skeel; *Evolution of life*, by W J Gladwin; *Energy and man*, by G H Dury and others; *Space*, by L J Carter and David A Hardy; and *Great explorers*, by A C Green. All the filmstrips can easily be converted into slides. Illustrated brochures of new releases are distributed.

In 1969, the *Methuen educational transparency atlas: land and water* was issued for use with an overhead projector; twenty superimposable transparencies, in four colours, isolate and clarify geographical factors. They are available with or without a binder. A number of experiments have been made with animated maps on film, especially in the United States. Symbols, flow-lines or other features may be shown individually, comparisons can easily be emphasised by choice of adjacent items and, for the evocation of ideas, the possibilities are infinite. Lettering may be used on the film, if suitable, or all explanation may be given in a commentary. An article in the November, 1968, issue of *Geography*—'Overhead projector transparencies for geography teaching: a review'—traced the development of this idea.

Filmstrips and slide sets, with lecture notes, are available also from Diana Wyllie, Limited, London. Detailed catalogues are prepared, also a leaflet describing the recommended D W Viewpack Storage System. Hulton's filmstrips may be had on sale or return; recent series include 'Regional geography of North America' and 'Geographical studies of Malaya'. The Encyclopaedia Britannica Instructional Materials Division offers a wide range of filmstrips, overhead transparencies, study prints and multimedia kits, also information on projectors and reference material, while an Audio-Visual Adviser will help with any queries. Packages and study kits include 'Earth and space sciences', which covers geology, oceanography, meteorology, astronomy and conservation. Geography in all aspects and Environmental Studies form separate sections of the library. The complete catalogue of current publications is published in two parts, Primary and Secondary.

Many organisations issue visual material for educational use in their own subject. For example, the United Nations has prepared three wall charts, 'Flags of the United Nations', a 'United Nations student map of the world' and one setting out the United National system and how it works. The Mastic Asphalte Advisory Council has 'The story of asphalte in building'. The Japan Silk Association, Inc., Tokyo, 'Silk in Japan'; each port authority provides the best material on its own services and The Commonwealth Institute (*qv*) provides study material, wall charts, maps, pictures, filmstrips, slides and tape recordings on the human aspects of Commonwealth relations, the resources and the trade of individual countries. The Ceylon Tea Centre, the Cotton Board, the Wool Secretariat, Chambers of Commerce, tourist offices and travel agencies, the Colonial Office and the Central Offices of Information in most countries provide a wealth of pictorial material.

Unesco has organised conferences on the use of audio-visual material, with special application to geography teaching. The series of *Unesco world geography charts* began with *Europe*, a set of sixteen charts, two each for Denmark, France, Hungary, the Netherlands, Spain, Switzerland, the United Kingdom and the USSR. Each chart was accompanied by four large coloured photographs and detailed information notes. Photographs and text had the approval of Unesco and of the Unesco Commissions in the countries concerned, and the charts were made available in Britain from Educational Publications Limited, East Ardsley, Wakefield. The venture proceeded by continents, the aim being to provide a careful selection of first-class but inexpensive material illustrating life in countries throughout the world, as part of the Unesco international co-operation programme.

The Council for Education in World Citizenship is another organisation which lends filmstrips free to member schools, while The Atlantic Information Centre for Teachers, London, and The Atlantic Education Trust provide a clearing-house for information on audio-visual aids available throughout the western world. The Centre is administered by an international governing body, consisting of leading educationalists in many countries. The Trust publishes three times a year *The world and the school*, a periodical for teachers containing material on current affairs, economics, economic geography, socio-economic issues, a chronology of world events, bibliographies, notes on teaching methods and teaching aids, also reviews and information on forthcoming conferences. Maps and diagrams are included. *Crisis papers* is an *ad hoc* series sent free of charge to subscribers to *The world and the school*; the documentation and summary contained in these pamphlets may often be correlated with issues of *World survey* (incorporating the previous series *The British survey*), also published by the Trust, an illustrated information service, each issue concentrating on an area particularly in the news.

Audio-Visual Productions, Richmond, Surrey, devote a large section of their stock of transparencies to geographical subjects. Notes provide a range of information on each topic.and explain the various signs and symbols. The *World physical geography* series comprises 'The earth', 'The atmosphere' and 'The land', each sub-section including several sets. There are also many sets of slides covering these topics. *Environmental case studies* overhead transparency sets contain diagrams, graphs, landscape views and teacher's notes, presenting a detailed analysis of the characteristic features of the local geography represented by a map extract. Then there are the *General purpose maps* transparencies, which consist of single sheets, each in several colours, showing main features of countries and regions. In the large collection of *Regional geography* transparencies, each section includes a base map, all the other items pictured in the section being drawn to the same scale.

Pictorial Charts Educational Trust issues an interesting range of pictorial material on aspects of British history and geography. Particularly useful has been *Developing Britain*, which consists of a large map of Britain and five smaller maps giving details of land use, industry, transport, fuel and power, manpower and education. *Britain's early industries* is the title of a group of charts concerned with wool, cotton and iron, showing their geographical distribution, stages of development of processes and products and their social repercussions. A set under the general title *Industrial revolution* deals with textiles, technology and agriculture, also *From steam to computer*—all emphasising the main features of development and their effects on society. *The Manchester Ship Canal* shows how the canal created an inland port serving a great hinterland; and an excellent chart, *The North Sea*, combines the geographical and historical aspects, outlining the industries and trade of the countries surrounding the North Sea and the exploitation of oil and gas in the Sea. The information is conveyed through large and small scale maps, block diagrams, graphs and illustrations.

Macmillan issues various kinds of audio-visual material. The overhead projector transparencies, $10'' \times 10''$, are mounted in frames with the overlays supplied unmounted to enable the teacher to manipulate them as required. Guidance notes are provided. A base transparency outlines the subject matter and each overlay develops it and introduces supplementary information. A teacher can add his own material to the transparencies and, to facilitate this, a base map on the same scale is provided on the reverse side of the teacher's notes for those transparencies which deal with geographical regions. High quality colour reproduction enables the transparencies to be shown in daylight. Macmillan's *Geography class pictures*, in full colour, are suitable for primary or early secondary ages; they illustrate life and work among the peoples of the world, their basic foods, fruit and drinks, their clothes, homes, manufactures and transport, each with teachers' reference books, edited by G Noyle, which are themselves illustrated. The *Topicards* series introduced a new presentation of geography in visual terms; they are designed to provide a framework round which the creative teacher can build. An introductory series

86

dealt with important themes and concepts in geography illustrating the underlying general patterns, with world-wide examples. Detailed sample studies followed and experimental topics continued to complement the introductory series. The cards are printed in full colour on one side and in black and white on the other. Examples are *Map interpretation, Coastlines, Agriculture—the physical environment, Latitude and longitude, Climate and weather, Rivers, Communications*. One exercise on each *Topicard* suggests fieldwork related to the pupil's own region. A full brochure is available on request.

Since 1926, when the Hadow Report emphasised the point that sound learning stems from pupils' interests, there has been a steady development in the teaching of themes requiring more than one subject discipline for their full appreciation. The Schools Council 'Integrated studies' scheme has prepared many sample packs following these ideas, for example, 'Exploration man', which are handled by the OUP Education Department. Ward Lock Educational, London, also issue photographs and charts in connection with their *Geography in colour* series. The Jackdaw Publications Limited, London, packs, begun by Cape, are now an accepted teaching aid. Many are of geographical interest, such as *Dairy farming*, compiled by John Lloyd Jones, including eighteen items, and *The motor industry*, by Greg Jeffries, with thirteen. *Canadian Jackdaws* are a more recent series. On similar lines are the Archive Teaching Units prepared by the University of Newcastle-upon-Tyne Department of Education. The first was *Coals from Newcastle*, compiled by L Turnbull and J C Tyson, which comprised a folder of reproductions of contemporary archives 'for the study of the economic and social history of the North East Coalfield in the early nineteenth century', distributed by Harold Hill and Son, Limited, Newcastle.

Frederick Warne and Co., London, have issued 'photosets', folders each containing twelve large oblique air photographs in colour of important geographical or industrial features. The photographs are printed on stiff paper, 266 mm by 190 mm in size and, where suitable, are accompanied by sketch maps and suggestions for individual lines of study. *Map extract folders* contain sets of six full colour extracts from large scale maps, with short descriptive texts, statistics, photographs or diagrams, emphasising the most important features for study.

Cassells of London, in co-operation with the Geographical Association, have produced complete packs for the study of air photo interpretation; each contains the basic equipment for reading vertical air photographs, namely, eight stereo pairs of nine by nine inches gloss photographic prints, a transparency with coded tracing of one photograph, an air photo interpreter's scale, a pocket stereoscope and a book of explanatory notes.

Each of the Macdonald Educational geography packs, 1969–, contains ten sets of integrated aids for teaching the geographical features of specific areas of the British Isles; they consist of ten Ordnance Survey map extracts, ten corresponding white polystyrene relief models, ten large aerial photographs showing key features and a teacher's booklet giving supplementary information. The map extracts, at the scale of $2\frac{1}{2}$ inches to the mile, are laminated. Overhead projector transparencies offer map coverage of 134 countries, each set consisting of four transparencies: a blank outline map defining territories, a full colour physical relief map, complete naming labels and a blank transparency for the teacher's use. A new series presents themes such as 'Temperature', 'Resource distribution'. Macdonald has evolved a number of 'Colour units', consisting of twenty-four or thirty-two page paperbacks designed mainly for children of average ability in secondary schools. They include all the most commonly recurring subjects; each page or double-page spread has been prepared as a complete topic and each is expected to occupy a child for two or three weeks, so that the course can be infinitely varied and exchanges made to suit individuals. The texts are straightforward, but, at the same time, aim to explain technical terms for geographical phenomena, such as the location of industry, continental drift or the uses of marginal land.

Esso *Geography studies*, available from Longmans, in sets of six 35 mm colour transparencies, deal with aspects of the geography of the British Isles, stressing particularly the changes that have taken place in agriculture, industry and in our way of life. Each study comes in a plastic wallet and includes full notes, each written by a teacher experienced in the subject. The BP Educational Service, Mersham, Surrey, also provides a variety of visual aids, most of which have been prepared specifically for educational use, either gratis, on free loan or for purchase. A special geographical series includes a 30-frame 'Origins of oil', a 55-frame 'The formation and types of clouds' and a 49-frame 'Association of clouds and weather'.

Posters by Post, London, issue coloured posters (available from other stockists throughout the country), including maps, such as Speed's *Map of England* and reproductions of seventeenth century celestial maps, such as those of Cellarius, and charts of the Moon.

Through Harrap are available many French seven-colour wall maps with laminated surfaces, also nearly two hundred colour slides, each with descriptive commentary, designed to be used with the maps. Many of the slides are oblique aerial photographs taken with this series in mind. Westermann double-sided washable outline wall maps permit the continuation of a subject over several lessons, since they can be rolled and stored with the chalk-drawing on them. The maps are made of strong black plastic-coated fabric which can be cleaned with a damp cloth. Each is supplied with wooden rods top and bottom and strips at each end for securing when rolled. The permanent outlines are in a pale blue, the intersection of selected geographical co-ordinates is shown in the four corners of each map and the principal rivers are drawn in. All desired detail can be built up by the teacher with a class. The Westermann Pictorial wall maps have proved their worth in teaching, forming a transitional step from pictures to abstract geographical maps. Through their graphic presentation, they allow scope for the child's imagination and lead from the three-dimensional to the two-dimensional map. The map 'Wild animals and natural vegetation' is a particularly attractive example, suitable for permanent wall decoration while pupils discover more and more details portrayed on it. Wall maps and charts from a number of other foreign publishers are made available to British schools through publishers in this country.

New audio-visual developments and materials are regularly reviewed in a number of the leading educational journals, including *The Times Literary Supplement, Teachers world and schoolmistress, The teacher, Educational equipment, New education, School building supplies and equipment, School and college, School government chronicle, Educational review* (School of Education, University of Birmingham) and *Trends in education* (HMSO for the Department of Education and Science).

Refer also

Walter W Newey: 'The use of geography visuals in television', *Scottish geographical magazine*, December 1968.

183 'Australia: a study of warm environments and their effect on British settlement', by Griffith Taylor, was published by Methuen in a seventh edition, revised 1958, reprinted 1961, in the *Advanced geographies* series. Sections have been added on central Australia, on Australian Antarctica and recent industrial growth.

Refer also

B R Davidson: *The northern myth: a study of the physical and economic limits to agricultural and pastoral development in tropical Australia* (Melbourne UP; CUP, 1965).

Erwin and Gerda Feeken: *The discovery and exploration of Australia* (Nelson, 1971).

184 'Australia, New Zealand and the South Pacific: *a handbook'* (Anthony Blond, 1960), was prepared by fifty distinguished contributors under the editorship of Charles Osborne. Nine articles deal with the physical conditions and characteristics of the States and Territories of Australia; eleven deal with the economy. Social patterns form a major topic. Three sections are given to New Zealand—'Political background', 'The economy' and 'Social patterns'. Much informed comment is included by C H Newbury on the Pacific Islands, viewed in their relation to Australia and New Zealand.

Note Further volumes in this series, *Handbooks to the modern world*, are entitled *Africa, Western Europe, Latin America, The Soviet Union, Eastern Europe, The United States and Canada* and *The Middle East.*

Refer also

Harold Brookfield, *ed*: *The Pacific in transition: geographical perspectives on adaptation and change* (Arnold, 1973).

185 'Australian bibliography: *a guide to printed sources of information'*, compiled by D H Borchardt (Melbourne: F W Cheshire, 1963, second revised edition, 1966), covers library catalogues and general retrospective bibliographies, current national newspapers, bibliographies of subject areas, regional bibliography, government publications and the state of bibliography in Australia. A list of works referred to is included.

186 'An Australian bibliography of agricultural economics 1788–1960', compiled by J L Dillon and G C McFarlane (Government Printer's Office, New South Wales, 1967), includes some ten thousand items, arranged within three sections: a listing classified by subject matter, an author listing and a subject listing of major statistical sources.

187 'The Australian encyclopedia', in ten volumes, edited by A H Chisholm and others, was published by the Michigan University

90

Press (Sydney: Angus and Robertson, 1958). Particularly detailed treatment is given to the Australian aborigines and those of Papua, New Guinea and New Zealand.

188 'The Australian environment' prepared by CSIRO (Melbourne University Press, 1960; third edition, reprinted, 1966), has become a standard reference work, owing its origin to an agricultural conference, 1949, on plant and animal nutrition. In the revised, illustrated editions, Australian plant and animal life is examined against the background of the environment.

Refer also

J S Beard: 'The penetration of the western deserts of Australia', *The geographical journal*, December 1970.

Maurice Berney: *Australia* (edited by Cyril Pearl), (Angus and Robertson, 1965).

D A Brown *et al*: *The geological evolution of Australia and New Zealand* (Oxford: Pergamon Pr., 1968).

N T Drohan and J H Day, *ed*: *Readings in Australian economics* (Cassell Australia, 1965).

G H Dury and M I Logan, *ed*: *Studies in Australian geography* (Heinemann Educational Books, 1968).

C Forster, *ed*: *Australian economic development in the twentieth century* (Allen and Unwin, 1970).

L St Clare Grondona: *Australia in the 1960's* (Blond, second edition, 1964).

Alex Hunter, *ed*: *The economics of Australian industry: studies in environment and structure* (Melbourne UP; CUP, 1963).

J N Jennings and J A Mabbutt, *ed*: *Essays in Australian geomorphology*) (Canberra: ANU Press 1967).

J N Jennings and J A Mabbutt, *Landform studies from Australia and New Guinea* (CUP, 1967).

Allen Keast: *Australia and the Pacific Islands: a natural history* (Hamish Hamilton, 1966).

Allen Keast: *et al, ed*: *Biogeography and ecology in Australia* (The Hague: Junk, 1959).

John Kirwan: *An empty land: pioneers and pioneering in Australia* (Eyre and Spottiswoode, 1934).

Egon and Elsie Kunz: *A continent takes shape* (Collins, 1971).

Charles Laseron: *Ancient Australia: the story of its past geography and life* (revision by R O Brunnschweiler, Angus and Robertson, 1969).

Graham H Lawton: 'First immigrants to Australia', *The geographical magazine*, September 1973.

G W Leeper, *ed*: *The Australian environment* (Melbourne UP, third edition in co-operation with CSIRO, 1960).

T L McKnight: *Australia's corner of the world: a geographical summation* (Prentice-Hall, 1970).

George Palmer: *A guide to Australian economic statistics* (Macmillan, 1963).

Douglas Pike: *Australia, the quiet continent* (CUP, second edition, 1970).

Vincent Serventy: *Landforms of Australia* (Angus and Robertson, 1968).

O H K Spate: *Australia* (Benn, 1968).

L J Webb *et al, ed*: *The last of lands: conservation in Australia* (Warne, 1970).

D B Williams, *ed*: *Agriculture in the Australian economy* (Sydney UP, 1967).

189 'Australian geographer', journal of the Geographical Society of New South Wales, has appeared twice a year since 1928; it contains original articles and book reviews. Annual and approximately three-yearly indexes are prepared.

190 The Australian Geography Teachers Association, founded in 1969, is a national body aiming to promote the teaching and study of geography and to provide a forum for Australian geography teachers; its journal, *Geographical education*, also began, on an annual basis, in 1969.

191 Australian Institute of Cartographers has the main headquarters at Melbourne, where also is the headquarters of the Victoria division. The New South Wales division is based on Sydney, the South Australian division on Adelaide and a Tasmanian division is centred at Hobart. The Institute's journal is *Cartography* (*qv*).

192 'Australian maps' has been published since January 1968 by the National Library of Australia. Issued quarterly, with an annual cumulation, the publication lists sheet maps and atlases prepared in or which represent areas within the Commonwealth of Australia and its external territories, or which are associated with persons or corporate bodies throughout this area.

Refer also

Barry Cohen: *Australia: a map geography* (Heinemann Educational Books, 1972).

R V Tooley: *One hundred foreign maps of Australia 1773–1887* (The Map Collectors' Circle, 1964).

Index to Australian resources maps of 1940–1959 (Canberra, Department of National Development, 1961; supplement covering 1960–1964, 1966).

193 'Background notes on the countries of the world' (Bureau of Public Affairs, Department of State, Washington, DC) are excellent factual pamphlets, each in a binder, about countries and territories; each *Note* contains information on land, people, history, government and political conditions, economy and foreign relations. There are maps in the text and, usually, a bibliography. The *Notes* are available on subscription or any special part may be had separately.

194 'Background to geography', by G R Crone (Museum Press, 1964; second edition, 1968; paperback edition, 1969), 'is an attempt to interest the general reader in the study of geography and to explain the value of a geographical outlook on the world today' (Preface).

195 'Background to political geography', by G R Crone (Museum Press, 1967) aims 'to discuss a representative selection of contemporary political problems', including such pressing topics as 'The world's food supplies', 'Frontier zones and boundaries', developing countries and the role of such diverse countries as China, Latin America, Australia, Western Europe and the United States, concluding with an assessment of the United Nations. A section, 'Books for further reading', is appended and there are a number of photographs and sketchmaps.

Among a growing body of studies on this aspect of geography, a useful complementary work is

J R V Prestcott: *The geography of state policies* (Hutchinson University Library, 1968).

196 Bagrow, Leo (1881–1957) was one of the great scholars whose work so stimulated the present interest in historical cartography; during a life-long study of early cartography, in Russia until 1918, in Berlin, 1918–1945, and in Stockholm, 1945–1957, he published more than seventy studies, making important contributions to cartographic history and encouraging inter-national activity and cooperation. He wrote numerous papers on the early maps of the Black Sea, Siberia and Asiatic Russia, mono-graphs on the history of ancient geography and on the literature of the history of cartography, and bio-bibliographical studies on the sixteenth century cartographers who contributed to the *Theatrum* of Abraham Ortelius, which were published as supplements to *Petermann's Mitteilungen*, 1928 and 1930. Probably his best-known work in the west is *Geschichte der Kartographie*, 1951 (*qv*) and the *Imago mundi: a review of early cartography* (*qv*), which he founded. Bagrow himself made a fine collection of maps, especially of Russian maps, which were acquired by the Houghton Library of Harvard College in 1956.

197 Bartholomew, John and Son Limited was founded in 1797 by George Bartholomew, map engraver, and is now in the fifth gener-ation of an unbroken family tradition of high quality cartography. The first John Bartholomew (1831–1893), son of George, founded the Geographical Institute in Edinburgh, which has remained the headquarters of the House of Bartholomew; John George Bartholo-mew (1860–1920) is noted for his development of layer colouring as a method of relief representation; the late John Bartholomew (1890–1962), was himself a geographer, being honorary secretary of the Royal Scottish Geographical Society and president 1950 to 1954, and was influential in the establishment of the Chair of Geography at Edinburgh University. Outstanding among the firm's contributions to mapmaking have been the editions of *The Times atlas of the world* (*qv*); the 'half-inch' map of Britain, the first topographic series to make use of layer colouring, 1878–; *The Edinburgh world atlas* (*qv*); numerous school and university atlases, such as the *Comparative atlas* (*qv*); the *Atlas of Scotland*, published in 1895 for the Royal Scot-tish Geographical Society; the *Physical atlas*, planned in five volumes, of which the *Atlas of meteorology* (*qv*), 1899, and the *Physi-cal atlas of zoogeography* (*qv*), 1911, were particularly important; and the *World reference map* series of topographic maps in their frequent revisions, now in a new format under the collective title *World travel* series. The Bartholomew *Road atlas of Great Britain* is revised annu-ally. Specially designed for motorists and tourists on a scale of a fifth of an inch to the mile, a double-page is given to each map section, so that a large area can be studied at one time. Full contour colouring shows relief, with spot heights. Six road classifications are indicated and Ministry of Transport road numbers are used throughout. An index of some four thousand names quotes map references. Useful also is Bartholomew's *Roadmaster motoring atlas of Great Britain*, which is regularly updated. The *Reference atlas—Greater London* has become a standard work; and the *Gazetteer of the British Isles*, with its supplement, contains details of more than ninety thousand cities, towns, villages, hamlets, etc of the British Isles and the Channel Islands, arranged in alphabetical order. A sixteen-page summary includes the 1961 population census figures. *The road atlas of Europe* is a later atlas specially designed for tourists, including all kinds of information likely to be useful. New maps for motorists and tourists are frequently prepared; *The tourmaster maps of Britain*, for example, and the GT series.

From 1969, the firm has undertaken a 'Bartholomew early maps' series; in co-operation with the Royal Geographical Society, London, maps from the Blaeu *Atlas novus* have been republished in colour, on specially selected antique cartridge paper. The maps are issued in a carrying tube. Bartholomew has been the United Kingdom wholesale distributor for the Cappelen *Road and tourist map of Norway* and has more recently been appointed distributor of the Mair/Shell maps of Europe. A valuable collection of atlases dating from the sixteenth century has been built up by the firm.

The catalogue of publications, revised annually, is clear and includes index maps; the latest editions contain a 'Table of map scale equivalents' in fractions, mileage and kilometres.

Refer also

'Batholomews—on the map' *in British printer,* September, 1963.

M J Chittleburgh: 'John Bartholomew and Son Limited', *Bulletin*, Special Libraries Association, Geography and Map Division, June 1972.

198 'Beaches and coasts', by C A M King (Arnold, second edition, 1972), is recognised as one of the foremost works on the subject. The new edition has been completely revised, including the figures, retaining only such of the older research and theory that has remained of value. Of the four parts, the first introduces the forms and the techniques for studying these features, the second deals with the processes operating on beaches and coasts to give them distinctive characters, the third is concerned entirely with beaches and the fourth with coasts. A new chapter has been added on sea level fluctuations. The whole is illustrated with diagrams and sketch-maps and each chapter is accompanied by references.

199 Behaim, Martin (*c* 1459–1506/7) was a famous globe-maker. One of his globes, made in Nuremburg about 1492, still survives.
> *Refer also*
> E G Ravenstein: *Martin Behaim: his life and his globe*, 1908.
> *See also*
> Globes

200 'Bell's advanced economic geographies', edited by R O Buchanan, are organised in two series, systematic and regional. Both series have the same aims—'to demonstrate the kind of thinking, critical and constructive, that informs current research in economic geography and to make the results of such research as widely available as possible'. Each volume is prepared by a recognised authority in the field. Systematic studies include Michael Chisholm: *Geography and economics;* P P Courtenay: *Plantation agriculture;* Peter R Odell: *An economic geography of oil;* L J Symons: *Agricultural geography;* among the regional studies are R C Estall: *New England: a study in industrial adjustment;* F E Ian Hamilton: *Yugoslavia: patterns of economic activity;* J E Martin: *Greater London: an industrial geography;* Wilfred Smith: *An historical introduction to the economic geography of Great Britain;* H P White and M B Gleave: *An economic geography of West Africa.*

201 'Berge der Welt', edited by H R Muller, was published in Munich by the Nymphenburger Verlagshandlung, 1969, for the Swiss Foundation for Mountain Research; the whole set of volumes, 1947– is extremely fine, the first eight volumes having been edited by Marcel Kurz. At the end of the set is a consolidated index of authors, biographies, placenames and subjects.

202 Berghaus, Heinrich Karl (1797–1884), one of the great German cartographers of the nineteenth century, worked with Alexander von Humboldt and Carl Ritter and at the Cartographic Institute Justus Perthes at Gotha. His outstanding achievement was the *Physikalischer Atlas . . . (qv).*

203 Bertelsmann Cartographic Institute at Gütersloh, West Germany, is one of the most influential of the European cartographic agencies. Four great atlases are especially outstanding: the family reference atlas, *Bertelsmann Hausatlas*, 1960, 1962; the large and small world atlases, *Der Grosser Bertelsmann Weltatlas* (*qv*) and the *Kleiner Bertelsmann Weltatlas;* and the *Bertelsmann Atlas International*, 1963.

> *Refer also*
>
> Werner Bormann: 'Aus der Arbeit des Kartographischen Institutes Bertelsmann', *International yearbook of cartography*, 1964.

204 'Bibliographia geodaetica' has been produced monthly from 1963 by the National Committee for Geodesy and Geophysics of the German Democratic Republic, in co-operation with the International Documentation Centre for Geodesy at Dresden Technical University, the International Association of Geodesy and the International Federation of Surveyors (Berlin: Akademie-Verlag); it is referred to also as the International Geodetic Documentation. The publication continues the *Bibliographie Géodésique Internationale* (*qv*) (1928–1960) and the *Monatwissenschaftliche Literatur-berichte*, which covers 1962, and includes about ninety abstracts in each issue, each repeated in English, French, German and Russian.

205 'A bibliographic aid to the study of the geography of Africa: a selected listing of recent literature published in the English language', was compiled by Sanford H Bederman for the Bureau of Business and Economic Research at Georgia State University, 1972. The work contains some 1,900 items listed under countries, thence alphabetically by authors, using different coloured papers for the sections.

206 'A bibliographic guide to population geography', by Wilbur Zelinsky (University of Chicago Department of Geography, Research Paper, no 80, 1962), includes 2,588 items from the latter half of the nineteenth century to mid-1961; the work is intended as a finding list, no attempt being made at critical evaluation.

> *Refer also*
>
> *International Population Census bibliography* (University of Texas Bureau of Business Research for the University of Texas Population Research Center, six volumes, 1965–1967) replaces the two Library of Congress similar bibliographies of 1943 and 1948.

Hans Dörries: 'Siedlungs-und Bevölkerungsgeographie (1908–1938)' *in Geographisches jahrbuch*, 1940.

H T Eldridge: *The materials of demography: a selected and annotated bibliography* (Columbia University Press for the International Union for the Scientific Study of Population and the Population Association of America, 1959).

207 'A bibliographical and historical essay on the Dutch books and pamphlets *relating to New-Netherland and to the Dutch West India Company, and to its possessions in Brazil, Angola, etc, as also on the maps, charts, etc of New-Netherlands'* compiled by G M Asher, was reprinted by N Israel, Meridian and Theatrum Orbis Terrarum in 1966 from the Amsterdam edition of 1854–1867. It is thought to be the only special bibliography of the Dutch expansion in the western hemisphere and in West Africa in the seventeenth century. There is a folding map.

208 'A bibliographical guide and index to the principal collections of town plans and views published in the sixteenth and seventeenth centuries in Die Alten Städtebilder: *ein Verzeichnis der graphischen Ortansichten von Schedel bis Merian'*, by Von Friedrich Bachmann, provides an invaluable first study on this topic, first published in 1939 in an edition of five hundred and re-issued in 1965 in Stuttgart by Anton Hiersemann. The bibliographical history of each collection is traced and the contents are analysed town by town, with an emphasis on German collections.

209 'Bibliographie cartographique internationale' was first proposed in 1938, but due to the war, publication did not begin until 1949, by Armand Colin, under the auspices of the Comité National Français de Géographie and the International Geographical Union, with the support of Unesco and the Centre National de la Recherche Scientifique. It remains the only official international record of maps and atlases published throughout the world, including also monographs of cartographical interest. The first volume listed maps published in 1946–47 in eight countries; the geographical societies of more than twenty countries now collaborate in listing local and regional maps, and editing is done at the Bibliothèque National. Each entry is accompanied by a brief annotation and the whole work is extensively indexed.

210 'Bibliographie de cartographie ecclésiastique' (Leiden: Brill, 1968–) began with the publication of the *Bibliographiekirchengeschichtlicher Karten Deutschlands,* prepared at the Institut für Landeskunde, Bad Godesberg, by Karl-Georg Faber, Bertram Hartling and Hans-Peter Kosach, together with the *Bibliographie kirchengeschichtlicher karten Österreichs*, under the direction of Ernest Bernleithner and Rudolf Kienauer. In brief, the background to this monumental work was the creation of the Commission Internationale d'Histoire Ecclésiastique Comparée at the International Congress of historical sciences at Rome in 1955; a subcommission, 'Cartographie ecclésiastique' was at the same time formed to prepare an atlas of the historical geography of religions. At the 1960 Congress at Stockholm, the Commission Internationale d'Histoire Ecclésiastique Comparée accepted the offer of Professor Hermann Heimpel, Director of the Max Planck Institute at Göttingen to set in train a programme of bibliographical work to parallel the cartographic.

211 'Bibliographie de l'oeuvre de Lucas Jansz Waghenaer', an outstanding bibliography compiled by Thomas James I Arnold, was reprinted from the *Bibliotheca Belgica*, first series, Ghent, 1880–1890 by N Israel, Meridian and Theatrum Orbis Terrarum in 1961. All the editions of the *De Spieghel der Zeevaerdt* are described page by page, noting all known variants of the charts as well as of the text.

See also under Waghenaer.

212 'Bibliographie de Népal', published by the Centre National de la Recherche Scientifique, Paris, forms the first volume in the series *Cahiers Népalais*, compiled by L Boulnois and H Millot. References are to western literature from the eighteenth century to 1968.

Refer also
J D A Stainton: *Forests of Nepal* (Murray, 1972).

213 'Bibliographie de Tahiti et de la Polynésie française', compiled by Patrick O'Reilly and Edouard Reitman, was published in 1967 by the Musée de l'Homme, Paris, being number 14 of the *Publications de la Société des Océanistes*. 'This weighty volume completes the series of bibliographies dealing with New Caledonia, the New Hebrides, Wallis and Fortuna'. In the standard format adopted by the editors, works of reference are included, also voyages, monographs on geology, botany, zoology, geography, ethnology (including social anthropology and linguistics), history (including administration and missions) and economic life. More than ten thousand items, with numerous analytical sub-headings, are accompanied by evaluative notes and further references.

214 'Bibliographie des bibliographies Canadiennes', directed by Raymond Tanghe (University of Toronto Pr., under the auspices of the Société Bibliographique du Canada, 1960), was grant aided by The Humanities Research Council of Canada and the Social Science Society of Canada. Included are scholarly works containing bibliographies, periodicals, brochures, newspapers, maps or their reproductions, with information for their identification, author, title, place, publication date; also bibliographies in monographs and periodical articles or reference works such as directories and biographical dictionaries. Booksellers' and publishers' catalogues are not included. Entries are numbered and arranged under broad subject headings. Of special interest in the present context are the sections dealing with 'Official publications', 'Commerce—communications', 'Geology—mines', 'Agriculture' and 'Geography', with indexes of compilers, authors and subjects.

Refer also

J Keith Fraser and Mary C Hynes, *comp: Lists of theses and dissertations on Canadian geography* (Ottawa: Lands Directorate, Department of the Environment).

Louis Trotier, *ed: Studies in Canadian geography* (University of Toronto Pr., 1972; series publications from the 22nd International Geographical Congress, Montreal).

215 'Bibliographie des oeuvres relatifs à l'Afrique et à l'Arabie' was compiled by J Gay in 1875. The work covers about 3,700 titles, with bibliographical references, notes, cross-references, an index of names and one of towns. It has been reprinted for the second time in 1970 by Theatrum Orbis Terrarum.

216 'Bibliographie géodésique internationale' in its first series was published by the International Association of Geodesy, as follows: 1, 1928–30, 1935; 2, 1931–34, 1938; 3, 1935–37, 1939, all edited by G Perrier and P Tardi; 4, 1938–40, 1947, edited by G Perrier, P Tardi and G Laclavère; 5, 1941–45, 1952; 6, 1946–48, 1954; 7, 1949–51, 1956, all edited by P Tardi and G Laclavère; 8, 1952–55, 1962, edited by the Central Bureau of the International Association of Geodesy (under the chief direction of J Villecrosse), as were volumes 9 and 10,

1956–57, and 1958–60, published respectively in 1963 and 1965. Beginning with the volume for 1961, the bibliography was published in a new format, as a monthly magazine, *Bibliographia geodaetica* (*qv*) and on cards, International Geodetic Documentation, edited by the Geodätisches Institut of Dresden. The bibliography aims to be a truly international publication; under the aegis of the International Association of Geodesy, the following regional institutes collaborate in the work: the Finnish Geodetic Institute (Sweden, Norway, Denmark, Finland); the Central Bureau of the IAG (Spain, Portugal, Italy, Belgium, Greece, France, French-speaking Africa); Institut für Angewandte Geodäsie, Frankfurt a/Main (Netherlands, Austria, Luxembourg, Switzerland, West Germany); Technische Universität Dresden Geodätisches Institut (Poland, Czechoslovakia, Bulgaria, Romania, Yugoslavia, Hungary, East Germany); Military Survey—Geodetic Office of Great Britain (Great Britain, Ireland, Commonwealth, South Africa); the Soviet Committee for Geophysics (USSR); the US Coast and Geodetic Survey (USA, Japan) and the Inter-American Geodetic Survey—Canal Zone (South America). *Bibliographia geodaetica* is published in French, English (Butterworths Scientific Publications), Russian and German, with abstracts in the four languages. Entries, arranged by the UDC, are each accompanied by a brief annotation. The cards are prepared and sold in two different forms: 'simple series', one card per title; 'complete series', two cards per title, in either English, French, Russian or German, grouped according to three main subjects, higher geodesy, surveying, and photogrammetry (in German only). Only group I is published by the International Association of Geodesy; the second and third groups are published with the co-operation of the International Federation of Surveyors and other relevant bodies.

217 'Bibliographie géographique internationale' is the central current geographical bibliography. The first issues, 1891–1913–14 were published as separate parts of the *Annales de géographie* (*qv*) under the direction of L Raveneau. After the first world war, the bibliography was published under the present title by the Association de Géographie Français (Armand Colin) and, since 1931, it has been a publication of the International Geographical Union in international co-operation, with the assistance of Unesco and the Centre National de la Recherche Scientifique, the latter assuming increased publishing responsibility with the 1954–55 volume, 1958. All aspects of geography are covered, except purely technical or local topics;

useful reference works, such as glossaries and year-books, are included. Arrangement is primarily by country, with subject divisions, under three main headings: historical; general geography; regional geography. Most of the entries carry brief annotations. Author indexes are included and the later issues have also detailed subject indexes.

218 'Bibliographies, catalogues, check-lists and indexes of Canadian provincial government publications', compiled by Mohan Bhatia (University of Saskatchewan, Saskatoon Library, 1970), was created out of the increasing interest in and awareness of the value of government publications as source material and the emphasis on the study of raw material in higher education. Canadian provincial government publications had not previously been easy to locate.

219 Bibliographies, national, from the point of view of geographical studies, and cartographical control
Arrangement by continent, then alphabetically by country
EUROPE
Albania The National Library publishes a quarterly current bibliography of books and pamphlets, official publications, maps and atlases, also bibliographies of bibliographies. University theses and dissertations are listed by the State University of Tirana and published in special booklets or in its bulletin. Periodicals are indexed by the National Library and published in the *Bibliographie trimestrielle du périodique*. *The Albanian book* has been published by the National Library from 1958, first annually, quarterly from 1960; and *Articles from Albanian periodicals* is also published by the National Library, quarterly 1961–1964, bi-monthly 1965 and monthly from 1966.

Austria The national current bibliography, *Österreichische bibliographie*, has been published fortnightly since 1946; official documents, new journals, theses and maps are included. *Refer also* to the *Österreichische bibliographie*, compiled by C Junker and L Jellinek, 1899–1901, which includes publications in German only, classified systematically by subject, issued first fortnightly, then monthly. The national cartographic agency is the Kartographische Kommission der Österreichischen Geographischen Gesellschaft, in Vienna.

Belgium The *Bibliographie de Belgique* is prepared by the Royal Library. Official publications and government documents are to be found in two retrospective bibliographies—Paul de Visscher and Jacques Putzeys: *Répertoire bibliographique du Conseil d'Etat*, with a supplement covering 1960–62, compiled by Jacques Putzeys (Institut Belge des Sciences Administrative, 1963); and Denise de Weerdt: *Bibliographie retrospective des publications officielles de la Belgique, 1794–1914* (Louvain: Editions Navwelaerts, 1963). Since 1963, the Centre International de Documentation Economique et Sociale Africaine has regularly published a *Bulletin of information on theses and studies in progress or proposed. Bibliographie géographique de la Belgique*, compiled by M E Dumont and L De Smet, with a first supplement in 1960, is issued by the Commission Belge de bibliographie; the *Bibliographie de Belgique: liste mensuelle des publications belges ou relatives à la Belgique* has been published since 1875, a new series being started from 1967; and *Bibliotheca Belgica: bibliographie générale des Pays-Bas*, edited by Marie-Thérèse Lenger was published in two volumes, 1966. *Abstracts of Belgian geology and physical geography*, 1967–, edited by L Walschot, began publication in 1969 by the Ghent Geological Institute of the University of Ghent. The volumes are to appear annually, each containing some 250 abstracts, a subject index and a geographical index. Cartographical studies are co-ordinated by the Section de Cartographie du Comité National de Géographie, Bruges.

Bulgaria The national current bibliography, *Balgarski knigopis*, published monthly since 1897, includes maps, new periodicals and any changes in the publication policy of periodicals. Since 1962, a quarterly supplement has listed official publications and dissertations and the bibliography itself has been issued fortnightly since 1969. The Centre for Scientific Information and Documentation also publishes a series of abstracting journals devoted to specific subjects; geography is not named separately. The Centre for Agricultural Scientific Information and Documentation of the Academy of Agricultural Science issues a series 'Rural economy and forestry' within the *Referativnyi bjuleten. Refer also* to the publication of the Library of Congress, Slavic and Central European Division, Reference Department, *Bulgaria: a bibliographic guide*, 1965, compiled by Marin V Pundeff, especially the sections 'General reference works', 'Land and people' and 'Economy and social conditions'. The Scientific and Technical Union of Bulgarian Geodesists and Surveyors, Sofia, is the co-ordinating body for research in these subjects.

Czechoslovakia There are two current national bibliographies, one weekly, *Czech works*, published by the National Library of Prague, the other, monthly, *Slovak works*, published by the Matica Slovenská. Some official documents are included. Bibliography of theses began with a special number each year of *České knihy*, 1965–(1964). Since 1965, maps and atlases have appeared regularly in *Česka grafika a mapy*, an annual index which lists the productions of the previous year. A similar list is in progress in Slovakia. Bibliographies on special topics are being increasingly undertaken by appropriate bodies. The Comité de Cartographie de la Société Tchécoslovaque Scientifique-Technique, in Prague, is the central organisation for co-ordinating cartographical work.

Denmark Biblioteca Danica, the national retrospective bibliography, published by the Royal Library 1872–1931, covering the period 1482–1830, was followed by a new and enlarged edition 1960–63. Annual catalogues for the years 1959–63, as well as a cumulative volume of the Danish current bibliography, *Dansk bogfortegnelse*, 1955–59, were prepared by the Bibliotekscentralen and published by G E C Gad; the volumes covering the periods 1841–58 and 1859–68 were republished by anastatic printing in 1960 and 1961 respectively. An index of official publications and government documents is prepared by the Danish Institute of International Trade and published by the Bibliotekscentralen. *Danish theses . . . a bibliography* was made available in 1929 and 1961, the two volumes covering the period 1836–1958. Bibliographies concerning geography and topography are so far devoted to specific themes, such as *Bibliography of Old Norse-Icelandic studies*, prepared by Hans Bekker-Nielsen and Thorkil Damsgaard Olsen, in collaboration with the Royal Library, 1963(1964)–. *Denmark: literature, language, society, education, arts: a select bibliography* was one of the publications of the Royal Library, 1966. In 1972, the Dansk Kartografisk Selskab was formed, based on Copenhagen.

Finland The Finnish national bibliography, prepared by Helsinki University Library, is a current bibliography which has, from 1932, included all literature published in Finland, regardless of language. The first volume of a retrospective bibliography, 1878, covers literature in Finnish for the years 1544–1877; each of the succeeding volumes lists works published during the previous three or eight years. This bibliography includes maps. From 1961, official publications have been listed in various forms by the Library of Parliament. The University of Helsinki publishes an annual list of theses and academic publications of all Finnish universities, 1966–; there is a special systematic section for maps. Catalogues of maps of the General Cartographic Service of Finland have appeared irregularly. The Suomen Kartografinen Seura, in Helsinki, is the central cartographic organisation.

France The *Bibliographie de la France*, the national current bibliography, celebrated its 150th anniversary in 1961, when the Cercle de la Librairie issued a special number devoted to the history of this work, which appeared originally under the title *Journal général de l'imprimerie et de la librairie*. The technical development of the bibliography was described in the *Bulletin des bibliothèques de France*, November 1961. Since 1960–61 the annual volumes have included an index of current serials; and since 1963 the official part of the publication has been classified according to the UDC rules. The Comité Français de Cartographie, Paris, is the co-ordinating cartographic body.

See also under Bibliothèque Nationale.

Germany Deutsche Bibliographie: Wöchentliches Verzeichnis, 1947–, a weekly systematic national bibliography, began in 1965 to separate into three series: books on sale, books not on sale and maps. There are monthly and quarterly indexes; five-yearly indexes record not only books and maps published in the two parts of Germany, but all published in German and issued abroad. Official publications and government documents are listed as a separate part of the *Deutsche Bibliographie . . .*, issued every other year. Information on maps and atlases is issued also in the *Berichte zur Deutschen Landeskunde*, Stuttgart. The national cartographic body of the German Democratic Republic is the Deutsche Akademie der Wissenschaften zu Berlin and that of the Federal Republic is the Deutsche Gesellschaft für Kartographie, Hamburg.

Greece has no current national bibliography, only individual catalogues, such as the *Bulletin analytique de bibliographie hellénique*, published by the French Institute in Athens. The Hellenic Geographical Society, Athens, acts as the national cartographic body.

Hungary The national current bibliography, 1946–, *Magyar nemzeti bibliográfia*, was published by the National Széchényi Library monthly to 1961, then fortnightly; it records, by UDC arrangement, books, pamphlets, maps and theses. A cumulative volume appears every two or three years. A cumulative retrospective bibliography of works published after the second world war appears under the title *Magyar könyvészet 1945–1960* (1964); volume IV contains the entries for art, literature, geography and history. A catalogue of Hungarian periodicals is published separately; and articles published in Hungarian periodicals are listed monthly in *Magyar folyóiratok repertóriuma*. There are various specialised abstract reviews. The national cartographic agency is the Hungarian National Committee of the ICA, Budapest.

Ireland Irish publications are included in the *British national bibliography*. In addition, the Stationery Office, Dublin, issues an annual list of official publications; the National Library of Ireland, Dublin, prepares a national retrospective bibliography, which includes printed works, manuscripts, periodical articles and maps. *Irish historical studies* contains an annual bibliography, *Writings in Irish history*. The *Irish publishing record*, compiled by the School of Librarianship, University College, Dublin, covers material published in Ireland, both in the Republic and in Northern Ireland, and includes books, pamphlets, the first issue of new periodicals, yearbooks and government publications; the *Record* is prepared on behalf of the Irish Association for Documentation and Information Services. The Ordnance Survey of Ireland, based on Dublin, is the national cartographic organisation.

Italy The *National bibliography* was published monthly between 1886 and 1957, arranged by subject, with annual indexes of authors and subjects; in 1958, a new series began, also monthly, entitled *Bibliografia nazionale Italiana*. Periodicals and official publications are noted in separate supplements. Maps published in Italy are appended as a special supplement to the monthly issues. The Associazione Italiana di Cartografia, Novara, is the national body.

Luxembourg The annual *Bibliographie Luxembourgeoise* lists publications received by the National Library, also works written by Luxembourg nationals or relating to the Duchy. Since 1958, it has included the contents of periodicals and from 1962 official publications have also been included, distinguished in the text by a special sign. There is no current bibliography of special subjects. The cartographic body is the Administration du Cadastre et de la Topographie.

Netherlands The Royal Library issues *Bibliografie van in Nederland verschenen officiële en semi-officiële uitgaven*. Netherlands periodicals are indexed monthly, with annual cumulations, in *Nijhoff's index op de Nederlandse periodieken van algemene inhoud*. *Brinkman's catalogus van boeken*, a private undertaking, began in 1846 with monthly issues with annual and quinquennial cumulative lists; books and periodicals published in the Netherlands have been included, also those in Dutch published in Belgium. Since 1945, university theses have been listed. There is also a select classified bibliography, *Nieuwe uitgaven in Nederland*. Another useful guide is

Sijthoff's adresboek voor de voor de Nederlandse boekhandel, with its separate lists of periodicals and official publications. The national body is the Kartografische Sectie het Koninklijk Nederlands Aardrigjskundig, at The Hague.

Norway The *Norsk bokfortegnelse* includes books, pamphlets, periodicals, university theses, official publications and maps. Official publications are also listed in a special current bibliography, *Bibliografi over Norges offentlige publikasjoner*, published annually since 1956. In the annual cumulation of the national bibliography, maps and atlases are treated separately. For retrospective bibliography, the *Bibliotheca Norvegica* was compiled by Hjalmar Pettersen in four volumes (Christiania, 1899–1924) listing works printed in Norway before 1814, works of Norwegian authors and translations of works in Norwegian published abroad, as well as foreign works dealing with Norway. Vilhelm Haffner compiled retrospective lists of works from 1814 to 1924 (1925) and from 1925 to 1935 (1936). Det Norske Nasjonale Komite for Kartografi and the National Survey of Norway are based on Oslo.

Poland The *Przewodnik bibliograficzny*, which includes maps and atlases, is published weekly, with a monthly list of authors and an annual cumulation, containing a list of subjects. On the basis of this publication, the Bibliographical Institute prepares the official statistical yearbook of Polish publications, *Ruch wydawniczy w Liczbach*, having text in Polish and English. An annual list of periodicals is published by the Bibliographical Institute, also a monthly bibliography of periodical articles. University theses are listed by the Ministry of Higher Education, beginning with a first volume in 1962, which covered the years 1959–1961, thence annually. Special bibliographies are being steadily compiled such as the *Bibliography of Polish meteorology and climatology up to 1939*, compiled by J Rajman, 1968. An annual *Bibliografia geografi polskiej* has already been initiated by the Bibliographical Institute and similar works have been started for economics, geology and forestry. The Bibliographical Institute is also preparing a retrospective bibliography of Polish works and works on Poland. The Institut Geodezki i Kartografii is in Warsaw.

Portugal The national bibliography, *Boletim de bibliografia portuguesa*, has been compiled by the National Library since 1935, except for the war years, annually until 1954, then monthly; it includes books, pamphlets, maps and official publications. A number of special bibliographies have also been published, on geology, seismology and meteorology, among others. The Portuguese National Library Commission, working in the Lisbon Academy of Science, is compiling a retrospective *Portuguese general bibliography*. Lisbon National Library publishes also the monthly *Portuguese bibliography bulletin*, which includes the most important articles from major periodicals. The Instituto Geografico e Cadastral is in Lisbon.

Romania The Central State Library issues the *Bibliografia Republicii Populare*, fortnightly; it includes books, pamphlets and maps. A separate fortnightly publication lists periodicals. A Centre of Information and Documentation in Social and Political Sciences began operations in July 1970, as an institution of the Academy of Social and Political Sciences. The Centre took over the whole activity carried out by the Scientific Documentation Centre of the Academy of the Socialist Republic of Romania in these fields. The 'Social sciences' section of *Romanian scientific abstracts* would be of interest to geographers.

Spain The monthly *Boletín del depósito legal* and the *Bibliografía española*, annually, both began in 1958 and include maps and atlases; the latter also lists periodicals and official publications. The Ministry of Information and Tourism (Press Department) publishes an *Anuario de la prensa española*, of which Part I is concerned with periodicals. From the numbers of special bibliographies, two are of direct interest: *Guía bibliográfica para una geografía agraria de España*, compiled by José Muñoz Pérez and Juan Benito, 1961, and *Bibliografía de geografía económica de Galicia*, by F J Rio Baija, 1960. The national cartographic body is the Seminario de Estudios Cartográficos, in Madrid.

Sweden There is no formal National Commission for archives, bibliography, research or documentation. Various bodies concerned with archival documents issue publications on their own work. The central cartographic agency is the Kartografiska Sällskapet in Stockholm.

Switzerland Das Schweizer buch, bibliographical bulletin of the National Library, 1901–, cumulates into the *Répertoire du livre suisse*, in two parts, authors and subjects. Maps and atlases are included. *Bibliographie des publications officielles suisses* has also been prepared by the Bibliothèque Nationale since 1946, and the *Catalogue des écrits académiques suisses*, from 1897. The Société Suisse des Libraires et Editeurs has issued irregularly the *Répertoire des périodiques suisses*. The Schweizerische Gesellschaft für Kartographie, in Zürich, is the national body.

USSR Two current bibliographies, both long-established, give systematic coverage of all books published in all languages in the USSR: *Knižnaja letopis*, weekly with a monthly supplement and *Ezegodnik knigi SSSR*, in two volumes annually. Current Union records of periodicals, theses and official publications appear regularly and geographical maps and plans are included in the *Kartografičeskaja letopis*, published annually by the All-Union Book Chamber. In addition, all the Republics keep their own records. Since 1925, books, pamphlets, official publications, maps and atlases have been listed in the *Annals of publications of the Byelorussian SSR*, issued in monthly parts. Publications dealing with the Byelorussian SSR, but appearing in other republics of the Soviet Union, have since 1946 been listed in a special section of the *Annals*. Every year, cumulative indexes annexed to the *Annals* contain lists of periodicals published in the Byelorussian SSR, including new publications and those that have changed their titles. The Ukrainian SSR national bibliography began in 1924, based on the Ukrainian SSR Book Chamber at Kharnov, set up in 1922. An index of periodicals has been issued for the years 1918 to 1950 and the Chamber is responsible also for the national retrospective bibliography.

    Note The Bibliographical Institute of the National Library of Poland, Warsaw, published in 1969 a work by Pelagia Girwic on the organisation and network of current Soviet bibliography. The National Council of the Cartographers of the USSR, Moscow, acts as the control agency.

United Kingdom The British national bibliography, 1950–, based on legal deposits, does not include maps. A *Guide to British periodicals*, by Mary Toase, was first published by The Library Association, 1962. Official publications are made known by daily, weekly, monthly and annual cumulations published by HMSO; *Sectional lists*, dealing with individual department publications, are revised as necessary. Aslib issues an annual *Index to theses accepted for higher degrees in the universities of Great Britain and Ireland* and periodical articles from major periodicals are listed in the *British humanities index*, the *British technology index* and the *Index to articles in British technical journals*, all begun in 1962 by The Library Association. The *Bibliotheca celtica* lists annually all publications concerning Wales, Celtic works and the Celtic language, prepared on the basis of the acquisitions of the National Library of Wales, arranged by subjects, with a list of authors. *A bibliography of works relating to Scotland*, compiled by P D Hancock in two volumes, was published by the Edinburgh University Press, 1960. There is a rapidly increasing number of local bibliographies, such as the *East Anglian bibliography . . .* (The Library Association, 1960–). Individual institutions issue their lists of maps and atlases; there is no centralised publication.

Refer also

Statistical news: developments in British official statistics, published quarterly by the Government Statistical Service 'to provide a comprehensive account of current developments in British official statistics and to help all those who use or would like to use official statistics'. Every issue contains up to three articles dealing with special subjects in depth. Shorter notes give news of the latest developments in many fields, including international statistics. Frequent reference is made to other works which, though not issued by government organisations, are closely related. Each issue is indexed and a feature is the reference to 'Articles in recent issues of *Statistical news . . .*'

The Cartography Subcommittee of the British National Committee for Geography is based at The Royal Society, London. A Commission for Geography is part of the National Council for the Coordination of Scientific Research; this and the Union of Geographical Societies serve to link all geographical workers by means of newsletters and journals.

Yugoslavia Since 1950, the Jugoslovenski Bibliografiski Institut has published a current national classified bibliography, the *Bibliografija Jugoslavige . . .*, fortnightly from 1954, which lists books, pamphlets and maps, succeeding the annual bibliography *Jugoslovenska bibliografia*, 1945–1950. Yugoslav periodicals have been listed, since 1956, in the quarterly *Bibliografija jugoslovenske periodike*, as well as in the national bibliography.

ASIA: MIDDLE EAST: FAR EAST

Afghanistan has remained isolated and until recent years did not attract scholarly research. Now the Afghans themselves are attempting research projects and documentation. The Russians made a beginning in bibliography for the general area in the nineteenth century, but up to 1968 only one important work was published, the *Bibliographie analytique de l'Afghanistan*, by Mohammed Akram, 1947–; only the first volume was issued then, dealing with works published outside Afghanistan and it is believed that no other volumes

110

were completed. Afghanistan is still inadequately mapped and there is no official list of maps as yet.

Burma The *Burmese national bibliography* has been undertaken by the Daw Nyunt Myint National Library, Rangoon. The plan is for cumulative volumes to be published every two or three years and further details should be available soon.

Ceylon The national bibliography has been published quarterly from 1962 by the National Bibliography Division of the Government Archives Department in Gangodawila; it includes books, pamphlets, published theses, dissertations and new periodicals. Three languages are used, Sinhala script, Tamil and English; it includes atlases, but not maps. *Ceylon periodicals index* is prepared by the National Museum Library, Colombo.

China A Bibliographic Centre was set up in the National Central Library in Taipei in 1960; the Centre publishes a *Monthly list of Chinese books*, in Chinese and English, and an annual *National bibliography of the Republic of China*, prepared by the National Central Library which has also published a national retrospective bibliography in two volumes listing more than fifteen thousand documents published in Taiwan between 1949 and 1963. An *Index to the Chinese periodical literature* was published by the Library of the National University of Taiwan.

India The *Indian national bibliography* is based on a very complex system, involving numerous publications including works in the main languages; the Ministry of Education prepared a list in 1958, subsequently handing over the work to the Central Reference Library, Calcutta, from which annual volumes appeared between 1960 and 1962, quarterly issues in 1963 and monthly issues from September 1964, cumulated annually. A second part deals with government publications. Many publications include lists of the subjects of theses and there is also the *Bibliography of current reports*, published by the Atomic Energy Establishment, Information Division. A *Guide to Indian periodical literature* (*Social sciences and humanities*), 1964–, has been prepared by the Prabhu Book Service, in quarterly issues, with annual cumulations.

Books India, annual, 1972–, by the National Book Trust, New Delhi, includes individual bibliographies, prepared mainly by the universities and libraries.

Refer also

N N Gidwani and K Navalani: *Indian periodicals: an annotated guide*, 1969.

Indonesia The current bibliography, *Berita bulanan*, is prepared by the Bureau of National Bibliography; an index of Indonesian scientific periodicals was initiated in 1960 and a national commercial bibliography, *Berita bibliografi*, has been published since 1955 by a wholesale bookseller, Gunung Agung.

Iran Index Iranicus, compiled by Iradj Afshar, is among the series of works published by the University of Tehran; it comprises a systematic list of Iranian articles on Iranological studies published in journals and other periodical publications, the first volume, covering 1910 to 1958, having been completed in 1961. The University of Tehran has also published a *Bibliography of Iranian bibliographies*, also compiled by Iradj Afshar. The same editor prepares the annual *Bibliography of Persia*, published by the Persian Book Society, 1955–, a systematic current bibliography of all books and periodicals published in Iran; a retrospective bibliography is in progress. A *Geographical bibliography*, under the direction of M Gandjei, lists geographical articles throughout the Iranian press. The National Cartographic Centre of Iran is at Teheran.

Iraq The *Iraq national bibliography*, containing books, pamphlets, official publications and university theses, is compiled by the Central Library of the University of Baghdad, which prepares also bibliographies and indexes of many special subjects.

Israel Kirjath sepher is the main current bibliography. The Publishers' Association of Israel has inaugurated the 'General catalogue of books', of which a new edition was published in 1969. The Centre of Scientific and Technological Information has issued a *Directory of current research in Israel: physical and life sciences;* the second survey, listing some four thousand projects, was published in Tel Aviv in 1969. A *Directory of serials in pure and applied sciences and economics published in Israel* was published in Tel Aviv in 1963, in Hebrew and English; and an *Abstracts of theses* . . . is prepared two-yearly by the Hebrew University, Jerusalem. The Government Press Office issues *Newspapers and periodicals appearing in Israel* and there is also the *Index of articles on Jewish studies*, by Issachar Joel, 1966—published by the Magnes Press, Jerusalem, 1969–. A project aiming at a complete Hebrew retrospective bibliography is being prepared at the Jewish University, with the co-operation of the National Library and under the auspices of the Hebrew Institute of Bibliography. The Israel Committee of the ICA, c/o the Survey of Israel, is based at Tel-Aviv.

Japan The National Diet Library is responsible for the current national bibliography, *Zen Nihon Shuppan-butsu Sô-mokuroku*, which lists all works published in Japan, in two parts, official and unofficial publications; it contains several indexes and a directory of publishers. The Library issues also *Nohon Shuho*, a weekly list of works deposited with the Library and, jointly with the Ministry of Education, the *Directory of Japanese periodicals: natural sciences, medical sciences and industry*, first issued in 1962. From 1963, the Shuppan News Company has issued a general catalogue of Japanese periodicals and from 1957 the Board responsible for issuing official publications has prepared a monthly list. Theses are listed by the Research Institute of Educational Administration, which puts out an annual publication; maps and atlases are mentioned in the national bibliography. There are many specialised catalogues and lists compiled by national bodies, for example, the 'Wheat information service'. Four volumes of a *Bibliography on geography*, including related subjects, taking the bibliography to 1966, have been compiled by Jimbun Chiri Gakhai and published by Taimeido. One of the best general bibliographies is *A selected list of books and articles on Japan* in English, French and German, published by Harvard University Press, 1954. *Japanese geography: a guide to Japanese reference and research materials*, compiled by R B Hall and Toshio Noh, constitutes *Bibliophysical series*, 6, of the Michigan University Center for Japanese Studies (Michigan University Press; Cumberlege, 1956). [*Reference books of Japan*], with supplements, 1962, 1965 and 1972, compiled by Nihon Toshokan Kyokai Nihon no Sanko Tosho Henshu Iinkai (Nihon Toshokan Kyokai, 1972) and *Books on Japan in western languages*, compiled by the International Christian University Library, 1971, covering the current contents of academic journals in Japan (University of Tokyo Press, 1971), are two more recent useful sources.

Korea The Korean national bibliography, published monthly by the National Central Library, gives detailed bibliographical information on all categories of books, pamphlets and periodicals published during the preceding month. In November 1964, the National Central Library issued a contribution to the national retrospective bibliography, covering 1945 to 1962. A list of periodicals and one of official publications are issued by the Ministry of Information. Lists of university theses are prepared by the Korean Research Centre. The Centre has also published a *Selected list of Koreana collections. Bibliography in business and economics (1945–1960)* was published in 1961 by the Industry Management Research Centre, which is sponsored by Yunsei University.

Kuwait The Libraries Department, Kuwait University, co-ordinates the bibliographical services. The University and government departments, together with the Institute of Scientific Research, have been foremost in preparing bibliographies and lists of publications of national interest, specialised bibliographies and lists of theses.

Laos The only bibliography at present available is the *Bibliographie du Laos*, compiled by Thao Kéne, a listing of books and review articles dealing with Laotian civilisation.

Lebanon The *Bibliographie nationale*, 1964, 1965, 1971, 1972, and *Thèses 1909–1970*, by Nawal Mikdashi, were published in Beirut by the American University of Beirut, Yafet Memorial Library, 1971. A Documentation Centre was set up in 1970, attached to the Ministry of Planning at Bir Hassan; there is also the Documentation Centre of the National Scientific Research Council of Lebanon.

Malaysia has no complete current national bibliography. 'Current Malayan serials', compiled by Lim Wong Pui Huen, was included in the *Singapore library journal*, October 1963, and a 'Guide to Singapore government departments and serials', by E Sormitasagama, in the issue for April 1964. Useful is the *Catalogue of government publications* issued at intervals by the Government Printing Office. The Singapore National Library has prepared many specific bibliographies, including *Books about Malaysia*, 1963, revised in 1964 and 1967, and *Urban community development*, 1962. *Books about Singapore and Malaysia, a selective bibliography*, compiled by the Reference Section of the National Library, was completed in 1965; it includes references to works on economics, commerce and industry, physical features and natural history, travel and serials. There is also *Malaya, a background bibliography*, compiled by Beda Lim and published in 1962 by the Malaya Branch of the Royal Asiatic Society.

Mauritius Bibliography of Mauritius (1502–1954) covering the printed records, manuscripts, archivalia and cartographic material (Port Louis, Government Printer, 1956) has been continued since 1955 in the form of annual supplements containing a list of all works and printed matter printed in Mauritius during each year. These supplements appear in the *Annual Report of the Archives Department* and contain a list of acquisitions concerning Mauritius, recording also scientific publications relating to it, theses, etc. The *Annual Reports of the Mauritius Institute* for 1960 and 1961 contain information on the publications concerning Mauritius, with special emphasis on zoology.

114

Nepal The Nepalese Study Centre at the Centre National de la Recherche Scientifique, Paris, is engaged on a comprehensive bibliography of Nepal, arranged by subjects. Volume I, 1969, comprised 'Sciences humaines—Références en langues Européenes', compiled by L Boulnois et H Millot.

Pakistan There is a current bibliography in preparation, but no information concerning it has come to hand. Otherwise, apart from PANSDOC, the only contribution to a national bibliographic coverage is the annual catalogue of official publications issued by the Government Printer. The Survey of Pakistan, Karachi, acts as the national cartographic body.

Philippines A current bibliography is being prepared and the retrospective bibliography has been compiled to 1957. The University of the Philippines, Institute of Public Administration, Inter-Departmental Reference Service prepares the *Index to Philippine periodicals* and the Research Co-ordination section of the University edits *Thesis abstracts*, of which the first issue appeared in 1962, covering 1947 to 1954. A *Checklist of Philippine government publications* is prepared by the National Library. A *Bibliography of Philippine geology, mining and mineral resources* was compiled by Juan S Teves (Manila: Bureau of Printing, 1953) and *Bibliography of Philippine geography, 1940–1963: a selected list*, by Robert E Huke (Dartmouth College, New Hampshire, Department of Geography, 1964). The Philippine National Committee for Cartography is at the Board of Technical Surveys and Maps, Manila.

Singapore There is a separate annual national bibliography, issued by the National Library, which includes government publications and maps. *Books about Singapore, 1972*, was also prepared at the National Library.

Thailand There is no systematic current bibliography, but some materials are covered. *Bibliography of Thai government publications* has been issued by the Thai Library Association since 1962; an *Index to Thai periodical literature 1957–62* was published in 1962 by the Ministry of Education, Department of Teacher Training, Bangkok; *Bibliography of material about Thailand in western languages* was published in 1960 by the Chulalongkorn University, Faculty of Arts; and a *Statistical bibliography: an annotated bibliography of Thai government statistical publications* was prepared in the Office of the Prime Minister (National Office of Statistics, 1964). The Royal Thai Survey Department at Bangkok is the national cartographic organisation.

Turkey The current national bibliography, *Turkiye biblioyograf-yasi*, was begun in 1928 by the Directorate of Legal Deposit at the Ministry of Education; in 1953, the work was undertaken by the National Library. It includes periodicals, official publications, theses, maps and atlases. A bibliography of articles in Turkish periodicals began quarterly production in 1952.

Viet-Nam Current national bibliography is undertaken by various organisations and comes in various forms. The *National bibliography of Viet-Nam*, issued quarterly by the Directorate of Archives and National Libraries, contains lists of non-periodical publications deposited with the Copyright Department; since 1961, these lists have been included in the *Journal officiel* of the Republic; also *Sách Mô*, 1962–, a monthly bulletin designed to keep the public informed of new acquisitions of the National Library and the General Library attached to the Directorate. The Ministry of Information publishes a monthly bulletin giving a list of publications submitted to the Ministry for purposes of censorship. The Directorate of Archives and National Libraries is preparing a retrospective bibliography, incorporating some individual separate existing studies. The *Catalogue des cartes et plans* published by the National Geographic Department of Viet-Nam is in the form of general tables of sheets on scales of 1:25,000, 1:50,000, 1:100,000, 1:250,000, 1:500,000, with current price lists.

AFRICA

Naturally, no bibliography covers the whole of the continent, but the following references help in general studies: *Catalog of African Government Documents and African Area Index* (Boston University Libraries, second edition, revised and enlarged, reproduced by G K Hall, 1964, in one volume): *Bulletin d'information sur les recherches dans les sciences humaines concernant l'Afrique* (Brussels: CIDESA, 1967). *Sub-Saharan Africa: a guide to serials* was published in 1970 by the Library of Congress, Washington, DC; compiled by the African section of the Library's General Reference and Bibliography Division, the guide contains 4,670 entries recording a selection of serials published before 1969 in western languages and in African languages using the Roman alphabet. It includes many of the titles appearing in *Serials for African studies*, issued by the Library in 1961, except that publications specifically on North Africa have been excluded. The journal *Afrique équatoriale*, 1955–, includes mention of works of all kinds, including those published abroad dealing with central Africa.

There are also H A Rydings: *The bibliography of West Africa* (Ibadan University Press for the West African Library Association); Mary Jane Gibson: *Portuguese Africa: a guide to official publications* (Library of Congress, General Reference and Bibliography Division, Reference Department, 1967); Julian W Witherall: *French-speaking West Africa: a guide to official publications* (Library of Congress, General Reference and Bibliography Division, Reference Department, 1967).

Algeria The *Bibliographie de l'Algérie*, published by the Bibliothèque Nationale, is prepared on the basis of the books, pamphlets and periodicals received by the Legal Deposit Department of the Library, half-yearly, 1963–1965; 1972–, in Arabic and French. For the Côte d'Ivoire, the following are authoritative sources: *Essai d'une bibliographie de la Côte d'Ivoire* (Paris: Organization for Economic Co-operation and Development, Development Centre, 1964) and the periodicals section, 2 and 3, of the *Bibliographie de la Côte d'Ivoire*.

Egypt Since the National Library in Cairo was made the centre for legal deposit in 1954, it has been responsible for compiling the current national bibliography, *Egyptian publications bulletin*, 1956–. In 1962, cumulative lists were issued: 1955–60; 1961–62; 1963–December 1964. There is also available a *Subject catalogue of Egypt*, an index of all foreign publications on Egypt in the National Library, in three volumes. A collection entitled 'Series of bibliographical lists of books and references about the Arab world', 1960–, began with *Algeria, Palestine, Syria, Lebanon, Iraq, Sudan, Al-Maghreb, Tunisia, Libya* and *Arabian peninsula*.

Ethiopia Ethiopian publications: books, pamphlets, annuals and periodicals articles published in Ethiopia is issued annually, in Amharic and English, by the Haile Sellassie I University, Institute of Ethiopian Studies, 1965–; also a *List of current periodical publications in Ethiopia*, 1964–, bi-annually. Specific bibliographies are prepared by the Ethiopian Research Institute.

Ghana The Ghana national bibliography is issued annually by the Ghana Library Board, by whom a retrospective bibliography is in progress; the Board issued also in 1960 *Books about Ghana*. The Director of Surveys, Accra, issues a catalogue of maps, with supplements. Government publications are listed annually in *Government publications: price list* and the University of Ghana Library prepares a *List of theses*.

Refer also

A F Johnson: *A bibliography of Ghana 1930–1961* (Longmans, 1964).

G M Pitcher: *Bibliography of Ghana 1957–1960* (Kumasi: Kwame Nkrumah University, 1960).

The Padmore Research Library issues a *Special subject bibliography* series, which includes *A select annotated bibliography of Ghana*.

The Research Library on Africa Affairs, University of Ghana Library, Institute of African Studies, has prepared a *Union list of Africana periodicals*, which is revised at intervals.

The Ministry of Agriculture Reference Library, Accra, issued *Ghana agriculture, 1890–1962: bibliography of crop and stock, co-operation and forestry, food and fisheries*, 1962.

A W Cardinall: *A bibliography of the Gold Coast* (Accra: Government Printer, 1931).

Guinea The national bibliography is prepared by the National Library and published as a supplement to the review *Recherches Africaines* (Institut National de Recherches et de Documentation). A first five-year survey, from September 1958 to December 1963, was attached to no 1, 1964, followed by annual cumulations.

Madagascar The University Library and the National Library began an annual current bibliography in 1965 (1964–), under the supervision of M S de Nuce and J Ratsimandrava. A retrospective bibliography, published by Grandidier, covers 1800–1904; 1903–1933 and 1934–1955; and another section, covering 1956–1963, was prepared with the help of Unesco. The *Bibliographie nationale de Madagascar, 1956–1963*, was planned and compiled by Jean Fontvieille, published, with assistance from Unesco, in three volumes; it is a continuation of the *Bibliographie de Madagascar*, by G Grandidier and the primary purpose of the new bibliography was to complete the latter's work and provide the Malagasy Republic with a retrospective national bibliography. Indexing is alphabetical and cumulative by authors, anonymous works and subjects.

Malawi List of publications deposited in the Library of the National Archives (Zomba, National Archives, 1965– is published annually, but includes material published only in Malawi. The *Malawi Government gazette* (Zomba, Government Printer) lists weekly all Government publications; and *Books about Malawi*, a select reading list, was issued by the Malawi National Library Service in 1969.

Morocco An annual list, *Informations bibliographiques Marocains*, is published, consisting of the publications received by the Bibliothèque Générale et Archives du Maroc, based on fortnightly lists prepared by the librarians. Contributions toward a retrospective bibliography appear in the review *Hespéris*. The Service Topographique, Ministère de l'Agriculture, at Rabat, acts as the national cartographic body.

Nigeria The National Library produces *Nigerian books in print* and *Serials in print in Nigeria*. Lists are also issued of theses and dissertations accepted for higher degrees in Nigerian universities. The University Library, Ibadan, also functions as a national bibliographic centre; a current bibliography is prepared which includes books and pamphlets, also official publications. The University Institute of Librarianship published *Nigerian library resources in science and technology*, compiled by F Adetowun Ogunsheye, 1970.

Refer also

Margaret Amosu, *compiler: Nigerian theses* (Ibadan University Press, 1965).

Helen F Conover: *Nigerian official publications, 1869–1965: a guide* (Library of Congress, 1959).

L C Gwam, *compiler: A handlist of Nigerian official publications in the National Archives Headquarters, Ibadan*, 1964.

W John Harris, *compiler: Books about Nigeria: a select reading list* (Ibadan University Press, fourth edition, 1963, fifth edition, 1969).

Senegal Official publications are listed by the Library of the Archives Service, Dakar; university theses by the University Library, Dakar. The National Geographical Institute, Hann, compiles information concerning maps and atlases. The Centre de Documentation Economique et Sociale Africaine (CIDESA) acts as a bibliographic centre. The *Bibliographie du Sénégal* (Dakar: Archives nationales) includes official and non-official books, periodicals and theses and *Les sources bibliographiques de l'Afrique de l'Ouest et de l'Afrique équatoriale d'expression française* was issued at Dakar by the Bibliothèque de l'Université, 1970.

Sierra Leone Sierra Leone publications, published annually by the Sierra Leone Library Board, does not include maps or audio-visual materials. *Official publications of Sierra Leone and Gambia*, by A Walker, was published by the Library of Congress, 1963; and *A bibliography of non-periodical literature on Sierra Leone 1925–1966*, compiled by H M Zell, excluding government publications, was published by the Fourah Bay College Bookshop Limited, Freetown, 1966.

South Africa Two current national bibliographies are produced by the South African Public Library and State Library respectively—*Africana nova*, 1958—and *South African national bibliography*, 1959–. As a result of the National Conference of Library Authorities, 1962, the State Library was requested to publish a cumulative retrospective bibliography to 1959. The South African National Committee for the IGU and the ICA is located at Pretoria.

Uganda Publications received in the University College of Makerere are recorded in the library bulletin; in fact, official publications of all East African countries are included.

> *Note* It may be noted here that the second *Tanzania national bibliography* began in 1970—no details available as yet.

> *The Rhodesias and Nyasaland: a guide to official publications*, compiled by A A Walker (Library of Congress, General Reference and Bibliography Division, Reference Department, 1965).

NORTH AMERICA

Canada Since 1950, the National Library has been responsible for the preparation of the national current bibliography, *Canadiana: publications of Canadian interest noted by the National Library*, which is published monthly, with annual cumulations; publications issued by commercial organisations are listed, also those published by the Federal Government and the ten Provincial Governments. The first issue of every periodical published in Canada is mentioned. In 1962, the Canadian Library Association published a cumulative list covering a period of twelve years, *Canadian index to periodicals and documentary films: an author and subject index, 1948–1959*. Official publications and government documents are listed by the Department of Public Printing and Stationery, as follows: *Canadian government publications monthly catalogue*, 1953–, of which an annual cumulation is published; and *Daily checklist of government publications*, 1952–. An annual list of theses is compiled by the National Library and published by the Queen's Printer under the title *Canadian theses*, arranged by broad subject headings. The National Film Board publishes every two years *Canadian filmstrips catalogue* and, since 1948, the Canadian Library Association has issued monthly *Canadian index to periodicals and documentary films*, with annual cumulations.

> *Note* also the work of the Canadian Association of Geo-

graphers; *Contributions to a short-title catalogue of Canadiana* (Montreal: Bernard Amtmann, 1971–); *Canadian basic books in the English language* (Toronto: Quill and Quire, 1971–); and *A checklist of Canadian literature and background materials, 1628–1960*, by Reginald Eyre Watters (second edition, revised, University of Toronto Press, 1972). The Canadian Institute of Surveying, Cartographic Committee, Ontario, is the body concerned with international cartographic work.

Refer also

Raymond Tanghe: *Bibliographie des bibliographies*, under the auspices of the Bibliographic Society of Canada (University of Toronto Press, 1960–), with annual supplements.

United States There is no current national bibliography in a formal sense, but a number of publications serve the purpose. The Library of Congress has been given public recognition as a national bibliographic centre, many other centres concentrating on individual subjects. The *National union catalog: a cumulative author list representing Library of Congress printed cards and titles reported by other American libraries* is compiled by the Library of Congress with the assistance of the American Library Association Committee on Resources of American Libraries. A quarterly and annual companion volume—*Library of Congress catalog—book: subjects . . . a cumulative list of works represented by Library of Congress printed cards*—is prepared by the Catalog Maintenance Division of the Library of Congress. A *National union catalog* covering the years 1958–1962 was published in fifty-four volumes by Rowman and Littlefield, Inc, New York; this work includes the titles indexed by the Library of Congress during these years, about 830,000 titles, plus some eight hundred monographs published between 1956 and 1958 recorded by other American libraries. *United States government organizations manual* contains a special twenty-five page section devoted to the main publications of the Federal Government departments and services; *United States research reports* are published fortnightly by the Office of Technical Services, and the Library of Congress, Exchange and Gift Division issues a *Monthly checklist of State publications*. In addition, the United States Superintendent of Documents prepares a *Monthly catalog of United States government publications*. *Dissertation abstracts* are published monthly, in subject sections, with an annual cumulation; *Maps and atlases* forms part six of the *Catalog of copyright entries* and acquisitions of atlases are listed also in the

National Union Catalog and in the *Library of Congress catalog—books: subjects*. The General Land Office issues a *List of cartographic records*. The Cartography Division of the American Congress on Surveying and Mapping, Washington, is the international body, under the Director of the US Geological Survey.

Bermudiana, prepared and published by the Bermuda Library, Hamilton, in 1972, was the first edition of a bibliography of Bermuda, intended as an introduction and guide to the special collection of Bermudiana housed in the Reference Department of the Library.

LATIN AND CENTRAL AMERICA; WEST INDIES

El Salvador An official current national bibliography is in the early stages of establishment, prepared by the National Library. A national retrospective bibliography, covering the years 1830 to 1954, has been completed under the title *Bibliografía salvadoreña 1830–1954*.

Guatamala Printed matter subject to legal deposit has been listed since 1932 in the *Boletín de la Biblioteca Nacional*. The National Library publishes *Indice bibliográfico guatemalteco*, which has listed publications of all kinds, including periodical articles, since 1951; the Library also contributes to the *Bibliografía de Centro América y del Caribe*, with assistance from Unesco. Government publications are recorded in legislation compendia; university theses in *Publicaciones de la Escuela de Bibliotecología de la Facultad de Humanidades de la Universidad de San Carlos de Guatemala*. For more than fifty years, periodicals have been indexed by the National Library of Guatemala and, since 1960, a special section, 'Hemeroteca nacional', has been created. The *Bibliografia de los estudios geográficos de la República de Guatemala desde 1571 hasta nuestros días*, compiled by M Reyes and Luis Jose, was published in 1960 by the Editorial José de Pineda Ibarra; it contains books and pamphlets published in Guatemala.

Guyana The *Bibliography of Guyana* was compiled by Vincent Roth; the *List of source material on Guyana of interest to geographers located in the United Kingdom*, by Dr Leslie Cummings; the *Guyana handbook—industry, tourism, commerce*, published by Guyana Manufacturers Association in co-operation with the Ministry of Information and Culture, Guyana Development Corporation and Guyana Graphic Limited; the *Selection of documents on Guyana*, compiled by Claire Collins and Yvonne Stephenson (University of Guyana Library, 1969); *Select bibliography of the works of Guyanese and on Guyana, on the occasion of Guyana Week, 19–25 February 1967* (Georgetown, Public Free Library, 1967); *Bibliography of documents relating to the economy of Guyana*, compiled by the Research Department of the Bank of Guyana (Georgetown, Bank of Guyana, 1968); and the *Bibliography of the geology and mining of British Guyana*, by C G Dixon and H K George (Georgetown, Government Printery, 1964, Geological Survey of British Guyana, Bulletin 32), based on material in the Geological Survey Library.

Honduras Books, pamphlets, official publications, periodicals, maps and atlases are listed in the *Anuario bibliográfico*, 1961–.

Jamaica Plans are in train for a systematic current bibliography. In addition, *Jamaica: a select bibliography 1900–1963* was prepared by the Jamaican Library Service, the Institute of Jamaica and the University of the West Indies (Jamaica Independence Festival Committee, 1963); *A selective bibliography of Jamaica*, revised to December 1967, compiled by the Institute of Jamaica, was included in the *Handbook of Jamaica* (Government Printing Office, 1967) and is to be revised annually. *The printed maps of Jamaica to 1825*, the work of K S Kapp, was published by the Bolivar Press, Kingston, 1968.

Mexico The *Bibliografía mexicana* has been produced fortnightly since 1967, also a *Bibliografía histórica Mexicana* from the same date, by the Mexico University. The latter includes thesis material prepared in Mexican universities. Theses from American and Mexican universities are included in the *Latin American research review* supplement, compiled by Allen D Bushong. Retrospective bibliography has been compiled for certain periods, the most important being that for 1900–1958. *Bibliografía geográfica de México*, 1955–, is published by the Dirección General de Géografia, Meterologia; and the *Bibliografía economica de México*, 1955–, by the Department of Economic Studies, Bank of Mexico. The Comité Nacional Mexicano de la ICA is based on the College of Geography, National University of Mexico.

The *Current Caribbean bibliography* is published at Puerto Rico by the Caribbean Organization. Apart from this work, retrospective bibliographies include *A guide for the study of the British Caribbean, 1763–1834*, compiled by Lowell J Ragatz (United States Government Printing Office, 1932); *Bibliography of the West Indies (excluding Jamaica)*, by Frank Cundall (Institute of Jamaica, 1909); and the

Catalogue of the library of the West India Committee, 1941. *Tropical agriculture*, quarterly review of the Faculty of Agriculture in the University of the West Indies, lists research reports and theses. The Central Library Service of Trinidad and Tobago have prepared various bibliographical aids: *A selective list of material illustrating Caribbean development* . . . (Trinidad Government Printing Office, 1963); *Select bibliography of books, pamphlets, etc., by Trinidadians on Trinidad and Tobago* . . ., 1961, with supplements; and a *List of maps of Trinidad and Tobago* (Lands and Surveys Department, 1965). Also to be noted are *A guide to records in Barbados*, by M J Chandler (Oxford: Blackwell, 1965) and *A guide to records in the Leeward Islands*, by E C Barker (Oxford: Blackwell, 1965). A basic source for Latin American materials is *Current national bibliographies of Latin America: a state of the art study*, by Irene Zimmerman, published by the University of Florida Press. The *Bibliografia brasileira mensal* (Rio de Janeiro, Instituto Nacional do Livro, 1967—replaced the *Bibliografia brasileira 1938–1955*, the *Bibliografia brasileira corrente, Revista do Livro, 1956–1963* and the *Bibliografia brasileira 1964–1966*. An informative article by Juan R Freudenthal: 'Chilean national bibliography: origins and progress', was included in *Libri*, 1972.

Peru The National Library of Peru publishes the *Anuario bibliográfico peruano*, which includes all Peruvian books and pamphlets, books and periodical articles about Peru, official publications, maps and atlases and printed theses. The Library issues also a *Boletín*, the review *Fénix* and reprints under the title, *Memoria*. Special bibliographies are published in the *Boletín bibliográfico* of the Universidad Nacional Mayor de San Marcos and in the Library's *Boletín*. Maps and atlases are shown in the geography sub-section of the *Anuario* under the heading 'Maps'.

Uruguay The National Library has published *Anuario bibliográfico uruguayo* since 1949, and the Biblioteca del Poder Legislativo began publication in 1962 of the *Bibliografía uruguaya* in three issues a year, of which the last is cumulative.

AUSTRALIA

The Australian Advisory Council on Bibliographic Services was established in 1956; its secretariat, the Australian Bibliographical Centre, forms part of the Commonwealth National Library. Since 1961, the Library has published the *Australian national bibliography*, which lists not only publications of Australian origin, but also publications relating to Australia; In 1972, the *Australian national bibliography* was redesigned in format and in method of production; it is now issued in a classified arrangement with an author/title/series index and a detailed subject index based in ORECIS. Production has been automated and issues are now computer typeset in Plantin type from a machine held file of MARC records. *Australian government publications*, monthly 1952–1960, was cumulated in the *Annual catalogue of Australian publications* in 1961 and has appeared annually since that date. From 1961–1967, maps and atlases were listed in the national bibliography; from the beginning of 1968, the National Library has published *Australian maps*, quarterly, listing all atlases and sheet maps both published within Australia and representing areas in Australia and the external territories. Individual States have prepared separate bibliographies, such as the *Western Australian Government Publications 1829–1959: a bibliography*, compiled by Elmar Zalumns (National Library of Australia, 1971). In addition, the National Mapping Council of Australia publishes annually its *Pictorial index of activities* and the Hydrographic Service of the Royal Australian Navy has issued a *Catalogue and index of Australian charts* since 1962. In 1961, the Department of National Development published an *Index to Australian resources maps of 1940–59*. The Commonwealth National Library prepares, in separate parts, a *Guide to collections of manuscripts relating to Australia*, which mentions the place of deposit and gives a description of private documents as well as of documents from government archives. *Marshall's union list of higher degree theses in Australian University libraries* was inaugurated in 1959 and there have been three supplements since; *Current Australian serials: a select list* has been issued by the National Library since 1963. The standard retrospective bibliography is Sir John Ferguson's *Bibliography of Australia . . . (qv)*. The Australian Institute of Cartographers acts as the national cartographic body.

New Zealand The *Bulletin of the General Assembly's copyright publications* was published annually between 1934 and 1949, when it became a monthly, with annual cumulations; it includes books, pamphlets, official publications, maps and new serials. The *New Zealand national bibliography*, complete from 1890, has been published by the Government Printer and the National Library of New Zealand. The *Copyright publications bulletin* records all New Zealand official publications and the New Zealand Printing and Stationery Department also publishes monthly a special selective

Government publications. The *Union list of theses of the universities of New Zealand* has been undertaken since 1963 by the New Zealand Library Association. *A bibliography of New Zealand bibliographies* was compiled by the New Zealand Library Association, 1967.

For further references to bibliographic material relating to individual countries, consult the Index.

220 'Bibliography and index of geology exclusive of North America', 1933– has been published by the Geological Society of America, 1934–. It is comprehensive; arrangement is alphabetical by authors, with a detailed subject and area index. Professor K M Clayton prepared abstracts of current British geological literature, sponsored by OSTI, as a basis for the United Kingdom contribution to the bibliography.

>*Note* The complementary bibliography, *Bibliography of North American geology*, 1919–, was published by the Society, 1931–.

221 'Bibliography of Africa', proceedings and papers of the International Conference on African Bibliography, Nairobi, December 1967, was edited by J D Pearson and Ruth Jones (Cass, 1970).

222 'Bibliography of African hydrology', compiled by J Rodier (Unesco, 1963), deals with precipitation, general climatological data and the effect of climatological factors, run-off, rivers, streams and lakes. The text is in English and French.

223 'Bibliography of agriculture', the monthly publication of the United States Department of Agriculture, ceased with the December 1969 issue. The work was taken over by the CCM Information Corporation, a subsidiary of Crowell Collier and Macmillan Inc. Data input will continue to be generated by the National Agriculture Library, the indexing and printing being handled by the CCM Corporation. The information contained remains substantially the same, but the subject index is to be enlarged by additional thesaurus terms. Production is by photocomposition.

>*Refer also*
>*World bibliography of agricultural bibliographies*, which covers libraries, societies, dictionaries of terminology etc, kept up to date by regular supplements in the *Quarterly bulletin of the International Association of Agricultural Librarians and Documentalists.*

Agrarmeteorologische bibliographie, prepared annually by Maximilian Schneider (Offenbach am Main, Deutscher Wetterdienst—Bibliographien des Deutschen Wetterdienstes).

John R Tarrant: *Agricultural geography* (Newton Abbot: David and Charles, 1973).

224 **'A bibliography of arid-lands bibliographies'**, prepared by P Paylore (Natick, Earth Sciences Laboratory, US Army Natick Laboratories, 1967), brings together arid-lands bibliographies from citations in subject chapters comprising the compendium *An inventory of geographical research on world desert environments*, adds appropriate bibliographies from other sources and indexes the whole by geographic area and subject.

Refer also

W C Palmer and L M Denny: *Drought bibliography* (US National Oceanic and Atmospheric Administration, Environmental Data Service, 1971).

225 **'Bibliography of Australia'**, compiled in four volumes by Sir John Alexander Ferguson (Angus and Robertson, 1941–1955), runs as follows: 1, 1784–1830; 2, 1831–1838; 3, 1839–1845; 4, 1846–1850. A fifth volume, covering 1851–1901, was published in three volumes 1963–, including printed books, pamphlets and broadsides, with certain exceptions.

226 **'Bibliography of the Australian aborigines and the native peoples of Torres Strait to 1959'**, was compiled by John Greenaway (Angus and Robertson, 1963). The numbered entries are arranged alphabetically by author and a map is included—'Location of Australian tribes and key to location of tribes'.

227 **'Bibliography of bibliographies on the Arctic'**, compiled by Artheme A Dutilly (The Catholic University of America, Washington, DC, 1945; 1946), is concerned with the region circumscribed by the 10 degrees C (50° F) isotherms for July. An appendix lists prominent names in Arctic exploration and their ships.

228 **'Bibliography of books on Alaska published before 1868'**, the work of Valerian Lada-Mocarski, was published by the Yale University Press; it includes primarily first editions, in chronological order, illustrated by annotated facsimiles and giving a critical history in all major languages.

Refer also

Bern Keating: *Alaska* (National Geographic Society, Special Publications Division, 1969).

G W Rogers, *ed: Change in Alaska* . . . (University of Washington Pr., 1971).

M B Sherwood: *Exploration of Alaska: 1865–1900* (Yale University Pr., 1965).

229 'A bibliography of British Columbia: *laying the foundations 1849–1899'* was prepared by Barbara J Lowther and Muriel Laing under the auspices of the Social Sciences Research Centre, University of Victoria, 1968. Arrangement is chronological by imprint and the data included brings in works published up to the end of 1964 which are concerned with the period of coverage; these may be significant general books, books with relevant chapters and serials. Items are numbered and annotated except when the titles are sufficiently descriptive and a useful feature is the inclusion of location.

230 'A bibliography of British railway history', compiled by George Ottley (Allen and Unwin, 1965), is a classified arrangement of books, parts of books and pamphlets on the history and description of rail transport in the British Isles from the earliest known records to the present. Annotations are appended as necessary. The classification used is printed on the endpapers and there is an extensive introduction on the scope and use of the bibliography. Appendices set out The Railways Act 1921, First Schedule and 'Railway undertakings nationalised under the Transport Act 1947'. Folded charts show the hierarchies of the London Passenger Transport Board, the various Midlands, Manchester and Great Western Railways and there is a very adequate index.

231 'A bibliography of Canadiana: *being items in the Public Library of Toronto, Canada, relating to the early history and development of Canada'*, edited by Frances M Staton and Marie Tremaine, was published by the Library in 1934. Books were selected from the Reference collection of the Library to form a chronological record of the history of Canada from its discovery to the Confederation of the Province in 1867 (1534–1867). Included are the journals of explorers, traders and missionaries from the Atlantic to the Pacific and from the Great Lakes to the Arctic Circle; the records of soldiers and administrators and the narratives of travellers. There is a special guide to government documents. The entries are numbered and the index refers to author or authority, title or catchword and subject. Following the same plan, a supplement edited by Gertrude M Boyle and Marjorie Colbeck was issued in 1959; this text includes Newfoundland and some errata.

Refer also
Marie Tremaine: *A bibliography of Canadian imprints 1751–1800* (University of Toronto Pr., 1952).

232 'A bibliography of Fiji, Tonga and Rotorua', edited by Philip A Snow, was published by the Australian National Press in 1969; some ten thousand entries provide sources for study of the central Pacific.

233 'A bibliography of Ghana 1930–1961', compiled by A F Johnson, was published for the Ghana Library Board by Longmans in 1964. It is, in some respects, a continuation of *A bibliography of the Gold Coast*, prepared by A W Cardinall as a supplement to the Census Report of 1931. In the later work, an attempt is made to list all publications on the Gold Coast and Ghana, including selected periodical articles and translations. The work is arranged in sections according to category of material—bibliographies, periodicals, maps, government publications—also by some subject headings, such as 'Geography', 'Cocoa', 'Forestry', 'Fisheries', 'Agriculture' and 'Travel'; altogether an invaluable compilation.

Note The *National atlas of Ghana* first folios are becoming available in Britain as this *ms* goes to press, directed by Professor E A Boateng and published in Accra by the Ghana National Atlas Project of the Council for Scientific and Industrial Research.

234 'Bibliography of Kerala State, India' was compiled by William A Noble for the Geography Department, University of Missouri, 1970, and is an example of the local studies which are gradually leading to greater knowledge of the sub-continent. 1878 items, in European languages, are arranged within fourteen subject groups, with a special section for periodicals and an index to maps.

235 'Bibliography of the literature relating to New Zealand', compiled by T M Hocken (Government Printer, 1909) has been regarded as a standard work. Arrangement is chronological, with an Addenda, a Maori bibliography, 'Varia' and an index to authors and subjects, not titles. Full bibliographical details are given, also annotations when necessary. A supplement was issued by Whitcombe and Tombs in 1927.

236 '**Bibliography of Malaya**: *being a classified list of books wholly or partly in English relating to the Federation of Malaya and Singapore*' was edited by H R Cheeseman and published by Longmans Green, 1959, for the British Association of Malaya, 1959.

237 '**The bibliography of Mauritius (1502–1954)**' was compiled by Dr A Toussaint and H Adolphe, superseding the *Select bibliography of Mauritius* by Dr Toussaint, which appeared as publication no 4 of the Société de l'Histoire de Maurice. This later bibliography includes printed records, manuscripts, archives and maps and is kept up to date by annual supplements.

238 '**A bibliography of New Zealand bibliographies**' was published in 1967 by the New Zealand Library Association. The Association has also sponsored a *Guide to New Zealand reference material and other sources of information*, compiled by William John Harris and published in a second edition in 1950; supplements, by A G Bagnall, were issued in 1951 and 1957.

239 '**Bibliography of place-name literature:** *United States and Canada*', edited by R B Sealock and P A Seely (American Library Association, 1948; revised edition, 1967), contains references to 3,600 books and articles. Arrangement is by state and province; there is a complete author index and a sensibly compiled subject index.

240 '**Bibliography of printed Maori to 1900**', a valuable work edited by H W Williams (Government Printer, 1924, with a supplement, 1928), includes all books printed wholly in Maori or in Maori with a translation, but excluding works of wider scope. Full bibliographical details are given, frequently with annotations; arrangement is chronological, with indexes to authors and titles, but not to subjects.
> *Refer also*
> C R H Taylor: *A bibliography of publications on the New Zealand Maori and the Moriori of the Chatham Islands* (OUP, 1971).

241 '**Bibliography of reference materials for Russian area studies:** *a preliminary checklist to which is appended a selective list of periodicals* and newspapers published in the USSR and by emigrés abroad', compiled by Peter Gay (The City College Library, University of New York, 1962), was prepared in the course of developing the college collection in the area of Russian studies. Annotations were added as desirable and the work, divided into two main parts, relative to material in the college library and other material not at the time available, includes guides, bibliographies of periodicals and newspapers, general bibliographies, biographies, encyclopedias and research lists, bibliographies of bibliographies, subject bibliographies, with a separate section for 'Geography', publishers, library resources and a list of periodicals in English or Russian.

Refer also

Russia: nineteenth-century source material (Irish University Pr., 1971, *Area studies* series, in thirty-eight volumes, also on microfilm.

242 '**Bibliography of seismology**' has been compiled by the Canada Department of Mines and Technical Surveys, half-yearly from 1929 (Dominion Observatory, Ottawa). More than sixty-two journals have been scanned and the items are arranged alphabetically by author. A cumulative index covers 1947–1956.

243 '**Bibliography of soil science, fertilizers and general agronomy**', 1931/1934–, prepared by the Imperial Bureau of Soil Science (subsequently the Commonwealth Bureau of Soils), Harpenden, Hertfordshire, Commonwealth Agricultural Bureaux, has been issued triennially from 1935. The bibliography in each volume concentrates on a specific topic, arranged according to an adaptation of the decimal classification, plus a geographical sequence for regional items, with author and subject indexes.

Refer also

Roy L Donahue *et al: Soils: an introduction to soils and plant growth* (Prentice-Hall, third edition, 1971).

Norman Hudson: *Soil conservation* (Batsford, 1971).

Sir E John Russell: *Soil conditions and plant growth* (Longmans, ninth edition by E Walter Russell, 1961).

W N Townsend: *An introduction to the scientific study of the soil* (Arnold, fifth edition, 1973).

244 '**Biblio-mer**: *bibliographie de la mer, des marines, des eaux de mer et intérieurs: sciences, technique, enseignement, littérature*', '*Livres et* *périodiques 1967–1968'* (Ostende, Editions Biblio-mer, 1969), was edited by R Roze and M Lelarge. The work is intended as an annual, classified bibliography, with analytical and critical notes of all French-language books, periodicals and other publications, wherever issued, on the subject of the sea and inland waters in the broadest sense; the sea, war and merchant fleets, instruction, history, science, techniques, organisation, economy and law. Full bibliographical descriptions are given, brief reviews and condensed analyses of most of the items. To allow mounting on standard cards, the type area of the pages does not exceed 103 mm.

245 '**Bibliotheca Americana:** *a dictionary of books relating to America from its discovery to the present time'*, compiled by Joseph Sabin and others, was reprinted by N Israel of Amsterdam in twenty-nine volumes in 1961–62 from the New York edition of 1868–1936. This is an indispensable tool, being the total printed material published in England, France, Holland, Germany, Italy, Spain, Portugal, Scandinavia and the American countries relating to the western hemisphere including the Pacific Ocean. Joseph Sabin worked on the bibliography for twenty years prior to the beginning of publication in 1867. Thirteen volumes had been brought out at the time of his death in 1881; Wilberforce Eames continued the work and published six more volumes between 1884 and 1892. Then followed a break until 1927, when, with the assistance of the Bibliographical Society of America, the work was continued under the editorship of Wilberforce Eames and R W G Vail; it was completed in 172 parts in 1936. The twenty-nine volumes have been reprinted in fifteen volumes, using fine quality thin paper.

246 '**Bibliotheca Australiana**' is the collective title given to four series of facsimile editions which chronicle four hundred years of Pacific exploration from Magellan's voyage at the beginning of the fifteenth century to the highly organised scientific expeditions at the end of the nineteenth century. Significant journals and histories written during these four centuries by the mariners themselves and their crews are included, providing a chronological record of the development of knowledge concerning the Pacific Ocean. The series is published jointly by N Israel, and the Da Capo Press of New York; related volumes are issued in groups of ten to twelve, two to four groups appearing annually. For each work, the most important edition is reproduced, giving preference to English language editions, but in its own language if a work has not been translated into English. Whenever possible, works are published in English and in the original language. A feature is the reproduction of many maps and charts.

Refer also
Edouard Roditi: *Magellan of the Pacific* (Faber, 1972).

247 'Bibliotheca cartographica', an international bibliography covering all new publications relating to all aspects of the theory and practice of cartography, has been published twice a year from 1958–. The work was planned by a working group, the Arbeitskreis Bibliographie des Kartographischen Schrifttums (Commission on the Bibliography of Cartographic Literature), set up in 1956 by the German Society for Cartography. More than five hundred publications are examined for each issue, by more than fifty experts and international organisations throughout the world; editing is done by the Institut für Landeskunde within the Bundesanstalt für Landeskunde und Raumforschung, with the Deutsche Gesellschaft für Kartographie, and publication is based on the Institute for Cartography and Topography, University of Bonn. Publication languages are German, English, French and Russian. A *General catalogue of cartographic literature* is also in preparation.

248 'Bibliotheca geographorum Arabicorum' is the title of a comprehensive selection of works originally published between 1870 and 1894 reprinted by Brill of Leiden, from 1967, edited by M J de Goeje in eight volumes, including descriptive and biographical works, systematic studies and a number of dictionaries and glossaries, such as the edition of T G J Juynboll of the great *Lexicon geographicum*, 1850–64, which together provide an invaluable reference source for the study of Arab geography and the contribution of Arab geographers.

249 'Bibliothèque Nationale', Département des Cartes et Plans, Paris, holds one of the world's great collections of maps, including a rich collection of ancient maps and portolan charts. Since 1830, the total French cartographical production has been kept, together with the most important of that of other countries. In 1963 was published an invaluable *Catalogue des cartes nautiques sur vélim conservées au Département des Cartes et Plans*, by Myriem Foncin and others; this includes the basic collection of the Bibliothèque Nationale, collections transferred to the library from the archives of the Service

Hydrographique de la Marine and from the library of the Société de Géographie, with considerable descriptive annotation and bibliographies. The library sponsors and contributes to a vast amount of bibliographical work, both national and international.

250 '**Biogeography and ecology in South America**', edited by E J Fittkau and others (The Hague: W Junk NV, 1968 (1969)), in two volumes, is a collection of essays demonstrating the natural wealth of South America, in English, German, Spanish or Portuguese. Volume one considers the wider aspects of physical conditions, climate, agriculture, environmental change; the second treats of individual groups of flora, fauna, birds and fishes. The two volumes form Volume XIX of the *Monographiae Biologicae*.

Refer also

Proceedings and papers of the Conference of Latin Americanist Geographers (CLAG), founded, 1970; centred on Michigan State University.

Jean Dorst: *South America and Central America: a natural history* (Hamish Hamilton, 1967).

Edward J Goodman: *The explorers of South America* (Macmillan, 1972).

Barry Lentnek *et al, ed: Geographic research on Latin America*, Benchmark 1970. *Proceedings* of the Conference of Latin Americanist Geographers, Vol I. (Muncie, Indiana: Ball State University, 1971).

Alice Taylor, *ed: South America* (Newton Abbot: David and Charles, with the co-operation of the American Geographical Society, 1973).

V L Urquidi and Rosemary Thorp, *ed: Latin America in the international economy. Proceedings* of a Conference held by the International Economic Association in Mexico City (Macmillan, 1973).

251 '**Biological and agricultural index**', the successor to the H W Wilson Company *Agricultural index*, began monthly publication in 1964 (except September). The coverage of the 115 periodicals already indexed was expanded to include the US Department of Agriculture publications, experiment station publications, etc, from the United States, Canada and the British Commonwealth. The form of indexing is similar to that used in most of the Wilson indexes, with subject headings based on those used in the dictionary catalogue of the

Library of Congress, and numerous subheadings and cross-references. There are annual cumulations.

252 Blaeu, Willem Janszoon (1571–1638) developed at Amsterdam a cartographical publishing house of outstanding importance. The House of Blaeu, carried on by his son, Jan Willenz (1596–1673), was responsible for some of the finest works of the seventeenth century, notably *Le grand atlas ou cosmographie Blaviane en laquelle est exactement descritte la terre, la mer, et le ciel*, originally published in Amsterdam, 1663, in twelve volumes, which were reprinted in facsimile by Theatrum Orbis Terrarum (*qv*), Amsterdam. This atlas is considered by scholars to be one of the most magnificent early atlases known; Amsterdam being a centre of learning and geographical information, it was possible to create the atlas with the collaboration of artists, engravers and men of learning and experience from many countries. The text is in French, including geographical and historical descriptions of each of the 609 double-page maps. Editions of the atlas in French, Latin, Spanish and Dutch had been made available before a fire in the printing works terminated Blaeu's career and dealt an irreparable blow to Dutch cartography. The contents of the twelve volumes are as follows: 'World map, North Polar region, Denmark, Norway, Sleswick' (61 maps); 'Sweden, Russia, Poland, Greece' (41 maps); 'Germany' (97 maps); 'Belgium and the Netherlands' (63 maps); 'England' (58 maps); 'Scotland and Ireland' (55 maps); 'France, Switzerland' (two volumes, 73 maps); 'Italy' (60 maps); 'Spain, Portugal, Africa' (41 maps); 'Asia' (28 maps); 'America' (23 maps). The reproduction is printed on specially designed paper, matching the paper used by Blaeu in texture and colour. The fine copies of *Le Grand atlas* in the Amsterdam and Leiden University libraries were used; all the beautiful frontispieces, some of Tycho Brahe's astronomical plates and thirty-two of the maps have been reproduced in full colour following the hand-coloured copy presented by Blaeu to Colbert, Minister to King Louis XIV. Dr C Koeman contributed an introductory study, in book form, to be used with the Atlas and Miss E L Yonge wrote about the colour plates in *The Library journal*, 1 June 1967. The Royal Geographical Society, London, and John Bartholomew and Son have co-operated to publish a series of reproductions of maps from the Blaeu Atlas of 1648, printed in full colours on antique cartridge paper.

Refer also
    Edward   Luther   Stevenson: *Willem*   *Janszoon*   *Blaeu*

1571–1638: a sketch of his life and work with an especial reference to his Large World Map . . . (The Hispanic Society of America, 1914).

C Koeman: *Joan Blaeu and his Grand Atlas* (Philip, 1970), in which chapters deal with 'Biography of Joan Blaeu', 'Printing house and cartographical institutes', 'Origin and growth of Blaeu's atlas', 'The Atlas Maior', 'The cartographical contents of the Grand Atlas', 'The fire of 22nd February 1672' and 'Further history of the Atlas Maior'.

'A catalogue by Joan Blaeu: a facsimile with an accompanying text by Dr. Ir. C Koeman', published by N Israel, Theatrum Orbis Terrarum Limited and the Meridian Publishing Company for their friends at the occasion of the New Year, Amsterdam, December 1967'. This is 'A catalogue of atlases, globes and maps published by Joan Blaeu (1670–71), preserved in the Plantin-Moretus Museum, Antwerpen' with commentary, which includes further references.

S J Tyacke: 'Blaeu and Kepler' *The British Museum Society Bulletin*, October 1971.

253 'The Blond world atlas', edited by Jean de Varennes and Jean Lavallée (Holt, Rinehart and Winston, Canada Limited; Blond Educational, 1971), was a completely new atlas, designed for general use and for secondary level classes. Divided into six main sections, the World, the Continents, Canada (in particular detail), the USA, Resources and Statistics, the maps are all in full colour in a 13″ × 10″ format. The first four sections contain single and double page physical maps with bar and line climate graphs and regional maps portraying special features such as political divisions, climate, geology, soils, vegetation, ethnology, land use, transportation, natural resources, industry, agriculture and population. Five maps show the urban land use of major Canadian cities and of New York. Relief is shown by contours and layer colouring. The 'Resources' section contains forty-eight commodity distribution maps, each accompanied by a statistical analysis of the commodity and the major world producers. The 'Statistics' section uses Canadian production as the comparison index for certain commodities, such as iron ore, automobiles and wheat.

254 'Blumea: *Tijdschrift voor de systematick en de geographie der planten*', a research journal of plant taxonomy and plant geography, international in scope, was begun at the Leyden Rijksherbarium in 1954. Articles are mainly in English, illustrated and with frequent bibliographical references.

Refer also

H A Gleason and A Cronquist: *The natural geography of plants* (Columbia University Pr., 1964, reprinted 1968).

N Polunin: *Introduction to plant geography and some related sciences* (Longmans, 1960, reprinted 1969).

255 Board of Agriculture: *The review and abstract of the county reports to the Board of Agriculture*, by William Marshall, which were brought together in five volumes as a uniform series in 1818, have been reprinted by David and Charles of Newton Abbot. Together the volumes summarise the findings of the county by county surveys of the Board of Agriculture in the closing years of the eighteenth century and the opening of the nineteenth century. They run as follows: Northern Department; Western Department; Eastern Department; Midlands: Southern and Peninsula Departments. The reprinting of the actual *Reports* is in progress; each is being printed in its entirety, no new material being added, but a book is planned which will discuss the project as a whole, together with critical comment. Already available are the volumes for Lincolnshire and Sussex, both by Arthur Young.

256 Board of Trade Library (London) of books, pamphlets and periodicals on all aspects of home and overseas trade and commerce is of the greatest value to geographers. When the library was reorganised in 1946, special divisions were created, including the statistics division library for the United Kingdom, Commonwealth and foreign countries, and a section devoted to the economic statistics of the United Nations; the whole collection of statistics is one of the best available. The Board's publications are listed in the HMSO sectional list no 51, 1932–; the weekly issues of the *Board of Trade journal*, 1886– and its indexes provide a central source of information. Since 1970, the Library has come within the newly formed Department of Trade and Industry.

257 Bodleian Library, University of Oxford; the Map Room in the New Bodleian, opened in 1947, has acquired during recent years more than eighteen thousand maps a year, making the total more than two million, invaluable for the study of the development of cartography. Holdings include many geographical treasures collected through several centuries; manuscripts, early local surveys of the British Isles and Europe and many famous collections of topographical books, such as the Gough Collection. The Gough Map (*qv*) is on view in the reading room. On open access are reference works and a selection of geographical texts, representative periodicals from many countries and some of the general and national atlases. The map catalogue, with its 'Area-scale-date' and 'Subject' headings, has been devised to give the reader the maximum help and information.

258 **'Boletin de información científica Cubana'** has been issued twice a year from December 1969; it contains abstracts of articles on all aspects of science and technology appearing in Cuban publications, arranged according to the UDC classification. Microfilms or photocopies of the original articles can be supplied.

Refer also

C G Clarke: 'The national atlas of Cuba', *Bulletin* of the Society of University Cartographers, Winter, 1971.

259 **'The book of British topography',** produced by John P Anderson in London, 1881, contains a classified catalogue of all topographical works in the library of the British Museum relating to Great Britain and Ireland. An unabridged reprint of the first edition has been published by N Israel, Meridian Press and Theatrum Orbis Terrarum.

260 **'Boundary layer meteorology'** began life in March 1970 (Reidel Publishing Company), edited by R E Munn and a panel of international experts. This quarterly journal, with others, such as *Agricultural meteorology* (*qv*), deals with those factors of meteorology which affect the environment; it is a handsome production, including diagrams and illustrations.

Refer also

R E Munn: *Biometeorological methods* (Academic Pr, 1970).

261 **Bowman, Isaiah** (1878–1950) exerted a wide influence on world geography during a period of rapid change, both in the international scene and in the profession, especially as director of the American Geographical Society between 1915 and 1935 and as president of the International Geographical Union, 1931 to 1934. His best known published work, *The new world* (*qv*), reflects his theories and knowledge of international political geography. Under his guidance, the

American Geographical Society became more influential, research and publications programmes were initiated, the monthly *Bulletin* became *The geographical review* (*qv*) and, in co-operation with other learned bodies, great impetus was given to American geographical work. The knowledge gained from wide travel and the far-reaching theories developed by his original mind are revealed also in his other published work, *Forest physiography: physiography of the United States and principles of soils in relation to forestry*, 1911, *The Andes of Southern Peru*, 1916, *Desert trails of the Atacama*, 1924, *Pioneer fringe*, an expansion of his 'pioneer fringe' thesis, 1931 and *Limits of land settlement . . .*, 1937. Another influential publication was *Geography in relation to the social sciences*, 1934. The Isaiah Bowman School of Geography at Johns Hopkins University, Baltimore, was named in his honour.

262 'Bradshaw's canals and navigable rivers of England and Wales: *a handbook of inland navigation for manufacturers, merchants, traders and others'*, compiled by H R de Salis, a director of a firm of canal carriers, 1904; the work has been reprinted by David and Charles of Newton Abbot, 1969 with an introduction by Charles Hadfield. Detailed itineraries are given of 129 waterways, preceded by thirty pages of general information on various aspects of canals and their use. A glossary of canal terms is included.

Refer also

David and Charles of Newton Abbot: *Inland waterways histories* series and *The canals of the British Isles* series; also the works of Charles Hadfield.

J H Farrington: *Morphological studies of English canals* (University of Hull, Occasional papers in Geography, no 20, 1972).

Ronald Russell: *Lost canals of England and Wales* (Newton Abbot: David and Charles, 1971).

263 Brill, E J, printers, publishers and booksellers of Leiden (Netherlands), are publishers of scholarly monographs and bibliographical works, with special interests in all aspects of Africa and the Near and Far East and in geographical subjects, biology, agriculture, economics and law. *Brill's weekly*, noting recent and forthcoming books, as well as new and second-hand books from stock, concentrates usually on a particular regional or thematic topic in each issue; *Brill's news*, each autumn, a helpful publication arranged by broad subject headings, draws attention to works in preparation or recently published, especially series, frequently with full annotation and sometimes with accompanying plates. The *Annual catalogue* of forthcoming books, from July, 1972, has appeared in the form of leaflets, each dealing with one or more of the subjects contained in *Brill's News*, enabling swift dissemination. Through the year, catalogues are constantly issued on specific topics and a separate catalogue of periodical publications is available. Individual leaflets are circulated, which give full particulars of every major book on publication. A recent work of the greatest significance to geographers in the study of geographical thought is the reprint *Bibliotheca geographorum Arabicorum* (*qv*). Special subject catalogues, published frequently, are particularly useful for regional studies, such as—'Peoples and travels'; 'Near East': 'Books on South and Central Asia from E J Brill'; 'Eastern Europe'; 'Africa and ethnography—geography'; 'Africa–America–Europe'; and 'The Iberian Peninsula, the Maghrib and Africa (except Egypt)', the latter mainly from the collection of Professor R Bassett. Relevant journals published include the *Journal of Asian and African studies*, the *Journal of the economic and social history of the Orient*, the *Newsletter on stratigraphy* and *Tijdschrift voor economische en sociale geographie*.

264 'Britain and the British seas', one of the most influential works of Halford J Mackinder (*qv*), was published in *The regions of the world* series (Heinemann, 1902), of which Mackinder was editor. In the preface, Mackinder states that Britain 'is known in such detail that it has been possible to attempt a complete geographical synthesis. The phenomena of topographical distribution relating to many classes of fact have been treated, but from a single standpoint and on a uniform method'. The book made a great impact, being the most detailed and successful study of this country to date, and it remains a pioneer work in regional treatment. The teacher is present throughout, in the clarity of the exposition and the inclusion of informative figures and sketch-maps in the text; some map plates were drawn specially by J G Bartholomew.

265 'Britain's green mantle, past, present and future', by A G Tansley (Allen and Unwin, 1949, 1968), traces the history of the natural vegetation of Britain from the end of the Ice Age, describing woodlands and grasslands, heaths and bogs, mountain vegetation, coastal dunes and salt marshes. An undoubted classic, written by the first chairman of the Nature Conservancy, it was completely revised for the second edition by M C F Proctor to adjust to interim changes. Though not written specifically with geographers in mind, the work, with its numerous fine photographs, makes essential background reading.

Refer also

A G Tansley: *The British Islands and their vegetation*, 1939.

266 'Britannia', a topographical work of considerable interest to geographers, by William Camden, first published in Latin in 1586; two more London editions followed, then one published in Frankfurt, and an English edition appeared in 1610. The 1607 edition was the first to contain the county maps, engraved by William Hole and William Kip. The work has been reprinted in facsimile by David and Charles of Newton Abbot, 1971, with a new introduction by Stuart Piggott. The folio edition of 1695, prepared by Bishop Edmund Gibson, which is acknowledged to be the best, was used, retaining the splendid first edition English prose style, with careful editing; it includes a fine set of county maps engraved by Robert Morden. A bibliographical note by Gwyn Walters, Assistant Keeper of the National Library of Wales, was included.

267 'Britannia', by John Ogilby (*qv*), embodied the first original survey of the main roads of England and Wales, presented in strip form, and with six or seven sections of road to each page. This work exerted considerable influence on the development of British cartography, in the adoption of the scale of one inch to one mile and of the statute mile of 1760 yards, in furnishing roads for many county maps which had hitherto lacked them and as a model for a long succession of similar road-atlases. Theatrum Orbis Terrarum Publishing Company has reprinted *Volume the First: or, an illustration of the Kingdom of England and Dominion of Wales* . . . of 1675, comprising one hundred double-page maps and 230 pages of text, with a biographical note by J B Harley. The Bibliographical Note discusses the genesis of the survey, its execution and publication, also evaluating the maps as a source for the study of the historical geography of Restoration England.

268 'The Britannica world atlas' consists of 349 maps dealing with 'The world scene'—social and natural features, 'Travel and tourism' and 'World political geography', followed in greater detail by political and physical maps, geographical summaries and comparisons of most of the notable man-made features and an index gazetteer. There are numerous statistical tables and charts and explanatory text.

269 British Antarctic Survey, which originated in 1943 and was known between 1945 and 1962 as the Falkland Islands Dependencies Survey, is now based at Birmingham University. A *Bulletin*, published normally two or three times a year, 1963–, makes known the work of the survey; preliminary reports, notices of new projects, notes on papers and correspondence are also featured. The *Bulletin*, obtainable only from the survey, supplements the *Scientific reports*, the series in which are published results of the scientific work, except in hydrography, carried out in the British sector of Antarctica by the Survey. The reports are published at irregular intervals, not necessarily in numerical order, and they are available from the Survey or from HMSO. The *Bulletin* is illustrated by line blocks and half-tone plates, and valuable folded maps, plates and other illustrations accompany the reports.

270 British Association for the Advancement of Science: the monthly journal, *Advancement of science*, is necessary background reading for geographers, especially the annual address by the president of section E, 'Geography'. Valuable also are the scientific surveys prepared for the annual meetings held in different parts of the country. Traditionally, the work of editing and production has been entrusted to the local geography department. The scope of the volumes has broadened during recent years and it has been interesting to trace progress both in method and presentation. Of many excellent regional studies, *Sheffield and its region: a scientific and historical survey*, edited by David L Linton, 1956, *Manchester and its region . . .* edited by Charles F Carter, 1962, *Nottingham and its region . . .* edited by K C Edwards, 1966 and *Durham County and City with Teeside*, edited by J C Dewdney, 1971 are perhaps particularly informative and well executed.
>Refer also
>
>W G V Balchin: 'Regional surveys of the British Association for the Advancement of Science', *Geography*, July 1973'.
>
>O J R Howarth: 'The centenary of section E (Geography)', *Advancement of science*, no 30, 1951.

271 'The British bulletin of publications on Latin America, the West Indies, Portugal and Spain' is published twice a year by the Hispanic and Luso-Brazilian Council, prepared in Canning House under the direction of the librarian, G H Green, with the collaboration of Dr A J Walford. Works are arranged under the headings of Latin America as a whole, then under an alphabetical listing of the individual countries and alphabetically by author. Bibliographical details are given for each entry, with a few lines of description.

272 British Cartographic Society was the first separate organisation in Britain concerned solely with cartography, founded at the end of 1963, following discussions at informal cartographic symposia at Edinburgh in September 1962, organised by the Departments of Geography and Edinburgh and Glasgow Universities, and a second at the University of Leicester in September 1963, 'to promote the development of cartography'. During the period 1965–66, a Map Curators' Group was formed and a Hydrographic Department was established. An annual general meeting is held in September; ordinary meetings, twice a year, and visits to map collections, also weekend symposia, have developed successfully. A *Newsletter* is being published as a valuable forum for the exchange of information. The progress of the Society may be traced in the issues of *The cartographic journal* (qv). A Library has been established, housed at the Edinburgh Public Library; holdings of books and atlases are increasing rapidly, as well as current periodicals from all parts of the world, and accessions lists have been issued. In February 1971, Aslib, in conjunction with the Map Curators' Group, co-operated in arranging an advanced course on work with maps; it was intended for staff dealing with maps at professional level and included discussions on some of the more specialised problems of administration, recent advances in map reading, carto-bibliography and the study of maps.

273 'British geological literature', compiled by Edward L Martin and Anthony Harvey, was issued quarterly from 1964 (Coridon Press, Bourne End, Bucks), with the aim of listing all books and articles on geology and allied subjects. It was available in two editions: A, a standard library edition, and B, a catalogue edition, supplied on loose sheets printed on one side of the paper only. The service ended in 1968 with volumes 4 and 5 both incomplete.

To take the place of this work, a new publication with the same title began in June 1972, quarterly, by the Bibliographic Press Limited, of which the Managing Director was Dr N Edwards; there was no connection with the previous venture, but the Press holds the remaining stock and back issues. Scope is now literature on geology and geomorphology of the British Isles and adjacent sea areas; titles and short abstracts of papers published in learned and technical journals, conference proceedings, etc, are listed under regional headings, which, so far as possible, are those used for the Institute of Geological Sciences *Handbooks* of British Regional Geology. A map showing a key to the regional divisions is given inside the back cover. Author, place and general subject indexes are included with each issue.

Refer also

John Challinor: *The history of British geology: a bibliographical study* (Newton Abbot: David and Charles, 1971).

Kirtley F Mather and Shirley L Mason, *ed: A source book in geology 1400–1900* (Harvard University Pr, 1971).

274 British Geomorphological Research Group, now a Study Group of the Institute of British Geographers, was established by the Department of Geography, University College of Swansea, in 1961. Four working sub-committees investigate different aspects of geomorphology: a geomorphological map of Great Britain; slope studies; form of the sub-drift; surface and morphometric analysis. Publications include an annual *Register of current research in geomorphology*, 1963–, which lists specialists in Britain working on geomorphological topics throughout the world; and the *Bibliography of British geomorphology*, edited by K M Clayton (Philip, 1964), undertaken as a contribution to the work of the 20th International Geographical Congress, 1964. Relevant books and periodical articles published between 1945 and 1962 are included, with a selection of earlier works; the service was continued by *Geomorphological abstracts (qv)*. Occasional papers include *Geomorphology in a tropical environment*, papers given to the symposium of May 1968, edited by Anthony Harvey.

275 'British history atlas', compiled by Martin Gilbert, with cartography by Arthur Banks (Weidenfeld and Nicolson, 1968), aims to be 'a visual introduction to British history'; the subject is widely interpreted, including treaties and wars in which Britain was concerned. 118 monochrome maps, having brief notes as keys to symbols or in windows suitably placed on the page, trace the main theme.

Refer also

Peter Mathias: *The first industrial nation: an economic history of Britain 1700–1914* (Methuen, 1969).

276 'British interests in the Persian Gulf', by Abdul Amir Amin (Leiden: Brill, 1967), describes British trade in the mid-eighteenth century by the British East India Company, the new developments in the Gulf and in India, the breakdown of Persian authority and the gradual removal of trade towards India. The work, which includes one folding map, provides a welcome piece of research into the economic history of the Anglo-Persian-Indian relationship.

277 British Museum (now The British Library, Reference Division): the original Cotton, Sloane and Harleian Collections all contained maps, the Royal Library was added in 1757 and the fine geographical and topographical collection assembled by George III was transferred to the Museum in 1828. Maps, therefore, have formed an integral part of the collection, but the Map Room was not established as an independent department until 1868, and the manuscript maps remained in the Department of Manuscripts. In 1902, the Map Room became a division of the Department of Printed Books. The collection includes the whole of current British map production and a representative selection of topographical and special maps from other countries. The section of historical maps is especially strong, including a comprehensive series of maps and atlases from the fifteenth century, King George III's Topographical and Maritime Collections and the Crace Collection of London Plans, also a considerable number of manuscript maps, particularly early estate surveys. Some oriental maps are kept in the Department of Oriental Printed Books and Manuscripts. The current acquisition policy is to keep all maps on a scale of approximately 1:50,000 and all special maps of value, likely to be useful to students. Holdings of Ordnance Survey maps are complete; Admiralty charts are also deposited, but not the inter-edition corrections. Exchange of maps with the United States is comprehensive, but uneven for the rest of the world. A study room and open-access reference collection are available in the department and an extensive information service is maintained. On occasion, articles in the *British Museum quarterly* and *The British Museum Society bulletin* are of relevance, particularly on early topographical literature or maps; also the excellent catalogues of exhibitions, finely illustrated, such as *Prince Henry the Navigator and Portuguese marine enterprise*, 1960, which included annotated entries.

See also Catalogue of the manuscript maps, charts and plans and of the topographical drawings held in the British Museum.

278 The British National Committee for Geography, set up by the Royal Society in 1920 to act as the British link with the International Geographical Union, has been re-constituted to make it more representative of geography in Britain today. The function of such committees, laid down in the statutes of the IGU (*qv*) is to nominate delegates to meetings of the Union and to promote the objects of the Union in the member countries. The Committee has a widely representative membership and *ex officio* membership is extended to the Hydrographer of the Navy, the Director-General of the Ordnance Survey, the Director of Military Survey, the Director of Overseas Surveys, a Secretary of the Royal Society, the Secretary of the British Academy and the Chairman of the Cartography Sub-Committee, also elected members from many geographical organisations within the British Isles. A Study Committee has been set up to consider issues of topical importance concerning geography in the United Kingdom. The development of formal cartographic education in the United Kingdom was given a new impetus by a conference held at the Royal Society in September 1968, under the auspices of the Cartography Sub-Committee of the British National Committee for Geography. A full report was issued—'Education in cartography in the United Kingdom'—and the final resolution requiring the Department of Education and Science and the Scottish Education Department to set up a Joint Committee for the formulation of qualifications in the fields of cartography, photogrammetry and surveying at Ordinary and Higher National Certificate levels was duly carried into effect. The funds made available for research through the 20th International Geographical Congress Fund are administered and close contact is also maintained with the trustees of the Dudley Stamp Memorial Fund.

279 'British pioneers in geography', by Edmund W Gilbert (Newton Abbot: David and Charles, 1972), consists of a collection of essays by Professor Gilbert on notable geographical personalities, their special ideas and the environment in which they lived and worked, from the time of the Hakluyts and their immediate predecessors. The work makes a valuable contribution to the progress of British geographical studies; however, a closely co-ordinated analysis of the

146

many facets of this progress has yet to be produced.

As this *ms* goes to press, the news has come of the death (October 1973) of Professor Gilbert; *British pioneers in geography* was the last in the distinguished line of his publications.

280 'British weather in maps' by James A Taylor and R A Yates (Macmillan, second edition, 1958; New York: St Martin's Press, 1967), presents a method of geographical analysis and interpretation of the 'primary documents' of British weather, especially the British Daily Weather Reports. The successive theories evolved to explain and classify the weather are described as a background to the appreciation of the format and function of the Weather Reports—'General considerations', 'Some fundamental properties of the atmosphere', 'The British Daily Weather Report', 'Air masses', 'Fronts', 'The anticyclone', 'Other synoptic types' and 'Classifications of British weather and climate'. Appendices present 'Dates and times of selected British Daily Weather Reports showing examples of standard front and air mass types'; 'A selection of symbols used on weather maps'; 'Procedure for the classroom analysis of weather maps'; 'Equivalents of temperature'. Throughout the work the weather codes used are those given in the publication *Instructions for the preparation of weather maps* (HMSO, 1954). There are figures and sketchmaps in the text; references are listed for chapter 7, 'Classifications of British weather and maps' and there is a short general bibliography, mainly of Meteorological Office publications.

281 Brunhes, Jean (1869–1930) studied with Paul Vidal de la Blache and in his turn contributed greatly to the reputation of the French school of geographical thought, especially in regional and human geography; a man of outstanding scholarship and a stylist, exerting very wide influence on academic work during his term as Professor of Human Geography at the Collège de France, 1912 to 1930. His chief published works include the pioneer study *La géographie humaine* (*qv*), *La géographie de l'histoire*, with C Vallaux, 1921, and *Géographie humaine de la France*, in two volumes, 1920 and 1926, each with a collaborator.

282 Brunswick International School Book Institute, created by the Council of Europe some years ago, includes a 'Europe centre'. The Institute has so far collected about sixty thousand textbooks. Policy is for the institute to receive all new publications and new curricula and the German Research Community has sponsored the acquisition of books from North and Latin America. There are also plans for making even more international the *International yearbook for the teaching of history and geography*, which has been published by the Institute for the past thirteen years (1971). The Institute, headed by Professor Georg Eckert, has arranged more than a hundred bilateral or international conferences, many of them to discuss the standard and use of geography textbooks, atlases and maps. Five more European centres, based on the Brunswick model, have been planned by the Council of Europe.

283 **'Bulgaria: a bibliographic guide'**, compiled by Marin V Pundeff (Library of Congress, Slavic and Central European Division, Reference Department, 1965, 1968; New York: Arno Press), presents a bibliographic survey—a discussion of sources, grouped under seven subject headings: 'General reference works'; 'Land and people', etc, followed by a 'Bibliographic listing of publications discussed', each numbered and given a brief bibliographical description.

284 **'Bulletin of material on the geography of the USSR'** was published by the University of Nottingham Department of Geography between 1958 and 1961, while its usefulness seemed assured. Readers are reminded of *Soviet geography* . . . and the increased number of new texts in English on Russian geography and of English abstracts or translations in Russian works. The twelve issues of the Bulletin included 'Agricultural statistics' by C A Halstead, 1958; 'New economic regions in the USSR', by J P Cole, 1958; 'Industrial statistics', by J P Cole, 1958; 'Transport statistics and notes', by R E H Mellor, 1959; 'Population statistics' by J P Cole 1959, in two issues; 'Selected data from the *Soviet statistical yearbook* for 1958', by J P Cole, 1960; 'Nationalities of the USSR in 1959' by J P Cole, 1960; 'Agricultural statistics', by C A Halstead, 1961; 'Economic geography in the USSR, 1960' by F C German, 1961; 'The Soviet iron and steel industry', by R E H Mellor and J P Cole, 1962.

285 **'Bulletin of quantitative data for geographers'** edited by J P Cole and published by Nottingham University from 1965, aims to inform geographers on quantitative data not readily available due to language or other difficulties and to introduce and show the application of mathematical and statistical processes in geography.

Refer also

148

Barry Floyd: 'The quantitative and model-building "Revolution" in geography: a student attitude survey', *Geography*, January 1970.

Derek Thompson: 'A selective bibliography on qualitative methods in geography', *Geography*, January 1969.

286 'Die Bundesrepublik Deutschland in Karten' is the most comprehensive documentary cartographical work to date on all aspects of the land and communities of Germany, 1965– by the Institute for Space Research at Hanover, the Federal Office of Statistics and other authoritative bodies (W Kohlhammer, 1965–).

Refer also

Atlas of Nordrhein-Westfalen (Düsseldorf: Ministerpräsidenten des Landes Nordrhein-Westfalen, 1950–).

Atlas der Deutschen Volkskunde (Marburg: N G Elwert Verlag, 1959–1966).

Atlas des Deutschen agrarlandschaft (Weisbaden: Franz Steiner Verlag, 1962–1965).

T H Elkins: *Germany* (Chatto and Windus, 2nd edition, 1968).

E Meynen *et al, ed: Handbuch des naturräumlichen Gliederung Deutschlands* (Bad Godesberg: Bundestalt für Landeskunde und Raumforschung Selbstverlag, five volumes, 1953–1962).

287 The Butterworth Group has published a number of books on geography, all well illustrated and produced: T R Tregear: *An economic geography of China*, 1970; J P Cole and F C German: *A geography of the USSR: the background to a planned economy,* second edition, 1970; J P Cole: *Latin America: an economic and social geography*, second edition, 1970; I B Thompson: *Modern France: a social and economic geography*, 1970; Sir Raymond Priestley and others: *Antarctic research: a review of British scientific achievement in Antarctica*, 1964; N C Pollock: *Studies in emerging Africa*, 1971; Chiao-Min Hsieh: *Taiwan-Ilha Formosa: a geography in perspective*, 1964.

288 'Cahiers de géographie de Québec', journal of the Institut de Géographie, Université Laval, Quebec, superseded the Institute's two series, *Cahiers de géographie* and *Notes de géographie*, in 1956. Two issues are published each year; articles are mainly in French, with English summaries, and informative book reviews are a feature. Indexes are prepared annually and five-yearly.

289 'Cahiers d'outre-mer: *revue de géographie de Bordeaux'* is an interesting and valuable journal, produced quarterly from 1948 by the Institut de Géographie de la Faculté des Lettres de Bordeaux. Annual indexes are published, with ten-yearly cumulations.

290 CALCOMP General Purpose Contouring Program is used to plot automatically functions of two independent variables in the form of contour diagrams or maps. It can make a map of any suitable data and has been used in widely varying applications to plot seismic, demographic, geological, thermal and pressure maps and diagrams. GPCP uses a gridding method that computes gridded data from randomly spaced input data, analytically constructing a smooth surface. The speed and accuracy of the method makes it specially useful for plotting quantities of contour data at minimum cost—as in oil prospecting, highway design and the compilation of weather maps.

291 'Cambrian bibliography: *containing an account of the books published in the Welsh language, or relating to Wales, from 1546 to the end of the eighteenth century, with bibliographical notes'*, by W Rolands, edited and enlarged by D Silvan Evans, 1869, has been reprinted by the Meridian Publishing Company, Amsterdam, in collaboration with N Israel, 1970.

292 'Cambridge expeditions journal', annual publication of the Cambridge University Explorers' and Travellers' Club, 1969/70–, has taken in *Visa*. The journal exists 'to provide a definitive list and factual description of all expeditions planned and undertaken in the year: to provide a medium for expressing our appreciation of the services rendered to these expeditions by the firms of the Cambridge Block Order Scheme, and of the financial and informational assistance given by countless individuals and organisations to each expedition'. The texts are accompanied by photographs, sketchmaps and figures.

293 Cambridge University Department of Geography was founded in 1888 with periods of re-organisation in 1919 and 1937. The library, classified by its own scheme, is primarily a working library for students and staff; in addition, some valuable collections are held, especially a collection of eighteenth and early nineteenth century books on discovery and travel. The Cambridge University Geographical Society has since 1920 made useful contributions to original work.

294 'Canada: a geographical interpretation', prepared under the auspices of the Canadian Association of Geographers, was edited by John Warkentin (Methuen, 1968) on the occasion of the centennial of Canadian Confederation and was subsidised by the Centennial Commission. The book is divided according to the following topics: 'The setting', 'Lands and people', 'People and places', 'Relations and trends'. Each part is followed by a list of references and there is also a 'Note on sources'. Photographs and diagrams accompany the text and there are maps in a pocket.

Refer also

John T Andrews: *A geomorphological study of post-glacial uplift with particular reference to Arctic Canada* (Institute of British Geographers, Special publication, no 2, 1970).

J Brian Bird: *The natural landscapes of Canada: a study in regional earth science* (Wiley, 1973).

J B Brebner: *Canada: a modern history* (University of Michigan Press, 1960).

R J E Brown: *Permafrost in Canada: its influence on northern development* (Toronto: OUP, 170).

R L Gentilcore, *ed*: *Canada's changing geography: selection of readings* (Prentice-Hall, 1967).

L E Hamelin: *Le Canada* (Paris: PUF, 1969).

D Q Innis: *Canada: a geographic study* (McGraw-Hill, 1966).

Kathleen Jenkins: *Montreal: island city of the St Lawrence* (Doubleday, 1966).

R R Krueger and R G Gorder: *Canada: a new geography* (Holt, Rinehart and Winston, 1968).

R J McCormack: 'The Canada Land Use Inventory: a basis for land use planning', *Journal of soil and water conservation*, July–August, 1971.

Dorothy E Ryder, *ed*: *Canadian reference sources: a selective guide* (Canadian Library Association, 1973).

W C Wonders, *ed*: *Canada's changing north* (Toronto and Montreal: McClelland and Stewart, 1971).

W D Wood and R S Thoman, *ed*: *Areas of economic stress in Canada: Proceedings* of a conference at Queen's University, Kingston, Ont (Industrial Relations Centre, Queen's Univ 1965).

295 Canada, Department of Mines and Technical Surveys, Geographical Branch, developed in 1951 from the Geographical Bureau of 1947, established 'to collect and organise data on the physical, economic and social geography of Canada'; The Department was reorganised in 1966 under the title Department of Energy, Mines and Resources; two divisions operate for the Canadian work, designated Regional Geography and Systematic Geography; the Foreign Geography Division works on studies of foreign areas of interest to Canada. A *Geographical bulletin* has been published irregularly from 1951, in English and French; the articles are authoritative and illustrated with photographs and maps in the text, also frequently with maps in a separate pocket. Abstracts are included. An index is cumulated for every four issues. *Memoirs* and *Papers* have also been published and a *Bibliographical series* began in 1950. The occasional monographs are valuable, as, for example, *An introduction to the geography of the Canadian Arctic*, 1951. Other divisions of interest to geographers include the Surveys and Mapping Branch, the Marine Sciences Branch, the Dominion Observatories and the Mineral Resources Division.

See also
Geological Survey of Canada.

296 'Canada in maps', with French and English text, contains documents drawn from an exhibition arranged by the National Map Collection, Public Archives of Canada, in October 1969–February 1970. The Map Division was created in 1908, but the collection began in the 1880s and it now provides a focal point and central management control for projects of national interest. Section I deals with 'The age of discovery' and 'Canada emerges'; II, 'Exploration'; III, 'Political development'; IV, 'Settlement'; V, 'Urban development'; VI, 'Architectural, military, engineering and naval plans'; VII, 'Hydrography'; VIII, 'Canada's maps today' and, finally, 'Atlases display' from four cases. Entries include annotation and the location of each item. The Collection numbers more than five hundred thousand items, rapidly increasing, and the Division is responsible also for Canada's contribution to the *Bibliographie cartographique internationale* (*qv*).

Refer also
Atlas and gazetteer of Canada (Ottawa: Queen's Printer, 1969).

Betty May: 'Canadian maps', *Bulletin*, Special Libraries Association, Geography and Map Division, March 1971.

297 Canadian Association of Geographers is the association of professional geographers in Canada, founded in 1950. The first conference was held in the following year, and the *Proceedings* of these conferences have been published in a semi-annual publication, the *Canadian geographer*, which is bi-lingual, with abstracts in either English or French. Book reviews are included.

298 'Canadian cartography', 1962–, is the title given to the Proceedings of the Symposium on Cartography, The Canadian Institute of Surveying, Ottawa, first held in Ottawa, 1962; the second volume reports on the Symposium of 1964, and so on every other year.
Refer also
Publications, Association of Canadian Map Libraries/ Association des cartothèques canadiennes, c/o National Map Collection, Public Archives of Canada, Ottawa; *ACML newsletter*, issued three or four times a year.
Cartologica, bi-monthly 1969– (Québec, Cartothèque, Bibliothèque générale, Université Laval).

299 'Canadiana', monthly, lists the works of Canadian interest received by the National Library (National Bibliography Division). A main development in *Canadiana* 1970 was the inclusion of sound recordings; Library of Congress classification numbers are also added to the entries in Part I, except those in the fields of Canadian history, literature and law. Queen's Printer catalogue numbers are appended. The first section includes the main body of material, catalogued and classified by DC, both adult and works for young people; the second section comprises pamphlet material and brochures; the third, microforms; 4, films; 5, publications issued by the Government of Canada and 6, publications of the Provincial Government of Canada.

300 'Canadiana before 1867', a series of reprints published to coincide with the centenary of Canadian Federation in 1967, issued by SR Publishers Limited, was prepared under the auspices of La Maison des Sciences de l'Homme, Paris. The Humanities Research Council of Canada, The Social Science Research Council, Ottawa, and the Toronto Public Library, on history and government. Also included are, for example, 'An account of the countries adjoining to Hudson's Bay', by Arthur Dobbs, 1744; 'General introduction to the statistical account of Upper Canada', by Robert Fleming Govilay, 1822; 'Statistical account of Upper Canada' by the same author, 1822; 'British Columbia and Vancouver Island', by W C Hazlitt, 1858 and 'An account of Prince Edward Island in the Gulf of St Lawrence, North America', by John Stewart, 1806, a survey of the geography, history, industries and natural resources of the Island.

301 'Cappelen road and tourist map of Norway', the first such series of an international standard to become available, covers the entire country. The map is based on the most recent material from the Norges Geografiche Oppmåling (The Norwegian Geographic Survey Department) and the tourist information represents the accumulated result of investigations carried out by several hundred contributors throughout the country. Six colours are used: road networks are classified according to the latest road regulations, highway and road numbers being in line with the new system brought into effect in June 1965. Thirty-five thousand placenames are inserted. The key, shown on the reverse of each map, includes some sixty symbols representing information likely to be of use to tourists, given in English, French and German. On the four most northerly maps, coastal steamer routes are indicated. The maps are folded into a stiff paper cover. In the United Kingdom, John Bartholomew and Son Limited are the distributors.

302 Caribbean Council developed from the former Caribbean Organisation, which itself succeeded the Caribbean Commission; all functions and the library have been transferred. A *Current Caribbean bibliography* was begun by the library in 1950 (1951–); other bibliographies, catalogues, bulletins, pamphlets, reports and surveys are issued from time to time.

303 'Caribbean review' has been published quarterly in Puerto Rico since April 1969; articles, essays and bibliographies are included, in Spanish or English. Reviews are a main feature, with the intention of covering all the main books relating to Latin America and the Caribbean and each issue contains a list of recent books, classified by subject.

154

Refer also
The Caribbean geographer (University of the West Indies, Geography Department, 1972–).

Social research and rural life in Central America, Mexico and the Caribbean region. Proceedings of a seminar organised by Unesco in co-operation with the UN Economic Commission for Latin America, October 1962 (Unesco, 1966).

Sir Harold Mitchell: Caribbean patterns: a political and economic study of the contemporary Caribbean (Chambers, 1967).

V Rubin, ed: Caribbean studies: a symposium (University College of the West Indies, Institute of Social and Economic Research, 1957).

J Wreford Watson et al: A geography of Bermuda (Collins, 1965).

304 'Caribbean studies', a quarterly journal published by the University of Puerto Rico Institute of Caribbean Studies, includes current bibliographies of books, pamphlets and periodical articles.
Refer also
Wilbur F Buck: Agriculture and trade of the Caribbean region—Bermuda, the Bahamas, the Guianas, and British Honduras (Washington: US Department of Agriculture, Economic Research Service, 1971).

Timothy Severin: The golden Antilles (Hamish Hamilton, 1970).

305 'Caribbeana 1900–1965: a topical bibliography', compiled by Lambros Comitas (University of Washington Press for the Research Institute for the Study of Man, 1968), contains more than seven thousand references to books, monographs, reports, articles and miscellaneous publications, arranged on the following plan: a general introduction, 'The past', 'The people', 'Elements of culture', 'Health, education and welfare', 'Political issues', 'The environment and human geography', 'Socio-economic activities and institutions', 'Soils, crops and livestock', 'Economic and social projects'—each being sub-divided as necessary, with author and geographical indexes. Each entry bears a reference number and a geographical code.

306 'Cartactual', an international bi-monthly topical map service begun in 1965 by Cartographia of Budapest ('Kultura'), is produced in English, French and German, under the editorial direction of Professor Dr Sándor Radó. Bi-monthly booklets, each providing a set of maps on various topics, printed as loose-leaf double page maps, trace recent changes in geographical information throughout the world. The first issues were in monochrome, each map being carefully drawn in simple style, with adequate documentation and scale. In volume 2, 1966, red colour was introduced to show changes, black remaining for existing detail. Aspects especially noted are modification of administrative boundaries, expansion or reduction of transport systems, changes in the numbers of inhabitants of settlements and the foundation of new settlements, new geographical names and other such data.

307 'Carte de France' on a scale of 1:80,000 and, by photographic enlargement, at 1:50,000, was completed as early as 1878, the sheets being printed in monochrome. Relief was shown by hachures. It is instructive to compare this series with that of the first official British mapping programme as the earliest national surveys to be carried out on scientific principles. The *Nouvelle carte de France* at 1:20,000 now provides the basic map for all cartographic work.

308 Carto-bibliography as a term came into current use with the increasing variety of maps and the universal recognition of their uses in contemporary life, leading to a corresponding increase in the literature concerning them and in the guides to collections, both current and retrospective. The first General Assembly of the International Cartographic Association was held in 1961 and the *Bulletin*, containing reports of the cartographic activity of member nations, first appeared in 1962. Among the organisations making regular contributions to the subject are the International Association of Geodesy, the International Society for Photogrammetry, the Centre de Documentation Cartographique et Géographique, the Institute of Geodesy, Photogrammetry and Cartography of Ohio State University, the Ontario Institute of Chartered Cartographers and the British Cartographic Society (*qv*). Of central importance are *New geographical literature and maps* (*qv*), the 'Cartographic progress' section of *The geographical journal* (*qv*), the 'Geographical record' section of *The geographical review* (*qv*), *Cartography* (*qv*) and the *Kartographische nachrichten* (*qv*) of the Deutsche Gesellschaft für Kartographie eV. *World cartography* (*qv*) is the first source of information for international work. Individual national coverage in cartobibliography still varies considerably; maps are included in perhaps about half of the national bibliographies. Countries such as Portugal and the Netherlands have been particularly active in compiling retrospective bibliographies, with such major works as the *Atlantes Neerlandici* (*qv*). The reports of individual mapping agencies are contributions to national bibliographical completeness, such as the monthly *Publication reports* and the guides and other informative material issued by the Director General of the Ordnance Survey (*qv*). *Imago mundi* (*qv*) is the international journal covering historical cartography and the *International yearbook of cartography* (*qv*) is a unique publication including finely illustrated articles by leading world authorities. The *Bibliographie cartographique international* (*qv*) provides an extensive coverage, as does the *Bibliotheca cartographica* (*qv*). A novel and highly successful venture is the *Zumstein katalog . . .* (*qv*). Retrospective bibliographies, each devoted to a particular period or type of material, include *Official map publications . . .* (*qv*), *The printed maps in the atlases of Great Britain and Ireland . . .* (*qv*) and *Map collections in the United States and Canada . . .* (*qv*). The catalogues and accessions lists of such great map collections as those of the British Museum, the Library of Congress, the Bibliothèque Nationale and the Bodleian Library are essential bibliographical sources, as are the catalogues of the great national cartographical publishing houses, such as Bartholomew, Esselte, Cartographia of Budapest, Rand McNally, Georg Westermann and the Stanford annual international catalogue. General bibliographical services usually include a section for maps and atlases, such as *Whitaker's cumulative book list* and section K of *British books in print*.

Refer also

Denoyer-Geppert, Chicago: *Maps, globes, charts, atlases, models, transparencies*—annual.

G L Alexander: *Guide to atlases: world, regional, national, thematic* (Metuchen, N J: Scarecrow Pr, 1971).

L Bagrow and H Wertheim, *ed: Jahrbuch der alten Kartographie* (Amsterdam: Israel, 1964).

G Fremlin and L M Sebert, *ed: National atlases* (Cartographica, Monograph no 4; Toronto: York University, 1972).

Harold Fullard: 'Atlas production for the 1970's', *The geographical magazine*, October 1969.

G R P Lawrence: *Cartographic methods* (Methuen, 1971; *Field of geography* series, includes information on atlases and map series).

Muriel Lock: *Modern maps and atlases* . . . (Bingley, 1969; Hamden, Conn, Archon).

Karl-Heinz Meine: 'Considerations on the state of development with regard to topographical maps of the different countries of the earth', *International yearbook of cartography*, 1972.

W W Ristow, *comp: À la carte: selected papers on maps and atlases* (Washington, DC: Library of Congress, 1972).

K A Salichtchev: *Atlas nationaux: histoire, analyse, voies de perfectionnement et d'unification* (Edition de l'Académie des Sciences de l'URSS for the Commission of National Atlases of the IGU, 1960).

——'Contribution of geographical congresses and the International Geographical Union to the development of cartography', *IGU Bulletin*, Volume XXII, no 2, 1971.

'The status of world topographic mapping', *World cartography*, 1970.

R W Stephenson: 'Atlases of the western hemisphere: a summary review', *The geographical review*, 1972.

K L Winch: *ed: International maps and atlases in print* (Bowker, in conjunction with Edward Stanford, 1974).

Yale University, Department of Geography: *Cartographica: a series of monographs*.

309 Cartographia of Budapest, one of the leading European cartographic houses, has made major contributions to modern mapping. Among their best known works are the London, Madrid and Rome sheets of the 1:2,500,000 world map, published by the East German Department of Geodesy and Cartography, 1962; and the 'Hydrographic map of Europe's surface waters', 1:10M, 1965.

310 'The cartographic journal', issued twice a year from 1964 by the British Cartographic Society, is of the highest standard both in content and production. Technical articles, world-wide in scope and usually accompanied by comprehensive references, on all aspects of contemporary cartography are suitably illustrated; society news is included, also cartographic news and notices of meetings and symposia. Useful features are careful signed reviews, 'Recent literature', including both books and periodical articles, and 'Recent maps', which covers also atlases. An index for volumes 1 to 4 was distributed with the December 1968 issue and a cumulative index is available covering volumes 1–8; articles were subject classified, authors' names arranged alphabetically, while maps, diagrams and illustrations were indexed by topic and there is also a separate index of speakers whose papers have been briefly reported.

311 'Cartography', journal of the Australian Institute of Cartographers, Melbourne, has been issued irregularly from 1954, usually twice a year. Important features are the 'Cartographical abstracts' and reviews of overseas publications in this field. An index is compiled every two years.

312 Cartography: summary of recent developments and techniques

THE FRAMEWORK OF MODERN CARTOGRAPHY: The definition of cartography, as pronounced by the experts at the meeting of the United Nations Secretariat and representatives in 1949, runs as follows: 'the science of preparing all types of maps and charts, and includes every operation from original surveys to final printing of copies. The types of maps and charts included are 1) topographic maps; 2) geologic maps, hydrographic charts, and aeronautical charts, all of which are prepared upon a topographic map base; and 3) office-compiled maps showing the location, extent and characters of physical, economic and social phenomena.' Topographic mapping was considered to be a social service and therefore a function of government, whether it was actually prepared by governmental agencies or under contract, for all purposes of development and administration. The need for accurate map coverage is the same in all parts of the world, but the kinds of maps needed vary with the terrain and stage of development. Stress is now laid on the essential advantages of surveying and mapping developing areas before any projects are planned.

The Council of the British Cartographic Society agreed the following definition on 24 April 1964: 'Cartography is the art, science and technology of making maps, together with their study as scientific documents and works of art. In this context maps may be regarded as including all types of maps, plans, charts and sections, three-dimensional models and globes, representing the earth or any heavenly body at any scale. In particular, cartography is concerned with all stages of evaluation, compilation, design and draughting required to produce a new or revised map document from all forms of basic data; it also includes all stages in the reproduction of maps. It encompasses the study of maps, their historical evolution, methods of cartographic presentation and map use.' Compare also

Professor Imhof's preface to the second *International yearbook of cartography*—'Maps are inexhaustible mines of information for geographers and scientists, indispensable elements of regional and country planning, comparisons and guides for all tourists and globe-trotters. More than ever we can nowadays state the truth of Napoleon's words: "When preparing maps, one should only produce good ones"'.

The American Congress on Survey and Mapping, on the other hand, in 1952 (*Survey and mapping*, XII, 1, 1952), decided on a definition restricted both at the beginning and the end of the entire process—'... the compilation of essentially new maps in general through final drafting and photo-processing stages preparatory to reproduction', omitting the specialised knowledge of surveyor and map printer.

During the past twenty years or so, a number of national and international glossaries have been undertaken. Since 1943, the Geographical Section, General Staff, of the War Office, has produced a series of *Short glossaries for use on foreign maps* in thirty volumes; these include all terms commonly found on maps, in thirty languages. In 1944, Alain Bargilliat compiled a *Vocabulaire pratique Anglais-Français et Français-Anglais des termes concernant la cartographie*, for the Institut Géographique National; this includes terms used in geodesy, topography and all processes involved in the drawing and printing of maps. The *Lexique Anglais-Français des termes appartenent aux techniques en usage à l'Institut Géographique National* was published in three volumes, 1956–58. Two practical works appeared in Washington in 1948: *Definitions of terms used in geodetic and other surveys* was published by the United States Coast and Geodetic Survey (Special publication no 242) and *Glossary of cartographic terms* was issued by the United States Army Map Service. The United States Geological Survey, Topographical Division, compiled a *Glossary of names for topographic forms*, in 1954, and in the same year, the American Society of Civil Engineers, New York, published *Definitions of surveying, mapping and related terms*. A very careful work, *English-Russian dictionary on cartography, geodesy and aerial phototopography*, compiled by G L Galperin and edited by G V Gospodinov, was produced by the State Publishing Office for Physical and Mathematical Literature, Moscow, 1958; and a *Multilingual dictionary*, compiled by a Special Committee of the International Federation of Surveyors, was published by the Federation in 1963. More than 5,500 entries, including definitions, are in French,

160

English/American and German.

The discussions involved in all these projects revealed a good deal of discrepancy in the meaning attached to terms and much consultation is still required before agreement is reached. Agreement on terminology is of central importance, not only for the complete understanding of research and textbooks published in different countries, but also looking ahead to co-ordinated indexing projects and programming for computer use. The Group of Experts on Geographical Names was appointed by the Secretary-General of the United Nations, following a resolution of the Economic and Social Council at the end of June 1960; the *Report* of the Group (UN Economic and Social Council, New York, 1961) stressed the need for standardisation of geographical names. The problems involved were briefly set out in twenty two sections intended for the guidance of national names authorities. Particularly stressed were the publication of gazetteers of standardised names after due research, and close liaison between national cartographical agencies and national names authorities. Considerable progress has already been made in international agreement and in the United Nations cartographical bulletin, *World cartography*, Volume VI, there is a bibliography of gazetteers.

In 1964, therefore, the International Cartographic Association appointed a Commission to establish some degree of standardisation in the use of terms by map-makers and users throughout the world; the first working meeting of the ICA Commission on the Definition, Classification and Standardisation of Cartographic Terms was held in September 1965, at which it was agreed that the principal task should be the compilation of cartographic terms published in a *Multilingual dictionary of cartographic terms*, contributed by the National Committees. The chief contributors were the Cartography Sub-Committee for Geography, the Comité de Cartographie, the Deutsche Gesellschaft für Kartographie, the Hungarian Geodetic and Cartographic Society, the Japan Cartographic Association, the Seminario de Estudios Cartograficos and the National Council of the Cartographers of the USSR. The United Kingdom contribution was published separately in 1966, with the title *Glossary of cartographic terms*. Four hundred terms are included; three appendices relate to 'Map projections', 'Isograms' and 'Paper sizes' and the work was introduced by W D C Wiggins, then Director of the Overseas Surveys. The standard form of entry agreed by the Special Commission included full definition, with explanatory notes in English,

French, German and Russian, possibly in Spanish also. Single word equivalents were to be listed in a number of other languages, but not defined. All such glossaries must be frequently revised in this age of constant development and change. The Deutsche Forschungsgemeinschaft and the Federal Government granted facilities as an exchange centre for evaluation of the lists.

The currently accepted definition for an atlas, given in the *Glossary of technical terms in cartography* is 'A collection of maps designed to be kept (bound or loose) in a volume'. In a paper presented at the ICA Symposium at Edinburgh in 1964, O M Miller, Secretary of the American Geographical Society, discussing the theme 'Concepts and purposes of a serial atlas', likened such an atlas to a journal appearing at regular or irregular intervals. He was referring in particular to the *Antarctic map folio series* and the *Serial atlas of the marine environment*. The loose-leaf format is the new element in atlas production; the analogy with the journal form can be carried too far in that the individual sheets are expected to be used in conjunction with one another. Production in this form allows, in the first place, for the research first completed to be made available and, secondly, for revision of individual sheets.

The Cartographic Office of the United Nations has as its aims the sponsorship of maps, charts and other geographic aids and information, assistance in the co-ordination of the activities of the United Nations and the specialised agencies in the field of cartography, interpretation of cartography in all aspects and the encouragement of projects and conferences. Promotion of continuous effort and uniformly high standards are the main ideals. United Nations meetings on surveying and mapping have been important, especially the 'Third United Nations Cartographic Conference for Asia and the Far East', held in 1961 at Bangkok. 120 participants from twenty five countries took part, including representatives from FAO, ICAO and UNESCO, the European Organisation for Experimental Photogrammetry Research, the International Geographical Union, the International Hydrographic Bureau and the International Union of Geodesy and Geophysics. Technical Committees were established on Geodesy; Topography and photogrammetry, Photointerpretation and topical maps; the IMW World Aeronautical Charts, and Geographical Names; Magnetic surveys and world magnetic charts, hydrography and oceanography. The establishment of a regional intergovernmental centre for surveying and mapping was discussed, also new techniques and developments, electronic distance measuring instruments, the materials of scribing, use of computers and the co-ordination of aerial photographic surveys with the production and maintenance of nautical charts. The *Proceedings* were issued in two volumes, the 'Report of the Conference', by G R C Rimington, and 'Proceedings of the conference and technical papers' (Canberra: Department of National Development, 1962).

These conferences continue every two or three years. The fifth conference was outstanding in its results, held in March 1967 at The Academy of Science in Canberra. 149 delegates represented thirty one countries. Cartographic progress throughout the world was reported and discussed, five technical committees were established, on geodesy and control surveys, on topographical cartography, on topical cartography, on general cartography and on hydrography and oceanography, the latter significantly reflecting the growing economic interest in the oceans and the ocean floors. Another obvious trend was the stress on thematic and rapid topical mapmaking, shown by such resolutions as the following: the use of airborne electronic measuring systems, such as Aerodist, for establishing control surveys in difficult country; the use of satellite geodesy for establishing or improving international geodetic connections; the repetition of accurate horizontal and vertical surveys in seismic areas to determine the topographical effect of earthquakes; and the use of colour and infra-red photography in the preparation of topical maps.

The International Union of Geodesy and Geophysics and its predecessors have undertaken important projects in international latitude services, a bureau for isostatic reductions and the adoption of standards of accuracy for geodetic operations. An international bibliography on geodesy has been published, and *Chronique* (1957–), which superseded the original *Bulletin d'information de l'UGGI*, is issued monthly in English, German, French and Russian, with bibliographical supplements on geodesy, hydrology and oceanography from 1958.

The International Cartographic Association had its origin in a meeting of cartographers from both national and commercial mapping organisations near Stockholm in 1956, under the sponsorship of the Swedish Esselte Corporation. A small committee of representatives from France, Germany, Great Britain, Sweden, Switzerland and the United States was formed to look into the potentialities of an internationally founded body and, in 1958, a second international

163

conference was held, with hospitality from the house of Rand McNally and Company, Chicago. At this conference, national delegates were advised to see what could be done in their own countries to co-ordinate cartographic work, and from this time on many new national cartographic organisations were formed. In Britain, the Sub-Committee for Cartography of the National Committee for Geography, under the auspices of the Royal Society, meets at quarterly intervals. These meetings, together with the discussions at four well-attended symposia, did much to co-ordinate cartographic ideas. A two-day cartographic symposium organised by the Ordnance Survey at Southampton in November 1961 gave an opportunity for contact between government representatives, commercial mapmakers and academic geographers. Topics such as the representation of relief, the potentialities in the use of plastic materials and the whole concept of 3-D maps were discussed and papers were given on the relative methods of drawing and scribing, on the preparation of six-inch maps for mountain and moorland areas, particularly in Scotland and Ireland and on production methods for small-scale maps. The use of machines in the various processes of mapmaking was naturally very much to the fore throughout the discussions. The symposium was held under the aegis of the Sub-Committee of the Royal Society and the *Report*, to which an explanatory preface was added by M A Shaw, of the Cartographic Department of the Clarendon Press, was published by the OUP, 1964. Then there were the two symposia held in 1962 and 1963 by the Universities of Glasgow and Edinburgh and of Leicester respectively, which led directly to the formation of the British Cartographic Society in 1963 to promote the development of cartography. The fourth symposium was held at Oxford in 1963 by the Cartographic Department of the Clarendon Press on the subject 'Experimental cartography'. The first object of the discussions was to look closely at the use of maps as research tools, in the mapping of data in industry, geology, demographic distributions, climate, transport, vegetation, flora and fauna, history and archaeology, hydrography and oceanography. The second object was to consider whether the cartographic analysis of different subjects has anything to contribute to topographic mapping. The discussions at the Ordnance Survey symposium proved so valuable that two more such meetings were arranged; at the third, called the Map Users' Conference, held in London in 1964, it was decided to continue regular November meetings.

Meanwhile, in 1958, the German Cartographic Society organised a conference at Mainz, at which the name 'International Cartographic Association' was adopted and an Executive Committee appointed. At the International Geographical Congress at Stockholm, 1960, a Special Commission on Cartography was set up to discuss the affiliation of the ICA to the International Geographical Union. The first General Assembly of the Association was held in Paris in 1961, the second in London in 1964, arranged to coincide with the Twentieth International Geographical Congress, with the hope of facilitating liaison between the two organisations. The objects of the ICA are the advancement of the study of cartography and its problems, the encouragement and co-ordination of cartographic research, the exchange of ideas and documents, the furtherance of training in cartography and the dissemination of cartographic knowledge. *The cartographic journal*, December 1964, included an outline of the progress and objects of the ICA to date and the *International yearbook of cartography*, 1965, contained a selection of papers and discussions from the 1964 technical conference. Member nations of the ICA each appointed a national committee to represent them at ICA meetings.

The First General Assembly of the ICA, held in Paris in May 1961, was organised by the Comité Française de Techniques Cartographiques; twenty five member nations were represented and Professor Dr Carl Troll represented the International Geographical Union. A *Bulletin* began in 1962. The ICA holds three types of meetings: the general assembly every four years, technical conferences held independently, and a technical conference held in conjunction with the International Geographical Congress. Special Commissions are set up as required, of which details are given in *Orbis geographicus* and in the issues of the *Newsletter* of the ICA. The Third General Assembly of the ICA was particularly important, held in New Delhi in 1968, co-ordinating with the Twenty-first International Geographical Congress. At this congress, a combined session of the IGU and the ICA was held to demonstrate the affiliation of the two organisations and to encourage collaboration between geographers and cartographers. The main themes of the technical conference highlight the questions currently under debate among both geographers and cartographers, namely, the education and training of cartographers, the standardisation of technical terms, automation in cartography, the collection and recording of information for map revision, maps of the future, considering any new styles and types required, the problems of map production in small quantities and

165

frequent editions, map libraries and their problems and the mapping of developing countries. The programme of work set in progress by the United Nations and the International Cartographic Association has done much to stimulate the development of separate national cartographic bodies.

The British Cartographic Society, formally founded in 1963, was the first individual organisation in Britain to be concerned entirely with cartography. Annual meetings and separate symposia, a library housed in the Edinburgh Public Library and *The cartographic journal*, issued twice a year since 1964 have been among the Society's achievements so far.

The American Congress on Surveying and Mapping has been held since 1941, having its headquarters in Washington DC; subdivisions of the Congress are devoted to Cartography, Control surveys, Property surveys, Topography, Instruments, and Education. Among the other organisations which have made outstanding contributions to the subject are the International Association of Geodesy, the International Society for Photogrammetry, the Centre de Documentation Cartographique et Géographique, the Institute of Geodesy, Photogrammetry and Cartography of Ohio State University and the Ontario Institute of Chartered Cartographers. The research of such organisations as the Cartographic Department of the Clarendon Press, Oxford; of the Hunting Surveys and Consultants Limited; Fairey Surveys Limited; the Generalstabens Litografiska Anstalt, Esselte AB, Stockholm; the Bertelsmann Cartographic Institute, Gütersloh and the International Society for Photogrammetry has made outstanding contributions, also that of the specialist instrument and equipment makers, without whose constant innovations and improvements the fine existing work could not be achieved.

The Commission on Interpretation of Aerial Photographs was established at the Geographical Congress in London, 1964, continuing the work of the previous Sub-Commission on Air Photo Interpretation of the Special Commission on Cartography, set up in 1961. Regional reports have been circulated in mimeographed form and some have been published in *Photogrammetria*. Miscellaneous information on congresses, conferences, research projects and practical surveys has been disseminated by the commission in general circulars. The commission has first concentrated on aerial photography as a means of collecting analytical data; later, the scope of the commission widened to include the study of aerial photography as a unique source of information for integrated and synthetical

166

geographical studies. Separate working parties have been investigating the photo-interpretation of glacial geomorphological features and of rural land use. Especially on the latter subject, a vast amount of information collected from many countries has been processed and compiled into an index, 'Geographical interpretation of aerial photographs', which comprises two parts, a list of research or practical mapping projects with details concerning type of photographs used, methods employed and maps produced, and secondly, a bibliography printed out from punched cards, published as part one of a new serial publication of the Bundesanstalt für Landeskunde und Raumsforschung, Bad Godesberg. Regional reports on photo-interpretation and mapping of rural land use have been published as *Collection of papers on photo interpretation and mapping of rural land use*: papers written for the Commission on Interpretation of Aerial Photographs, reprinted from *Photogrammetria*. An *Air photo atlas of rural land use* aimed to bring together annotated aerial and, possibly, space photographs showing various types of rural land uses in regions of the world, at suitable scales.

A conference at Toulouse in 1964 on the subject 'Aerial surveys and integrated studies', organised jointly by UNESCO, the Centre National de la Recherche Scientifique and the University of Toulouse, was attended by 190 scientists from forty-five countries. Papers covered the uses of aerial photography in the study of geology, geography, vegetation, hydrology, ecology, geomorphology and soils and the application of these methods to the integrated surveys being carried out all over the world, particularly in Australia, Africa and Latin America. Selected papers were published in English and French in the Natural Resources Research Series VI, 1968.

In Delft, two famous departments in adjacent buildings on Kanaalweg, the International Training Centre for Aerial Survey and the Survey Department of the Rijkswaterstaat have produced the major research and publications from the Netherlands in photogrammetry, survey and topographical cartography in postwar years. The latest developments include large-scale plotting automatically by computer. Of central importance is the *International bibliography of photogrammetry*, prepared by the ICT, to which centres of bibliographical work in photogrammetry throughout the world contribute.

On the last occasion of checking, the following organisations co-operated in the bibliography, representing a roll-call of important organisations in this field: Clair A Hill and Associates, Civil Engineers, Redding, California; Yale University, Forestry Library; Air

Force Missile Test Center Library, Florida; Photogrammetry Inc, Rockville; MIT, Department of Civil and Sanitary Engineering, Photogrammetry Laboratories, Lexington, Mass; University of Missouri, Forestry Department; Dartmouth College, Hanover, New Hampshire, Baker Library Division of Acquisitions and Preparations; Eastman Kodak, Research Library, Rochester, New York; Lockwood, Kesslen and Bartlett Inc, New York; Fairchild Camera and Instrument Corporation, Long Island, New York; Syracuse University, Department of Civil Engineering; The Thomas Engineering and Surveying Company, Columbus, Ohio; Ohio State University; Aero Service Corporation, Philadelphia; Stephen F Austin State College, Nacogdoches, Texas; American Society of Photogrammetry, Washington; Coast and Geodetic Survey, Washington; Library of Congress, Exchange and Gift Division; US Geological Survey, Washington; National Bureau of Standards, Washington; the Australian Institute of Cartographers; University of Queensland Library, Brisbane; Lands and Surveys Department, Tasmania; Ontario Department of Mines and Technical Surveys, Ottawa; University of New Brunswick, Surveying Engineering, Fredericton, NB; Department of Forestry Library, Ottawa; National Research Council, Division of Applied Physics, Ottawa; Université Laval Library, Quebec; Survey of India, Dehra Dun; The Royal College, Nairobi, Kenya; Surveyor General, Northern Nigeria Surveying; Ministry of Land and Survey, Kaduna; Survey General, Salisbury, Rhodesia; Director of Conservation and Extension and Department of Trigonometrical and Topographical Surveys, Salisbury, Rhodesia; University of Cape Town, Department of Land Surveying, Rondebosch, Cape Province; University of Natal, Department of Land Surveying, Durban; Ferdinand Postma Biblioteek, Potchefstroom University, Potchefstroom; Australian Institute of Cartographers; the Library of the University of Queensland; the Lands and Surveys Department of Tasmania; the Royal Institute of Chartered Surveyors; the Ordnance Survey and the Directorate of Overseas Surveys, and several other relevant interested departments in British universities; the Geodetic Library, no 1, Survey Production Centre, Feltham, Middlesex; Road Research Laboratory, Harmondsworth, West Drayton, Middlesex; Department of Surveying and Geodesy, University of Oxford; BR Section, Ordnance Survey; University of Leeds, Department of Civil Engineering; Queen's University, Belfast, David Keir Library; and the Department of Geography, Glasgow University. University College, London, includes a

Department of Photogrammetry and Surveying, also the headquarters of The Photogrammetric Society, which publishes the *Photogrammetric record*.

The Premier Congrès de Géographie Aérienne, organised by the Union Syndicale des Industries Aéronautiques, took place at the end of 1938. Emmanuel de Martonne summarised the development of the subject at that time in his *Géographie aérienne* (Paris: Michel, 1948); a summary nearly twenty years later is given in Volume XVI, 1967, of the *Archives internationales de photogrammetrie*, which contains the seventy three papers in English, French and German, presented at the International Symposium on Photo-interpretation at the Sorbonne, 1966, illustrated with photographs, maps, diagrams and bibliographies.

The International Society for Photogrammetry, founded in 1910, has proved an important forum for the discussion of the latest developments in both techniques and theory. There are seven autonomous technical commissions and every four years the International Congress of Photogrammetry is organised under the direction of the Committee of the Society. Publications are normally in English, French, German and Italian; *Photogrammetria* is the official journal of the Society and *Archives* are published after each Congress, usually in several volumes, consisting of proceedings, national reports, reports of the technical commissions and invited papers.

GROUND AND AERIAL SURVEYING FOR MAPMAKING

In difficult terrain, progress in topographical mapping was slow or impossible until the development of aerial photographic techniques, which are still best combined with ground survey if possible. Most areas of the world have now been mapped at small scales or at least have photographic coverage, but improved mapping, revision or special purpose mapping goes on continuously. Marine surveying is a never-ending task, especially in coastal waters, where the siting of navigational aids must be plotted on charts and the checking and amendment of charts are vital, especially when shifting seabeds are concerned. The Thames Estuary Surveys, for example, are regularly checked, as are other particularly busy shipping lanes and some less stable offshore areas may need frequent checking. Much greater attention has been given to the precise mapping of coastal waters, of recent years. The various methods used in portraying coastal features should be noticed, as, for example, on the new maps of British coasts in the *Atlas of Britain and Northern Ireland*. The polder coastal areas are finely portrayed in the *Atlas van Nederland*, and the Russian meticulous mapping of estuaries and deltaic areas is most striking in both the *Atlas mira* and the *Fisiko-geografičeskij atlqs mira*.

The chief problem affecting the plotting of air charts is the ever-increasing speed at which aircraft pass over the ground mapped and charting has had to adapt to a form suitable for projection from a 35 mm film on to a display screen operated by push-button controls.

The use of satellites for geodetic exploration develops rapidly through two American organisations, the National Aeronautics and Space Administration (NASA), and the Environmental Science Services Administration (ESSA). The first international symposium on the use of artificial satellites for geodesy was held in Washington in April 1962, the *Proceedings*, edited by G Veis, being issued in 1963. NASA's first explorer spacecraft, GEOS-A, was launched from Cape Kennedy in November 1965, the objective being to compare different techniques of measurement. The next, PAGEOS, satellite aimed to establish a world-wide geodetic satellite network with more than forty stations. The sun-illuminated satellite, at an altitude of over 2,500 miles, serves as a survey beacon for ground stations located approximately 2,500 miles apart. Meanwhile, a more limited series of observations has been conducted with ESSA by the United States Coast and Geodetic Survey, in co-operation with the Canadian, British, Danish, Norwegian and Icelandic Governments. By photographing satellites Echo 1 and Echo 2 simultaneously from two or more positions on the earth's surface, ground distances can be determined more exactly than by any other method. The geodetic networks of the European and North American continents, have been 'tied in' by using accurate inter-continental measurements.

Early in 1909, the first aerial photographs were taken from an aircraft. Before this time, however, aircraft had been used for photo-mapping in many countries, including the United Kingdom, Canada and Switzerland, using the photo-theodolite for ground surveys. Between the wars, much progress was made; for example, the United States Coast and Geodetic Survey had mapped the Mississippi delta from aerial photographs and the Hydrographic Office had surveyed Cuba in 1928, using the same methods. During the second world war, the need for rapid surveys of difficult terrain led to vastly improved techniques and, by the end of the war, the aerial camera was established as a powerful new mapping tool.

Aerial pictures, used in conjunction with stereoplotting machines and co-ordinatographs, are of use not only to cartographers, but to mining geologists, agriculturists, road and railway engineers; changes in vegetation, and therefore of underlying soil and rock, are clearly brought out. A network of ground control points or co-ordinates which can be identified on the photographs must be available before plotting can begin and some ground survey is necessary to fill in the local details. But hundreds of square miles of inaccessible territory in jungles, swamps, icefields and mountain ranges have been mapped by aerial photography, which would otherwise have remained unknown. Successful results, however, obviously depend very much on suitable weather conditions.

Aerial photographs are either vertical or oblique and they may be taken and used as pinpoints, strips or block coverage. Vertical photographs can be used directly for mapping with exact contours plotted by viewing stereoscopic pairs. Each print must overlap adjacent prints sufficiently to give a three-dimensional view. Hydrographic features stand out particularly well with this method. Oblique photographs show ground features as they would appear from the windows of an aircraft. Needless to say, great skill must be used in interpreting the photographs and improvements in instruments are being made all the time.

In areas difficult of access, both vertical and oblique air photography are used; and in the Himalaya, for example, and other high mountain ranges, even these methods are impossible. In such areas, use is made of the terrestrial phototheodolite and, more recently, increasing use has been made of modern distance-measuring equipment using radio or light waves. Ultra-high-frequency radio can be used for sounding the depths of ice sheets to about three thousand metres. A Royal Society symposium was held at Oxford in September 1965, at which geodesists and physicists from twenty five countries presented thirty seven papers on such subjects as these; and in the same year, electromagnetic distance measurement was demonstrated at a symposium of the International Association of Geodesy. The Stanford Research Institute of California has developed a method for converting radar signals to map symbols, by which weather data can be automatically plotted on a map and this data may also be transmitted over telephone or teletype wires to any distance.

Land capability studies must be carried out by a team of workers, as so many factors are involved. Maps have been prepared as part of routine government survey programmes and for oil or mining companies in planning their prospective work; the geological surveys range from rapid small scale mapping of many thousands of square miles of territory to detailed surveys of complex areas involving specialised studies in petrology, micropalaeontology and applied geology. The new methods are now commonly used in urban mapping for town planning, resettlement, surveys for re-development of railways and roads, and the special requirements needed for irrigation planning, reconnaissance surveys, hydro-electric schemes and mineral exploitation.

Two of the most influential private surveying organisations are the Hunting Group of Companies and Fairey Surveys, which operate throughout the world, using the latest developments in instruments and equipment, photographic and printing facilities. The Hunting Group, founded in 1874, with headquarters in London, comprises many specialised companies. The most international of the group's activities are those of the Hunting Survey Group. In Britain, there are four operating companies under the overall management of Hunting Surveys and Consultants Limited; their work includes mapping, ranging from topographical maps to large-scale plans for civil engineering works, precision topographical and architectural model-making. Hunting Technical Services Group is a group of scientists providing a land-use and agricultural consultancy service. Teams of experts work in all parts of the world, especially in South America, Africa, the Middle East and Asia, including the Lower Indus Project, the largest land rehabilitation programme ever mounted. The firm specialises in applied geological sciences, including airborne, ground and marine geophysical surveys, hydrogeological and engineering geology studies; and the aerial photographic library is believed to be the largest in the world, fully indexed.

Fairey Surveys, founded in India in 1923, also works in all parts of the world; its Research and Engineering Division has planned and patented the Fairey Plotterscope, a viewing aid for stereo-plotting machines with separate co-ordinatograph tables. The Plotterscope provides an accurately magnified image of both pencil and plot, enabling the operator to plot control points, spot heights, contours and other detail without leaving his seat to examine the trace. The Survey has had long experience in the field of aerial photography, including a ten-year period of continuous operation as flight trials contractors to the British Ministry of Aviation, and it now covers the whole range of surveying, mapping and photography. Among its most interesting projects was the topographical survey for the Kariba Dam on the Zambesi.

172

The Airborne Profile Recorder, which was developed within the Hunting Group, records a continuous profile of the ground along the line of flight and supplies data from which ground heights can be determined, therefore providing a rapid means of covering an area with a dense network of height control. For precision work the Doppler Navigator is used—a radar aid which measures continuously throughout flight the ground speed and distance travelled by the aircraft to an accuracy of 1:1 per cent. Hunting Surveys Limited was among the first organisations to carry out aerial surveys in colour.

Photomosaics consist of an assembly of aerial photographs, with the detail matched in order to provide a comprehensive picture of the area, and they are of great value in the first reconnaissance stage of planning a new road or route-finding through poorly mapped country, as the basis for compiling information on land use, selection of sites for industrial development, selection of routes for power or pipe lines, records of tide levels and location of sand and mud banks or preliminary studies in irrigation and drainage projects. Photomaps are produced from standard aerial photo-mosaics, using photomechanical meshes to separate the main types of terrain into different colours.

The 'Preliminary Plot' method developed by the Directorate of Overseas Surveys, which produces an outline base map mainly for use in plotting subsequent field observations, resulted in an economy of time and has enabled the Directorate to complete more than a thousand square miles of 1:50,000 scale mapping since its creation in 1946. In some cases, the maps thus produced show little more than the drainage pattern, vegetation types and an index to the aerial photography used in compilation. The photographic cover of the world is considerably greater than the existing coverage by topographical maps, for adverse weather factors are still more than offset by the time taken in traditional ground survey, draughtsmanship and cartographic reproduction.

Pre-eminent in the vast periodical literature on photogrammetry are the *Proceedings* of the various Congresses on Aerial Photography and Photogrammetry: the *Monthly abstract bulletin*, issued by the Eastman Kodak Company, Rochester, New York, is a most useful source. The quarterly *Photogrammetric engineering*, 1934– by the American Society of Photogrammetry, includes articles, statistics, notes and reviews concerning photographic procedures, instruments and air photo-interpretation; from the Brussels Société Belge de Photogrammétrie comes a scholarly *Bulletin*. Mention should also be made of the *Österreichische zeitschrift für vermessungswesen* of the Austrian Society of Photogrammetry at Baden bei Wien, and of the *Revista Brasileira de fotogrametria*, issued by the Sociedade Brasileira de Fotogrametria, at Rio de Janeiro. *Allgemeine vermessungsnachrichten* is the quarterly journal of the German Society of Photogrammetry, Berlin; and a new series of the quarterly *Revue française de photogrammétrie* began in 1950, issued by Section Láussedat de la Société Française de Photographie et de Cinématographie, Société Française de Photogrammétrie.

The *Transactions* of the Moscow Institute of Geodetic, Aerial Photographic and Cartographic Engineers and of the Central Scientific Research Institute of Geodesy, Aerial Photography and Cartography are the respective bulletins of Moscow and Leningrad. Papers on techniques and equipment, photogrammetric mapping, photo-interpretation techniques, photogeology, on use in forestry and soil surveys and on aeromagnetic surveying form the record of the United Nations Seminar on Aerial Survey Methods and Equipment, Bangkok, 1960, published under the title *Proceedings of the United Nations Seminar on Aerial Survey Methods and Equipment.* *Photo interprétation*, produced in Paris in six issues a year since 1963, constitutes a well-conceived attempt to present a wide range of problems of air-photo interpretation in an accessible and useful format for teaching purposes. Each issue contains eight stereoscopic pairs of photographs showing areas dissimilar in location and character. For each pair, there is a transparent overlay illustrating the principal features shown on the photograph, a short article explaining the interpretation and a punched card classifying the photograph according to its location and principle features of interest, thus providing a growing collection of useful examples for teaching the elements of air photo-interpretation, geographical features and relationships. The Oxford symposium on experimental cartography, mentioned above, led to the publication of *Experimental cartography*: report on the Oxford Symposium, October 1963 (OUP, 1964), which contains the papers and discussions; pertinent bibliographical references are also appended.

Organisation Européenne d'études photogrammétriques expérimentales was the official publication of the Frankfurt am Main Institut für Angewandte Geodäsie, 1966. Thirty four maps and diagrams enclosed inside the back cover illustrate the report of the Commission of the Organisation on the preparation of a photogrammetric map at 1:100,000 for developing countries, where

174

speed and straightforward methods are important. The report is in French and English, summarising the tests with small scale aerial photographs. 'Air photography and geography' was the theme of another symposium of significance, of which the papers were reported in *Drumlin*, II, 2, 1966, with a sketch-map, diagrams and bibliography. In March 1967, with financial support from UNESCO, a two-day meeting was held in Ottawa in conjunction with the Second Canadian Symposium on Photo Interpretation, organised by the Canadian Institute of Surveying and the Inter-Departmental Committee on Aerial Surveys. A report prepared for UNESCO contained the papers presented, the discussions and the relevant literature references.

Most of the great cartographical departments of the world have prepared technical manuals, such as *A guide to the compilation and revision of maps* published by the United States Department of the Army, Washington, 1955; the *Technical manual of the War Department*, Corps of Engineers, Washington and the *Topographic instructions* of the United States Geological Survey, with their supplementary pamphlets and technical memoranda. The Surveys and Mapping Branch, Department of Mines and Technical Surveys, Ottawa, published a *Cartographic manual*, 1954, and a *Surveying manual*, by L C Ripa, 1964, which includes diagrams, a bibliography and glossary. A fourth revised edition, by Major-General G Cheetham, of the *Textbook of topographical surveying*, was published by the Ministry of Defence in 1964 (HMSO, 1965), illustrated by maps, diagrams and a bibliography. Some other relevant references are:

A L Allan *et al*: *Practical field surveying and computations*. (Heinemann, 1968).

American Society of Photogrammetry: *Manual of photographic interpretation* (Washington: The Society, 1960), edited by R N Colwell, with illustrations, bibliographies and glossaries. Development and interpretation in various applications, including geography, geology, agriculture, soils, forestry, hydrology, urban area analysis.

E Arnberger: *Lehrbuch der kartographie* (Vienna: Deuticke, 1965).

T E Avery: *Interpretation of aerial photographs: an introductory college textbook and self-instruction manual* (Minneapolis: Burgess Publishing Company, 1962, reprinted 1965).

H F von Bandat: *Aerogeology* (Brill, 1962). The practical use of air photography: the methods used in constructing photogeologic maps for use in the field.

A Bannister and S Raymond: *Surveying* (Pitman, 2nd edition 1965).

C E Bardsley and E W Carlton: *Surveyor's field-note forms* (Scranton, third edition, 1952).

L Barth: *Bild und karte im erdkundeunterricht* (Berlin: Volk und Wissen, 1963).

Jacqueline Beaujeu-Garnier: *Practical work in geography* (Arnold; New York, St Martin's Press, 1963).

Hallert Bertil: *Photogrammetry* (McGraw-Hill, 1960). Includes many photographs of instruments for air survey.

T W Birch: *Map and photo reading* (Arnold, new edition, 1960). Contains samples of ten Ordnance Survey maps on various scales, with matching photographs.

Guy Bomford: *Geodesy* (Oxford: Clarendon Press, second edition, 1962).

F Bonasera: *Fondamenti di cartografia* (Palermo, Univ degli Studi di Palermo, 1965).

W Bormann: *Allgemeine kartenkunde* (Lahr, Schwarzwald, Astra; Bailey and Swinfen, 1954).

H Bosse: *Kartengestaltung und Kartenentwurf* (Philadelphia, Chilton, 1962).

G C Brock: *Physical aspects of air photography* (Longmans, 1952).

L A Brown: *Mapmaking: the art that became a science* (Boston, Little Brown, 1960).

R Chevallier, *editor*: *Photographie aérienne: panorama intertechnique* (Paris, Gauthier-Villers, 1965). Twenty two contributions by specialist authors.

J J Cirrito: 'Radar photogrammetry: a cartographic process', (*Professional geographer*, January 1963).

James Clendinning: *The principles and use of surveying instruments* (Blackie, second edition, 1959).

James Clendinning: *The principles of surveying* (Blackie, second edition, 1960).

C A Close and H S L Winterbotham: *Textbook of topographical and geographical surveying* (HMSO, third edition, 1925). Still a standard and an indispensable reference book.

C H Cotter: *The astronomical and mathematical foundations of geography* (Hollis and Carter, 1966).

D R Crone: *Elementary photogrammetry* (Arnold, 1963).

Ryer Daniel: *La photogrammétrie appliquée à la topographie* (Paris, Eyrolles, 1952).

G H Dury: *Map interpretation* (Pitman, third edition, 1968).

G H Dury and J A Morris: *The land from the air: a photographic geography* (Harrap, third impression, 1958).

A G F Elwood: *Essentials of map-reading* (Harrap, fourth edition, 1964).

F Fiala: *Mathematische kartographie* (Berlin, VEB Verlag Technik, 1957).

W Flichmer *et al.*: *Route-mapping and position locating in unexplored regions* (Basle, Birkhauser, 1957).

David Greenwood: *Mapping* (University of Chicago Press, revised edition, 1964).

E A Gutkind: *Our world from the air: an international survey of man and his environment* (New York, Doubleday, 1952).

J A Gwyer and V G Waldon: *Photo-interpretation techniques: a bibliography* (United States Library of Congress: Technical Information Division, 1956). Exhaustive, annotated bibliography of literature published 1935–1953.

Bertil Hallert: *Photogrammetry: basic principles and general survey* (McGraw-Hill, 1960).

R H Hammond: *Air survey in economic development* (Muller, 1967). Air survey methods, equipment and examples of air surveys.

C A Hart: *Air survey* (Royal Geographical Society pamphlet).

Viktor Heissler: *Kartographie* (Berlin, de Gruyter, 1962).

C B Hitchcock and O M Miller: 'Concepts and purposes of a serial atlas' (ICA Technical Symposium, Edinburgh, 1964).

H L Hitchins and W E May: *From lodestone to gyro-compass* (Hutchinson Scientific and Technical Publications, 1952).

Jean Hurault: *Aerial photography and map-making* (Paris, Institut du Transport Aérien, 1959). In effect, a summary of the methods employed by the Institut Géographique National, with English translation.

Jean Hurault: *Applications de la photographie aérienne aux recherches de sciences humaines dans les régions tropicales* (Paris, Ecole Pratique des Hautes Etudes, Sorbonne 1963). With folder of photographs.

Jean Hurault: *L'exam stereoscopique des photographies aériennes* (Théorie et pratique) (Paris, Institut Géographique National, two volumes, 1960). Also a box each of photographs and of maps.

Jean Hurault: *Manuel de photogrammétrie* (Paris, Institut Géographique National, new edition, two volumes, 1956).

Eduard Imhof: *Gelände und karte* (third revised edition, 1968).

J J Klawe: 'Photography in the service of cartography', *Graphic arts focal point*, no 6, 1962.

H P Kosack and K H Meine: *Die kartographie, 1943–1954: eine bibliographische übersicht* (Lahr, Schwarzwald, Astra; Bailey and Swinfen, 1956).

David Landen: 'Fotocartas para la planificacion urbana', *Revista cartografía*, XIV, 1965, with English summary.

S Laurila: *Electronic surveying and mapping* (Ohio State UP, 1960).

W T Lee: *The face of the earth as seen from the air: a study in the application of airplane photography to geography* (American Geographical Society of New York, 1922). A pioneer work and still interesting.

Sir Clinton Lewis: *The making of a map* (Royal Geographical Society pamphlet).

A Libault: *La cartographie* (Paris, PUF, 1962; 'Que sais-je? series').

A Libault: *Les mesures sur les cartes et leurs incertitude* (Paris, Editions Géographiques du France, 1961).

J D Lines: 'Spot photography for map revision' (*Cartography*, September 1962).

Karl-Heinz Meine,: 'Aviation cartography', *The cartographic journal*, June 1966.

V C Miller: *Photogeology* (McGraw-Hill, 1961).

G F Morris and F R Flooks: *Background to surveying* (Blackwell, 1964).

P G Mott: 'Some aspects of colour aerial photography in practice and its applications' (*The photogrammetric record*, October 1966).

I I Mueller: *Introduction to satellite geodesy* (Constable, 1964).

Multilingual dictionary of technical terms in cartography (Steiner Verlag, 1973).

W E Powers and C F Kohn: *Aerial photo-interpretation of landforms and rural cultural features in glaciated and coastal regions* (Northwestern University, Studies in geography no 3, 1959).

N J D Prescott: 'The geodetic satellite—"SECOR"', *The geographical journal*, March 1966.

T F Rasmussen: *Kartlaere* (Oslo, Universitetsforlag, 1963; Scandinavian University Books).

François Reignier: *Les systèmes de projection et leurs applications à la géographie, à la cartographie, à la navigation, à la topométrie* . . . (Paris, Institut Géographique National, two volumes, 1957); text and 48 plates in looseleaf form.

W W Ristow: *Aviation cartography: a historico-bibliographic study of aeronautical charts* (Library of Congress, second edition, 1960).

178

F Ruellan: *Photogrammétrie et interpretation de photographies stéréoscopiques terrestres et aériennes* (Paris, Masson, 1967).

J K S St Joseph: *The uses of air photography: nature and man in a new perspective* (John Baker for the Cambridge University Committee for Aerial Photography, 1966). Thirteen contributions by experts.

J A Sandover: *Plane surveying* (Arnold, 1961). Contains chapters on photogrammetry by D H Maling.

J A Sandover: *Theodolite practice* (Cleaver-Hume Press, 1960).

A I Shersen: *Aerial photography* (Jerusalem, Israel Program for Scientific Translations, 1961). Authorised by the Ministry of Higher Education of the USSR as a textbook for aerophotogeodesy.

C H Strandberg: *Aerial discovery manual* (Wiley, 1967).

K Thoeme: *Karte und Kompasse: eine praktische Anleitung zum Gebrauch von Karte und Kompass* (Berne, Hallwag, 1965).

C Thomson: *Map and compass work* (Arco, 1964).

N J W Thrower: *Original survey and land subdivision* (Chicago: Rand McNally for the Association of American Geographers, 1966).

United States Army Engineer Corps: *Photogrammetric mapping* (Defense Department, Engineer Manual series, 1963). Looseleaf basic manual on mapping from aerial photographs, well illustrated.

Vermessungskunde für kartographen, two volumes: 1, edited by E Lehmann *et al*; 2, edited by E Thum *et al* (Gotha, Haack, 1957–60).

F von Ikier: *Kartenkunde: Handbuch für den gebrauch und die benutzung von karten und luftbildern* (Bonn, Verlags und Vertriebs-Gesellschaft die Reserve, 1964).

MAP CONSTRUCTION AND DESIGN

Any study of map projections *per se* would be beyond the scope of this work, but a word should be said concerning the effect of choice of projection on map accuracy and design. Choice must depend upon the area to be mapped and the purpose of the map. Distribution maps should be plotted on equal area projections, otherwise relative densities cannot be truly compared. The Bonne Projection, for example, allows freedom from distortion along its central meridian, whereas scale and angular distortion increase rapidly with distance away from the central meridian; it is therefore more suitable for mapping an area with greater north-south extent than east-west. The Albers Projection includes two standard parallels free from angular distortion, so that its greatest usefulness is demonstrated in the mapping of middle latitude areas with greater

179

extent in an east-west direction. Other equal area projections in frequent use include the Lambert Azimuthal Equal-Area Projection, the Sinusoidal, Mollweide and Eckert. Preservation of the shape of small areas on a map is known as conformality; the angles round any point are correctly represented. Air and sea charts, in particular, require this quality. The most widely used projection for charts has been the Mercator, since its inception in 1569. Most of the Admiralty Charts are drawn on the Mercator, but it has the disadvantage of enlarging areas in the higher latitudes on a map covering a wide area; much misconception regarding the size of Greenland, for example, in comparison with the Indian sub-continent, is due to this drawback. Conformality is not so vital on topographic maps.

A third quality in a projection, azimuthality, enables all places to be shown in their true direction from the centre of the map and linear and area scale variations are symmetrical round the central point. The Gnomonic is such a projection, frequently used for navigational charts, because all straight lines drawn from the centre of the map represent parts of great circles, the shortest distances between any two points on the globe. 'Interrupted' projections have been used intermittently from the sixteenth century. Mathematically constructed, they include the use of multiple axes, according to the area and purpose of the map. The various interrupted projections of Goode were of particular value, not only because of their skilful design, but because they encouraged the acceptance and further development of this useful device. In 1916, he prepared an interrupted version of the Sinusoidal, which divided the world into seven segments, splitting Eurasia along the 60 degrees east meridian. His interrupted version of the Mollweide preserved the continuity of Eurasia. In 1923, he produced an interrupted homolosine and an interrupted Werner followed in 1928, under the title of Goode's Polar Equal-Area Projection. These projections appeared at a time when the limitations of the Mercator Projection were becoming increasingly obvious; their use in *Goode's school atlas* and in the widely used wall-map series, familiarised the use of such adjusted interruptions. American map companies quickly adopted other interrupted arrangements for basic world maps. Philip and Sons Limited used the interrupted Mollweide as the basic world projection in the *Chambers of commerce atlas*, 1925, but without inserting meridians; later, the House of Bartholomew devised a 'recentred' Sinusoidal and, in the *Nordisk Världs atlas* produced in Sweden in 1926, the Sinusoidal projection in interrupted form was used, the central meridians and interruptions being chosen to make the graticule symmetrical about the equator. The majority of contemporary atlases use some form of un-symmetrical projections for world maps, with the exception of navigational or air route maps, for which the Mercator still best serves the purpose.

Little need be said about scales here, as there are so many excellent books currently including this aspect of mapmaking. Suffice it to draw attention to the fact that four scales occur particularly frequently: the 1:25,000, used by several European surveys, particularly by the German; 1:50,000, used by many topographical surveys as a 'standard' scale for base maps, at which reasonable detail may be shown; 1:62,500, an approximate one-inch to the mile scale, used by the United States Geological Survey and any surveys modelled on its work; and the exact one-inch to the mile scale used by the Ordnance Survey and by most of the Commonwealth Surveys. Clear distinction must be made between basic maps directly drawn from a field survey of all features, and derived maps, usually on smaller scales and for different purposes. The trend has been towards transfer to the metric system by those mapping agencies not already using it. Frequent experiments have been made in modern mapping to familiarise users with world maps 'in the round', to emphasise the actual relationships of countries with one another. These concern particularly the polar regions; the *Readers' Digest world atlas* and R E Harrison's *Fortune atlas*, 'Look at the world' section, presented some unusual orientations.

The base materials upon which the maps are prepared for reproduction must be carefully chosen for stability and ease of working. Some particularly important atlases have had paper specially made for the purpose. Before the second world war, most cartographic drawing was carried out on cartridge paper, although such agencies as the Ordnance Survey and the Esselte Corporation were using coated glass plates even at this time, because of their high stability. Hand engraving on copper plates remains now in only a few cartographic departments; hydrographic charts, for example, may still be made on copper, which allows of easier revision than some of the more recent materials. By 1946, zinc plates coated with a white enamel drawing surface were in use and soon after, high stability plastic sheets were devised, which required special inks. The ultimate development in this line was the introduction of plastic or glass sheets coated with visually translucent and actinically opaque lacquer-like substances. A scribing tool replaced the pen in drawing very fine lines more quickly and economically. The points, of sapphire or steel, were prepared in different widths, so that uniformity could easily be achieved and the drawing be used directly, in negative or positive form, by using different methods for the preparation of the printed plate. In drawing the Ordnance Survey maps of Ireland, scribing was done on white coated astrafoil with a blue key, and sometimes on the white astrafoil direct over the basic field document. This was quicker and cheaper than drawing and the standard higher. The use of plastics involves air conditioning and temperature and humidity control in drawing offices as well as in production stages and storage.

The new era of automatic cartography caused adjustments in techniques as great as the change from hand drawing to copper-engraving. Mr D P Bickmore, Head of the Cartographic Department of the Oxford University Press, and Dr R Boyle, a Director of Dobbie McInnes, together worked out the prototype of the system which evolved as the Bickmore Boyle System of Automatic Cartography, a result of the co-operation of the two organisations, with financial assistance from the (then) DSIR. The basic concept of the system was described by Mr Bickmore in a talk given on the BBC Third Programme, reprinted in *The listener* of 30 January 1964, in which he spoke of the system as consisting of 'a table on which a hand-made map compilation is placed; the lines on this draft are then followed or "read" with a pointer. As this pointer moves over the map, streams of x and y co-ordinates are fed to magnetic tape, giving thousands of positions per inch of line, and to an accuracy of three-thousandths of an inch. The information on the magnetic tape is coded into such features as rivers, coastlines, contours, outlines of built-up areas, and so on. A second plotting table is then brought into operation by the tape. On this table is mounted a projector with a fine beam of light; this moves again with great precision and plots lines of varying thickness on to sensitized film. The scale of the map can be altered and variations of map projection can be achieved by feeding the tape through a computer. The system will short-circuit many of the laborious production and checking stages that at present separate the map compilation from the finished negatives or positives from which it is printed.'

The four component parts were the compilation reader, the magnetic tape deck and editor's control panel, the automatic plotting table and the name placement projector, both the choice of data and the symbols for rivers, coastlines etc being monitored from the

182

editorial control panel. The drawing equipment worked to an accuracy of 0·07 mm; lines of any thickness or of varying character were drawn or coloured areas produced as negative masks. The editorial control unit enabled the editor to select data from the stored library information and to control the drawing units. He selected the area of the map required from the relevant magnetic tape and punched cards; chose the scale, which was not dependent on the scale at which the compilation was read; selected the detail required from the tape or cards, combining information from one tape with that of another; specified the symbols and line weight. If a change of projection was necessary, the tape and cards were in a form that could be fed through any internationally compatible computer. New or revised information could be fed in at any time, replacing superseded information. This bank of information, which was in precise digital form, was stored in terms of the different features of the map and not in terms of the type of line or symbol by which it was to be represented. This meant that subsequent choice of symbols was not restricted. Names were also keyed on to the punched cards or magnetic tape, in relation to the appropriate point information. All the various automatic plotting instruments worked as co-ordinate principles, so that any geographical information capable of being expressed by co-ordinates was capable also of being programmed for automatic plotting. It was fortunate, too, that these technical developments evolved at a time when increasing social, economic and political changes demand quick and accurate revised maps.

One of the best-known automatic co-ordinatographs is the Aristomat, produced by Dennert and Pape of Hamburg, distributed in the United Kingdom by Technical Sales Limited. This machine, with linear numerical control, is a drafting unit for locating and marking points. Grid nets can be drawn parallel to the axes. Punched cards or tape are used for input. A similar machine is the Auto-Tool Model 6000 High Speed Plotter, produced by the Auto-Tool Corporation, Aruada in Colorado, and another American plotter is the Model 502 Digital Plotter, from Calcomp, California Computer Products, Inc.

The Army Map Service and the United States Naval Oceanographic Office have greatly influenced the development of specialised cartographic equipment in America. Concord Control Inc, of Boston, perfected a basic drafting machine, Model E-51 Precision Digital Coordinatograph. Input was from computer-programmed magnetic tape or punched paper tape; continuous lines could be drawn or scribed on paper or coated plastic; or, by using a small, general purpose computer, with special equipment, such as the Photo-scribe Head, a complete automatic drafting machine, the Concord Mark 8 Coordinatograph system. The Benson-Lehner Data Reduction System, developed by Benson-Lehner Corporation, Van Nuys, California, is another plotter using magnetic tape, punched tape or punched cards, used by a number of United States government departments, universities and private concerns. 'Read-out' equipment is usually supplied by the same companies, such as the Aristometer by Dennert and Pape, the Model 3700 Series Digitising System by the Auto-Trol Corporation. More specialised still is the Concord Automatic Type Placement System made by the Concord Control Inc for the United States Army Map Service. The Concord equipment was designed as a comprehensive automatic system.

d-Mac Limited of Scotland and Kongsberg Vapenfabrik of Norway collaborated in offering complete systems for analysing graphic material for computation and producing drawings from computer-generated data. The Cartographic Digitiser provides the input to the computer and the Kingmatic drawing machine draws from the computer output. The Cartographic Digitiser Type CF was developed as an aid to reducing vast amounts of data, obtained over many years of field survey and cartographic work to a form suitable for computer processing. Providing a rapid means of digitising selected information contained in maps, charts, drawings and photographs, it became a key unit in the growing employment of computers for the analysis of problems relating to conservation of natural resources and food production.

The necessary height data for the computation of the analytical shaded picture can be collected not only from contour maps but also directly from stereoscopic models of air photographs. Parallel profiles of the relief at suitable densities are measured and the necessary density of height data, obtained either by direct measurement or by interpolation, by the electronic computer. 'Topocart' was one of the latest of the VEB Carl Zeiss Jena stereocartographic instruments for the plotting of aerial photographs at small and medium scales.

A Research Grant was awarded to the Royal College of Art by the Natural Environment Research Council for a project to develop an automatic technique for presenting data in a cartographic form by means of a computer. Basically, it consisted of an electronic plotting table and 'lock on' time follower, both being developed by AEG in Germany, connected to a PDP-9 computer. Lines traced from maps

184

were converted into the form of x and y coordinates and stored on magnetic tape. At a later stage the tapes were to be read to control the movement of a beam of light thrown on to photosensitive film, thereby re-drawing the original. The work has been carried out at the college and at a special laboratory in Oxford.

When the surveyors have completed their work, it is the task of the cartographer to select from this raw material the information he wishes to include in particular maps, to design the maps on those projections and scales most suited, using the most appropriate symbols and colours and to add such text as may be necessary. Finally, the maps must be reproduced. Although these three processes may be clearly distinguished, they must in practice be considered in conjunction from the outset, if the completed maps are to be efficient and effective. Every part of the total production demands knowledge, skill and experience; at their best, modern maps demonstrate artistic excellence as well.

A well-considered map should present individual factors clearly, so that they can easily be studied simultaneously. Contents may express the variations of a single commodity over an area or may show the distribution of different elements. Relief representation, colours and symbols all play their parts. Great skill must be applied to the selection of items for inclusion or emphasis; it is increasingly the practice to prepare explanatory text for use with the map, outlining purpose, degree of proven accuracy or the date of information incorporated.

During the past ten years or so, much of the discussion at cartographic conferences and technical congresses has been concerned with the relative qualities of new plastics for map production. A second major consideration has been the choice of inks and the methods of using them. The development of plastics has resulted in the replacement to a large extent of drawing and glass engraving by negative or positive scribing on pre-coated plastics and new tools have been developed. Sapphire cutters, though more expensive, have been found much more satisfactory than steel needles, when fine line-work is required. The choice of suitable printing format is also vital in planning maps. The tendency is to use larger printing plates, and this is again an economy, providing that consistency in colours and exact registration are not impaired.

Ilford Supermattex and other similar materials are making films with a polyester base, excellent for scribing and photomechanical

185

application, produced by Ilford Graphics Limited, London. A successful process has been the Fluorographic Process patented by Printing Arts Research Laboratories Inc, California, using Mylar or Melinex transparent sheets. The latest in many experiments in waterproof paper is 'Silbond', a synthetic paper made by Fraser-produkte GmbH and Company, in West Germany and available in the United Kingdom through Reeve Angel International Limited. This astonishing product, made from polyester fibre, is waterproof, weather-resistant, dirt-repellant and washable; it will not crumple or fray and it will take all the normal printing processes. It is naturally more expensive than ordinary papers.

The aesthetic appreciation of modern maps, as compared with their forerunners, is of an entirely different quality; thorough appreciation must now depend on some knowledge of the technical miracles performed in producing an accurate and complex, yet artistically pleasing map face. The engaging dolphin creatures and the gay little ships may be missed, but the representation of relief has turned, in one sense, full circle; the modern three-dimensional relief techniques have the same purpose as the 'sugar-loaf' hill features, plus, of course, now, scientific accuracy. Small pictorial trees may still indicate the presence of individual types within a woodland area. At this time, when not only specialists but the general public are using maps more frequently than ever before, contemporary maps are expected to convey their information as directly and as effectively as possible, without ornamentation, but with full documentation and essential explanatory text; absolute registration is expected up to twelve colours, involving extreme accuracy in all stages of production.

The representation of land relief is fascinating in its variety. In spite of the introduction of contours, about 1850, the Ordnance Survey continued to use some additional method of portraying relief. For reasons of economy, hachures were omitted from the fourth or 'popular' edition published after the 1914–18 war, but the omission did not meet with full acceptance. Publication of layered or shaded maps of selected tourist areas followed, and, in due time, the fifth relief edition, in which hachures on the shadow sides of the hills were overprinted in violet. The second world war put an end to the fifth edition, and after this war, the sixth edition, the 'new popular', was produced as quickly as possible, with contours only. The seventh edition also has contours only, but the policy of producing tourist maps of selected areas with hill-shading has been continued. Hill-shading has also been introduced into the fifth edition of the quarter-inch map series. Much thought has been given to the problem of depicting landforms with greater fidelity, using hill-shading to create an impression of three dimensions. Among the more elaborate systems are those requiring the making of three-dimensional models in exact replica of the landforms. The model is then photographed, as if light were directed from the north-west corner, through a half-tone screen for overprinting on the maps in suitable colours, usually brown or grey. Other techniques begin by shading the ground relief in pencil on grained Astrafoil or by painting it with an air brush on a suitable drawing surface, as if it were lit from a north-westerly direction. These originals are then photographed in readiness for making a printing plate. For the best results of all, hill-shading is blended with layer-colouring, with or without contours.

The use of relief model maps has increased, especially for educational purposes. The most frequent method of achieving such a map is to make a key print of the map area on to a sheet of Astrafoil, indicating rivers and main contour intervals. A felt pad is then placed underneath the Astrafoil and, by using suitable tools and a good deal of skill, the Astrafoil is pushed into the felt and stretched as necessary to take on the shape of the ground relief. Wooden pegs cut to scale are used to push up the peaks and outline the hill slopes. The model is sprayed with white paint and set in front of the camera with specially controlled side lighting to give a shadow effect on the hills. Any individual features desired can be painted on the models, which are especially useful for demonstration purposes or framed as wall maps for teaching.

The representation by colours of relief features, especially height, has caused much discussion through the years. By using a colour scheme related to height alone, deserts have been known to be shown in green! If any approximation to verisimilitude is to be attempted, seasonal and other variations should logically be taken into account as well. Some of the 1:100,000 maps of Sweden have been published in summer and winter editions. As colour-photogrammetry is increasingly developed, some more effective means for depicting the natural colours of a landscape may be found, particularly on large-scale maps. Modern reproduction techniques enable much more gradual colour changes to be shown. The 'strip' method has been used to show the presence of several factors within an area, or a 'transition' area. A black and white shaded relief map is frequently used as a base for combination with other factors, by overprinting. Several of the distribution maps in *The Atlas of Britain and Northern Ireland*, for example, use a grey relief base, against which colour symbols show up well. Hachures have by no means disappeared. Relief on some European maps, notably on the mountain areas of Switzerland, is most successfully shown by hachures, with or without contours; the details of rock faces are frequently exquisitely superimposed in this way. The change from contour lines and hypsometric tints to methods based on plastic relief models for the representation of relief results in a more accurate and graphic effect, but requires more accurate base maps and also demands from the draughtsman not only skilled precision, but also an imaginative feeling for surface relief forms.

An international system of colour measurement has been under discussion for many years. A standardised scheme for the distinction of rocks of various periods was agreed in 1881 at the Geological Congress at Bologna. The Munsell system is the most widely known and was adopted for the IMW at 1:1M. The Ordnance Survey published the scale of hypsometric tints agreed in Bonn in 1962, for the IMW; in the solid colours used, the colour is indicated in Munsell's terms. There are five principal hue names in the Munsell system; the value notation relates to the degree of lightness or darkness of a colour, ranging from a theoretically pure black, having notation 0/, to a theoretically pure white, with notation 10/. The chroma notation of a colour indicates the strength or degree of saturation of a particular hue from a neutral grey of the same value; the scales here range from /0 for a neutral grey to /10, /12, /14 or more. The use of colour in cartography was one of the topics discussed at the Third International Conference for Cartography at Amsterdam, of which reports were included in the *International yearbook of cartography*, VII, 1967.

The factors affecting the selection and use of colour on maps are complex, not the least important being the differing subjective reactions of map-users. During years of guiding students' evaluation of maps and atlases, interesting results have been obtained by noting individual instinctive reactions to certain distinctively coloured map sheets, prior to more objective analysis; particularly useful in this exercise have been the physical sheets of the *Atlas of Britain*, the sheets of the first Land Utilisation Survey and, in the Clarendon Press *Atlas of Britain and Northern Ireland*, the sheets depicting geology, the double sheet depicting the surrounding seas and the final section of regional maps. In each case, without hesitation, some of the group reacted favourably, others unfavourably; of the latter, after closer examination, reasons for choice of colours might be admitted, but the aesthetic reservation remained. By the use of graduated screens, the combination of the three standard colours in all their variations can be made to produce a great number of colour tints; in addition, hatching and other devices can increase the powers of distinguishing factors on the map face.

Portrayal of coast lines on topographic maps presents special problems, notably on the smaller-scale maps. Care must be taken that measurements all relate to, for example, the high tide level. Agreed symbols should indicate the nature of the cliffs. The map of the coasts in the *Atlas of Britain and Northern Ireland* was an interesting pioneer work; in the *Atlas van Nederland*, as would be expected, particular care was taken in drawing the polder areas; and, in the 1954 and 1962 *Atlas mira*, the skill with which deltas were shown is particularly impressive. The practice of showing shadow relief as a background to thematic mapping of, for example, commodities or resources, has become more common, showing clearly the correlation between elevation and crop or livestock production. The scale of the map must also greatly affect the choice of relief symbols; at small scales, contours and hypsometric tints are of little value. The cost limitations of the work in hand must also affect the method chosen to portray the information to be included. With skill, black and white can be perfectly effective. Only on the largest scales can the key signs accurately represent the position of features on the ground. At smaller scales, a reduction in the amount of information shown must result, to avoid misrepresentation and overcrowding. Statistical information presented in visual form can represent only abstractions, not actual values, unless figures are actually affixed at convenient points. A detailed summary of such problems as these, with an extensive bibliography, is given by Erik Arnberger: 'Das topographische, graphische, bildstatistische und bildhafte Prinzip in der Kartographie', *International yearbook of cartography*, IV, 1964.

The constitution and terms of reference of the Commission on Thematic Mapping were approved by the Fourth General Assembly, 1972, for the period 1972–1976, namely, to propose standard systems of thematic mapping of natural resources and human activities (in accordance with a resolution of Unesco, October 1970), having regard not only to printed maps but also to electronic visual display; to encourage the establishment or development of national working groups on thematic mapping and the compilation of national reports; and to co-operate with the Commissions of the ICA and the

IGU, especially with the Commission of National and Regional Atlases of the IGU. Standardisation of signs and symbols in geological, pedological, phytogeographical, geomorphological, physiographical and other earth science mapping being well advanced, the Commission envisaged a concentration on comparable problems in economic mapping. Working Groups on thematic mapping have made considerable progress, especially in Belgium, Canada, Finland, France, the FRG and the GDR, Hungary, Japan, the Netherlands, Poland and the Soviet Union.

Refer also

Jaromír Demek, *ed*: *Manual of detailed geomorphological mapping* (Prague: Academia, 1972).

Lajos Stegena, *ed*: 'Industrial signs in atlas cartography' (Hungarian Working Group for Thematic Mapping).

'Project of signs for maps aiming at regional development' (prepared by the Cartographic Chair of the Eötuös Loránd University on behalf of the Department for Regional Development of the Hungarian Ministry for Building and Town Planning).

One of the most exacting aspects of cartography is the reduction to smaller scales from original surveys. Decisions depend on a number of factors—feeling for terrain, for example, and the purpose of the map are paramount considerations. In using maps in conjunction with geographical interpretation, therefore, it is essential to remember that the cartographers have already made a selection from the total features present in the area; the greater the geographical knowledge of the cartographers, or the greater the co-operation between specialised geographers and cartographers, the more reliable and valuable the resulting maps should be. As quantitative data accumulate throughout the world, so do the problems of representing the variety cartographically or by diagrammatic maps. The data may be continuously collected, as in the case of weather information, or may be collected at intervals, as in censuses and surveys. Maps rather than tables are normally compiled when the aim is the comparison of particular factors from place to place; or it may be required to compare the distribution of the data with physical variations, climate or soils. Very great care must be taken in choice of scale, colouring and symbols, otherwise a distorted view may be given. Exactly similar data, mapped in different ways, can give quite different visual impressions. Yet, skilfully prepared maps are the most powerful media for expressing comparisons or evoking deductions.

The choice of names for inclusion on a map, their linguistic form, the kind of typeface chosen and the placing of names are all-important to the clarity and legibility of the map. Several specifications have been adopted for the form of names; for example, those for the International Map of the World 1:1M and for the ICAO World Aeronautical Chart; also for the hydrographic charts issued by the International Hydrographic Bureau and the Universal Postal Union world map using the form of place names adopted in the Directory of Post Offices. At the national level, among others, the Permanent Committee on Geographical Names for British Official Use has published rules for dealing with geographical names in various languages and the United States Board on Geographic Names has worked on similar lines for the United States. All countries have their own points of view. A Draft Programme was circulated for discussion at the Second United Nations Regional Cartographic Conference for Asia and the Far East, at Tokyo, 1958. The establishment by the United Nations of a central international body, an 'International Committee on Geographical Names', was recommended; also that the Secretariat of the United Nations should act as a central clearing house of information concerning national systems of transliteration and that national gazetteers should be compiled. Full details of the progress of the discussions, recommendations and decisions are given in volumes VI, 1958; VII, 1962 of *World cartography* and in the *Official records of the Economic and Social Council, Twenty-seventh Session*.

A H Robinson in particular has emphasised that very few typefaces have been designed especially for cartography and that a main principle of typography is violated when any type is reduced by photography. For the 1964 International Geographical Congress, an experiment was conducted by The Monotype Corporation Limited, in conjunction with the Cartographical Department of the Clarendon Press, to demonstrate the effect of typography on maps. The results were published in the form of a broadsheet, on which eight maps of France are shown, identical except for the variations in typography. The area chosen was a varied one, giving full rein to the contrasts demonstrated. Serif can be compared with sans serif, condensed with expanded letters, upper case with lower case, roman and italic capitals. The chief functional requirements of type faces for cartographic work are legibility in small sizes; legibility in areas particularly complex topographically; easy recognition of individual characters; the use of several readily distinguishable styles of type to isolate individual factors or to emphasise the more important cities;

legibility against a multi-coloured background and unity and pleasing appearance in the finished map. It must be borne in mind that, on small-scale maps, the name of a city, even in the smallest of readable type, may spread over hundreds of miles. On the other hand, names of political areas or of an extended range of mountains must be spaced out. Neither will the printed names always have a horizontal base line, for river-names for example, normally follow their flow.

The Monotype photo-lettering machine is one of the most commonly used. The machine photographs individual characters direct on to film or paper; characters are selected manually by a dialling operation, after which the cycle of operations is controlled automatically by sequential electrical and electro-mechanical components. Both Fairey Air Surveys Limited and the Cartographic Department of the Clarendon Press installed Monotype photo-lettering machines. John Bartholomew and Son Limited use hand-set type, cast on Monotype machines, from which reproduction proofs are taken for sticking up on to artwork prepared for photo-mechanical reproduction. All kinds of lettering, numbers and symbols are offered for sticking up by 'Format' Modern Multi-Use Acetate Graphic Art Aids, attached with a wax-free adhesive. Interesting commentaries on these problems were made in the *Report of the group of experts on geographical names* in *World cartography*, VII, 1962; and in 'The question of adopting a standard method of writing geographical names on maps in the United Nations', *World cartography*, VII, 1962. Most maps carry lettering of many sizes ranging from about 14 point to 4¼ point, the vast majority being in the range of 6 point and smaller. Particular type faces are usually kept consistent for the same features. Sans serif has been establishing itself, especially sans serif capitals. Experiments on lettering and type faces for complex maps continues by cartographic departments, by the Chart Reproduction Committee of the Joint Advisory Board and by the Cartographic Sub-Committee of the Royal Society.

The insertion of grid lines on maps has become an increasingly common practice during recent years, especially with the various editions of national maps in series. These lines must be accurate so that adjacent map sheets show continuous grid lines when used together and they are plotted by a co-ordinatograph, a measuring machine which enables them to be plotted in two directions at right angles to one another. They work to an accuracy of 0.002 inches and can draw a line up to fifty one inches. Co-ordinatographs have proved indispensable in precision mapping for geodetic, photogrammetric and cartographic purposes. As well as plotting orthogonal grid systems, they are used for the production of masters for graticules for all purposes. Among the most used are the Carl Zeiss Precision Co-ordinatographs, which map points in systems of orthogonal co-ordinates on the following scales: 1:800, 1:1,000, 1:2,000, 1:2,500, 1:4,000, 1:5,000 and multiples of these scales. Use has expanded since various models of the Precision Co-ordinatograph have been equipped with selsyns; when combined with an electro-mechanical recording and computing unit, it is possible to record the co-ordinates of points fixed on a map or plan with the co-ordimeter. Recording is done either in clear text or on punched tape. The 'Carl Zeiss Precision Co-ordinatograph Instruction Manual' enlarges on all aspects of these machines, with a folder of illustrations tipped into the back cover.

Comparable advances have been made in map reproduction processes, where accuracy must now be perfect, even in small-scale work, involving up to twelve colours. Lithography is the form of printing most usually used for conventional map reproduction. The invention of the offset method of lithographic printing and the discovery that zinc could be used instead of limestone were two major stages in the development of modern map-printing. The offset printing machines used for map printing are usually sheet fed rotary machines having a capacity of 10,000 impressions per hour. The stages of map production, using lithographic processes, are compilation, photographic copying, fair drawing, followed again by photographic copying, preparation of the printing plates and the final printing. The precision of the finished map detail depends upon an accurate drawing and accurate superimposition of transparent sheets carrying the various components, line networks, colours and lettering. Where, for example, many pages of an atlas are to be reproduced in several colours on a large sheet, the correlation of pages on successive colour printing plates requires great skill. Examples that spring to mind in English cartography are the vegetation maps in the *Atlas of Britain and Northern Ireland* and the maps showing glaciation. Step-and-repeat machines, working to a tolerance of less than 0.001 inches, are invaluable for this kind of work.

A regular revision policy should be planned at the time of preparation of any new series of maps, the time interval varying according to the kind of terrain covered and the content and purpose of the maps. Transitional revisions may usually be seen at most survey offices between published editions, as in the case of the Ordnance Survey.

193

Any kind of social and industrial mapping benefits from the increased use of computer processing of data, so that maps can be produced quickly and revised editions supplied equally quickly, when changes occur. The vast numbers of items involved in meteorological and oceanographical recording and charting have especially required the installation of automated equipment. All the above-mentioned considerations for map production apply to the making of atlases, with the additional factor that an atlas should be carefully planned in its entirety before detailed preparation begins. The purpose of the publication must determine the scope, contents, overall arrangement and emphasis on individual sections. The sequence of maps should follow logically and projections and scales should be chosen to suit the size and shape of the area to be mapped. Both scales and projections will inevitably be changed for specific purposes, but the maximum uniformity should be aimed at and, within a section of, for example, economic distribution maps, the scale should be uniform to enable comparability. Loose-leaf format facilitates revision.

Now that cartographers are so closely involved in the modern technical aspects of map plotting, the Hunter-Penrose-Littlejohn Limited *Graphic arts technicians handbook*, now in its fifth edition, will be found useful, also the *Jena review* and the *Hunting Group review*. Hunting Surveys Limited also issue regular 'Information sheets'. Some further sources include:

M Archambault *et al*: *Documents et méthode pour le commentaire de cartes* (*géographie et géologie*) (Paris, Masson, 1965–).

S Augustin and R Schoonman: 'Automation and design', *Penrose annual*, 1964.

E D Baldock: *Manual of map reproduction techniques* (Ottawa, Queen's Printer, 1964).

E D Baldock: 'The technical performance of map revision', *Kart nachrichten*, V, 4, 1963.

B Bannerjee and H R Betal: 'Perspective on the nature of map projection', *Geographical review of India*, XXVII, 2, 1965.

J Beaujeu-Garnier: *Practical work in geography* (New York, St Martin's Press; Arnold, 1963).

M W Beresford: *History on the ground: six studies in maps and landscapes* (Lutterworth Press, 1957). Field studies in England.

S Bertram: 'The universal automatic map compilation equipment', *Photogrammetric engineer*, March 1965.

D P Bickmore and A R Boyle: 'An automatic system of cartography', *International yearbook of cartography*, V, 1965; Address to the ICA Technical Symposium, Edinburgh, 1964.

T W Birch: *Maps, topographical and statistical* (Oxford, Clarendon Press, second edition, 1964).

R G Blakesley *et al*: 'The planning databank challenges the surveyor and mapmaker', *Surveying and mapping*, March 1967.

Roger Brunet: *Le croquis de géographie* (Paris, Société d'Edition d'Enseignment Supérieur, 1962). Sketchmap technique; block diagrams; statistical presentation.

William Bunge: *Theoretical geography* (Lund, C W K Gleerup, 1962). Lund Studies in Geography, Series c, General and Mathematical Geography, no 1).

John Bygott: *An introduction to mapwork and practical geography* (UTP, ninth revised edition, 1964, by D C Money).

C F Capello and M L Chionetti: *Elementi di cartografia* (Torino, Giappichalli, three volumes, 1958–60).

C C Carter: *Land-forms and life: short studies on topographical maps* (Christophers, 1959, repr 1961, revised by M O Walter).

R J Chorley and P Haggett: 'Trend-surface mapping in geographical research', *Transactions*, Institute of British Geographers, XXXVII, 1965.

W G Clare: 'Map reproduction', *The cartographic journal*, December 1964.

M C Collins: 'The production of 1:50,000 contoured maps using high level photography and analytical triangulation', *Report of proceedings*, Conference of Commonwealth Survey Officers, 1963 (1964).

Bruce Cornwall and A H Robinson: 'Possibilities for computer animated films in cartography', *The cartographic journal*, December 1966.

Alexander d'Agapeyeff and E C R Hadfield: *Maps* (OUP, second edition, 1950). Map making, map reading and the history of maps.

R O Davis: 'Problems of map maintenance' (ICA Technical Symposium, Edinburgh, 1964).

E R De Meter: 'Automatic contouring', *Nachr karten u vermessungswesen*, V, 9, 1964.

E R De Meter: 'Latest advances in automatic mapping', *Photogrammetric engineer*, November 1963.

G F Delaney: 'Problems in cartographic nomenclature', *Canadian cartography*, 1962.

G H Dury: *Map interpretation* (Pitman, third edition revised, 1967). Includes chapter on cartographical appreciation by H C Brookfield and G H Dury.

Max Eckert: *Die kartenwissenschaft* . . . (Berlin, Walter de Gruyter, two volumes, 1921 1925). A classic work and a major source book for later studies.

A Elwood: *Essentials of map-reading* (Harrap, fourth edition, 1964).

J K Fraser: 'Canadian Permanent Committee on Geographical Names', *Geographical bulletin*, May 1964.

G J Friedman: 'How far automation?' *Surveying and mapping*, December 1964.

D W Gale: 'Register control in map reproduction', *The cartographic journal*, December 1965.

Alice Garnett: *The geographical interpretation of topographical maps* (Harrap, third edition revised, two volumes 1953). With twenty-five maps in folder.

A C Gerlach: 'Technical problems in atlas making' (ICA Technical Symposium, Edinburgh, 1964).

J B Goodson and J A Morris: *Contour dictionary: a short textbook on contour reading with map exercises* (Harrap, third edition, 1960).

C B Hagen: 'Maps, copyright and fair use', *Bulletin*, Special Libraries Association, Geography and Map Division, December 1966.

A G Hodgkiss: 'Cartographic illustration: aims and principles', British Society of University Cartographers, 1966.

M Hotine: 'Rapid topographic surveys of new countries', *Surveying and mapping*, 1965.

Eduard Imhof: 'Tasks and methods of theoretical cartography', *International yearbook of cartography*, 1963.

Eduard Imhof: *Thematische Kartographie* (Walter de Gruyter, 1972).

J S Keates: *Cartographic design and production* (Longmans, 1973).

J S Keates: 'The perception of color in cartography' *Proceedings* of the Cartographic Symposium, Edinburgh, 1962.

G Krauss: 'Difficulties of maintaining topographic maps and possibilities of overcoming them' (ICA Technical Symposium, Edinburgh, 1964).

N P Lavrov: 'The perspective of the automation of the techniques of compilation and preparation to reproduction of geographic and topographic maps' (International Geographical Congress, London, 1964, Section IX, Cartography).

André Libault: *La cartographie* (Paris, PUF, 1963).

B Lockey: *The interpretation of Ordnance Survey maps and geographical pictures* (Philip, seventh edition, 1965).

D H Maling: 'Recent trends in map use and presentation', *Penrose annual*, 1964.

A C Marles: 'Photomechanical processes on plastics', paper and discussion presented to the Fifth meeting of the Symposium of the British Cartographic Society, Swansea, 1965, on 'Current developments in cartographic practice and photomechanical techniques', reprinted in *The cartographic journal*, June 166.

W W Ristow: *Three-dimensional maps: an annotated list of references relating to the construction and use of terrain models* (Washington, Library of Congress, 1964).

J A Roberts: 'The topographic map in a world of computers', *The professional geographer*, November 1962.

A H Robinson: *Elements of cartography* (Wiley, second edition, 1963).

A H Robinson: *The look of maps: an examination of cartographic design* (University of Wisconsin Press, 1952).

R R Rollins: 'Printing management for maps and charts', *Surveying and mapping*, June 1964.

A Rosenfeld: 'Automatic imagery interpretation', *Photogrammetric engineer*, March 1965.

K A Salichtchev: *Cartography* (Moscow, 'High school' Publishing House, 1966). In Russian.

Axel Schou: *The construction and drawing of block diagrams* (Nelson, 1962).

J V Sharp, *et al*: 'Automatic map compilation', *Photogrammetric engineer*, March 1965.

R B Simpson: 'Radar geographic tool', *Annals* of the Association of American Geographers, 1966.

P Speak and A H C Carter: *Map reading and interpretation* (OUP, 1964).

W R Tobler: 'Automation in the preparation of thematic maps', *The cartographic journal*, June 1965.

W R Tobler: 'The geographic ordering of information: new opportunities', *Professional geographer*, July 1964.

F Topfer and W Pillewizer: 'The principles of selection', *The cartographic journal*, June 1966.

C Travers: 'Cartographic maintenance requirements' (ICA Technical Symposium, Edinburgh, 1964).

J Tricart *et al*: *Initiation aux travaux pratiques de géographie: commentaires de cartes* (Paris, Société d'Edition d'Enseignement Supérieur, second edition 1960). Survey of the kinds of maps and mapping techniques.

United Nations: *Modern cartography: base maps for world needs* (New York, Department of Social Affairs, 1949). English and French editions.

R L Voison: 'Production control' (ICA Technical Symposium, Edinburgh, 1964).

M Wood: 'Visual perception and map design', *The cartographic journal*, June 1968.

J W Wright: 'Three types of reconnaissance mapping', *The cartographic journal*, June 1965.

P Yoeli: 'Analytical hill shading and density', *Surveying and mapping*, June 1966.

P Yoeli: 'The mechanisation of analytical hill shading', *The cartographic journal*, December 1967.

A Zvonarev, *editor*: 'New problems and methods of cartography', Leningrad, *Nauka*, 1967, Academy of Sciences of the USSR Geographical Society. In Russian. Eleven contributions by specialists.

For individual items of source material, *consult* Index.

313 'Cartography of the Northwest Coast of America to the year 1800', by Henry R Wagner, originally published in Berkeley, 1937, was reprinted by N Israel of Amsterdam in 1967. The two volumes, bound in one, contain thirteen folding maps. The first volume traces the evolution of the cartography of the region to the explorations of the Vancouver expeditions; the second comprises a critical and descriptive list of more than nine hundred maps, with an index, a list of place-names still in use, one of those now obsolete and a bibliography.

Refer also

H Harrisse: *The discovery of North America . . . with an essay on the early cartography of the New World*, 1892.

E D Fite and A Freeman: *A book of old maps delineating American history*, 1926.

314 Cary, John (1754–1835), one of the most brilliant of English map-makers, made great advances in technique in his maps of the British Isles, plans of London, large and small county maps and a number of special-purpose maps depicting such features as canals and post-roads. He surveyed nine thousand miles of turnpike roads for the Postmaster-General, incorporating much of his observed detail in his atlases, especially in the *New and correct English atlas*, 1787 and many other editions to 1831, *Cary's travellers' companion*, 1790, *Cary's new itinerary*, 1798, and the *New British atlas*, in collaboration with John Stockdale, 1805. Cary's county maps of Cardiganshire, Middlesex, Oxfordshire, Glamorganshire and the plan of London and Westminster, published between 1786 and 1803, reveal new advances in geographical delineation. The firm of G and J Cary produced also guide books, road books, globes, celestial charts and instruments of many kinds, all set out in their *Catalogue of maps, atlases, globes and other works published by G and J Cary*, London, 1800.

Refer

Sir H G Fordham: *John Cary, engraver, map, chart and print-seller and globe-maker, 1754–1835: a bibliography, with an introduction and biographical notes* (Cambridge, 1925).

315 Casella, C F, and Company, Limited, London, are not only one of the foremost firms making scientific instruments for meteorology, research and industry, but also issue useful catalogues on specific types of instruments, such as 'Meteorological instruments', 'Humidity, dew point and frost point', 'Barometers and manometers', 'Photogrammetry'. Leaflets include 'A selection of meteorological instruments for schools', 'Wind velocity and direction', 'Atmospheric pressure', 'Temperature', 'Humidity', 'Precipitation and evaporation', 'Sunshine, solar radiation and cloud' and 'Alnor dew point meter'. A range of colour films and slides has been produced with the aim of assisting in the selection of instruments for particular purposes, their setting up and use, including guidance on the choice of site, each with explanatory notes. Filmstrips include a 'Screen colour guide to clouds', 'Unstable weather' and 'Stable weather'. The firm also produces the Air Photo Packs compiled by The Geographical Association.

316 'Cassell's new atlas of the world', 1961, edited by Harold Fullard, containing 130 maps by George Philip, was a completely new work in the long line of authoritative atlases published by the House of Cassell since the first *Universal atlas* of 1891. The new atlas is especially useful for commercial interests and has an index-gazetteer of some seventy thousand entries.

317 Cassini, Jean Dominique (1625–1712) was the founder of the distinguished family of scientists. His son, Jacques (1677–1756), evolved the Cassini projection for the first scientific triangulation of France, and with his son, César François Cassini de Thury (1714–1784), initiated the Survey of France, the first precise national survey, which greatly influenced the progress of the Ordnance Survey in Britain and led in due time to the trigonometrical survey of France and Britain by General Roy in 1787.

318 'Catalan atlas' of 1375, traditionally attributed to Abraham or Yehuda Cresques and dedicated to King Charles V of France, is a masterpiece of the cartography of the period. The first two of the six vellum leaves comprise the text in Catalan; illustrations of men and animals are illuminated in gold, silver, red, orange, violet, blue and green. The remaining four leaves—the Nautical Atlas—contain four maps which, placed next to one another, give a picture of the world as then known, with many illustrations and explanatory texts. The maps of the areas from the British Isles to the Black Sea are of the portolan type and of a high standard of accuracy and cartography; the maps of the Near and Middle East and of north Africa show information gathered from Venetian and Genoese merchants, while towards central Asia and China the knowledge brought back by the Polos and other missionaries and travellers has been inserted.
Refer also
J A C Buchon and J Tastu: *Notice d'un atlas en Langue Catalane*, 1375 (Paris, 1839).
Pinhas Yoeli: 'Abraham and Yehuda Cresques and the Catalan Atlas', *in The cartographic journal*, June 1970.

319 'Catalog of African Government Documents and African Area Index' (Boston University Library, second revised edition, 1964, published by G K Hall) contains in one volume references to about four thousand monographs. The African Area Index is an alphabetical index to book materials by topics under the area to which they belong.

320 'Catalogs of the Scripps Institution of Oceanography Library', University of California, San Diego, have been reprinted by G K Hall: the Author-title catalogue, in seven volumes, 1970; the Subject catalogue, in two volumes, 1970; and Shelf-list, in two volumes, 1970 and the Documents-Reprints-Translations Shelf-list, in one volume,

1970. The library holds outstanding collections in oceanography, marine biology and marine technology, with imprint dates ranging from 1633 to the present. In addition to a basic reference collection in mathematics, physics and chemistry, the collection is strong in atmospheric sciences, fisheries, geology, geophysics and zoology; it holds a major collection of oceanographic expedition literature, reports, special documents and translations.

321 'Catalogue of books, maps, plates on America *and of a remarkable collection of early voyages . . . presenting an essay towards a Dutch-American bibliography'*, by Frederik Muller, printed in Amsterdam 1872–1875, has been reprinted by N Israel, 1966, with a subject index and an index of personal names compiled by G J Brouwer.

322 'A catalogue of Latin American flat maps 1926–1964', compiled by Palmyra V M Monteiro (Institute of Latin American Studies, University of Texas at Austin, 1967), is arranged regionally; bibliographic details are given, but there are no annotations.

323 'Catalogue of the Malaysia/Singapore Collection, University of Singapore Library', was printed in one volume by G K Hall in 1969. The collection, of some 7,500 items, is particularly strong in source material tracing the various aspects of the development of the Malay States, Singapore and the Bornean regions, but excluding Brunei and Indonesian Borneo. Arranged by the Library of Congress classification, holdings include public records, government publications, long runs of serials, theses, manuscripts and translations. Titles are given mostly in English and some bear imprint dates as early as 1596.

324 'Catalogue of the manuscript maps, charts, and plans and of the topographical drawings held in the British Museum' was planned in three volumes. Volumes I and II were originally published in 1844, reprinted in 1962; volume III was printed in 1861, but never published, the impression being destroyed in a fire. The 1962 reprint was made from a copy comprising a set of surviving sheets and was in fact the first publication of volume III. The *Catalogue of the printed maps, plans and charts in the British Museum*, compiled by R K Douglas, published in two volumes, 1885, has been supplemented thereafter by annual volumes of the *Catalogue of printed maps in the British Museum: accessions*, 1884–. The working copies in the Museum have been maintained in guard-books, now numbering eighty-four, incorporating the columns of the original catalogue and the accession entries added from year to year. A photolithographic edition of the *Catalogue of printed maps, charts and plans*, recording the holdings of the Museum to the end of 1964, in fifteen volumes, 1967, is a valuable tool for carto-bibliographical work.

325 Cataloguing books on geographical subjects presents no particular problems, but the cataloguing of a map collection demands specialised knowledge. All the great map departments have formulated their own rules for cataloguing their collections; a comparison of their findings reveals interesting differences, not so much of opinion as of emphasis. The rules evolved by the British Museum, the Bibliothèque Nationale and the War Office are especially clear and detailed. In addition, the following works are informative: Samuel W Boggs and Dorothy Cornwell Lewis: *The classification and cataloging of maps and atlases*, Special Libraries Association, second edition, 1945; Mary Ellis Fink: 'A comparison of map cataloging systems', *Bulletin*, Special Libraries Association, Geography and Map Division, December 1962; *The catalog library and the map librarian*, part IV of the *Cartographic research guide*, Special Libraries Association, Geography and Map Division, 1957; B M Woods: 'Map cataloging', *Library resources and technical services*, Autumn, 1959; R J Lee: *English county maps: the identification, cataloguing and physical care of a collection*, Library Association, 1955, pamphlet no 13. Reports on American cataloguing practice regarding maps, atlases, globes and relief models were included in the *Bulletin* of the Geography and Map Division for December 1948, October 1953 and April 1956. 'To avoid excessive handling of maps, the catalog entry should give as much aid as possible to the reader in the selection or rejection of a particular map'.

Refer also

Charles Buffum: 'Map cataloging: an informal view', *Bulletin*, Special Libraries Association, Geography and Map Division, June 1972.

W W Ristow and D K Carrington: 'The Library of Congress computerized map cataloging project', *International library review*, July 1970.

326 Cave Research Group of Great Britain was founded in 1946 for the encouragement of the scientific study of caves and of their past and present contents and inhabitants. Two general meetings are held each year for the reading of papers, which are printed in the *Transactions*. The *Occasional papers* have included such studies as E A Glennie and M Hazleton: *Cave fauna*, 1947; N Kirkham: *Derbyshire lead mining glossary*, 1949; and A L Butcher: *Cave survey*, 1950. The group possesses a Library, housed in Berkhamsted, Hertfordshire, which holds long runs of British and foreign speleological journals and a considerable collection of books on caves and limestone regions throughout the world.

Refer from the vast literature of journals and monographs:

Cave science, quarterly, 1947–, journal of the British Speleological Association.

Irish speleology, journal of the Irish Speleological Association, edited by the Department of Geography, Trinity College, Dublin, 1966–.

Annales de spéléologie, quarterly, Centre National de la Recherche Scientifique.

Proceedings, annual, of the University of Bristol Spelaeological Society.

Transactions, British Cave Research Association, Bridgwater, Somerset.

Studies in speleology, 1964– (Association of the Pengelly Cave Research Centre, annual).

David Judson: 'Cave surveying for expeditions', *The geographical journal*, June 1974.

James R Reddell: *A bibliographic guide to the caves of Texas* (Texas Speleological Survey, 1968).

——*A preliminary bibliography of Mexican cave biology with a checklist of published records* (Association for Mexican Cave Studies Bulletin, 1971).

P Renault: *La formation des cavernes* (Paris: PUF, 1970).

327 Central Office of Information *reference pamphlets* series is among the most useful to geographers of all the publications of the Department, particularly *The making of a nation* booklets: Nigeria, 1960; Sierra Leone, 1960; Tanganyika, 1961; Jamaica, 1962; Trinidad and Tobago, 1962; Uganda, 1962; Kenya, 1963; Zanzibar, 1963; Malta, 1964; Malawi, 1964; The Gambia, 1964; Zambia, 1965; Guyana, 1966

328 The Centre d'Analyse Documentaire pour l'Afrique Noire, Paris (CADAN), aims to provide documentary information of research workers in the social and human sciences on Africa South of the Sahara. The Centre systematically lists and analyses the relevant articles and scientific works, including some two hundred periodicals on African matters, plus as many of more general interest, together with national bibliographies, publishers' catalogues and the acquisition lists of the large libraries. This scanning yields some four thousand abstract cards a year, so far used in two different ways: either placed at the disposal of workers in standard card index files or processed by automatic data methods (SYNTOL), worked out in the CNRS automatic data section to facilitate automatic location of the information they contain.

329 The Centre for East Asian Cultural Studies, Tokyo, has published the following valuable aids: *A survey of Japanese bibliographies concerning Asian studies,* 1963; *Research institutes for Asian studies in Japan,* 1963; *Japanese researchers in Asian studies,* 1963; *Research institutes and researchers of Asian studies in Thailand,* 1964; *Bibliography of bibliographies of East Asian studies in Japan,* 1964; *A survey of bibliographies in Western languages concerning East and South East Asian studies,* 1966.

330 Centre for Environmental Studies, London, an independent body sponsored jointly by the Ford Foundation and the United Kingdom Government, was set up in 1967 to promote research and education in the planning and design of the physical environment and as a forum for discussion on an international basis. More than thirty researchers, full- or part-time, worked in eleven institutions on such problems, among others, as industrial location, population mobility, the housing market, activity networks, communication in re-housing and atmospheric pollution. The internal research programme of the centre itself began in 1968 with the appointment of a research team trained in town planning, sociology, transport engineering, mathematics, economics, physics, geography, systems analysis or market research. 'Patterns of urbanisation' is the subject of a current working party.

331 Centre National de la Recherche Scientifique publishes a number of series of interest in geographical studies. In addition to the

Bibliographie géographique internationale (*qv*) and the *Mémoires et documents du Centre de Recherches et Documentation Cartographiques* (*qv*) are the *Annales de spéléologie, Annales de géophysique, Annuaire d'Afrique du nord* and individual maps and monographs. *Le bulletin signalétique* includes sections on earth sciences and agriculture.

332 'Ceres', the FAO review, published in six issues a year in three editions, English, French and Spanish, is concerned with the adaptation of peoples to their environment, urbanisation, re-housing, the role of technology in agriculture and the dramatic social and economic changes that precede and accompany development. 'State of the market' commodity reports are included, a 'World report', short topical articles, reports and news items, short notes in a section entitled 'Forum', reviews of appropriate books and a list of 'Books received', the whole being accompanied by illustrations and the occasional lively cartoon.

333 The Challenger expedition, 1872–1876, which sailed round the globe under the leadership of Charles Wyville Thomson (later Sir Wyville), heralded the large-scale, systematic science of the seas. Reports of the expedition, *The Challenger reports*, begun by Sir Wyville Thomson and completed by Sir John Murray, run to some fifty volumes. Sir John Murray compiled also *Report on the scientific results of the voyage of HMS Challenger during the years 1873–76* in two volumes.

Refer also

Herbert S Bailey: 'The background of the Challenger Expedition', *American scientist*, September–October, 1972.

Henry Charnock: 'Using the ocean', *Journal of the Royal Society . . . of Arts . . .*, July 1973.

Margaret and Sir George Deacon: 'The first oceanographic expedition', *The geographical magazine*, September 1972.

Eric Linklater: *The voyage of the Challenger* (Murray, 1972).

G S Ritchie: *Challenger: the life of a survey ship* (Hollis and Carter, 1957).

Herbert Swire: *The voyage of the Challenger, a personal narrative of the historic circumnavigation of the globe in the years 1872–1876, by Navigating Sub-Lieutenant Herbert Swire, R N . . .* (Golden Cockerell Pr, 1938, two volumes).

334 The Challenger Society was founded in 1903 to promote the scientific study of oceanography; it is based now on the National Institute of Oceanography, Wormley, Surrey (*qv*). The *Annual reports* and *Occasional papers* are documents of central importance. Scientific meetings are held quarterly in the rooms of the Linnean Society and joint meetings with representatives of marine laboratories are held three times a year at various laboratories and other institutions.

335 'Chambers's historical atlas of the world' is intended for the use of students as a companion to their studies, being of pocket-size format, containing 108 six-colour maps and a seven thousand entry index. Treating first the span of the earliest known civilisations from the third century BC, the maps trace the main streams of world history, influenced by geographical, economic and political factors, to the complex and numerous developments and movements of the twentieth century.

336 'Chambers's world gazetteer and geographical dictionary', 1954, was revised by T C Collocott and J O Thorne in 1957. Emphasis is on Great Britain. Information given includes location, description and population, with some longer articles on more important places and some short definitions of geographical terms. A supplementary index includes variant names and alternative spellings.

337 'The changing nature of geography', by Roger Minshul (Hutchinson University Library, 1970, in hardback and paperback editions), examines the nature of geography and of geographers, the content of geographical studies and the methodology which has evolved through the years to the new quantitative and qualitative techniques. There are references and notes at the end of each chapter and a separate bibliography, including articles as well as books.

Refer also

Studia geographica (Institute of Geography, Czechoslovak Academy of Sciences, Brno, with summaries in Czechoslovak, French, English and German).

W Peter Adams and Frederick M Helleiner, *ed: International geography* (Toronto UP; OUP, 1972, two volumes. Papers submitted to the 22nd International Geographical Congress, Montreal, 1972).

Hanno Beck: *Geographie: Europäische Entwicklung in Texten*

und Erläuterung (Freiburg, Munchen: Verlag Karl Alber, 1973).
R J Chorley, *ed*: *Directions in geography* (Methuen, 1973). P E
Janem: *All possible worlds: a history of geographical ideas* (The
Odyssey Pr, 1972).

338 '**Character of a conurbation:** *a computer atlas of Birmingham and
the Black Country'*, compiled by Kenneth E Rosing and Peter A
Wood and published by the University of London Press, is a collection of some fifty maps derived from the sample survey of 1966. Explanatory text and diagrams interspersed with the maps show either
the whole conurbation based on electoral wards or the City of Birmingham based on enumeration districts, coded by means of the
SYMAP computer programme and reproduced directly from the
output of the line-printer. The maps demonstrate the value of automation in making use of such data.

339 Charts. Modern bathymetric charts had their origin in the portolano maps (*qv*) devised by the seamen of the Mediterranean soon
after 1200 to illustrate their *portolani* or sailing directions.

The amount of information on the oceans is still in reality sparse,
masked to a great extent, with obvious exceptions, by the small scale
of ocean charting. Until fairly recently, depths were laboriously
sounded, the observations were plotted and from the detailed plot
gradually a generalised picture of the sea bed bathymetry was
formed. Once echo sounding superseded the lead line, giving profiles
of the sea bed instead of isolated depth values, progress became
more rapid, as the mechanisms were perfected. Ships of all nations
send information to very many hydrographic offices, but maintenance of accuracy is still difficult, due mainly to human error.

The General Bathymetric Chart of the Oceans (GEBCO), first proposed in 1899 at the Seventh International Geographical Congress,
comprises twenty-four sheets covering the world oceans at 1:10M.
The production of the first four editions has been organised by a
number of bodies and in 1932 the International Hydrographic
Bureau (now the International Hydrographic Organization)
assumed responsibility for the centralisation of oceanographic
depth data and for updating the charts, assisted by the Hydrographic Offices of eighteen countries. The collection and exchange of
ocean bathymetric data have been increasing, with improved equipment and technology. The IHO and the Intergovernmental Oceanographic Commission, under Unesco, have jointly constituted a new

207

committee for the GEBCO—Fifth Edition, with new specifications where desirable.

Refer to the index under Charts, also

A R Boyle: 'Automation in hydrographic charting', *Canadian surveyor*, December 1970.

F A Pielou: 'Special purpose navigation charts', *The cartographic journal*, June 1971.

'International charts', *The geographical journal*, February 1974, 'Cartographical survey', p 157.

340 'A check list of Canadian literature and background materials 1628–1950', in two parts, presents a comprehensive list of books which constitute Canadian literature written in English, together with a selective list of other books of Canadian origin which reveal the backgrounds of that literature. The work was compiled by Reginald Eyre Watters for the Humanities Research Council of Canada (University of Toronto Press; OUP, 1959). Part II is particularly relevant here; it contains bibliographies with a Canadian focus, on local history and description, social history, travel and description. Entries are arranged alphabetically by author's name and there is an 'Index of anonymous titles' and an index of authors' names, initials and pseudonyms.

341 'Checklist of Southeast Asian serials', in the South East Asia Collection, Yale University Library, printed by G K Hall, 1969, includes all holdings catalogued before 1966; holdings catalogued after 1966 are given for those serials held in the main library. The collection is notable for government documents, society publications and limited editions of publications pre-1945 concerning Burma, Thailand, Laos, Vietnam, Cambodia, Malaysia, Singapore, Brunei, the Philippines, Indonesia, Portuguese Timor and New Guinea. Author and title references are given.

342 Chicago University, Department of Geography was established in 1904 and has taken its place among the most influential of academic centres of geographical studies. The research papers and irregular monographs issued since 1948 have proved invaluable; numerous works have been published by members of the staff, including the *International list of geographical serials* (*qv*) by C D Harris.

343 'China and Japan' is the title of a set of facsimile reproductions of nineteenth century British Parliamentary papers, involving fifty-two volumes, an invaluable guide to primary source materials concerning China and Japan and British–Far Eastern relations during the nineteenth century, edited by Professor P Ford, Mrs G Ford and W G Beasley, in the Irish University Press *Area Studies* series.

Refer also

C D Cowan, *ed: The economic development of China and Japan: studies in economic history and political economy* (Allen and Unwin, 1964).

344 'China reconstructs' is published monthly in English, Spanish, Arabic and Russian, by the China Welfare Institute, Peking. The periodical, generously illustrated, covers all aspects of the nation's life; of particular interest to geographers are the articles and photographs concerning agriculture, farming, the economy, industries and manufactures. An index is circulated with the final issue of the year.

Refer also

China pictorial

Peking review.

The physical geography of China (Praeger, 1969, in two volumes, for The Institute of Geography, USSR Academy of Sciences).

E S Kirby, *ed: Contemporary China: economic and social studies, documents, chronology, bibliography* (Hong Kong: OUP, five volumes, completed 1963).

A L March: *The idea of China: myth and theory in geographic thought* (Newton Abbot: David and Charles, 1974).

Yuan-Li Wu, *ed: China: a handbook* (Newton Abbot: David and Charles, 1973).

345 'Chisholm's handbook of commercial geography' has been a standard work since its first appearance in 1889. The work was entirely re-written by L Dudley Stamp and S Carter Gilmour in a fifteenth edition, 1956, and is now in the eighteenth edition, revised by Dudley Stamp (Longmans, 1966).

346 'A chronological history of voyages into the Arctic Regions', by John Barrow, 1818, has been reprinted by David and Charles of Newton Abbot. John Barrow was responsible for the renewed search for the North West Passage—his name is commemorated in Point

Barrow and the Barrow Strait—and his work is one of the best available histories of the quest. Beginning with the Norse discovery of Vinland, Barrow tells of the voyages of such explorers as Frobisher, Davis, Baffin and Hudson, bringing the story to the time of his own voyages.

Refer also

Ritchie Calder: *Men against the frozen north* (Allen and Unwin, 1957).

347 Chubb, Thomas is best known for his monumental *The printed maps in the atlases of Great Britain and Ireland . . .* (*qv*). Other major works include *A descriptive list of the printed maps of Somersetshire, 1575–1914,* 1914, and *A descriptive list of the printed maps of Norfolk, 1574–1916,* 1928.

348 'Cities in evolution' was edited by Patrick Geddes for The Outlook Tower Association, Edinburgh, and The Association of Planning and Regional Reconstruction (Williams and Norgate, revised edition, 1949). Geddes, a pioneer in the developing concept of city planning with regard to environment, included illustrations from his second exhibition and text drawn from his Catalogue to the first exhibition. Appendices include 'The Geddes diagrams', 'Geddes final Dundee lecture' and a brief biography of him.

Refer also

Jane Jacobs: *The economy of cities* (Cape, 1970).

349 'Cities of destiny', edited by Arnold Toynbee (Thames and Hudson, 1967), well illustrated with reproductions, photographs and sketchmaps, considers selected examples of well defined types of cities, under the following headings: 'Cities in history'; 'The city-state'; 'Capital cities' and 'Megalopolis', each chapter being contributed by an expert. Notes are appended to the text, also a bibliography.

Refer also

B J L Berry, *ed: City classification handbook: methods and applications* (Wiley, 1972).

Stephen Thernstrom and Richard Sennett: *Cities on the move* (OUP, 1970).

———*Nineteenth century cities: essays in the new urban history* (Yale UP, 1970).

350 'Cities of the Soviet Union: *studies in their functions, size, density and growth'*, by C D Harris (Rand McNally for the Association of American Geographers, 1970), assembles factual data collected over many years from Soviet census and other primary documents, dealing mainly with the 1,247 centres having more than 10,000 inhabitants for which data were published in the 1959 Census. A brief introduction describes the basic framework of the urban geography of the USSR and the work already completed on this topic by Soviet geographers; the growth of urban population as a whole is then considered, followed by comments on the development of individual towns from the early nineteenth century. A substantial bibliography contains references mainly to works in Russian, but many also in English, French or German.

351 'The citizen's atlas of the world', by John Bartholomew, is especially useful for library and educational use. Two hundred pages of coloured maps, the majority printed in band colouring for clarity, are designed primarily to show settlements and boundaries, both internal and international. Every second double page is presented as a single spread to give a larger unbroken map face. Introductory sections: 'Dates in history of exploration', 'World exploration chart', a glossary of geographical terms and other information are included for quick reference.

352 'City', 1967–, the bi-monthly journal of The National Urban Coalition, Washington, DC, contains illustrated articles, a 'Digest of recent urban commentary', a correspondence section and notes.

353 'The city in history', by Lewis Mumford, first published in America, 1961, and, in the same year, by Secker and Warburg, was reprinted by Pelican Books in 1966. The work expands the information and ideas in the historical sections of *The culture of cities (qv)*; parts of the four original chapters have been incorporated in the eighteen chapters of the later work. Four groups of reproductions or photographs are included, also a bibliography.

354 'City, region and regionalism: *a geographical contribution to human ecology'*, by R E Dickinson (Routledge and Kegan Paul, 1947, fourth edition, 1960), for the International Library of Sociology and Social Reconstruction, was superseded in 1964 by the title *City and region: a geographical interpretation*, in the same series.

Refer also

Garbis Armen: 'A classification of cities and city regions in England and Wales, 1966', *Regional studies*, June 1972.

R E Dickinson: *Regional ecology: the study of man's environment* (Wiley, 1970).

Bryn Greer-Wootten: 'Metropolitan regional analysis', *Progress in geography*, 1972.

C Vereker *et al*: *Urban redevelopment and social change* (Liverpool University Press, 1960).

R Vernon: *The changing economic functions of the central city* (New York: Committee for Economic Development, 1959).

355 'Civitates orbis terrarum', originally compiled between 1572 and 1618 by Georg Braun and Franz Hogenberg, was reproduced in black and white facsimile in the *Theatrum Orbis Terrarum* series, Amsterdam, 1965, with an introduction by R V Tooley. Six hundred towns in all parts of the world are included; the beautiful engravings are by Hogenberg and others, many of them representing the first known engraved views. Apart from its main topographical value, this magnificent work is of great interest as a record of the domestic life of the period.

356 The Clarendon Press, Oxford, Cartographic Department, became an individual concern in 1952, though still working in close collaboration with the Oxford University Press, and has since become noted throughout the world for consistent excellence of cartography and for experimental and pioneer work, both in conventional and automated cartography. The Department carries out all the processes of map and atlas preparation; the location, in Oxford, gives access to the advice of specialists in many disciplines and to the reference libraries of the University. Courses in the training of cartographers are offered. The Press also publishes monographs and series, such as the *Oxford studies in African affairs* and *A Pacific bibliography* (*qv*).

See also

Atlas of Britain and Northern Ireland; The Oxford atlas; The Oxford economic atlas of the world; The Oxford junior atlas; Oxford plastic relief maps; The Oxford school atlas; Oxford system of automated cartography.

Refer also

David Bickmore and Experimental Cartography Unit, *ed*: *Automatic cartography and planning* (The Architectural Press, 1971).

Christopher R Bourne: 'The Cartographic Department of the Clarendon Press, Oxford', *International yearbook of cartography,* 1968.

357 Classification. The variety of material in a geographical collection and the broad scope of the subject content have rendered inadequate any of the general bibliographical schemes of classification for the organisation of a specialised geography library. The Library of Congress classification, section G, and the Universal Decimal Classification 91 are used in some academic departments, usually with modifications; the latter has also provided the base for some special applications, such as that used by the Scott Polar Research Institute, in addition to the international classification below-mentioned. The British Museum Map Room, the Bodleian Map Room and the Bibliothèque Nationale have all evolved empirical schemes to suit their needs. The system used for the arrangement of entries in the *Bibliographie géographique internationale* dates, with modifications, from the system devised by Raveneau in 1891. The classification created by S W Boggs for the Council of the Association of American Geographers, published under the title *Library classification and cataloging of geographical materials,* is used by the American Geographical Society of New York in its research catalogue and in the bibliographical service *Current geographical publications;* it has also provided the starting-point for the classifications devised for several other notable collections, both in America and Britain. The Oxford University School of Geography uses the American scheme for the classified index of periodical articles maintained, but has found the scheme as a whole too detailed for organising the collection itself, for which a straightforward scheme giving regional priority is used; a numeral notation denotes the regional scheme, letters the thematic aspects, with running numbers added to give precise location, so that each item in the collection bears a unique call number. G R Crone, former librarian and map curator of the Royal Geographical Society, worked out an interesting classification, which, unlike the majority of geographical schemes to date, has a philosophical basis; in Mr Crone's words, 'The ruling idea has been to move from the separate subjects in which the geographer may be interested, through their inter-relations and on to the final synthesis'.

The schemes evolved for the vast collections in the US General Staff and the British War Office again demonstrate the practical approach, using letters, numerals and symbols in combination, so that each item is identified individually both in location and in all indexes and references. The Geographical Association has given much thought to the whole question of arrangement of geographical material; the classification used by the Geographical Association itself was based on experience gained by studying the scheme used by the University of Southampton Department of Geography and that of the Association of American Geographers; again, a combination of numerals and letters is used, with detailed sub-division, and a regional preference when possible. A simpler scheme drawn up for school use is class P of the Cheltenham Classification, which is in three main parts, each subdivided into nine sections and using the decimal point as necessary for further sub-division. Among the more recently evolved special classifications has been the classification of world vegetation, prepared by the Unesco Standing Committee on classification and mapping of vegetation on a world basis, worked over especially at a meeting held during the eleventh International Botanical Congress, August 1969; it provides a comprehensive framework for the more important categories to be used on vegetation maps at scales of 1:1M or smaller. The categories in this classification are units of vegetation, including both zonal formations and the more extensive azonal and modified formations; the system may be applied to larger scales by expanding it through further subdivisions. The framework is related to a scheme of colours, shades and symbols of world vegetation and an explanatory manual is under the editorship of Professor A Kücher. The Oxford forestry classification and the polar classification devised by the Arctic Institute of North America are two other widely accepted special classifications.

The Commission on Classification of Geographical Books and Maps in Libraries was constituted during the International Geographical Congress held in Washington in 1952. After much discussion at successive meetings, the section 'Geography' in the Universal Decimal Classification was adopted for expansion and modification. Professor E Meynen was foremost in the execution of this work, aiming at and, to a great extent, succeeding in integrating the different viewpoints in many countries into a synthesis. The resulting scheme, which has been recognised by the FID, was published in English, French and German, as the *Final report on the classification of geographical books and maps* for the XIth General Assembly and XXth International Geographical Congress, London 1964, preceded by a masterly article by Professor Meynen 'On the classification of geographical books and maps and the application of the Universal Decimal Classification (UDC) in the field of geography'.

Refer also

S W Boggs and D C Lewis: *The classification and cataloging of maps and atlases* (Special Libraries Association, second edition, 1945).

E J S Parsons: *Manual of map classification and cataloguing prepared for use in the Directorate of Military Survey* (War Office, 1946).

R T Porter: 'The library classification of geography', *Geographical journal*, March 1964.

—— 'The Universal Decimal Classification and Geography', *The geographical journal*, June 1972, 'The Record', p 274.

358 'The climate near the ground', by Rudolf Geiger (Harvard University Press, 1950, 1957, 1965, 1966; translated from the fourth edition of *Das Klima der bodennahen Luftschicht*, 1961), is a classic work, of which successive editions have taken account of new research. The following are the main topics: 'Heat budget of the earth's surface as the basis of microclimatology'; 'The air layer over level ground without vegetation'; 'Influence of the underlying surface on the adjacent air layer'; 'Quantitative determination of heat-balance factors'; 'The air layer near plant covered ground'; 'Problems in forest meteorology'; 'The influence of topography on microclimate'; 'Relation of man and animals to microclimate'. A section 'Hints on measurement techniques used in microclimatologic and micrometeorologic investigations' was contributed by Gustav Hofmann and there is a comprehensive bibliography of books and articles.

Refer also

Problems in palaeoclimatology. Proceedings of the NATO Palaeo-Climatic Conference held at the University of Newcastle-upon-Tyne, January 1963, edited by A E M Nairn (Wiley, 1964).

John F Griffiths: *Applied climatology: an introduction* (OUP, 1966).

James A Taylor: *Climatic resources and economic activity* (Newton Abbot: David and Charles, 1974).

J Tricart and A Cailleux: *Introduction to climatic geomorphology* (Longmans, 1972, translated by Conrad J Kiewiet de Jonge).

359 **'The climates of the continents'**, by W G Kendrew, was a pioneer work in English when it was first published in 1922; now in a fifth edition (Oxford: Clarendon Press, 1960). Comparison may usefully be made with the *Handbuch der Klimatologie*, edited by W Köppen and R Geiger in five volumes, 1930–1938.

Refer also

Eric C Barrett: 'Rethinking climatology: an introduction to the uses of weather satellite photographic data in climatological studies', *Progress in geography*, 1970.

R R Crowe: *Concepts in climatology* (Longmans, 1971).

G M B Dobson: *Exploring the atmosphere* (OUP, second edition, 1969).

G H Dury: 'Climatic change as a geographical backdrop', *The Australian geographer*, 1967.

P Estienne and A Godard: *Climatologie* (Paris: Colin, 1970).

F K Hare and J C Ritchie: 'The boreal bioclimates', *The geographical review*, July 1972.

H H Lamb: *The changing climate: selected papers* (Methuen, 1966).

——*Climate: present, past and future* (Methuen, two volumes, 1972–).

R W Longley: *Elements of meteorology* (Wiley, 1970).

G J H McCall: *Meteorites and their origins* (Newton Abbot: David and Charles, 1973).

Gordon Manley: *Climate, man and history* (Angus and Robertson, 1973).

W H Matthews, *ed*: *Man's impact on the climate*, 1971.

Albert Miller and Jack C Thompson: *Elements of meteorology* (Columbus, Ohio: Merrill, 1970).

H Newberger and J Cahir: *Principles of climatology: a manual in earth science* (New York: Holt, Rinehart and Winston, 1969).

C P Peguy: *Précis de climatologie* (Paris: Masson, second edition, 1970).

Robert Raikes: *Water, weather and prehistory* (Baker, 1967).

Herbert Riehl: *Introduction to the atmosphere* (McGraw-Hill, 1972).

R H Shaw: *Ground level climatology* (Bailey Bros and Swinfen

216

for the American Association for the Advancement of Science, 1967).

R O Slatyer and I C McIlroy: *Practical microclimatology* (Unesco, 1961).

E T Stringer: *Foundations of climatology: an introduction to physical, dynamic, synoptic and geographical climatology* (San Francisco: Freeman, 1972).

G T Trewartha: *The earth's problem climates* (University of Wisconsin; Methuen, 1961; second printing, 1962).

Studies in Antarctic meteorology (American Geophysical Union, *Antarctic Research* series, no 9, 1967).

Hermann Flohn: *Climate and weather* (Weidenfeld and Nicolson, 1969, translated B V de G Walden).

E C Barrett: *Viewing weather from space* (Longmans, 1967).

W J Maunder: *The value of the weather* (Methuen, 1970).

Hans Robert Scultetus: *Klimatologie* (Das Geographische Seminar: Praktische Arbeitswesen. Braunschweig: Westermann, 1969).

360 'Climatic atlas of Europe', published 1970– by Unesco, WMO and Cartographia of Budapest, is in looseleaf form, the corners of the sheets being reinforced. The volume contains two sets of thirteen maps each, showing the distribution of monthly and annual values of the mean atmospheric temperature and precipitation, together with a map representing annual temperature ranges. For its preparation, the meteorological services of the individual countries provided data obtained from several thousand stations; the information from which these maps were compiled covers the period 1931 to 1960, using a fuller body of data than has been available for any previous work of this kind and the maps have been prepared in accordance with the specifications laid down by WMO in the *Guide to climatological practices.* Colour scales have been applied consistently, place-names appear in the form used by the country concerned and headings and other explanatory matter have been given in the four working languages of WMO, English, French, Russian and Spanish. The map sheets are easily detachable from the metal spiral binding, 60 by 42 cm. This is the first volume of a world climatic atlas, under the direction of WMO, which will indicate the principal factors determining the climate of each continent.

361 'Climatic factors and agricultural productivity', a report on

217

papers and discussion presented at a symposium held on March 13, 1963, edited by James A Taylor, was made available in duplicated form by the University College of Wales, Aberystwyth in 1964 (Memorandum no 6). Sketchmaps and diagrams are included; the main topics under discussion, following papers by a number of experts, were 'Economic and ecological productivity under British conditions: an introduction'; 'Light and temperature efficiency, with reference to forest grasses'; 'The effect of weather conditions on the growth of lucerne and clover'; 'Drought, soil water and grass growth'; 'Climatic factors in the development of local grass conservation'; 'Climatic factors affecting Danish and Irish agricultural development' and 'Rainfall probability and agricultural productivity (overseas work with its possible implications in Britain)'. Edited extracts from the general discussion and conclusions are included.

Refer also

Earlier memoranda: 'The growing season', 1958; 'Shelter problems in relation to crop and animal husbandry', 1959; 'Hill climates and land usage, with special reference to the Highland Zone of Britain', 1960; 'Aspects of soil climate', 1961; 'Climatic factors and diseases in plants and animals', 1962; 'Climatic factors and agricultural productivity', 1963.

Jen-Hu Chang: *Climate and agriculture: an ecological survey* (Chicago: Aldine Publishing Co, 1968).

William P Lowry: *Weather and life: an introduction to biometeorology* (Academic Press, 1970).

James A Taylor, *ed*: *Weather forecasting for agriculture and industry: a symposium* (Newton Abbot: David and Charles, 1972).

362 'Climatological atlas of Africa', compiled and edited in the African Climatology Unit, University of Witwatersrand, under the direction of S P Jackson (Government Printer, 1961), contains fifty-five plates presenting data on monthly and annual rainfall, daily temperatures and humidity.

363 'Climatological atlas of the British Isles', published by the Meteorological Office, was begun before the second world war, in co-operation with interested governmental authorities. A new edition, 1945– (1952), incorporated an additional feature; new information and maps were compiled on the recommendations of the

218

National Agricultural Advisory Council, with the interests of agriculture in mind. 220 maps, arranged in ten sections, deal with all aspects of the climate and weather of the British Isles, each section being accompanied by an introduction and a bibliography, with tables and diagrams to supplement the maps. Most of the maps show average conditions 1901–1930, selected as being the standard period for climatological averages for all the meteorological services of the world. In some sections, data have been incorporated for later periods, covering as many years as possible; particularly interesting maps show snowfall, thunder frequency, monthly average means of vapour pressure, relative humidity and saturation deficit.

Refer also
   H H Lamb: *The English climate* (EUP, 1964).

364 'Climatological atlas of Rumania', published by the Meteorological Institute, Bucharest, 1966, in English and French, presents a very detailed climatological picture, reflecting observations during the past sixty years of intensive research. Temperature, humidity, cloud cover, precipitation, winds and sunshine have been mapped at 1:1,500, with topographical and political supporting detail. More than twelve layer colours are used on some maps and the printing is excellent throughout.

365 'Climatological atlas of the world' *see* under *Atlas of Meteorology* . . .

366 'Cloud studies in colour', by Richard Scorer and Harry Wexler (Oxford: Pergamon Press, 1967), comprises a collection of fine coloured pictures of cloud types, with brief explanatory comments on the facing pages. Introductory text discusses 'Cloud names' and 'Magnitudes'; appended are a 'Diagram of cloud mechanics', a section 'Types of motion' illustrated by figures and a combined index and glossary.

Refer also
   The colour encyclopaedia of clouds, by the same authors (Pergamon Press, 1968).
   B J Mason: *The physics of clouds* (OUP, second edition, 1971).
   D B Miller and R G Feddes: *Global atlas of relative cloud cover, 1967–70* . . . (Washington, DC: US Department of Commerce *et al*, 1971).

219

Richard Scorer: *Clouds of the world: a complete colour encyclopedia* (Melbourne: Lothian Publishing Co (Pty) Ltd; Newton Abbot: David and Charles, 1972).

367 'The coast of England and Wales in pictures', with commentary by J A Steers (CUP, 1960), presents a collection of superb photographs, with geographical explanations.
Refer also

E C F Bird: *Coastal landforms: an introduction to coastal geomorphology, with Australian examples* (Australian National University, 1964).

——— *Coasts* (MIT Pr, 1969).

K R Dyer: *Estuaries: a physical introduction* (Wiley, 1973).

W Harrison: 'Prediction of beach changes', *Progress in geography*, 1970.

B H Ketchum, *ed*: *The water's edge: critical problems of the coastal zone* (Cambridge, Mass: MIT, 1972).

C A M King: *Beaches and coasts* (Arnold, second edition, 1972).

Anthony Smith: *Beside the seaside* (Allen and Unwin, 1972; 'Operation Seashore, coastline of Britain in 1970).

J A Steers, *ed*: *Applied coastal geomorphology* (Macmillan, 1971).

J A Steers, *ed*: *Introduction to coastline development* (Macmillan, 1971).

368 'Coelum Stellatum' *see* under *Theatrum Orbis Terrarum*.

369 The Coffee Information Bureau, London, representing the Coffee Publicity Association Limited, provides a general information service on coffee in all its aspects. An educational visual aids section includes leaflets, cards on specific topics, colour films and demonstrations.

370 Colin, Armand, one of the leading French publishers, has a special interest in geographical subjects; for many years, individual geographical monographs have included a number based on doctorate theses. Outstanding works include L de Launay: *Géologie de la France*, 1921; Henri Baulig: *Le plateau central de la France et sa bordure méditerranéenne*, 1928; Philippe Pinchemel: *Géographie de la France*, 1964. Armand Colin is also associated with high-level bibliographical work, such as the current *Bibliographie géographique internationale* (qv).

371 Collet's Holdings Limited, Wellingborough, Northants, is an invaluable centre for the checking or purchase of Russian publications, such as the *Geologicheskaya Karten SSSR*, 1:2,500,000, published in sixteen sheets by the Ministry of Geology in 1965 (1968). Other notable publications introduced into this country by Collet's include the *Atlas of the lithological and palaeogeographical maps of the USSR*, in four volumes; *Deposits of useful minerals of the world*, four sheets at 1:20M; *Tectonic map of Eurasia*, twelve sheets at 1:5M, with legend in Russian and English; *Tectonic map of Europe with an explanatory book in Russian* (the French edition is out of print); *Tectonic map of the USSR*, sixteen sheets at 1:2.5M, with legend in English; and the *Atlas SSSR* in Russian.

372 Collins, Sons, and Company Limited, London, publishes one series of especial interest to geographers and cartographic works. The series is *The new naturalist: a survey of British natural history*, edited by a number of experts, some titles having gone into new editions. As the series has progressed, the idea of conservation of wild life and natural conditions has been stressed; number 49 is Sir Dudley Stamp: *Nature conservation in Britain*. The photographic editor, Eric Hosking, has included magnificent studies, some in colour, and there are usually maps in the text, varying in number according to the topic; the texts are of high standard and eminently readable, the overall production also being pleasing, including some very useful bibliographies. A few titles of particular interest are J A Steers: *The sea coast*, 1953, fourth edition, 1969, dealing with the relation of the coast to the general structure of Britain, followed by examination of the factors which develop different kinds of coasts and studies of contrasting coastal forms in all parts of Britain; L A Harvey and D St Leger-Gordon: *Dartmoor*, 1953, second edition, 1962, 1963, 1970, covers all parts of the moor; S W Wooldridge and Frederick Goldring: *The Weald*, 1953, 1966, deals similarly with the origin and development of this unique region; Sir Dudley Stamp contributed also *Man and the land*, 1955, third edition, 1969, a follow-up to his *Britain's structure and scenery*, number 4 in the series, and, with W G Hoskins, *The common lands of England and Wales*. Other particularly relevant titles include H J Fleure: *A natural history of man in Britain*; Gordon Manley: *Climate and the British scene*; and K C Edwards:

The Peak District. The second main value of Collins publications for geographers lies in atlas production. *Collins world atlas*, 'an atlas for the person who cares about the world we live in and who wishes to know more of the background to today's events', contains general, regional and thematic maps. Collins-Longmans have published a graded series of educational atlases—*Atlas 1*, for the youngest scholars; *Atlas 2*, in a second edition, 1967, for upper primary or junior secondary school use; *Atlas 3, Atlas 4* and *Atlas advanced* for CSE, fifth form and o level, and for sixth form, college and university, respectively. The latter, 1968, contains seventy-two pages of thematic maps drawn from the researches of leading geographers, with a forty-two page section on the world's climate, vegetation and resources and country by country graphs of the world's produce. Educational atlases include also the *Study atlas* and the *Visible regions atlas* and special editions prepared for Malaysia (in Malay), Thailand, Kenya, Malawi, Sierra Leone and Australia.

373 The Colombo Plan, initiated by a number of Commonwealth foreign ministers, who met in 1950 with the aim of planning co-operative economic development of south and south east Asia, following the difficulties created by the second world war, established a Consultative Committee and a Colombo Plan Council, the former consisting initially of Ministers from Australia, Britain, Canada, Ceylon, India, New Zealand and Pakistan. Subsequently, with the increase of the area under discussion from Iran to South Korea and from the Maldive Islands to Indonesia, membership of the Council was also increased; it meets annually at Colombo. The Consultative Committee is the senior policy-making body, meeting annually to review economic, technical and cultural progress. The Colombo Plan Bureau consists of an international staff of a Director and three officers; their function is to service the Council for Technical Co-operation, to record all technical assistance given to areas under the Plan and generally to disseminate information, acting also as a centre through which countries can initiate special regional programmes. A journal is issued, *The Colombo Plan.*

> *Refer also*
> Frederic Benham: *The Colombo Plan and other essays* (OUP for the Royal Institute of International Affairs, 1956).

374 'Columbia-Lippincott gazetteer of the world', edited by Leon E Seltzer, was a joint project by the Geographical Research Staff of

222

Columbia University Press and the American Geographical Society (Columbia UP; Oxford UP, 1952). The second printing, with supplement, brings the work up to date to the end of 1960. Articles are included on the nations, continents, regions and major cities of the world, with shorter notes on towns and villages; descriptions are given of geographic features, also the essential facts on such aspects as population and products. The first part of the supplement is a series of articles on the major political changes in the world since 1952; the second part lists figures for all towns in the United States with a population of over a thousand. Frequent cross-references are made and the work is thumb-indexed.

375 'Columbus' (Allen and Unwin, 1967) traces 'the story of Don Cristóbal Colón, Admiral of the Ocean, and his four voyages westward to the Indies according to contemporary sources retold and illustrated by Björn Landström'. Details are taken from the journals, from the letters to Ferdinand and Isabella and from other primary sources, superbly complemented by full colour illustrations and maps.

The Columbus Collection in the Berio Library, Genoa, begun in 1892, is today the centre for research on the voyages and discoveries of Columbus. Its carefully edited catalogue is a valuable bibliographic tool also for the early exploration of America.

Refer also

Christopher Columbus: documents and proofs of his Genoese origin (City of Genoa, 1932).

The journal of Christopher Columbus, translated by Cecil Jane (Anthony Blond, 1968).

Select documents illustrating the four voyages of Columbus, translated and edited by Cecil Jane (Hakluyt Society, two volumes, 1930).

Jean Merrien: *Christopher Columbus: the mariner and the man* (Odhams, 1958, translated from the French by Maurice Michael).

G E Nunn: *The geographical conceptions of Columbus* (American Geographical Society, 1924).

E G R Taylor: 'The navigating manual of Columbus', *Journal of the Institute of Navigation*, January, 1952.

The bibliography of the first letter of Christopher Columbus describing his discovery of the New World, compiled by R H Major, 1872, has been reprinted by The Meridian Publishing

Company, Amsterdam, together with a facsimile of Columbus' letter published at Basle, 1494.

L A Vigneras: *The journal of Christopher Columbus* (Blond, 1960, translated by C Jane).

376 'Commons and village greens: *a study in land use, conservation and management based on a national survey of commons in England and Wales 1961–1966'* was edited by D R Denman and others (Hill, 1967), financed by the Nuffield Foundation. Management schedules for many types of land are discussed, followed by a more detailed description of individual special areas, such as 'Livestock husbandry on Dartmoor and the commons of Devon'. The text also includes appendices on the conduct of the surveys and a glossary of special terms used, illustrated by photographs and maps.

Refer also

William C Found: *A theoretical approach to rural land use patterns* (Arnold, 1971).

377 The Commonwealth Agricultural Bureau, Farnham Royal, Buckinghamshire, was established as a co-operative venture providing a scientific information service for agricultural research workers. This is done mainly through abstracts of world literature covering the whole range of agriculture, agricultural economics, food science and technology, animal health and nutrition and forestry. The CAB comprises the following institutes: Commonwealth Institute of Entomology, Commonwealth Mycological Institute, Commonwealth Institute of Biological Controls and the Commonwealth Bureaux of Agricultural Economics, Animal Health, Animal Nutrition, Dairy Science and Technology, Forestry, Helminthology, Horticulture and Plantation Crops, Pastures and Field Crops, Plant Breeding and Genetics and of Soils. The CAB came into existence in its present form in 1929. Most of the Bureaux are located at a research institute working in the same field and library facilities are shared. Many overseas contacts are maintained and numerous publications issued, of which those of most value to geographers are probably the eighteen abstract journals, including *World agricultural economics and rural sociology abstracts, Dairy science abstracts, Herbage abstracts* and *Forestry abstracts.*

378 The Commonwealth Geographical Bureau project arose from the discussions of a meeting of Commonwealth geographers attending the 21st International Geographical Congress in New Delhi. The immediate establishment of a small Commonwealth Geographical Bureau and committee management was agreed; the recommended terms of reference included the study and practice of geography at all levels within the Commonwealth, the dissemination of information by means of a *Bulletin* and exchange of geographic staff. The Bureau has given priority to making contact with university geography departments and other higher education institutions, and was reconstituted at a meeting in Montreal during the 1972 IGU Congress.

379 The Commonwealth Institute, London, is concerned with the human aspects of Commonwealth relations and with the promotion of reciprocal knowledge and understanding. Its function is therefore educational and it carries out its ideals by means of the exhibition galleries, the cinema, the library, publications and travelling exhibitions. Talks to school classes are arranged and a Schools Advisory Service provides information and advice of all kinds. Publications include *Pamphlets* and *Papers* on aspects of the Commonwealth; and *Fact sheets on the Commonwealth*, which vary in size from four to twelve pages, giving important information on individual countries, with maps.

Refer also

J K Thompson: 'The new Commonwealth Institute after ten years', a paper given to The Royal Society . . . of Arts . . . and printed in the *Journal*, December 1972.

380 Commonwealth Scientific and Industrial Research Organisation (CSIRO), Canberra, the principal official scientific research body in Australia, is recognised as of world importance in soil research, pasture problems and basic research for industry. The work of the various divisions, such as the Northern Australia Regional Survey, 1946, and the Land Research and Regional Survey Section and its successors, 1950–, has been of central interest to geographers and the Organisation's publications are of the first importance, frequently produced as technical papers in such journals as *Australian journal of agricultural research* and the *Australia journal of applied science*. There are also the special series 'Land research' and 'Soil publication'; most issues are illustrated and include bibliographies; also *Arid Zone newsletter*, 1971–, annually. Closely associated with the CSIRO research is the Waite Agricultural Research Institute of the University of Adelaide, founded in 1925. As the Organisation has increased the scope of its activities, more specialised divisions have come into being, such as the Wheat Research Unit at Sydney, the Sugar Research Unit, Melbourne, Dairy Research at Melbourne, Fisheries and Oceanography at Cronulla, etc.

381 'Commonwealth survey', a record of United Kingdom and Commonwealth affairs, is a fortnightly factual listing of important developments in British and Commonwealth projects, trade and industry; the index cumulates into a useful source of reference.

382 'Concise encyclopedia of explorations', compiled by Jean Riverain (Collins; Follett, English language edition, 1969, for the Librairie Larousse, 1966), and re-edited by Miss P Bascom, is a mine of information about explorers and early discoveries. Salient facts given in the entries are strictly confined to geographical journeys and discoveries. The translation was made by Thérèse Surridge, with an introduction by Sir Vivian Fuchs and, throughout the text are small monochrome illustrations and a few maps.

383 'A concise glossary of geographical terms' was compiled by J C Swayne (Philip, third edition, 1968), honorary secretary of a committee of professional geographers set up by the British Association and the Royal Geographical Society to provide agreed definitions of geographical terms. Pending the completion of the *Glossary of geographical terms* (*qv*) by this committee, this work was issued, containing brief definitions, intended mainly for students and based on terms used in national geographical examination papers and in standard geographical works.

384 Conference on the History of Cartography: Theme—'Early maps as historical evidence' was held at the House of the Royal Geographical Society, London, 1967. The Programme included papers on 'A 13th-century plan from Waltham Abbey, Essex'; 'An early Tudor sketch map'; 'Scottish large-scale plans: their value for studying the evolution of the Scottish rural landscape'; 'The value of early maps as evidence for English urban topography'; 'Les plus anciens plans de villes granés et les événements militaires'; 'Estate maps as historical evidence: the example of Shapwick, Somerset'; 'Early maps as a source for the study of field systems with special reference to the West Riding of Yorkshire'; 'The maps of the Ancien Cadastre as evidence for the study of France in the early nineteenth century';

'The "Blathwayt" Atlas: maps used by British colonial administrators in the time of Charles II'; 'Nineteenth century maps of Palestine: dual-purpose historical evidence'; 'The historical variations of
Spurn Point: the evidence of early maps'; 'The growth of Orford Spit:
cartographic and historical evidence from the 16th century'; 'Some
episodes in the early history of the Six-Inch Ordnance Map'; 'Levels
of historical evidence in early maps (with examples)'; 'Maps as
sources for the study of land use in the past'; 'The evaluation of early
maps: toward a method'; 'Surrey estate plans'; 'The tithe surveys';
'Estate maps in Public Record Office of Northern Ireland'.

385 'Connaissance du monde', an interesting monthly journal begun
in 1955 by the Société d'Edition Géographique et Touristique, Paris,
includes articles, notices of books, films and records; it is frequently
illustrated and is indexed.

386 'Contemporary China: a research guide', by Peter Berton and
Eugene Wu and edited by Howard Koch, jr (The Hoover Institute on
War, Revolution and Peace, Stanford University, 1967; Hoover Institution bibliographical series, XXXI), includes bibliographical and
reference works, selected documentary materials and serial publications dealing mainly with the social sciences and humanities; more
than two thousand entries concern post-1949 mainland China and
post-1945 Taiwan. Each chapter and sub-section is preceded by an
introduction placing its bibliographical material in proper context.
Entries are annotated in detail and contain descriptive and evaluative comment. Appendices contain a list of publications devoted to
the resources of research libraries and institutions in the United
States and abroad, and a selected list of directories and theses on
contemporary China accepted by American universities. Four categories of works are distinguished: general and subject bibliographies, lists and indexes of newspapers and periodicals; general
reference works; and selected documentary materials in law,
government, economics, education and foreign relations; selected
serial publications from the mainland, Taiwan, Hong Kong,
Japan, the United States and the USSR. Two special lists are included: of descriptive accounts and catalogues of research libraries
and institutions throughout the world and of doctoral and masters'
theses.

387 'Contributions to bibliography of Australia and the South Sea

Islands', compiled by Willem C H Robert in five volumes (Amsterdam: Philo Press, 1967–), includes invaluable material arranged upon the following plan. In volume I, printed matter relating to discovery, exploration and travel issued in the Netherlands to 1921, with special emphasis on lesser known material, was made available by the author in 1964 in a limited edition, with a second edition in 1969; volume II consists of an *Index and bibliography of Dutch manuscripts and manuscript charts relating to the discovery*, 1968; volume III—*Printed material relating to discovery, exploration and travel, issued in Europe, except the Netherlands, to 1835*, again, first available in a limited edition, 1967, later revised and enlarged; volume IV, *Printed material relating to discovery, exploration and travel, issued in Europe, except the Netherlands, 1836–1921;* and volume V, *Charts and maps relating to Australia and the South Pacific issued in Europe to 1921*. The aim of these reference bibliographies and indexes was to enable the research worker in the field of Pacific history, geography and discovery to trace numerous references and facts pertaining to the subject. Within the volumes, arrangement is by alphabetical order of authors' names, and each concludes with indexes and lists, with cross references.

388 The Copper Development Association, Radlett, Hertfordshire, set up in 1933 to compile and distribute technical information, is typical of the specialist bodies whose work and publications are so vital to economic geographers. Books, pamphlets and brochures are produced at intervals, but of particular importance are *Copper*, issued three times a year, covering all aspects of the use of copper and its alloys, and *Copper abstracts*, a monthly selection of abstracts from over 120 technical and other periodicals and from relevant books, supplemented on occasion by abstracts from other abstracting services.

389 Coradi, G, Limited, of Zurich, is one of the most influential instrument-making firms in the world. Some recent machines include the 'Coradograph', precision coordinatograph for use in surveying and industry; the 'Automatic High-Precision Coordinatograph with Linear Interpolation Unit'; the 'Digimeter' in several forms, a data acquisition instrument developed by Coradi in collaboration with expert surveyors and the 'Electronic Coordinate Digitizing Unit' by which data are transferred in digital form to the data output units using punched cards or punched tape as data carrier. There is also the 'Coradomat' automatic drafting machine and numerous other models, many of them new designs using magnetic or punched tape.

390 Cornish, Vaughan (1862–1948) was a geographical scholar of wide interests, who, by his many papers and published books, as well as through his influence in the course of work with section E of the British Association and with the Geographical Association and other bodies, exerted great influence on the rising generation of young geographers. His first major work, *The great capitals: an historical geography*, published in 1923, aroused considerable interest. He made a special study of wave formations and used his great geographical knowledge to illuminate the appreciation of natural scenery, a theme to which he devoted much of his later life. Notable among his publications are also *National parks*, 1930; *The poetic impression of natural scenery*, 1931; *The scenery of England*, 1932; *Scenery and the sense of sight*, 1935; *The preservation of our scenery*, 1937; *The scenery of Sidmouth*, 1940; *The beauties of scenery: a geographical survey*, 1943. A selected bibliography is appended to a lecture delivered to the Oxford Preservation Trust by Edmund W Gilbert, 'Vaughan Cornish 1862–1948 and the advancement of knowledge relating to the beauty of scenery in town and country' (The Trust, 1965).

391 The Corona Library (HMSO) was a series of pleasantly produced monographs, each on a country of the Commonwealth—*Sierra Leone*, by Roy Lewis, 1954; *Nyasaland*, by Frank Debenham, 1955; *British Guiana*, by Michael Swan and *Jamaica* by Peter Abrahams, both 1957; *Uganda*, by Harold Ingrams and *North Borneo*, by K Tregonning, both 1960; *Fiji*, by Sir Alan Burns, 1963. The last volume in the series was Austin Coates: *Western Pacific Islands* (HMSO, 1971). They are illustrated with photographs and maps.

392 'Cosmographei oder Beschreibung aller Länder Stetten', by Sebastian Münster, 1544, is regarded as the first of this type of geographical encyclopedia, marking the peak of Renaissance geographical knowledge. The work went through thirty-six editions in six languages during the following century. Münster's aim was to provide a 'Compendium and brief description of all the lands of the Earth', using all available sources—the Bible, classical works, the comments of contemporary travellers and the reports of such explorers as Marco Polo, Columbus and Vespucci. The result was a glorious collection of geographical, topographical, historical, genealogical, ethnographical, anthropological data—both fabulous tale and scientific fact. The numerous maps and illustrations are a delight and the whole production has provided source material of all kinds for later scholars. Theatrum Orbis Terrarum Limited has now published a facsimile of the first edition, Basel, 1550, from the copy preserved in the Sächsische Ländesbibliotek, Dresden, with a new introduction in German and English by Professor Dr Ruthardt Oehme. It is in 'A series of early books on the history of urbanization', as part of the *Mirror of the world*, and is bound in facsimile leather and boxed.

393 'Countries of Europe as seen by their geographers', compiled by E C Marchant (Harrap, 1971), under the auspices of The Council of Europe *Education in Europe* series, the result of conferences sponsored by The Council for Cultural Co-operation, comprises a series of articles by eminent European geographers in which each outlines the manner in which he would have his country's geographical characteristics presented.

Refer also

Norman J G Pounds: *An historical geography of Europe, 450 BC–AD 1330* (CUP, 1973).

D I Scargill, *ed: Problem regions of Europe* (OUP, five volumes, 1973; further volumes to follow).

M R Shackleton: *Europe: a regional geography* (Longmans, seventh edition revised by Professor W Gordon East, 1964).

394 The Countryside Commission, under the Countryside Act 1968, replaces and assumes the functions of the National Parks Commission. The Commission selects and designates national parks and areas of outstanding natural beauty and draws up proposals for long-distance footpaths and bridleways, acts as the central source of advice on the provision of other recreational areas and makes recommendations on the distribution of grants from the Ministry of Housing for amenity purposes; it is also empowered to do research itself or in conjunction with other relevant bodies, such as the Nature Conservancy, Forestry Commission, British Waterways Board, Water Resources Board and others. A central information system, based on feature cards, is maintained and a monthly newsletter, *Recreation news*, is produced.

395 **'County atlases of the British Isles 1579–1703: a bibliography'**
compiled by R A Skelton (Map Collectors' Circle; Carta Press, 1964,
1970), was intended to provide a basic bibliography of the maps in
the county atlases of the British Isles from Elizabethan to mid-
Victorian times, a project interrupted by Dr Skelton's death at the
end of 1970. Donald Hodson, collaborator in the continuation of the
bibliography after 1703, will, it is hoped, complete the work, which,
to a certain extent, replaces Thomas Chubb: *The printed maps in the
atlases of Great Britain and Ireland* . . . (*qv*). The first volume deals
with the period from the publication of the *Atlas of England and
Wales* by Christopher Saxton to the maps prepared for Bishop
Gibson's 1695 edition of Camden's *Britannia* (*qv*), comprising 124
county atlases. The cartographic history of each item is given, including commentary and bibliographic sources as necessary. Additions
to the original work were made on publication: 'Maps of parts of the
British Isles in general atlases before 1650: a select list' and 'The
London map trade before 1700; with a biographical list of London
map-publishers'. The volume is generously illustrated and indexed.
   Refer also
      G Walters: 'Engraved maps from the English topographers
   c1660–1825', *The cartographic journal*, December 1970.

396 **'The crossing of Antarctica:** *The Commonwealth Trans-
Antarctic Expedition 1955–58'*, by Sir Vivian Fuchs and Sir Edmund
Hillary (Cassell, 1958; second edition, 1959), presents the full story
by the leader of the expedition and Sir Edmund Hillary, leader of the
New Zealand support party. There are coloured and monochrome
photographs and some sketchmaps in the text.

397 **'The culture of cities',** an exhaustive survey and a pioneer work,
remains probably Lewis Mumford's greatest achievement (Secker
and Warburg, 1938); it is eminently readable and the extensive,
annotated bibliography and illustrations add to its usefulness as a
source book. Other outstanding works by Mumford on similar
themes include *The story of Utopias: ideal commonwealths and social
myths*, 1923; *Technics and civilization*, 1934; *The city in history: its
origin, its transformations and its prospects* (*qv*); and *City development: studies in disintegration and renewal*, 1945.
   Refer also
      J C Russell: *Medieval regions and their cities* (Newton Abbot:
   David and Charles, 1972).

398 'A cumulation of a selected and annotated bibliography of economic literature on the Arabic-speaking countries of the Middle East, 1938–1960', prepared by the School of Oriental and African Studies, University of London, from the Bibliography issued by the Economic Research Institute, American University of Beirut. Selected, annotated and classified lists of articles, books, reports and official documents in English, French and Arabic amount to about 9,600 entries, the emphasis being on English-language material. The work has been reproduced by G K Hall.

399 'Current European directories', compiled and edited by G P Henderson, was published in 1969 by CBD Research Limited, Beckenham, Kent, in English, French and German. Here is a representative selection from the compiler's records of several thousand titles of directories published in Europe, based on personal assessment of contents or inspection of recent editions, response of publishers to questionnaires and the validity of bibliographical information available on those not actually inspected.

400 'Current geographical publications' is the record of additions to the Research Catalogue of the American Geographical Society, begun in 1938 by Elizabeth Platt and still the responsibility of the librarian and library staff. Ten issues a year are published, in which references to periodical articles as well as books, pamphlets, government documents and maps are arranged according to the classification system used in the Research Catalogue; regional placing takes preference over thematic.

The four sections in each issue run as follows: Topical, Regional, Maps and Selected Books. Prior to 1964, entries for maps were included in sections I and II. Material in the Topical section is arranged according to the abridged subject classification, as printed on a foldout back cover; this applies in general to sections II and III. Until September 1972, section I (formerly called General) contained references on the general aspect of Geography, but it has since been expanded to include a selection of citations heretofore found only in section II, Regional, arranged in accordance with the Systematic Classification scheme. Section IV is an alphabetical listing, by author; each book in this last section is also listed elsewhere in the bibliography under the appropriate topical or regional category. The original editions of volumes 1–28 are out of print, but have been reprinted by Kraus Periodicals, Inc, New York.

401 'Cyclopedia of New Zealand' in six volumes (The Cyclopedia Company, 1897–1908) includes industrial, descriptive, historical and biographical information, with figures and other illustrations throughout the text. Each province is treated separately; each volume has four separate indexes and the whole work may be useful in suggesting ideas towards a historical geography of New Zealand.
Refer also
> D J Hooton, *ed*: *New Zealand: the physical environment* (Auckland UP; OUP, 1970).

402 'Czechoslovakia: a bibliographic guide', compiled by Rudolf Sturm, is one of the great number of special bibliographies produced by the Library of Congress, Slavic and Central European Division. Published in 1967, the work is in two parts: the first consists of chapters dealing with bibliographies, general and reference works, 'The land', 'Its peoples', 'History', 'Politics and government', 'Law', 'The economy' and 'Social conditions'. The second part consists of a bibliographic listing of items discussed.
Refer also
> J Demek *et al*: *Geography of Czechoslovakia* (Prague: Academia, Publishing House of the Czechoslovak Academy of Sciences, 1971).
> H G Wanklyn: *Czechoslovakia: a geographical and historical study* (Philip, 1954).
> W Wynne: *The population of Czechoslovakia* (US Government Printing Office, 1953).

403 'The Daily Telegraph world atlas', edited by D L Baker, comprises seventy-eight pages of maps provided by the Esselte Map Service of Sweden. The maps are political and physical, showing railways, but only one category of roads, which gives therefore rather an inadequate impression. Included are three pages of statistics and a section 'Space supplement' compiled by Dr A R Michaelis.

404 'The Dartmoor bibliography: non-fiction', compiled by J V Somers Cocks and published by the Dartmoor Preservation Association, 1970, is 'an attempt to fill the need for an up-to-date reference to the printed literature of the area', the first reasonably comprehensive bibliography since Rowe's *Perambulation of Dartmoor*, 1896. The first part is a listing of books and pamphlets, arranged under authors' names, the entries appending annotations as necessary. Relevant periodicals, handbooks, guidebooks and directories are named, but not individual articles. The entries in the second section are arranged under subject headings and here more than two hundred additional articles and papers are included. In addition to its intrinsic value, this work has been mentioned as an example of bibliographical studies undertaken by local societies in Britain, providing key documents for the local geographer.

Refer also

Crispin Gill, *ed: Dartmoor: a new study* (Newton Abbot: David and Charles, 1970).

405 David and Charles, publishers, of Newton Abbot, Devon, issued their first complete catalogue in 1969; supplements are circulated at intervals, also special communications, such as 'Christmas news'. The firm publishes books on history, geography, natural history, travel and transport, topography and local history, with special emphasis on borderline subjects, to 'bridge gaps', such as that between geography and history or between history and industrial archaeology. They are also the European representatives of the Smithsonian Institution Press. Series include 'Industrial archaeology of the British Isles'; 'Railway holiday', for example, in France, in Switzerland; 'Railway history'; 'Railway histories of the world'; 'Railway history in pictures'; 'Inland waterway history'; 'Industrial history'; 'Industrial history in pictures'; 'Canals of the British Isles'; 'A regional history of the railways of Great Britain' in several volumes; 'Studies in historical geography', edited by Alan Baker and J B Harley; 'Problems in modern geography', edited by Professor Richard Lawton; 'Industrial Britain'; 'Islands'; 'The many worlds of wildlife'; 'Ports of the British Isles'; 'Old . . .', for example, 'Old Liverpool', 'Old Mendip'. A special line is naturally concerned with the West Country, such as *Geology explained in South Devon and Dartmoor*. The *Focus* series, edited by Alice Taylor, published in co-operation with the American Geographical Society, is designed to provide concise up-to-date readable reports on developing areas of the world, emphasising the interaction of environment and economic, social and political forces in the regions as a whole and in individual countries. Each book opens with several chapters dealing with problems common to the nations making up the area. A discussion of individual nations is then followed by case studies which examine in greater detail any projects of special significance. 1969–70 saw the production of paperback editions. Important reprints include Camden's *Britania; Murray's Handbook for Devon and Cornwall*, 1859, and *Murray's Handbook for Scotland*, 1894; *Baedeker's Russia*, 1914, with *Teheran, Port Arthur and Peking: a handbook for travellers; The Royal English atlas: eighteenth century county maps of England and Wales; Annals of coal mining and the coal trade,* by R L Galloway, in two volumes, 1898 and 1904; the classic, *Dartmoor,* by R Hansford Worth; and a *Reprint of the first edition of the One Inch Ordnance survey of England and Wales.* Journals published include *Industrial archaeology* and *Maritime history.* The firm has recently taken over the book club, Readers Union, with its magazine, *Readers news* and has a book and record shop in London.

406 Davis, William Morris (1850–1934), Professor of Physical Geology at Harvard from 1893, exercised one of the greatest influences on modern geomorphology. His conclusions, expressed in some five hundred pages, were strongly criticised both at the time and later, but his theories concerning cycles of denudation and erosion are still fundamental, though modified by later research. *Geographical essays*, 1909, included papers on normal erosion and on desert, coastal and glacial erosion, also papers on education; an unabridged republication of this collection was issued by Dover Publications and Constable in 1954.

407 'The dawn of modern geography: *a history of exploration and geographical science from the conversion of the Roman Empire to A D 900, with an account of the achievements and writings of the Christian, Arab and Chinese travellers and students',* by C R Beazley, published in three volumes by Murray, 1897–1906 (reprinted in New York by Pater Smith, 1949), was a monumental work dealing with the history of geographical exploration and scholarship from the fourth century to the early fifteenth century. The chapters on the history of medieval cartography remain particularly valuable.

408 de Gruyter, Walter, and Company, Berlin, publish many scholarly works in the fields of geography, geology and cartography and are notable to geographers particularly for the series of monographs which make up the *Lehrbuch der allgemeinen geographie* (*qv*). Other works of considerable importance are R Maack: *Kontinentaldrift und geologie des Südatlantischen Ozeans,* 1969; Richard Finsterwalders and others: *Photogrammetrie,* 1963–1968; Horst Falke: *Die Geologische Karte . . .,* 1969; *Kartographische Geländedarstellung* (*qv*); Martin Schwind: *Das Japanische Inselreich . . .,* in three volumes, 1967–; Hans-Günter Gierloff-Emden: *Mexico: eine landskunde,* 1969; Viktor Heissler: *Kartographie,* 1968. The firm publishes also *Die Erde . . .,* the *Hamburger Geographische Studien . . .* and the *Hamburger Geophysikalische Einzelschriften.*

409 de Martonne, Emmanuel (1873–1955) became the leading French geographer after the death of Paul Vidal de la Blache, whose student and son-in-law he was. His major interests lay in physical and regional geography and, through his academic work at Rennes, Lyon and the Sorbonne, where he directed the Institut de Géographie, 1927–1944, and by his publications, he exerted a permanent influence on these two aspects of geography. He was elected an honorary president for life to the International Geographical Union, to which his support was invaluable. His chief published work was the *Traité de géographie physique* (*qv*); he contributed the *Europe Centrale* volume to the *Géographie universelle* (1930–31), also the volume dealing with the physical geography of France, 1942 and *Geography in France* to the American Geographical Society Research series, 1924.

410 Debenham, Frank (1883–1965) led a varied life, both practical and academic; his wide interests in both arts and sciences, his vital personality and his gift for exposition are revealed in his writings and in the even more numerous works which he directed, edited or to which he contributed. He specialised in geology and went as geological expert with Captain Scott to the Antarctic, where he carried out research on the geology of Granite Harbour; he subsequently became a founder-member and, in 1925, first Director of the Scott Polar Research Institute. He was then at Cambridge and in 1931 he became first professor of geography there, exerting great influence on Cambridge academic geography. After publishing his polar researches, he wrote on many subjects. Greatly concerned to encourage cartographical knowledge and use, he wrote *Map making: surveying for the amateur,* which went into a third edition in 1955 (reprinted 1963); and he was one of the first geographers in Britain to see the possibilities of the new experiments in three-dimensional cartography, demonstrated, for example, in Harrap's *3-D junior atlas*, which he edited. This interest and his flair for vivid presentation are shown also in *The world is round: the story of man and maps,* first published by the Istituto Geografico de Agostini, Novara, and by Macdonald/Rathbone Books, 1958; in *The McGraw-Hill illustrated world geography* 1960; *The Reader's Digest great world atlas* (*qv*) and *Discovery and exploration . . . (qv)*.

411 'Decorative printed maps of the 15th to 18th centuries' (Spring Books, 1952, 1965) is an edition of *Old decorative maps and charts,* by A L Humphreys, 1926, revised by R A Skelton, with a new text and eighty-four reproductions. Humphreys, a connoisseur of fine books, compiled his work from the collector's point of view and with the interests of the collector in mind. The new edition is intended 'both as a specimen book and as an elementary guide to the study of maps printed from wood blocks or copper-plates . . .'. Individual sections deal with the map as a work of art, the printed map, the map trade, map-collecting and aspects of map features and conventional signs; Ptolemy, woodcut maps; Italian, Netherlands, English, German and French cartography. More than half the volume is devoted to reproductions. Bibliographies are included of reference material on the history of cartography and for each of the special sections.

Refer also

P J Radford: *Antique maps* (Garnstone Press, 1971).

R A Skelton: *Maps: a historical survey of their study and collecting* (University of Chicago Press, 1972).

412 'Deep-sea research and oceanographic abstracts', edited by Mary Sears, of the Woods Hole Oceanographic Institution, and Mary Swallow, of the National Institute of Oceanography, Wormley, Surrey, is a bi-monthly journal founded in 1953 (Oxford: Pergamon Press) at the instigation of the Joint Commission on Oceanography of the International Council of Scientific Unions. Papers are concerned with the results of research, improvements in instruments and new laboratory methods. Book reviews are included and there is a separate 'Instruments and methods' section, 'Abstracts' and a bibliography section.

413 Demangeon, Albert (1872–1940) was one of the great French geographers who trained in history and geography under Paul Vidal de la Blache. His monograph on Picardy, 1905, demonstrated his regional method; *Le déclin de l'Europe*, 1920, followed, then *L'Empire Britannique*, 1923, both of which were translated into English. He contributed to the *Géographie universelle* the first two volumes on the British Isles and that for Belgium, Holland and Luxemburg; *The British Isles*, translated and edited by E D Laborde, was published by Heinemann (third edition, third impression, 1961). His *Problèmes de géographie humaine* went into a fourth edition (Colin, 1952), in which was included a section on Demangeon and his published work. Many papers and notes made his ideas and his scholarship widely known, but perhaps his most lasting contribution to geographical studies lay in his direction, as editor, of the *Annales de géographie* (*qv*). *Les sources de la géographie de la France aux Archives Nationales*, 1905, was reprinted in the USA in 1967.

414 'The demographic yearbook', published annually since 1949, is one of the many United Nations publications essential to the geographer. Besides standard tables giving the latest available details for each country, each volume usually specialises in one particular aspect.

415 'Denmark: collective papers: *some contributions to the geography of Denmark and other topics discussed by Copenhagen geographers'* was edited by N K Jacobsen and R H Jensen (Københavns Universitets Geografiske Institut, 1968) on the occasion of the 21st International Geographical Congress. The papers, illustrated with photographs, sketchmaps, figures and an end section of folded maps, range over many aspects of the geography of Denmark and of Danish geographers. Each paper includes an abstract.
  Refer also
  Geofrafisk tidsskrift, København, 1877–
  Kulturgeografi, Aarhus, 1948–

416 'A descriptive atlas of New Zealand', edited by A H McLintock (Wellington: Government Printer, 1959), was the first systematic atlas of New Zealand, which proved so much in demand that a second edition was put in hand immediately and was issued in 1960. The atlas comprises an analysis and assessment of the country's resources on maps of varying scale; the topographical map is on the scale 1:1M, while maps of geology, soils, population and other factors

238

are mainly on 1:3,200,000. Descriptions accompany each map sheet and a comprehensive text, illustrated by diagrams, graphs, maps and photographs, was contributed by members of various government departments. There is a full gazetteer.

417 'A descriptive atlas of the Pacific Islands, New Zealand, Australia, Polynesia, Melanesia, Micronesia, Philippines', edited by T F Kennedy (Praeger, 1966, 1968), contains monochrome maps by Julius Petro and Lionel Forsdyke, with textual explanation and statistical information.

Refer also

H C Brookfield and Doreen Hart: *Melanesia: a geographical interpretation of an island world* (Methuen, 1971)

Phyllis Mander-Jones, *ed: Manuscripts in the British Isles relating to Australia, New Zealand and the Pacific* (Canberra: Australian National University Pr.; Angus and Robertson, 1972).

A Grenfell Price: *Island continent: aspects of the historical geography of Australia and its territories* (Angus and Robertson, 1972).

418 Desert Development Institute, Tokyo, created in 1971, aims to conduct research studies, tests and experiments, also, when possible, technological improvements for the development of arid and semi-arid land. During the next few years, the following projects are planned: research and collection of data, research into and technological development of equipment and devices for desert development, planning and programming of desert projects, co-operation with relevant overseas organisations and international bodies, publication of papers and reports on desert development and the arrangement of lectures, conferences, research seminars and training courses.

419 'Deserts of the world: *an appraisal of research into their physical and biological environments',* edited by William G McGuinnies, B J Goldman and Patricia Paylore (University of Arizona Press, 1968, second printing 1970), was a United States contribution to the International Hydrological Decade programme. A massive work, it was intended 'for those seriously interested in planning, managing and executing research or development efforts in the arid parts of the world'. The text is prefaced by 'locator maps' of relevant parts of the world, followed by some general comments pertaining to the major deserts. 'Appraisal of research on weather and climate of desert environments'; 'Appraisal of research on geomorphology and surface hydrology of desert environments'; 'Appraisal of research on surface materials of desert environments' continues with examination of vegetation, fauna and desert coastal zones. An appendix gives a 'General summary of the state of research on ground water hydrology in desert environments'. In addition to subject and author indexes, there is an index of scientific names of plants.

Refer also

An inventory of geographical research on desert environments published by the University of Arizona, 1968, for the Office of Arid Zone Studies.

Problems of desert development, prepared by the Academy of Sciences of the Torkmen SSR, Scientific Council of Desert Study and Development (Ashkhabad: 'Nauka'. 1967–).

R A Bagnold: *The physics of blown sand and desert dunes* (Methuen, 1941, a classic).

R U Cooke and Andrew Warren: *Geomorphology in deserts* (Batsford, 1973).

Jean Dresch: 'Utilization and human geography of the deserts', *Transactions*, Institute of British Geographers, December 1966.

K W Glennie: *Desert sedimentary environments* (Elsevier, 1970).

Peveril Meigs: *Geography of coastal deserts* (Unesco, 1966)

Heinrich Schiffers, *ed: Die Sahara und ihre Randgebiete* . . . (München Weltforum Verlag, three volumes, 1971–73).

Martin Simons: *Deserts: the problem of water in arid lands* (OUP, 1967).

Jean Tricart and A Cailleux: *Le modèle des régions sèches* (Paris: Centre de Documentation Universitaire, 1960).

Josef D Zimmerman: *Irrigation* (Wiley, 1966).

420 'Deutscher generalatlas' at 1:200,000 (Mairs Geographischer Verlag, 1967/68) consists mostly of double spreads, many folded. The hill shading and the deeper blues for hydrographic features are effective and roads, place-names and state boundaries stand out well. Much factual information is incorporated, but there is no sense of overcrowding. The town plans included are useful and the whole work is well documented.

421 'Deutscher Planungsatlas' is a superb atlas in ten volumes, 1956–, by the Academy for Area Research and Land Use Planning in Hanover. Scales range from 1:500,000 to 1:1M. The material was organised mainly by the individual states, bringing together a wealth of information based on the latest census data and other relevant sources, arranged as follows: 1, North Rhine-Westphalia; 2, Lower Saxony; 3, Schleswig-Holstein; 4, Hesse; 5, Rhineland-Palatinate; 6, Wurttemberg-Baden; 7, Bavaria; 8, Federal Republic of Germany; 9, Berlin; 10, Hamburg.

Refer also

> W Witt: 'Deutscher Planungsatlas', *International yearbook of cartography*, 1962.

422 'The development of Australia: a study commissioned by the Australian Development Research Foundation, Sydney', by J B Condliffe (Free Press of Glencoe; Collier-Macmillan, 1964), is a closely analysed summary supported by photographs, clear sketch-maps and diagrams, beginning with an introduction to the general setting of Australia from an international point of view, before treating 'The peopling of Australia'; 'Planned migration'; 'Urbanisation'; 'The mineral industry'; 'The search for oil'; 'Water and power'. Manufactures are considered, also transport, national development programmes and the organisation of applied research. Appendices deal with 'Regional development', 'Significant mineral resources', 'Power resources', 'Agricultural development schemes' and 'Water resources'.

Refer also

> Erwin Feeken and Gerda Feeken: *The discovery and exploration of Australia* (Nelson, 1971).

423 'Diary of the 'Terra Nova' Expedition to the Antarctic 1910–1912, of Edward Wilson, was published by the Blandford Press, edited by H G R King and with a Foreword by Sir Charles Wright; it contains detailed accounts of natural phenomena in the region and many of the twenty-seven watercolours included were made public for the first time. In addition to being a document of fundamental importance in the history of Polar exploration, the *Diary* must be highly valued for its revelations of the character of the author himself. Blandford Press have published also his *Diary of the 'Discovery' Expedition to the Antarctic regions 1901–1904*, edited by Ann Savours and *Edward Wilson's birds of the Antarctic*, edited by Brian Roberts.

424 'Diccionario Geografico-estadistico-historico de España' provides an essential guide to the historical geography of Spain (Madrid, second edition, 1846), covering in several volumes also the overseas possessions of Spain.

425 'Dictionary catalog of the Department Library, United States Department of the Interior',** Washington DC, was reproduced in thirty-seven volumes by G K Hall, 1966. These volumes represent more than 724,000 items, published and unpublished, covering the scientific, technical, economic and social aspects of natural resources, land management, mines and mineral resources, including journals and early works, also a unique collection on the American Indians.

426 'Dictionary catalog of the Stefansson Collection on the Polar Regions in the Dartmouth College Library',** Hanover NH, consisting of 120,000 entries, was published in eight volumes by G K Hall, 1966. Historical coverage is the main emphasis of the collection, with primary concern for the history of Polar exploration, Alaskan history, biography, description and travel with various other specialisations. Resources on the Arctic and Antarctic are included, within chronological and geographical limits, while documentation of the international relations aspect of the Polar Regions is included without regard to period. An extensive subject index is a particularly valuable feature of the catalogue.

427 'Dictionary catalogue of the Hawaiian Collection in the Sinclair Library, University of Hawaii',** Honolulu, was published by G K Hall in four volumes, 1963, with a first supplement in one volume. Dating from 1908, this catalogue represents the largest and most complete collection of Hawaiiana, including books, pamphlets and serials. Since 1915, the collection has been a depository for Hawaiian government documents and all are fully catalogued. Special reports and a newspaper clippings file are both included in the catalogue, also the acquired microfilm items.

428 'Dictionary of discoveries',** compiled by I A Langnas (New York: Philosophical Library, 1959) and revised by Peter Owen, provides an interesting and most useful alphabetical listing.

Refer also

L H Parias, *ed: Histoire universelle des explorations* (Paris, three volumes, 1955).

Jean Riverain: *Dictionnaire des explorations* (Larousse, 1968).

429 'A dictionary of geography', by F J Monkhouse (Arnold, 1965; second edition, 1970) included in the first edition about 3,400 entries in one alphabetical sequence, together with an analytical list of entries by subject grouping. The 'main criterion for inclusion has been usage'; current geographical textbooks and periodicals were scanned and those foreign words have been included which have been incorporated into English geographical literature. The new edition contains some six hundred new entries, most of them in the fields of town planning and quantitative research; also metric measures and quantities are given, though imperial equivalents are used where appropriate.

Refer also

Thesaurus des termes géographiques (Paris, 1971).

S J François de Dainville: *Le langage des géographes: termes, signes, couleurs, des cartes anciennes 1500–1800* (Paris: Picard, 1964).

J M Henry *et al: Thésaurus des symboles agrobioclimatiques, géographiques et techniques* (Tervuren, CIDAT, 1972).

W G Moore: *Dictionary of geography: definitions and explanations of terms used in physical geography* (Penguin Books, 1949, reprinted 1950; new edition, revised and enlarged, 1952, 1954, 1956, 1962, 1963; again revised and enlarged, 1967).

S Paré and N Voionmaa: *Thésaurus géographie rurale* (Paris: CNRS, Service de documentation et cartographie géographiquues, 1971).

430 'A dictionary of mapmakers' is a comprehensive work by R V Tooley, including cartographers, publishers and engravers from the earliest times to 1900. Part I (Map Collectors' Circle, volume 2, no 16, part 1) was available to members only but the whole work was eventually made available outside the Circle.

431 'Dictionnaire de géographie ancienne et moderne à l'usage du libraire et de l'amateur de livres', one of the most interesting of the early dictionaries of geography, in two volumes, by Pierre Deschamps, forms part of the supplement to Brunet: *Manuel du libraire* *et de l'amateur de livres*, published between 1860 and 1880. The dictionary includes gazetteer and glossary type entries in one alphabet, with a supplement of additions and corrections and a French index of Latin names; a feature is the references to early printing presses in various towns. The entire work has been reprinted by Rosenkilde and Bagger of Copenhagen.

432 'A dictionary of natural resources and their principal uses', compiled by Nora Jackson and Philip Penn (Oxford: Pergamon Press, 1966; second edition, 1968), examines a comprehensive number of products, mineral and vegetable, together with conditions of growth, users and potentials. The second edition has been up-dated and contains illustrations.

433 'Dictionary of rubber technology', by A S Craig (Butterworth, 1969), includes brief annotations on the meanings of common technical terms used in the natural or synthetic polymer industries. Sketches and diagrams supplement the explanations and there are references to specialised periodicals. Appendices give sources of information about rubber, notes on the composition of the types of products, grouped according to their uses, and a list of special publications.
　Refer also
　Rubber developments.

434 Directorate of Overseas Surveys originated in 1946, in response to the urgent demand for accurate medium-scale maps to assist economic development in many countries. The Directorate helps developing countries overseas at their request in basic surveying and mapping of their territories and co-operates with local survey departments, so that maps may be produced as rapidly and as economically as possible and also that work may cross national boundaries if necessary in order to plan geodetic surveys and air photography on a continental basis. In recent years, as more detailed development plans have been required, large-scale maps have been produced. The Directorate acts also as a centre for the collection and dissemination of technical information on surveying, field survey and mapping; comprehensive map and air photograph libraries are maintained covering overseas territories. Separate sections are concerned with cartography, photography, forestry, land use and resource survey. The Land Resources Division now has eight or more project teams of

244

scientists overseas, while many more projects are at preliminary or final stages. Geology, geomorphology, climatology, soil science, hydrology, irrigation engineering, ecology, forestry, agriculture, livestock husbandry and agricultural economics are among the specialist disciplines represented on the scientific staff. The *Annual reports* are central sources of information on the work of the Directorate; it is in four parts: General view of the year's work by region; Report on activities; Details by countries; Establishment and finance. Summaries and lists are presented in Appendices and a number of folded maps are included in a back cover pocket. A *Fact sheet* is revised as required; a quarterly *Newsletter* is issued and a *Catalogue of maps*, compiled in 1960, is supplemented by monthly lists of additions.

Refer also

K M Clayton, *ed*: *Guide to London excursions*, section 28 (20th International Geographical Congress, London, 1964).

D R Warren: 'Surveys for development', *The geographical magazine*, October 1969.

435 'Director's guide to Europe', a comprehensive business guide to Western Europe and Scandinavian countries, endorsed by the Institute of Directors, London, was compiled by Thornton Cox, 1968, specialists having contributed individual sections. Articles, 'The European Free Trade Association'; the 'European Economic Community'; 'Profit and loss of the Kennedy Round'; 'Doing business with Eastern Europe'; 'The Nordic Council and Nordic cooperation', are followed by chapters on the countries of Europe, each being dealt with in the same sequence and format. A vast amount of factual information has therefore been collected together on raw materials, agriculture, population, trade and exports etc, of practical use to the economic geographer.

436 'Directory of meteorite collections and meteorite research' (Unesco, 1968) was based on information received in reply to two questionnaires; the first was sent by the Unesco Department for the Advancement of Science to government departments and scientific institutions in Member States and the second by the Committee for Museums of Natural History of the International Council of Museums to all museums of natural history affiliated to the International Council. Collections and catalogues of research institutions in forty-nine countries are listed.

437 'Discovery and exploration': *an atlas-history of man's journeys into the unknown*, by Frank Debenham (Hamlyn, 1960), is a profusely illustrated work, for general background interest; a bibliography on explorers and exploration is a useful feature.
Refer also
    Michael Langley: *When the pole star shone: a history of exploration* (Harrap, 1972).
    Organ Olsen: *La conquête de la terre: histoire des découvertes et des explorations depuis les origines jusqu'à nos jours* (Paris: Payot, six volumes, translated by E Guerre, 1933–1937).
    J H Parry: *The age of reconnaissance* (Weidenfeld and Nicolson, 1963).
    Boies Penrose: *Travels and discovery in the Renaissance, 1420–1620* (Harvard University Pr., 1952, second printing, 1955).

438 'The discovery of America', by G R Crone (Hamilton, 1969), in the *Turning points in history* series, sets the main theme against the background of medieval and Renaissance scientific thought and European power politics, including a specially important topic, the Vinland Map controversy and the development of cartographical techniques. An introduction mentions the source material available, following which the characteristics of the medieval world are discussed, Irish and Norse navigation in the Atlantic, the Portuguese achievements and the voyages of Columbus, Amerigo Vespucci and expansion to the recognition of the two Americas. An Appendix, 'Navigation and cartography of the Discovery', provides a useful summary. There are reproductions and sketchmaps throughout the text and a short bibliography, divided within broad subject headings.
Refer also
    United States of America, one of the series of Irish University Press Area Studies, edited by Professor P Ford and Mrs G Ford, with Professor H C Allen.
    Hans Landsberg: *Natural resources for US growth: a study of America's needs up to the year 2000, and of supplies available to meet the demand* (Johns Hopkins Press; OUP, 1965. Paperback summary of resources in America's future . . . , by H H Landsberg *et al*.).
    N J G Pounds, *ed: USA: its geography and growth* (Murray, third edition, 1960).
    C Langdon White *et al: Regional geography of Anglo-America*

(Prentice-Hall, third edition, 1964).

Wilbur Zelinsky: *The cultural geography of the United States* (Prentice-Hall, 1973).

439 'The discovery of North America: *a critical documentary and historical investigation*', by Henry Harrisse, was reproduced by Theatrum Orbis Terrarum in 1969 from the London-Paris edition of 1892. The work is one of the outstanding contributions to the history of American geography, including a study of the early cartography of the New World, a chronology of one hundred voyages westward between 1431 and 1504 and bibliographical accounts of three hundred pilots who first crossed the Atlantic, with a copious list of the original American geographical names.

Refer also

W P Cumming *et al*: *The discovery of North America* (Elek, 1971).

S E Morison: *The European discovery of America: the northern voyages A D 500–1600* (OUP, 1971).

Charles Norman: *Discoverers of America* (New York: Crowell, 1968).

Carl O Sauer: *Sixteenth century North America: the land and the people as seen by the Europeans* (University of California Press, 1971).

L B Wright, *ed*: *English colonization of North America* (Arnold, 1968; 'Documents of modern history series').

440 'Documentatio geographica: Geographische Zeitschriften und Serien-Literatur' (Bad Godesberg, Institut für Landeskunde, 1966–) was first suggested by the Association of German University Teachers of Geography and begun under the auspices of the Institut für Dokumentationswesen of the Max Planck Gesellschaft zür Förderung der Wissenschaften. Bibliographical lists appeared bimonthly from January 1966, later tape-punch typewriters and data processing equipment programming being set up with the assistance of ZMD.

441 'Documentation on Asia' was begun in 1960, edited by Girja Kumar and V Machwe (Allied Publishers, 1963–). It is arranged under regional topics, then again by systematic. Under the auspices of the India Council of World Affairs, an unofficial body founded in

1943 to encourage and facilitate the scientific study of Indian affairs, it is hoped that the work may be kept updated.

442 'Domesday geography of England' is a most interesting reconstruction, by H C Darby and a team of editors, of the social geography and economic life of early medieval England, by interpreting the entries in the Domesday Book (Cambridge University Press, 1952–). The volumes run as follows: 1, Eastern England, 1952, second edition, 1957 third edition, 1971; 2, Midland England, 1954, second edition, 1971; 3, South-east England, 1962; 4, Northern England, 1962; 5, South-west England, 1967.
Refer also
Alan R H Baker and J B Harley, *ed: Man made the land: essays in English historical geography* (Newton Abbot: David and Charles, 1973).

443 'Early charts of New Zealand, 1542–1851' is a magnificent production, compiled by Peter Bromley Malins (A H and A W Reed, 1969), consisting of plates arranged in thirteen sections, with notes opposite each plate. The charts are grouped as Pre-Tasman, Tasman, Post-Tasman and pre-Cook, Cook's officers, French visitors to New Zealand, Vancouver and Makaspina, 1800–1820, 1820–1830, Dumont d'Urville, 1830–1840, Early sheet maps and two Maori charts. An Appendix lists Admiralty Charts, both British and French and there is a bibliography.
Refer also
John O'C Ross: *This stern coast: the story of the charting of the New Zealand coast* (Reed, 1969).

444 Earth Science Editors: the two Associations, European (EDITERRA) and United States, covering North America (AESE), have a Coordinating Council, thus providing an international structure for handling questions of common interest. The International Union of Geological Sciences is also represented on the Council. The Council is working to extend the system to include those parts of the world not already covered by the present associations and to promote the institution of similar ones, as desirable. Affiliation with similar organisations in biology and other sciences is also under consideration.

445 'Earth science reviews', published by Elsevier, Amsterdam, from 1966, is an international journal, presenting review articles relating to mineralogy, igneous and metamorphic petrology, geochemistry, geophysics, volcanology and economic and applied geology. Four issues make a volume.

446 'Earth science symposium on Hudson Bay', edited by Peter J Hood and others (Department of Energy, Mines and Resources, Geological Survey of Canada, 1969), consists of the proceedings of the symposium held in Ottawa in 1968, under the sponsorship of the National Advisory Committee on Research in the Geological Sciences and the Associate Committee on Geodesy and Geophysics of the National Research Council. There are illustrations, maps and diagrams in the text.
>   *Refer also*
>   James Cornell and John Surowiecki: 'State-of-the-earth report from the Smithsonian Institution for Short-lived Phenomena' (Nelson, 1973).
>   T W Donelly, *ed*: *The earth sciences—problems and progress in current research* (University of Chicago Press for William Marsh Rice University, 1964).
>   *Geophysical surveys* (Dordrecht: Reidel Publishing Co., 1972–)

447 'Earthquakes—atlas of world seismicity' (Oxford: Pergamon Press, 1969), edited by C Lomnitz, aims to assemble the basic available data in an accessible form and to 'secure a theoretical foothold for a concept of earthquake risk'.
>   *Refer also*
>   *Earthquake information bulletin* (National Earthquake Center, 1967–).

448 'The East African geographical review' has been published by the Uganda Geographical Association from 1963 as an annual issue; articles and book reviews are the chief features.
>   *Refer also*
>   *The East African economic review* (twice a year, OUP, East African Branch, Nairobi).

449 'East Asia, China, Japan, Korea, Vietnam: geography of a cultural region', by Albert Kolb (Methuen, 1971, translated by C A M Sym from *Ostasien*, 1963), begins with an introduction on the nature of a cultural subcontinent, followed by sections as suitable—'The natural features of East Asia and the East Asian cultural subcontinent'; 'China: the cradle of East Asian culture'; 'Population: society, settlement and economy'; 'The geographical regions of Chinese and central Asian culture'; 'Vietnam: culturally a part of East Asia'; 'Korea: a bridgeland'; 'Japan: the island world'. Coloured maps, some folded, occur throughout the text and there is a copy of 'China, Mongolia and Korea', in the Bartholomew world travel series, in a back cover pocket. A synoptic chronological table dating from about 500,000 BC provides a time scale background and there is a bibliography.

450 'East Midland geographer', founded by Professor K C Edwards in 1954, is produced twice a year by the Department of Geography, University of Nottingham, and is an excellent example of the academic publications which have multiplied in Britain during recent years and which are particularly valuable for local studies. A cumulated index is issued every four years.

451 'Eastern Europe: essays in geographical problems', edited by George W Hoffman (Methuen, 1971), contains papers presented at a conference held at the University of Texas at Austin, April 1969, under the title of 'East Central and Southeast European geography'; the conference had two main aims, to show the wide range of problems within the area of interest to geographers and the state of current geographic research, and also to assess research opportunities, educational exchanges and graduate and undergraduate training. The countries under review included The German Democratic Republic, Poland, Czechoslovakia, Hungary, Romania, Bulgaria, Yugoslavia, Albania and Greece. The editor has provided an introduction to the volume: 'Regional synthesis: an introduction', and the papers are as follows: Norman J G Pounds: 'The urbanization of East-central and Southeast Europe: an historical perspective'; Dean S Rugg: 'Aspects of change in the landscape of East-Central and Southeast Europe'; Jacek I Romanowski: 'Geographic research and methodology on East-Central and Southeast European agriculture'; F E Ian Hamilton: 'The location of industry in East-Central and Southeast Europe'; Thomas M Poulsen: 'Administration and regional structure in East-Central and Southeast Europe'; Fred E Dohrs: 'Nature versus ideology in Hungarian agriculture: problems of intensification'; Jack C Fisher: 'The emergence of regional spatial planning in Yugoslavia: the Slovenian experience'; Orme Wilson, jr: 'The Belgrade-Bar Railroad: an essay in economic and political geography'; Huey Louis Kostanick: 'Significant demographic trends in Yugoslavia, Greece and Bulgaria' and George W Hoffman: 'Regional development processes in Southeast Europe: a comparative analysis of Bulgaria and Greece'. Each paper is followed by comments and notes; statistical tables and sketch-maps are included as required.

452 '**Economic atlas of Ontario**', a fine research atlas, edited by W G Dean (University of Toronto Press, 1969), with the assistance of the Department of Geography of the University, the Government of Ontario and a number of graduate and undergraduate students, is arranged in ten sections—aggregate economy, population, manufacturing, resource industry, wholesale and consumer trade, agriculture, recreation, transportation and communications, administration and reference maps. Data are presented usually in the form of ratios or indices of comparison rather than as absolute numbers. Cartography is varied according to the topic and is generally clear, readily informative and artistically pleasing, under the direction of G J Matthews. Dr Dean's preface describing the evolution and organisation of the project is particularly interesting. Sources and notes are added for each map, usually on the map face or on the reverse. The atlas measures the two principal factors of production and market potential, its major purpose being to provide a useful aid to decision-making in economic affairs. In so doing it presents a record of the current economic geography of the province.

Refer also

W G Dean: 'An experiment in atlas structure: *The economic atlas of Ontario*', *The cartographic journal*, June 1970.

453 '**Economic bulletin for Latin America**', the excellent publication by the Secretariat of the Economic Commission for Latin America, has been published twice a year since 1956, to provide a résumé of the economic situation of the region designed to supplement and bring up to date the information issued in the Commission's annual economic surveys; specialised articles are included on topical issues relative to the economy. Since October 1958, the bulletin has regularly included a 'Statistical supplement'; this subsequently became sufficiently important to warrant separate publication, one issue being prepared for 1960, another for 1961, two for 1962, each bi-lingual.

From 1964, the *Statistical bulletin for Latin America* began regular publication.

Refer also

Egbert De Vries and J M Echavarria, *ed: Social aspects of economic development in Latin America.* Papers submitted to the Expert Working Group on Social aspects of Economic Development in Latin America, Mexico City, December 1960 (Paris: Unesco, 1963).

John R Wish: *Economic development in Latin America: an annotated bibliography* (New York: Praeger, 1966).

M Yudelman and F Howard: *Agricultural development and economic integration in Latin America* (Allen and Unwin, 1970).

454 'Economic geography', published quarterly, 1925–, by Clark University, Graduate School of Geography, Worcester, Mass, is the only English-language periodical devoted to the subject; editorial policy is directed towards geographers, economists, teachers, professional and businessmen and for all others interested in the intelligent use of the world's resources, with the aim of increasing the understanding of the world's economic patterns. A small section of careful reviews is included.

455 'Economic geography of China', by T R Tregear (Butterworth, 1970), emphasises the political development of China during this century, especially since 1949, as an essential background to the geographical description and analysis of the country and its economy. Dr Tregear has drawn his information from first-hand experience of the country and constant monitoring of Chinese journals and reports, carefully sorting facts from propaganda. Numerous illustrations, tables and maps are included in the text; there is a glossary and a selected bibliography.

Refer also

Charles A Fisher: 'Containing China?', *The geographical journal*, December 1970 and September 1971.

Ramon H Myers: *Chinese peasant economy: agricultural development in Hopei and Shantung, 1890–1949* (Harvard University Press, 1970).

456 'Economic implications of the size of nations with special reference to Lebanon', by Nadim G Khalaf (Leiden: Brill, 1971), is an attempt to analyse the economic stability, diversity of production and trade, degree of dependence on foreign trade and economic growth or development of a small nation. Part II of the work applies these theories to the Lebanese economy. A useful bibliography is appended.

457 'Economic, social and political studies of the Middle East', edited by C A O Van Nieuwenhuijze, of the University of Guelph, forms one of a new series published by Brill of Leiden designed as a channel of information taking the form of social scientific publications dealing superficially with contemporary problems of the Middle East. The editorial committee includes a number of specialists on the Middle East, social scientists living in that area and others having particular contributions to make to the series. The text is in English or French.
Refer also
  C A O Van Nieuwenhuijze: *Sociology of the Middle East: a stocktaking and interpretation* (Brill, 1971).

458 'Economic survey of Latin America', published by the United Nations from 1964, annually, supplemented by two issues a year of the *Economic bulletin* (*qv*), presents a comprehensive survey of regional and internal economic developments in Latin America and the impact of world events on the trends of economic growth of the areas from the years 1960 to 1963. Prepared in English and Spanish editions, central themes are on agriculture, manufacturing, energy, industry, transport, housing, commodity trade and the balance of payments.
Refer also
  Harold Blakemore and Clifford T Smith, *ed*: *Latin America: geographical perspectives* (Methuen, 1971).

459 'The economy of Pakistan: *a select bibliography, 1963–65*', compiled by A H Siddiqui, was published by the Pakistan Institute of Development Economics, Karachi, 1967. This bibliography is a continuation of *The economy of Pakistan: a select bibliography, 1947–1962*, published by the Institute in 1963. More than 1,100 entries are included referring to books, government documents, reports, conference literature and articles from periodicals published in Pakistan or abroad, arranged according to a special classification devised by the International Committee for Social Sciences Documentation, with some modifications. There is an author index and a detailed list of periodicals examined.

Refer also

K S Ahmad: *A geography of Pakistan* (OUP Pakistan, 1964; second edition, 1971).

C M Ali: *The emergence of Pakistan* (Columbia University Pr., 1967).

D Dichter: *The north-west frontier of West Pakistan: a study of regional geography* (OUP, 1967).

Herbert Feldman: *Pakistan: an introduction* (OUP Pakistan, second edition, 1969).

Stephen R Lewis, *jr: Economic policy and industrial growth in Pakistan* (Allen and Unwin for The Pakistan Institute of Development Economies, Karachi, 1969).

Mushtaqur Rahman: *Bibliography of Pakistan geography 1947–67*; mimeographed, Karachi University).

A Tayyeb: *Pakistan: a political geography* (OUP, 1966).

460 'The Edinburgh world atlas' or *Advanced atlas of modern geography*, first published by Bartholomew in 1949, with a second edition in 1957, was issued also with *Everyman's encyclopaedia* in 1958 and 1959. It is a useful general purpose reference atlas, comprising world maps for geology, physiography, vegetation, population and ethnology, climate and oceanography and economic geography, also including regional physical maps. Revised editions have followed since 1959, reaching a seventh edition in 1970, in which the world maps have been redrawn; British temperature charts have been restyled and contours removed from the general maps, making for improved clarity. Heights and depths have been converted to metres and temperature charts show degrees centigrade.

461 'Eduard Imhof: werk und wirken'; a festschrift volume for Professor Imhof at the age of seventy-five, was prepared by Hans Hauri and others (Zurich: Orell Füssli Verlag, 1970), with contributions from his colleagues and former students. Professor Imhof will be remembered in particular for his unique influence on the science of cartography and his development of the 'Swiss style'. The emphasis in this book is very much on the combination of artistic qualities and scientific accuracy upon which he insisted in all his work. His drawings, maps and relief models are reproduced throughout the text, showing especially his oblique hill-shading technique. Included is a bibliography of Professor Imhof's works.

462 Education in geography and cartography: During the seventeenth and eighteenth centuries, geographical facts were taught mainly by rote with the utilitarian purpose of furthering some other career, such as navigation, trading or commerce. Texts such as the two following examples, were the basic 'tools' in those days: *A tutor to Astronomie and Geographie, or an Easie and speedy way to know the use of both the Globes Caelestial and Terrestrial*, in six books, the first teaching the 'Rudiments of Astronomie and Geographie'; 2 to 6 'shewing by the globes the solution of problems astronomical, geographical, navigation, astrological, gnomonical and trigonometrical. More fully and amply than hath yet been set forth either by Gemma Frisius, Metius, Hues, Wright, Blaew, or any others that have taught the use of the globes: And that so plainly and methodically that the meanest capacity may at first reading apprehend it, and with a little practice grow expert in these Divine Sciences. With an Appendix shewing the use of the Ptolomaick Sphere'. The second edition, corrected and enlarged, was prepared by Joseph Moxon, Hydrographer to the King's most Excellent Majesty . . . at the Signe of Atlas, 1670; *A new geographical and historical grammar: wherein the Geographical part is truly modern; and the present state of the several kingdoms of the world is so interpreted, as to render the Study of Geography both entertaining and instructive*; containing, I, A description of the figure and motion of the Earth: II, Geographical definitions and problems, being a necessary introduction to this Study: III, A general Division of the Globe into land and Water: IV, The Situation and Extent of the several Countries contained in each Quarter of the World; their Cities, Chief Towns, History, Present State, respective Forms of Government, Forces, Revenues, Taxes, Revolutions, and memorable Events. Together with An Account of the Air, Soil, Produce, Traffic, Curiosities, . . . by Mr Salmon (T Salmon) with twenty-two folding maps, figures and tables, 1749.

The Committee of Council requirement in 1843 that normal schools liable to inspection should include geographical teaching, followed by a Minute in 1846 requiring pupil teachers and stipendiary monitors to have an elementary knowledge of geography gave the first indication in Britain of official recognition of Geography as a subject in its own right, though there was a considerable time-lag, as always, in any improvement in standards of teaching. In 1847, the Council began to issue select lists of books and maps on which a grant was payable; this was indeed a great step forward, but the availability and quality of maps and atlases for teaching were particularly unsatisfactory. The Royal Geographical Society provided the required impetus towards improved teaching standards, especially through its influence on the universities of Oxford and Cambridge, which culminated in 1885 in the publication of the report of J Scott Keltie, 'Geographical education . . .' (*qv*). Britain was compared with Germany, where already at that time twelve university chairs had been established and the subject was compulsory in all schools, largely under the influence of Pestalozzi.

Several trends and developments thereafter worked together to shape the course of modern Geography and to parallel the unprecedented growth of new knowledge with unforeseen concepts within the profession itself. The founding in Paris of the *Annales de géographie* was an event of supreme importance. Not only was it launched with the scholarly aim of avoiding 'nouvelles à sensation', it was typical of a new academic interest in Geography exemplified in an increasing high level periodical literature in many countries and it drew attention to a group of French geographers to whom modern geography owes an incalculable debt. Paul Vidal de la Blache, founder of the *Annales*, and his colleagues changed the exploration-travel-archaeology concept of Geography to one of an analytical and vital discipline, incorporating both imagination and scientific method. The Société de Géographie de Paris had been founded in 1822, with Von Humboldt as one of the founders; his influence had been strong in France, as had that of Ritter, Réclus, Darwin and Wallace. At the same time, the geological and topographical mapping of France, systematic compilation of census and other statistics and the movement towards more complete collection of data were laying the foundation for comparative studies. Vidal de la Blache succeeded to the Chair of Geography at the Sorbonne in 1898 and, in his inaugural lecture, he advocated detailed regional studies to bring together and interpret the complexity of physical, human, historical and economic factors, the keynote of the monumental *Géographie universelle*. While underlining the importance of physiographic studies, he pointed the way to the modern scientific approach to Geography, at the same time stressing the role of man in changing his environment. Lucien Gallois followed Blache; he also had approached Geography through History, having studied *Les géographes Allemands de la Renaissance* for his doctorate thesis, but he soon turned his attention to physical studies and continued the editorial work on the *Nouvelle géographie universelle* after the death of Vidal de la Blache. Many of the leading French geographers of the present century have been pupils of this great geographer; his breadth of vision transformed Geography from a largely static to a dynamic study and his views on the interactions between men and their environments came aptly at the beginning of a period of particular analysis and re-appraisal. His vivid, personal style, allied with erudite exposition, became the model for more than French geographical writing.

Halford Mackinder visited America in 1892. Here also, at Harvard, Princeton and Johns Hopkins, he found Geography an active academic pursuit and he determined to achieve the foundation of a geographical institute in Britain. He addressed meetings on the subject at every opportunity and spoke also at the International Geographical Congress of 1885. Being made President of the Geographical Section of the British Association, he based his Presidential Address on the theme 'Modern Geography: German and English'. His hope had been to see an institute established in London, but this was not found practicable, and Britain's first School of Geography was officially opened in Oxford in October 1899, with Mackinder as Director and A J Herbertson as his Deputy. Progress followed rapidly in many ways: clarification of ideas on subject content, emphasis on first-hand regional study, improvement of geographical publications. The Geographical Association (*qv*) owed its origin to the growing recognition of the need to improve visual aids in geography teaching and its influence began to be fully effective in 1900, when membership became open to all interested in the teaching of geography at all levels. Another significant date was 1918, when the Board of Education approved the inclusion of Geography among the grant-earning advanced courses in secondary schools. Geography has since become one of the foremost subjects in the GCE and comparable examinations, increasing in popularity as teaching methods measured up to the modern concept of the subject and, especially, as greater facilities for local field work and the provision of libraries and equipment have improved.

In spite of the achievement, however, adequate teaching facilities are still as yet not universally available; this fact becomes obvious in discussion with students applying for advanced courses in Geography. The influences of such organisations as the Geographical Association and the Geographical Field Group have been beyond measure and the Further Education Section of the Geographical Association Annual Conference has conducted detailed enquiries into

257

conditions, equipment, incidence of full-time qualified staff and library and map-making facilities in training colleges. Geography textbooks have been under fire since the middle of last century—in 1880, J R Green, the historian, wrote 'No drearier task can be set for the worst of criminals than that of studying a set of geography textbooks such as the children in our schools are doomed to use'. For many years, such texts as existed were restricted to the 'capes and bays' facts at elementary level. Gradually, such publishers as Methuen and Longman, McGraw-Hill and Wiley began to set new standards; co-ordinated series were planned, better produced and illustrated, keeping pace with the new geographical ideas. The Oxford Geographies, Hutchinson Advanced Geographies, Nelson's 'Regions of the British Isles', Murray's 'Life and livelihood' series and many others at various levels began to appear, until now the variety of attractive textbooks is almost overwhelming. To consider the improvement of school textbooks, the Council of Europe held four conferences—at Goslan, 1961; Tenerife, 1962; Bray, Co. Wicklow, 1963; Reykjavik, 1964—to define the qualities desirable, culminating in a final conference in Italy in 1965. Co-ordination of terms in English, French, German, Dutch and Italian was discussed. (*See* under Marchant in the reference section below).

The documentation available for teachers has also rapidly improved. Unesco has given special attention to geography teaching, on the assumption that, as with history and social studies, it is a subject likely to have a strong effect on the formation of children's attitudes towards their own and other countries. Two international seminars were held in 1950, one on the teaching of Geography and one on the improvement of textbooks. Also in 1950, an international seminar was held in Montreal on the teaching of Geography, following which a small group of specialists in co-operation with the International Geographical Union, prepared a study on the improvement of teaching, published in a provisional edition in 1962. In connection with the East-West project, Unesco held three seminars in Tokyo, Paris and Wellington, to examine how eastern geography books dealt with western countries and *vice versa*. Over the same period, in the United States, leading geographers and teaching specialists were concerned with the same problems. A team came together in 1961 to lead study and experiment, from which a general pattern for geography teaching emerged, involving group activities, role-playing games, model building, field work and discussion. Emphasis was on conceptual thinking and the use of 'new' materials.

258

One major practical outcome was the 'Geography in an urban age' one-year, multi-media geography course, prepared by the High School Geography Project of the Association of American Geographers, supported by the National Science Foundation (published information by Macmillan).

The present is a time of further change of emphasis and re-thinking in the study of Geography. The Government report on the subject, 1972, stated in the introduction—'. . . if the geography learned in schools is to be of value in adult life it should awaken an interest in the world of today and provide tools of learning which can be used to understand the world of tomorrow'. During the 1968 General Assembly of the International Geographical Union, the former Commission on the Teaching of Geography was abolished and replaced by the Commission on Geography in Education; the extent of work was expanded, having in mind developments in all parts of the world.

Refer also

Journal of the Scottish Association of Geography Teachers, 1971–.

P J M Bailey: 'The organization and management of Geography Departments in comprehensive schools', *Geography*, July 1972.

John Bale *et al, ed*: *Perspectives in geography education* (Edinburgh: Oliver and Boyd, 1973).

J M Ball *et al, ed*: *The social sciences and geographical education* (Wiley, 1971).

D S Biddle, *ed*: *Readings in geographical education: selections from Australian sources, 1954–* (Whitcombe and Tombs for the Australian Geography Teachers' Association, 1968–).

A Culley: 'The present state of fieldwork in secondary schools: a survey of current practice and opinion in a selected region' (East Midlands), *Geography*, January 1972.

Alice Garnett: 'Teaching geography: some reflections', *Geography*, November 1969.

Norman Graves, *ed*: *New movements: the study and teaching of geography* (Temple Smith, 1972).

N Grenyer: 'An introduction to recent developments in geography teaching: an annotated bibliography', *Geography*, November 1972.

A Hammersley *et al*: *Approaches to environmental studies: a handbook for teachers, students and others interested in the world around them* (Blandford, 1968).

Incorporated Association of Assistant Masters: *The teaching of geography in secondary schools* (CUP, fifth edition, 1967).

David Keeble: 'School teaching and urban geography: some new approaches', *Geography*, January 1969.

E W Lewis: 'The development of geography in the Polytechnics of England and Wales', *The geographical journal*, October 1973.

I L M Long and B S Roberson: *Teaching geography* (Heinemann, 1966).

Clare T Lukehurst and N J Graves, *comp*: *Geography in education: a bibliography of British sources 1870–1970* (Geographical Association, 1972).

E C Marchant, *ed*: *Geography teaching and the revision of geography textbooks and atlases*. Summary report of four Council of Europe Conferences (Strasbourg: Council of Europe, 1967).

E C Marchant: *The teaching of geography at school level* (Harrap, for the Council for Cultural Co-operation of the Council of Europe, 1971).

J W Morris, *ed*: *Methods of geographic instruction* (Waltham, Mass.: Blaisdell, 1968).

M C Naish: *Some aspects of the study and teaching of geography in Britain: a review of recent British research* (Geographical Association, 1972) complements *Geography in education: a bibliography of British sources 1870–1970* (Geographical Association, 1972).

New thinking in school geography (HMSO for the Department of Education and Science, 1972).

A D Nicholls: 'Environmental studies in schools', *Geography*, July 1973).

P A Sauvain: *A geographical field study companion* (Hulton Educational, 1964).

N V Scarfe: *Geography in school* (Normal, Illinois: Illinois State University, National Council for Geographic Education, Publication Centre, 1965).

P R Thomas: 'Education and the new geography', *Geography*, 1970.

Rex Walford, *ed*: *New directions in geography teaching*. Papers from the 1970 Charney Manor Conference (Longman, 1972).

Juliet Williams: 'Technical approach to a geography degree', *The geographical magazine*, October 1973.

L J Wright and J H Jones: 'Geography in the new Polytechnics', *Geography*, April 1972.
Innovation in geography and in university education. Meeting of the Committee of Geography in Education, Bratislava, 1971 *(Acta geographica Universitatis Comenianae Economico-Geographica*, no 12).

The professional training of cartographers, except within the great national and commercial cartographic publishing houses, has developed more recently. An exception has been in France, where the tradition of the ingénieurs des géographes dates from the beginning of the sixteenth century, when the ingénieurs-géographes militaires created the first topographic map of France. The ingénieurs-géographes are graduates of the Ecole Polytechnique who, on admission to the Institut Géographique National, are given two years' training in the Ecole Nationale des Sciences Géographiques run by the Institute. Similar organisations have developed in the Swiss, German and Swedish mapping agencies.

The mapping requirements of the two world wars, however, revealed the weaknesses of lack of co-ordination and of systematic advanced training in cartography. In 1963, the Cartography Sub-Committee of the British National Committee for Geography of the Royal Society established a Working Party to consider the education of cartographers in Britain. Its task has been to examine education in cartography in the United Kingdom in general and, in particular, to prepare for any consideration of the subject by the International Cartographic Association. Defining the scope of training, the Working Party agreed that it ranged from the study of the information collected by surveyors, of any kind, to the final reproduction of maps and charts by any means. The Group estimated that between 3,500 and 4,000 cartographers were currently at work in Britain, with an annual intake of about 250, the majority being civil servants; most of them were draughtsmen, some eight hundred were reproduction staff and the rest professionals of various kinds. In the resulting *Report on education in cartography* issued by The Royal Society in 1965, the Working Party held that 'cartography ranged from the study of information . . .' etc, as above, and agreed that field surveyors and photogrammetrists, along with geologists, botanists, meteorologists, archaeologists and statisticians were not cartographers in this sense. It was found that many training courses treated cartography as synonymous with draughtsmanship and were not concerned with 'printing' and that university geography courses generally included some introduction to the subject, with more or less technology. There was at that date no organised research programme. The Working Party insisted on parallel education in Geography, Measurement, Design and Reproduction.

Discussion of the subject at international level came with the establishment of the Commission of the ICA, 'Training of cartographers', with the terms of reference being 'to collect information on the different systems of training of cartographers now used in all member countries; to collate this information according to the various technical and professional levels and age groups of those under training; and to make this information available in as concise and convenient a form as possible.' Unesco officially gave its support to this suggested line of development by including in its programme at this time the study of the problems arising from education in cartography and the methodology of the preparation of thematic maps. A *Catalogue of Institutions providing instruction in cartography* was prepared by the IGU Commission 'Education in Cartography', distributed at the end of 1968. In 1970, a brochure, 'Typical syllabuses of instruction for the education of cartographers' was issued, also an 'International bibliography for education in cartography'. *See also* British National Committee for Geography: *Education in cartography in the United Kingdom*, 1969.

463 'Education and training in the mapping sciences, a working bibliography', compiled by Harry Steward (American Geographical Society of New York, 1969), consists of sixty pages containing 720 entries on the subject published between January 1955 and December 1969. Surveying and photogrammetry are included.

464 Educational field studies (15 Wulfruna Gardens, Wolverhampton) aims at providing advanced field study courses for students interested in botany, geography and geology. In 1971, field courses were based on Weymouth, for Dorset; on Scarborough, for East Yorkshire; on Malham, for North Pennines; on Llanryst, for Snowdonia; and on Church Stretton, for the Welsh Borderland. A Prospectus is available.

> *Compare: Geographical field classes in Benelux and the Eifel* (Educational Travel Limited, 1971).
> *Refer also*
> *Geography Forum* (Down County Education Office, Belfast).

Reports of the British Schools Exploring Society and the Young Explorers' Trust.

Teaching science out of doors: a collection of teachers' information leaflets (Warne, 1968–).

A Hammersley *et al: Approaches to environmental studies: a handbook for teachers, students and others interested in the world around them* (Blandford Press, 1968).

M F S Hopkins: *Learning through the environment* (Longmans, 1968).

465 'Elements of cartography', by A H Robinson and R D Sale (Wiley, third edition, 1969), has become a 'standard' work since its first publication in 1953. Cartographical teaching and the additions made to the new edition render it even more suitable for modern courses, especially a new chapter 'Compilation from air photography' and much new material bringing the text into line with contemporary thinking. There is a useful bibliography.

466 Elsevier Publishing Company Limited, Amsterdam, has issued many publications of interest to geographers. The House of Elsevier was founded by Louis Elsevier (1540–1619), the son of a printer of Louvain. The family became famous, printing many scholarly scientific works. In 1655, the concern, then directed by Abraham Elsevier III, moved to Amsterdam. For the geographer, the name stands for quality journals, monographs and maps. Periodicals in the geosciences include *Marine geology*, international journal of marine geology, geochemistry and geophysics; *Sedimentology*, journal of the International Association of Sedimentologists, and *Agricultural meteorology*, an international journal with a unique subject content. The *Elsevier oceanography* series and the *Developments in sedimentology* series are particularly valuable. The firm also published the *Reports* of the Soviet Antarctic Expedition, 1955. The looseleaf *Grosse Elsevier atlas*, 1950– is in two folders, with explanatory text containing sketchmaps and diagrams; the *Picture atlas of the Arctic*, compiled by R Thorén, 1969, nine chapters deal with 'The Arctic Ocean', 'Drifting ice stations', 'Arctic Alaska', 'Arctic Canada', 'Greenland', 'Iceland' (the northernmost headland), 'The Norwegian Arctic Islands of Jan Mayen and Svalbard', 'Arctic Scandinavia' and 'The Soviet Arctic'. 567 photographs are included, a location map for each section and some diagrams. *Elseviers weekly* is a valuable check on current publications.

467 'Emerging Southeast Asia: *a study in growth and stagnation'*, by Donald W Fryer (Philip; McGraw-Hill, 1970), aims to assess the role of South East Asia in the modern world: 1, 'The region', dealing with its part in the world economy, land use, urbanisation and industrialisation; 2, 'Progress', considering the natural resources and their use in Thailand, the Philippines, Malaysia and Singapore; 3, 'Stagnation', concerning Indonesia, the Union of Burma, Vietnam, Laos and Cambodia; and 4, 'Prospect', attempting to assess the region's potential trade and regional co-operation. There is a selected bibliography.

Refer also

Iain Buchanan: *Singapore in Southeast Asia: an economic and political appraisal* (Bell, 1972).

P P Courtenay: *A geography of trade and development in Malaya* (Bell, 1972).

S G Davis, *ed*: *Symposium on land use and mineral deposits in Hong Kong, Southern China and South East Asia* (Hong Kong University Press, OUP, 1964).

Bruce Grant: *Indonesia* (Melbourne University Press, new edition, 1966).

Milton E Osborne: *Singapore and Malaysia* (New York: Ithaca: Southeast Asia Program, Department of Asian Studies, Cornell University, 1964).

Charles Robequain: *Malaya, Indonesia, Borneo and the Philippines . . .* (Longmans, second edition, 1961, translated by E D Laborde; in co-operation with the International Secretariat of the Institute of Pacific Relations).

T H Silcock, *ed: Thailand: social and economic studies in development* (Australian National University Press, 1967).

Saw Swee-Hock: *Singapore: population in transition* (University of Pennsylvania Press, 1970).

Jeffrey C Stone: 'Foundations of a Malaysian nation', *The geographical magazine*, May 1970.

468 'Encyclopaedia of Australia', compiled by A T A and A M Learmonth (Warne, 1968), contains more than 2,700 entries and fifty special articles, illustrated, sometimes in colour, as in the case of 'Arms and flags of Australia' and the flora and fauna; there are small black and white maps and drawings in the text. Cross-referencing is helpful and there are frequent guides to further reading at the end of entries; collections and special libraries are included.

469 **'Encyclopaedia of Ireland'**, edited by Victor Meally and others (Dublin: Allen Figgis, 1968), deals with all aspects of the country under broad subject groupings. The text is illustrated and there are bibliographies—'Books and periodicals', 'Transport' 'The land' and 'Agriculture and fisheries' among others.

470 **'An encyclopaedia of the iron and steel industry'**, compiled by A K Osborne and M J Wolstenholme (The Technical Press, 1956, 1967), is a central source of information on the industry. Photographs and diagrams are included throughout the text and references are noted. Particularly useful for reference purposes are the Appendices on 'Conversion tables', 'Weights and measures', 'Properties', 'Signs and symbols' and 'List of scientific, technical and trade societies and other bodies related to the iron and steel industries'.

471 **'Encyclopaedia of Latin-American history'**, in one volume, compiled by Michael Rheta Martin and others, first issued in 1952, was revised by L Robert Hughes in 1968 for the Bobbs-Merrill Company. The work is particularly useful for geographers for the statistics included, and for the historical information concerning major cities and industries.

472 **'An encyclopaedia of London'** was first published in 1937, edited by William Kent, revised and reset in 1951. In 1970, it was further revised by Godfrey Thompson (Dent), illustrated with photographs and including references and bibliographies.

473 **'An encyclopaedia of New Zealand'**, edited by A H McLintock, is in three volumes (Wellington: Government Press, 1966). Many of the headings are specific, such as 'Anchovies, pilchards and sprats', some longer, such as 'Geology'. The whole work is a mine of information, including plates, monochrome illustrations and diagrams, statistics and endpaper maps.

Refer also

E J Baggaley: *A geography of New Zealand* (Nelson (Australia), 1968).

J C Beaglehole: *The discovery of New Zealand* (OUP, second edition, 1961).

K B Cumberland and J W Fox: *New Zealand: a regional view*

(Christchurch: Whitcombe and Tombs, second edition, 1968).

David E Gaskin: 'The origin of the New Zealand fauna and flora: a review', *The geographical review*, July 1970.

J W Hadfield: *Handbook of New Zealand agriculture* (Whitcombe and Tombs, 1968).

R D Mayhill and H G Bawden: *New Zealand geography* (Auckland: Blackwood and Janet Paul, 1966).

R F Watters, *ed*: *Land and society in New Zealand: essays in historical geography* (Wellington: Reed, 1965).

474 'Encyclopaedia of Southern Africa', first published by Warne in 1961, is now in its fourth updated edition, under the direction of Eric Rosenthal and a team of experts. All aspects seem to be covered in this handbook, which contains some five thousand entries, cross-referenced, and illustrated with eleven colour plates, many half-tones and numerous sketchmaps and drawings throughout the text.
Refer also

W J Burchell: *Travels in the interior of Southern Africa* (two rare volumes, limited edition, 1822–1824; facsimile reproduction by C Struik (Pty) Limited, 1967).

475 'The Endeavour journal of Joseph Banks 1761–1771', in two volumes edited by J C Beaglehole (Angus and Robertson, 1962), was produced as a memorial to Sir Joseph on behalf of the Government and people of New South Wales; it comprises the entire *Journal*, illustrated by portraits, landscapes and natural history notes. Dr Beaglehole, an acknowledged authority on Cook and Banks, also contributed the introduction.

476 'England and the Baltic in the Elizabethan era', by H Zins (Manchester University Press, 1972, translated from the Polish by H C Stevens), examines in detail one of the most important aspects of Elizabethan economic development, the growth of England's Baltic trade, which was achieved only after a severe struggle with the Hanseatic League. The first five chapters are devoted to a discussion of England's relations with the Baltic countries and an examination of the social, political and economic factors which led to the formation of the Eastland Company in 1759. The second part of the book gives a detailed analysis of the Baltic trade in the second half of the sixteenth century, paying particular attention to the all-important Polish trade. Written from the Polish viewpoint, the book combines

English, German and Polish sources, many previously unpublished.

477 'The English atlas', compiled mainly by Moses Pitt, with the help of Bishop William Nicholson, who undertook the second volume, and by Richard Peers, who prepared the fourth, which include most of the geographical descriptions, and others, was printed, in four volumes, at Oxford, 'at the Theater, for Moses Pitt at the Angel in St Paul's Church-yard', 1680–1683. The maps were based chiefly on Janssen's Atlas and the work was planned for eleven volumes, but only these four were completed and some parts of a fifth.

478 'The English gazetteer', compiled in two volumes by Oliver Mason (Newton Abbot: David and Charles, 1972), comprises a list of placenames, adding basic details of the services available in every city, town, village, hamlet—totalling some 16,500 entries. Map references are given, together with distances from nearby towns and such information as population figures.

479 'The English pilot' was planned by John Seller, the London chart and instrument maker as a sea-atlas, in four books, to compete with the Dutch publishers. About 1675 he began, but never finished, the printing of *The Third Book*, dealing with the 'Oriental navigation', and this book has been reproduced by Theatrum Orbis Theatrum. Originally printed by John How for the author in 1703, including thirty-five charts and ninety pages of text, John Thornton acquired the rights in it; he enlarged and completed the work, providing sailing directions compiled from journals of the East India Company's pilots and captains and charts prepared from Dutch and English originals. Later editions, with new charts, were published by Thornton's son Samuel in 1711 and by the firm of Mount and Page up to 1761. Thus the atlas served as the standard directory for British seamen in eastern waters for over half a century and it was used by Captain Cook on his first circumnavigation, 1768–71. In the reproduction, a bibliographical note by Coolie Verner and R A Skelton describes the sources, evolution and publication history of the atlas.

480 'Environment' is the official quarterly of the Institute of Environment, established in 1969 by the Ministry of Cultural Affairs, Paris. The Institute encourages new methods of teaching in urbanism, in its several aspects, and trains teachers, encouraging research in these fields. The review supports these activities and makes comparative studies with work being carried out elsewhere.

Refer also

Ambio: a journal of the human environment research and management (Royal Swedish Academy of Sciences, bi-monthly 1971–).

The human environment (Washington, DC: Woodrow Wilson International Center for Scholars, two volumes, 1972).

481 **'Environment and economic life:** *an economic and social geography'*, by Howard F Gregor (Van Nostrand, 1963), considers the role of the environment in the economic activities of mankind. The text is illustrated and contains maps and diagrams; there is a bibliography.

482 **'Environment and land use in Africa'**, edited by M F Thomas and G W Whittington (Methuen, 1969), sets out the problems facing geographers and agricultural planners; these topics were the subject of a symposium on the natural and social environments of selected African areas. An introduction considers agricultural geography in tropical Africa; part 1 presents studies generally; part 2, studies of the social environment and in part 3, selected case studies are analysed in detail, from Malawi, Nigeria, East Central Sudan, Swaziland and Kenya. There are photographs and numerous line drawings in the text.

483 **'The environmental handbook'**, edited by Garrett de Bell (New York: Ballantine Books Inc, 1970; 'Friends of the earth' series), was proposed at the first National Environmental Teach-in, April, 1970. Included in this stimulating work are articles, written by students, suggestions towards an ecological platform, a number of reprinted essays by authorities on economic, ecological, cultural and political change, a bibliography of books and one of films.

Refer also

The environmental handbook: action guide for the United Kingdom, edited by John Barr (Ballantine with Pan), based on the above.

Fieldworker: the environmental studies magazine.

Man's impact on the global environment: assessment and recommendation for action. Report of the Study of Critical Environmental Problems (SCEP) (MIT Press, 1970).

Chemosphere—chemistry, physics and biology focussed on environmental problems (Oxford: Pergamon Press, bi-monthly 1972–, in English, French or German editions.

Exploration universe: an atlas of our environment (Bartholomew/Holmes McDougall).

Répertoire de l'environment: associations et organisations (Paris: la documentation française, 1971).

H C Brookfield: 'On the environment as perceived', *Progress in geography*, 1969.

Raymond F Dasmann: *Environmental conservation* (Wiley, third edition, 1972).

Ellen T Drake, *ed*: *Evolution and environment* (Yale University Press, 1968).

John Haddon: *Local geography: geographical survey in rural areas* (Philip, 1964).

F K Hare and C I Jackson: *Environment: a geographical perspective* (Ottawa (Canada) Lands Directorate, Department of the Environment, 1972).

H W Helfrich: *Agenda for survival: the environmental crisis (Yale University Press, 1970).*

Grace E King, *ed*: *Conflict and harmony: a source book of man in his environment* (Philip, 1972).

Joy Manson and R B Salmon: *An experiment in environmental studies* (Oliver and Boyd for the Moray House College of Education, Edinburgh, 1968).

Max Nicholson: 'Environment on record', *The geographical magazine*, November 1971.

Timothy O'Riordan: 'Environment management', *Progress in geography*, 1971.

N Polunin, *ed*: *The environmental future: proceedings of the First International Conference on Environmental Future*, held in Finland, 1971 (Macmillan, 1972).

Richard E Preston, *ed*: *Applied geography and the human environment* (University of Waterloo, Ontario, with the assistance of the Organizing Committee of the 22nd Congress of the IGU, 1973).

Sam H Schurr, *ed*: *Energy, economic growth and the environment* (Johns Hopkins University Press, 1972).

Maurice Strong *et al*: 'Human environment: the impending crisis', *The geographical journal*, December 1972.

Richard H Wagner: *Environment and man* (New York:

Norton, 1971).

Note The first United Nations conference on the environment, held at Stockholm in June 1972, ended with a 'Declaration on the Human Environment' and the passing of an 'Action Plan for the Environment'. The problems of the developing countries were a major element in the Declaration.

The Professional Institutions Conservation Group arose as a direct result of the Countryside in 1970 Conference; similar groups having the same beginnings are Co En Co (The Committee for Environmental Conservation) and the Council for Environmental Education.

484 '**The environmental revolution:** *a guide for the new masters of the world*', a monumental work by Max Nicholson (Hodder and Stoughton, 1970), presents a summary of the author's views on the urgent necessity for pursuing a more ecological approach to the problems arising in an overcrowded world; the author's work in establishing the Nature Conservancy and as Chairman of the World Conservation Committee of the International Biological Programme, in addition to his years of study in this field, enable him to give an exceptionally clear analysis of man's use of the earth and the existing relationship between man and his environment. The computer is considered as a tool with which statistics and multiple factual data may be made meaningful. Conservation in Britain and in the United States is discussed, followed by descriptions of the development of international organisations whose aim is to deal with the many problems.

Refer also

'Planning and geography in the last three decades', the subject of The Eva G R Taylor Lecture, 1971, given by E C Willatts on 15 February and printed in *The geographical journal*, September 1971.

Pierre Dansereau, *ed*: *Challenge for survival: land, air and water for man in megalopolis* (Columbus University Press, 1970).

R W Durrenberger: *Environment and man: a bibliography* (Palo Alto, California: National Press Books, 1970).

David W Ehrenfeld: *Conserving life on earth* (OUP, 1973).

P Ward English and R C Mayfield, *ed*: *Man, space and environment: concepts in contemporary human geography* (OUP, 1972).

H J Fleure: *Some problems of society and environment* (Institute of British Geographers, 1947).

C D Forde: *Habitat, economy and society: a geographical introduction to ethnology* (Methuen, eighth edition, 1957, reprinted 1961).

Brian Goodey: *A checklist of sources on environmental perception* (University of Birmingham, Centre for Urban and Regional Studies, 1972).

Harold M Proshansky *et al, ed*: *Environment psychology: man and his physical setting* (City University of New York Environmental Psychology Program, 1970).

Arthur N and Alan H Strahler: *Environmental geoscience: interaction between natural systems and man* (Santa Barbara, California: Hamilton Publishing Company, 1973).

John R Tarrant, *ed*: *Computers in the environmental sciences* (University of East Anglia, School of Environmental Sciences, 1972; directory listing user name, address, computer used, program description).

485 Eratosthenes (*c*276–*c*194 BC), Greek geographer and scientist, and a librarian at Alexandria, laid the foundations of mathematical geography. He is especially notable for his calculations of the circumference of the earth, which he recognised as a sphere. He compiled a history of geography from the time of Homer and constructed a map of the world based on a system of parallels and meridians.

486 'Die Erde: *Zeitschrift der Gesellschaft für Erdkunde zu Berlin'*, one of the most scholarly of geographical periodicals, has been published quarterly since 1839 by Walter de Gruyter. The articles, bibliographies and reviews provide an unrivalled source on the development of geographical progress; abstracts are included and the annual index appears in the fourth issue. For use with *Die Erde* is the Haack *Kleiner Atlas, Die Erde*, now in a second edition.

487 'Erdkunde: *archiv für Wissenschaftliche geographie'*, one of the periodicals of international stature, is published quarterly by Ferd Dümmlers Verlag, Bonn. The articles are usually in German, some in English, of a high standard of scholarship and wide range of interest. Full and accurate summaries precede each article and English titles of articles are also listed in the tables of contents.

488 'Essays in political geography', edited by C A Fisher (Methuen, 1968), based on papers prepared for the 20th International Geographical Congress, 1964, deal first with the geographical aspects of the internal structure and the external relationships of states; secondly, with individual case studies in decolonization and with aspects of politico-geographical change in the old world. There are extensive notes, references and sketchmaps throughout the text.

489 Esselte Corporation, Stockholm, is a private map firm which has had great influence on Swedish map production. For many years, the firm has maintained an active exchange of technical experiences with the leading map printers in other Scandinavian countries and in Great Britain, America, Germany, Switzerland and France and has itself taken the lead in glass engraving and the use of plastics in mapping techniques. Scribing at Esselte has been further improved by the design of new engraving tools, which are also exported to other countries. Esselte did much to encourage the formation of the International Cartographic Union and takes its place in co-operative ventures between the foremost map services of the world, as, for example, in the production of the *International yearbook of cartography* (*qv*).

490 'The European bibliography' was compiled, in English and French, at the European Cultural Centre, Geneva, under the direction of Hjalmar Pehrsson and Hanna Wulf (Leiden: A W Sijthoff, 1965). The sections 'Europe and the world', 'Economics' and 'Documentation' are of particular interest to geographers; entries are arranged under broad subject headings and there is a name index. Notes are given in the original language in the case of books written in German, Spanish, Italian or Dutch.
Refer also
European research resources (J Tricart for the Council of Europe, 1968).

491 European communities: *Press and information* produces a wide range of publications describing work and policy. Of central importance is the monthly magazine *European community*, an illustrated journal containing short articles and notes. *The European Community in maps*, in a revised edition, 1968, is a folder of twelve four-colour maps depicting the main political, social and economic features of the Community and adjacent countries, including England

and Wales. Set into the folder is a four-page leaflet describing the aims and structure of the Community and a second four-page leaflet gives notes on the maps, with two pages of statistical tables. Sources are named on the inside back cover. 'Economic union and enlargement', 1969, represents 'The European Commission's revised opinion on the application for membership from the United Kingdom, Ireland, Denmark and Norway'; and 'Uniting Europe: the European Community since 1950', an illustrated brochure, describes the achievements of the Community. There are also the booklets 'Farming in the Common Market', 'Research and technology and the European Community' and a smaller summary leaflet, 'Europe's tomorrow'.

Refer also

Claude Chaline *et al: L'Europe des marchands et des navigateurs* (Paris: PUF, 1964).

Griffith Taylor: *Environment and nation: geographical factors in the cultural and political history of Europe* (University of Toronto Press, 1936).

J K Wright: *The geographical basis of European history* (New York: Holt, reprinted by The American Geographical Society, 1943).

492 'European companies: a guide to sources of information', in a second edition, 1966, reprinted, 1968, was compiled and edited by G P Henderson (CBD Research Limited, Beckenham, Kent). Arrangement of entries is alphabetical by countries, with code numbers attached.

493 European Conservation Year was 1970, when twenty-seven countries from Iceland to Turkey, in addition to fifty-seven international organisations, organised under the guidance of The Council of Europe, attempted to focus attention on the way in which human activities affected the natural environment and to discuss policies of conservation. In April, 1963, the United Kingdom held its first National Wildlife Exhibition, the highspot of National Nature Week, which led to the first of the conferences, 'The countryside in 1970', in November 1963. When the scope of the work had been fully explored, the European project was prepared. A conference in Strasbourg, in February, 1970, concentrated particularly on urbanisation, industry, agriculture and forestry, and on the increasing demands for leisure. In November, a conference in London summed up the main themes of the year and proposed guidelines for the ensuing decade. The Countryside Commission issued a 'Calendar of events' in England, ending with a list of the organisations taking part. A booklet, 'Wales in European Conservation Year', was issued by The Countryside in 1970 Committee for Wales; The Countryside Commission for Scotland published a guidebook 'Scotland's Countryside 1970' and a news-sheet setting out Scotland's involvement; a 'Calendar of Events in Northern Ireland' was issued by the Nature Reserves Committee.

Refer also

The whole issue of *The geographical magazine* for January 1970 was devoted to 'Conservation in Europe'.

494 'The European peasantry: the final phase', by S H Franklin (Methuen, 1969), describes and discusses the evolution of the people since the war, the economic and social consequences of their incorporation within the dynamic postwar industrial economies, the regional aspects of their evolution and the role of the state in helping to solve their problems. In outline, the scope of the work includes 'Peasants: concepts and context'; 'Bauern: worker-peasants, family farms in Federal Germany'; 'Paysans: property, family and farms in France'; 'Contadini: peasant and capitalist farming in the Mezzogiorno'; 'Peasants in the EEC . . .'; and 'Peasants in the countries of Eastern Europe'. There is a section of references, sub-divided according to the chapters, and a glossary of names not widely familiar or generally known by initials. A number of sketchmaps are included throughout the text.

495 'Everyman's atlas of ancient and classical geography' was first published in 1907. The latest revision (Dent, 1961) includes a particularly valuable essay by J Oliver Thomson on the development of ancient geographical knowledge and theory.

496 'Evolution of Australia', by R M Crawford (Hutchinson University Library, third edition, 1970), examines the policies, events and biographical details which have contributed most to the course of development. Four particularly important chapters, from the geographer's point of view, are devoted to the formative period 1850 to 1900—'The history of Australia is a chapter in the history of migration'.

497 'The evolution of Scotland's scenery', by J B Sissons (Oliver and

Boyd, 1967), examines the following topics: 'Pre-glacial evolution', 'Glacial erosion and early ideas about glaciation', 'Landforms produced by glacial erosion', 'Glacial deposits: their origin and significance', 'Glacial deposits and associated landforms', 'Landforms produced by glacial rivers', 'The glacial sequence', 'Changing sea-levels and changing climates', 'Causes and measurement of sea-level changes', 'Changing sea-levels in Southeast Scotland', 'Changing sea-levels in Scotland as a whole', 'Periglacial and postglacial changes'. The text is accompanied by beautiful and well-chosen photographs, sketchmaps and figures and there is a bibliography of references, mainly to periodical articles.

Refer also

The early maps of Scotland to 1850 (Royal Scottish Geographical Society, two volumes, 1973, 1975).

Archibald Geikie: The scenery of Scotland.

T L Johnston et al: Structure and growth of the Scottish economy (Collins, 1971).

Ronald Miller and Joy Tivy, ed: The Glasgow region: a general survey (Prepared for the meeting of the British Association, Glasgow, 1958).

J A Steers: The coastline of Scotland (CUP, 1973).

David Turnock: Patterns of Highland development (Macmillan, 1970).

498 'Exeter and its region', edited by Frank Barlow (University of Exeter on behalf of the Local Executive Committee of the British Association, 1969) from the work of thirty-one contributors, had the usual dual purpose of assisting the members of the Association during their stay in the city and area and of providing a substantial contribution to local studies. The text, in seven main parts, is subdivided as necessary—'The South West: the physical background'; 'The South-west: the biological background'; 'The archaeology and history of Devon'; 'The place-names of Devon'; 'The economy and political structure of Devon'; 'Exeter: the city and university' and 'Literature and art in the South West'. A chapter is devoted to an examination of The Exeter book. References are given at the ends of chapters; there are a number of plates, diagrams and sketchmaps throughout the text—a thorough study.

499 'Experimental cartography: report on the Oxford Symposium, October 1963' (OUP, 1964) includes papers and discussions; pertinent bibliographical references are also appended. The first object of the symposium was to discuss the use of cartography as a research tool, in the mapping of data in industry, geology, demographic distributions, climate, transport, vegetation, flora and fauna, history and archaeology, hydrography and oceanography. The second object was to consider whether the cartographic analysis of different subjects has anything to contribute to topographic mapping.

Refer also

D Bickmore, *ed: Automatic cartography and planning*, prepared by the Experimental Cartography Unit, Royal College of Art, being a report on a feasibility study commissioned by the former Department of Economic Affairs on behalf of the East Anglia Economic Planning Council (The Architectural Press, 1970).

G M Gaits: 'Thematic mapping by computer', *The cartographic journal*, June 1969.

500 'Experimental orthophotomap of Camp Fortune Skiing Area of Gatineau Park', at 1:10,000, prepared by the Photogrammetric Research Section of the National Research Council, one of the chief organisations promoting the use of such photomaps, was issued with *The Canadian surveyor*, volume XXII, no 1 (Ottawa: The Canadian Institute of Surveying, 1968). The map was designed by D Honegger under the direction of T J Blachut. In the *Proceedings* of the International Symposium on Photomaps and Orthophotomaps held at Ottawa in September 1967 is an article by T J Blachut, Director of the Research Section, entitled 'Further extension of the Orthophoto Technique'. The author points out that the Camp Fortune map was designed as a tourist 'winter map' to provide information for skiers. Relief shading was applied, based on contours produced on a conventional stereoplotter.

Refer also

R Welch: 'Photomap image quality', *The cartographic journal*, December 1972.

501 'Explanation in geography', by David W Harvey (Arnold, 1969), formulates a methodological framework for geographic thought in the light of recent advances in geographic research and statements in the philosophy of science. In six parts—'Philosophy, methodology and explanation'; 'The methodological background and explanation in geography'; 'The role of theories, laws and models in explanation in geography'; 'Model languages for geographic explanation'; 'Models for description in geography'; 'Models for explanation in geography'—are subdivided; for example, there are separate chapters on definition and measurement, classification, maps and pattern analysis. Figures illustrate the text and there is a list of references.

Note Methuen, from November 1971, announced a new series, 'The field of geography' edited by W B Morgan and J C Pugh—'designed to meet the need for inexpensive textbooks which provide a thorough grounding in modern techniques, concepts and principles in the many divisions of geographical study. Twenty volumes are in preparation and more are planned.'

Refer also

Michael Chisholm, *ed*: *Focal problems in geography* (Macmillan series).

Wayne K D Davies, *ed*: *The conceptual revolution in geography* (ULP, 1972).

502 'The explorers: *an anthology of discovery'*, compiled and edited by G R Crone (Cassell, 1962), portrays 'a number of explorers in action, either at critical moments in their journeys or when displaying their individual qualities conspicuously', excluding, for example, for the most part, sea voyages and mountaineering expeditions. Actual extracts of texts are presented, each with a brief note of introduction, arranged chronologically within sections dealing with the countries explored: Asia, Africa, North America, South America, Australia and the Polar regions. A map is included in each section.

Note The literature concerned with exploration is vast, either general accounts, summaries of the opening up of individual countries or assessments of the achievements of particular explorers. J R L Anderson, in *The Ulysses factor: the exploring instinct in man* (Hodder and Stoughton) has conceived an interesting theory, presenting evidence of the urge to explore as a combination of recognisable qualities, of which the Greek Ulysses is the type-figure.

503 'Explorers' maps: *chapters in the cartographical record of geographical discovery'*, by R A Skelton (Routledge and Kegan Paul, 1958), reprints, with revisions, a series of fourteen articles written for *The geographical magazine* between July 1953 and August 1956. 'It is designed chiefly as a picture book, and not as a systematic history of

277

exploration', having numerous black and white reproductions throughout. The text is planned as a summary of geographical ideas and events associated with the maps, under the following headings: 'The way of the East'; 'The way of the West'; 'The way of the North'; 'The Spice Islands and Cathay'; 'The South Sea'; 'The continents and the Poles'. There is a short bibliographical note.

504 **'Explorers' maps of the Nile sources 1856–1891'** is a unique collection of reproductions, from the archives of The Royal Geographical Society, of maps made in the field by Livingstone, Speke, Grant and other great explorers.

Refer also

Dorothy Middleton: 'The search for the Nile sources', *The geographical journal*, June 1972.

505 **Faber and Faber,** London, are known to geographers chiefly for *The Faber atlas,* which traces its origin to the *Österreichischer Mittelschul-Atlas* (*Kozenn-Atlas*) compiled by the Slovak geographer, Blasius Kozenn, 1864. A long line of atlases developed from the first edition, including Lautensach's *Atlas zur Erdkunde*, the Bordas *Nouvel atlas général* and *The Faber atlas*, published for some time by E Hölzel of Vienna; the English edition was specially designed for the English-speaking market. A new edition edited by D J Sinclair was published in 1970 by GEO Publishing Company, Oxford; this edition was updated to 1965. Intended primarily for teaching, the maps give most areas reasonable coverage for the size of the atlas, with emphasis on the British Isles and Europe. The gazetteer-index contains some twenty thousand entries. The firm's catalogues dealing with specific topics are issued from time to time; an excellent example is 'Faber books on farming', 1969, which includes land use, conservation, forestry, country life and other rural studies.

506 **'Facsimile atlas to the early history of cartography,** *with reproductions of the most important maps in the XV and XVI centuries',* prepared by A E Nordenskiöld, is a translation from the Swedish original, Stockholm, 1889, indispensable for the study of the Ptolemy editions and for the development of the cartography of the period.

507 **Fairey Surveys Limited,** Maidenhead, Berkshire, comprises a number of subsidiary companies and the Fairey Group of Companies includes yet more companies in many parts of the world. The whole range of surveying, mapping and photography is carried out, in any kind of terrain. Town planning, railway development, irrigation projects, cadastral and reconnaissance surveys, road construction and aerial surveying have contributed particularly to the development of countries in Africa and Asia. The firm produces pamphlets concerning its work: 'This is Fairey Surveys', for example, and 'Loose print mosaicing', by E L Freeman. Generally speaking, the firm does not manufacture instruments, but there is the Fairey Plotterscope, a viewing aid for stereoplotting machines, with separate co-ordinatograph tables, a compact lightweight instrument designed to aid the machine operator by providing an accurately magnified image of the pantograph pencil together with the surrounding detail which can be viewed from a normal seated position.

508 'The Far East and Australasia, 1969' (Europa Publications Limited) was the first of a new series of surveys annually bringing together factual information of all kinds. A general introduction is followed by a listing of regional organisations, then the main part of the work considers regional areas, South Asia, South-east Asia, East Asia, Australasia and the Pacific Islands. Essays are included on specific topics, reference material is noted and the final section is a 'Who's who' and a list of research institutions, associations and centres of study of the Far East and Australia. There are maps, diagrams and statistics in the text and a bibliography is appended to each part.

509 'Far East trade and development', the monthly independent international for trade expansion, reports in each issue on trends in world production and trade, including reports on new projects, reports on individual countries and on particular industries and commodities; a regular feature is the 'Machinery report'. There are usually some photographs and the advertisements, as always in such a periodical, are valuable indicators. Supplements on some current topic are occasionally issued.

510 'Far Eastern survey', a fortnightly research service (New York: American Council of the Institute of Pacific Relations, 1932–1961), contained factual information and expressions of opinion, mainly on economic topics, excellent background material for the understanding of events and development. Publication ceased in 1961, but the scope and purpose, with certain modifications, of this journal were continued in *Asian survey* (*qv*). The previous volumes were reprinted by Krauss in 1966.

Refer also

The Far East and Australasia annual, (Europa), which covers all the countries of the Far East, Australasia and the Pacific.

Proceedings of the Fourth Symposium on the Development of Petroleum Resources of Asia and the Far East (UN, in three parts, 1973).

The catalogues of the Far Eastern Library at the University of Chicago, printed by G K Hall, 1974.

511 'Farming systems of the world', by A N Duckham and G B Masefield (Chatto and Windus, 1970), is intended as a reference book for students and research workers, including, therefore, plenty of maps and diagrams, some photographs and a glossary. The two main divisions consist of 'Analysis of location factors' and 'Farming systems', containing a classification of farming systems and a number of regional reports based on actual surveys. A third part, 'Conclusion', examines, among other topics, world food and population problems and there are end of chapter references throughout.

Refer also

H F Gregor: *Geography of agriculture: themes in research* (Prentice-Hall, 1970).

512 Fawcett, Charles Bungay (1883–1952) was one of the leading British academic geographers in the period immediately following the inspiration of Mackinder and Herbertson, especially in Southampton, Leeds and London. His original thought in political and population geography was expressed in numerous articles in geographical and demographic journals and in such published works as *Frontiers: a study in political geography*, a pioneer work, 1918; *The bases of a world commonwealth*, 1941; and *Provinces of England: a study of some geographical aspects of devolution*, 1919, revised, with a new preface by W Gordon East and S W Wooldridge (Hutchinson University Library, 1960). A bibliography of his works was included in the *Transactions of the Institute of British Geographers*, 1952.

513 'The Fenland in Roman times: *a study of a major area of peasant* *colonization with a gazetteer covering all known sites and finds*, by P Salway and others, under the editorship of C W Phillips, is a unique record of Roman settlement and of an ancient landscape, published by The Royal Geographical Society, 1971; twenty-four plates and eighteen figures are included in the text and there are twenty-four maps, some in colour, in a separate envelope.

514 Festschriften: English scholars or groups of scholars have not been so ready to use this form of publication as, for example, those on the Continent—and geographers have been no exception—*Festschrift für Hans Kinzl: celebrating his 70th birthday*, for example, from the Geography Department of the University of Innsbruck and *Essays on agricultural geography: a memorial volume to Dr B N Mukerji*, edited by B Banerjee, from the University of Calcutta, 1969. During recent years, however, several examples of the genre have appeared in Britain, including *Geographical essays in honour of K C Edwards (qv)*; *Essays in geography for Austin Miller*, edited by J B Whittow and P D Wood (University of Reading, 1965); *Northern geographical essays (qv)*; *Studies of a small democracy (qv)*; *Irish studies in honour of E Estyn Evans (qv)*; *The allocation of economic resources: essays in honor of Bernard Frances Haley* (Stanford University; OUP, 1959, 1965); *Land use and resources: a memorial volume to Sir Dudley Stamp* (Institute of British Geographers, the first volume in the 'Special' series of publications); *Exeter essays in geography in honour of Arthur Davies*, edited by K J Gregory and W L Ravenhill (University of Exeter, 1971); *Studies in the vegetational history of the British Isles: essays in honour of Harry Godwin*, edited by D Walker and R G West (CUP, 1970). Festschriften with a difference are *Liverpool essays in geography: a jubilee collection (qv)* and *Geography in Aberystwyth: essays written on the occasion of the Departmental Jubilee 1917/18 . . . (qv)*. One of the latest to appear is the very valuable volume for *Eduard Imhof. . . (qv)*.

515 'Field natural history: a guide to ecology', by Alfred Leutscher (Bell, 1971), sums up the author's lifetime study and training as a naturalist and biologist, being a synthesis of the kind of information widely scattered in the literature. Intended for all persons interested for educational or professional reasons, the work is in three main parts: 'The organism and its environment', 'Major habitats in Britain' and 'Field work'. Included are eighty-three drawings and diagrams by the author, appendices and a bibliography.

516 Field Studies Council (formerly The Council for the Promotion of Field Studies) issued the first number of *Field studies* in 1959, its contributions 'well spread in interest and locality', illustrated with maps and diagrams. Field work being now an integral part of the training for a university degree in geography, geology, botany, zoology and others of the earth sciences, the field centres organised by the Council, with their resident wardens, collections of essential books and maps, simple laboratories and conference room facilities, are an absolutely essential unit in our system of higher education.

Refer also

Field Group studies, (Nottingham University).

'Field studies for schools' series, edited by Margaret S Dilke, published by Evans, each volume dealing with excursions in one area, with descriptions.

517 'Field studies in the British Isles', edited by J A Steers (Nelson, 1964), was published for the 20th International Geographical Congress, 1964; it contains thirty-three studies by specialist scholars. Many kinds of landscape are examined, including coasts, the Weald, scarplands, highlands and lowlands. The second group of essays in the book concentrates on Wales, followed by sections on Scotland and Ireland. There are textmaps and end of chapter references.

518 'The fitness of man's environment', prepared by Robert McC Adams and others, was published by the Smithsonian as Annual II (available in Britain through David and Charles of Newton Abbot). The contributors discuss what has gone wrong with man's environment and how our future surroundings might be made more attractive.

519 'Fiziko-geografičeskij atlas mira', published by the Academy of Sciences of the USSR, together with the Department of Geodesy and Cartography GGK, SSSR (Moscow, 1964), is the most detailed atlas of physical geography yet produced; an entirely new atlas, compiled by the foremost scientists of the USSR, incorporating much new research, especially regarding the atmosphere, hydrosphere and upper layers of the lithosphere, and including the latest earth science theories. In the section of general geography, some maps from the 1954 *Atlas mira* (*qv*) have been used in revised form, but all other maps are original and previously unpublished. The atlas is in three main parts:

seventy maps devoted to the natural features of the world, including the Arctic and Antarctic, on relatively small scales of from 1:60M to 1:150M, and a summary world map, 1:80M, of natural landscape zones; maps of individual continents, 1:10M to 1:40M, each series comprising about twenty pages of maps, together with a final zone map for each continent; an extensive study of the USSR, on more than eighty maps on scales of 1:15M, 1:20M and 1:35M, and a summary map of natural zones and provinces. Forty pages of explanatory text in Russian summarise the basic conclusions derived from the content of the maps and discuss the methods used in data selection and map compilation. The whole atlas notably demonstrates new carto-graphical techniques. A complete translation of legend matter, contents and explanatory text is presented in a combined two-month issue of *Soviet geography: review and translation*, May-June 1965.

520 Fleure, Herbert John (1877–1969), one of the great modern scholar-geographers, was the acknowledged leader among human geographers in Britain. Throughout his professional life he encour-aged generations of students, served in various offices, a great num-ber of learned organisations, travelled much and wrote an amazing number of major works, in addition to innumerable reviews and papers: *Human geography in Western Europe*, 1918; *Peoples of Europe*, 1922; *The races of England and Wales*, 1923; *The races of mankind*, 1927; *French life and its problems*, 1942; *The corridors of time,* with H J E Peake, in ten volumes completed in 1958; *The natu-ral history of man in Britain*, 1951, 1959, revised edition by Dr Marga-ret Davis (Collins *New naturalist library*, 1971); *Guernsey*, 1961. Mrs Sinnhuber compiled a bibliography of his publications, 1954, and The Geographical Association Library in the headquarters building has been renamed the Fleure Library; 'Fleure Library news and in-formation' is a regular feature in *Geography*. Among the many tri-butes to Professor Fleure's work, one of the most informative is that contributed by Professor E G Bowen and Professor Alice Garnett to *Geography*, November 1969.

521 'Flora Europaea' is a supranational atlas, in which all the flora of central Europe will be charted. Apart from Austria, where the undertaking is being co-ordinated, participant countries include the Federal Republic of Germany, the GDR, Switzerland, Liechten-stein, Italy, Yugoslavia and Czechoslovakia. Denmark, Holland, Belgium and Luxembourg are making the results of their virtually completed work available; the total project will provide a standard botanical work kept permanently up to date by supplementary and explanatory volumes. Climate, soil science, agriculture, nature conservancy and the effects of Ice Ages are some of the ancillary topics touched upon.

522 'The flora of Greenland', by Tyge W Bocher and others (Hurst, 1968), is considered a standard reference work; every species of flowering plant and fern is discussed, a total of five hundred. The determination of species is facilitated by keys and a number of clear and realistic line illustrations by Ingeborg Frederiksen. For each species a morphological description, the chromosome number and distribution of the species are given.

Refer also

Knud Hertling *et al, ed*: *Greenland past and present* (Copenhagen: Eduard Henriksen, 1972).

523 'Focus' is a monthly (except July and August) periodical published by the American Geographical Society from 1950, 'presenting a brief, readable, up-to-date survey of a country, region or resource, helpful in understanding current world events'. Each issue carries valuable bibliographies on the chosen theme and gives information on the country's place in the world, its physical setting, climate and people, economic activities and resources, referring to any relevant historical developments and adding notes on any special policies or projects in the area. Small photographs are introduced into the text, also at least one page of suitable sketchmaps. In 1971, Praeger published the first of a series of monographs based on the issues of *Focus*.

524 Food and Agriculture Organization of the United Nations sponsors research and produces publications of vital importance to geographers. Initiated by the first Conference on Food and Agriculture among the United Nations, at Hot Springs, Virginia, in 1943, the Organisation was formally created at Quebec in 1945, with temporary headquarters in Washington. In 1951, the headquarters removed to Rome. Publications cover agriculture, economics, fisheries, forestry and nutrition, in addition to the official records of the functioning and work of FAO. Periodicals such as the *Monthly bulletin of agricultural economics and statistics, Cocoa statistics, Unasylva, World fisheries abstracts* (qv), *Food and agricultural legislation,* the

FAO plant protection bulletin and the statistical yearbooks of agricultural, fisheries and forestry products constitute a world intelligence service on production, prices and trade that covers almost every commodity in the world. The state and outlook of world agriculture is recorded in a major annual publication, *The state of food and agriculture*. Technical monographs, reports, regional studies and pamphlets such as the *Commodity series* are the result of extensive cooperation between governments and experts throughout the world. *The FAO review* began publication in six issues a year, 1967–, in English, French and Spanish editions; the journal reports on agricultural technology in relation to the food demands made by increasing world population, progress of development projects, international trade and agro-allied industries. Most interesting and valuable of all, from January 1967 the 'FAO Documentation-current Index', issued monthly with bimonthly cumulations, has provided a 'current awareness' index, an excellent example of indexing in depth. It consists of three parts: an analytical index, an index by authors and a bibliographical list, produced automatically by means of special computer programmes. The FAO Documentation Centre was also established in 1967. The Centre produces a monthly *Current bibliography* covering all FAO publications and most unpriced technical documents and has also produced a series of retrospective *Special indexes*, which contain bibliographical references to the more than forty thousand publications and documents issued by FAO since 1945. Microfiches of the out-of-print works may be obtained at cost. The *Catalogue of FAO publications* appears every two years in English, French and Spanish; it lists all priced publications since 1945 and titles in preparation, under the headings: 'World food situation—basic information', Agriculture', 'Economics and statistics', 'Fisheries', 'Forestry and forest industries', 'Nutrition', 'Legislation', FAO official records and basic documents', 'Vocabularies, glossaries, bibliographies, catalogues', 'Periodicals and annuals'. Complete catalogues covering the years 1945–1968 and 1945–1972 are also available; brochures and leaflets describing new publications are circulated from time to time. The *Annual report* should be consulted for details of the work of the Organisation.

The *Production yearbook* presents data on population, land utilisation, the area and yield of some eighty crops, as well as information on livestock numbers and products, agricultural requisites, food consumption, index numbers of agricultural production, prices, farm wages and maritime freight rates; and the *Trade yearbook* provides information on 180 reporting countries, plus as much data as possible on non-reporting countries, concerning the quantities and value of imports and exports of more than 130 leading agricultural products and requisites. Individual value summaries of agricultural trade are included for about 120 countries. A new quarterly journal, *World animal review*, 1972–, attempts to bring into focus the various aspects of animal production, animal health and animal products, in the form of special articles, information notes, reports, charts, tables and illustrations, with particular interest for developing countries. The 'Better farming' series has been published by arrangement with the Institut Africain 'pour le développement économique et social'. *Ceres* (*qv*), 1968–, is one of the Organization's most valuable periodicals.

Map-making is a special activity of the Organization—of land use, pedological survey, hydro-geology, forest industry and so forth—the largest project, jointly with Unesco, being the *Soil map of the world*, 1:5M. A third edition of the *Atlas of the living resources of the seas*, in English, French and Spanish, has been in progress since 1972.

The most comprehensive annotated bibliography on food utilisation is *Food Aid: a selective annotated bibliography on food utilization for economic development*, prepared for the World Food Program by Elisabeth Henderson, 1964 (FAO, 1965). The emphasis is on the publications of the past ten years and on the viewpoint of recipient as well as producer countries. The 423 items are fully indexed.

525 'Foreign maps and landscapes', by Margaret Wood (Harrap, 1968), provides an introduction to the study of foreign maps; selected map sheets demonstrating a variety of landforms, are reproduced, with explanatory notes, from Switzerland, France, Germany, Norway, Netherlands and the United States. Terms are explained when necessary and there are fine half-tone plates, map extracts and diagrams in the text, also a short bibliography.

526 'Forest resources of the world', by Raphael Zon and William N Sparhawk (McGraw-Hill, 1923), prepared under the authority of the Secretary of Agriculture of the United States and in co-operation with The National Research Council, in two volumes, remains a classic. The text, illustrated by folded maps and diagrams, begins with 'The general forest situation in the world', followed by a series of chapters analysing forestry in various parts of the world and ending with an examination of 'Forest resources other than timber', such as resins and rubber. To its date, it provides a wealth of information, including many statistical tables and references.

Refer also

L R Holdridge: *Forest environments in tropical life zones: a pilot study* (Oxford: Pergamon Press, 1971).

527 'Forestry and timber technology', the title of the catalogue of Stobart and Son, Limited, London, includes government publications, Forestry Commission Publications, Forest Products Research Publications, timber journals, timber specimens and forestry and timber trades accessories; for example, Hough's *Encyclopaedia of American woods; Technical and commercial dictionary of wood*, by G Trippodo; *World timber: trends and prospects*, by T Streyffert; the *Concise encyclopaedia of world timbers*, by F H Titmuss; *Tropical forestry, with particular reference to West Africa*, by C J Taylor.

528 The Forestry Commission, London, was established by Act of Parliament in 1919, with the primary object of providing wood for industry, but with the declared intention of conserving and controlling wildlife, safeguarding the natural landscape and of meeting reasonable requirements for access and other recreational activities. The publications of the Department are set out in Sectional List no 31, revised in 1970; these comprise reports, Acts, regulations, bulletins, leaflets and guides. New booklets include 'The Forestry Commission and conservation', 'Britain's new forests', 'Forestry in England', 'Forestry in Wales' and 'Forestry in Scotland', all amply illustrated.

Refer also

Check list of Forestry Commission publications, 1919–1965 (HMSO, 1966).

H L Edlin: 'The Forestry Commission in Scotland, 1919–1969', *The Scottish geographical magazine*, September 1969.

George Ryle: *Forest service: the first forty-five years of the Forestry Commission of Great Britain* (Newton Abbot, David and Charles, 1969).

529 'France: a geographical survey', by Philippe Pinchemel, translated by Christine Trollope and Arthur J Hunt (Bell, 1969), is based on the second French edition, 1964, by Colin of Paris, with the inclusion of some of the author's revisions for the third French edition. The aim has been to give 'as coherent a picture as possible of the land of France, its organisation . . .'; the words of Paul Vidal de la Blache—'By what means did a fragment of the earth's surface, neither a peninsula nor an island, which no physical geographer could ever consider a whole, become a political unity and finally reach the status of a nation?' may be considered the keynote of this later study, by another of the leading geographers of France. With this philosophy in mind, the approach is traditional: an introduction treating of general characteristics; followed by 'The role of nature'; 'The role of man'; 'Industry'; 'The towns and cities'. A carefully selected bibliography is appended, in addition to bibliographical end of chapter notes. The sketchmaps and diagrams, though small, are evocative, in the best tradition of French geographical scholarship.

Refer also

La géographie française au milieu du XXe siècle (Paris: Baillière, 1957).

Georges Cazes and Alain Reynauld: *Les mutations recentes de l'économie française: de la croissance à l'aménagement* (Paris: Doin, 1973).

H Clout: *Historical geography of France* (Seminar Press, 1973).

Hilda Ormsby: *France: a regional and economic geography* (Methuen, second edition, revised, 1950, reprinted 1956).

530 France: its geography and growth', by Jean Dollfus, one of the *Geography and growth* series (Murray, 1969), surveys France under such headings as physique, climate, history and other general factors, before going on to consider the regions individually. Splendid photographs demonstrate the reaction of man and geographic factors throughout the area. The book is available in a students' edition and a library edition.

531 Freytag-Berndt has been issuing educational maps since 1894, including general, physical and thematic maps. Methods of cartography were completely revised after the last war and the latest techniques are now used. The maps are striking, using contours, distinctive hypsometric tints and spot heights for relief representation and clear drawing of river systems, roads and other main features. The firm is noted for the series *Touristen-Wanderkarten*, 1:100,000, of Central Europe, the *Auto-Atlas Österreich mit kartenteil Mitteleuropa* and other series such as the *Landerkarten*, 1:600,000 and the *Strassenkarten* 1:2M.

Refer also

Fritz Aurada: 'Entwicklung und Methodik der Freytag-Berndt Schulwandkarten', *The international yearbook of cartography*, 1966.

532 'From geography to geotechnics', by Benton MacKaye, edited by Paul T Bryant for the University of Illinois Press, 1968, is a collection of thirteen essays arranged in three sections: 'Geography to geotechnics'; 'Control of the landscape'; and 'Uses of the wilderness'. MacKaye's thesis on 'new science', the philosophy of homesteading, valley authorities, 'folkland', watershed management, the Tennessee Valley Authority, the Appalachian Trail and 'outdoor culture' reveals the American bias of the essays and shows echoes of his acquaintance with original thinkers such as W M Davis, Patrick Geddes, Lewis Mumford, Stuart Chase, Henry Gannett and Isaiah Bowman.

533 'Frontiers in geographical teaching', the Madingley Lectures for 1963, edited by Richard J Chorley and Peter Haggett (Methuen, 1965, 1967; second edition, 1970), is divided into three parts: concepts, techniques and teaching. Summaries and analyses are presented of many topics in the forefront of current geographical thinking, with useful lists of references accompanying each section.

534 'Fundamentals of economic geography: *an introduction to the study of resources'* by William Van Royen and Nels A Bengtson, was published in 1935, 1942, 1950, 1956 and in a fifth edition, 1964, extensively re-written. The first section considers 'Economic activities and their physical background'; the second, 'Distribution of mankind: its significance and its dynamic aspects' and the third, 'The field and function of economic geography', dealing with topics such as 'The earth as the habitat of man', 'Factors responsible for climatic differences', 'Climates of the world: classification and distribution', 'Climate, soils and agriculture', 'The regions of humid tropical climates: characteristics of the three types', 'Major agricultural products of the humid tropics', 'The regions of dry tropical climates: areas of agricultural potential' and so on, carefully analysing the main kinds of resources in their environments, including, finally, the metals and manufacturing industries. An appendix examines maps, sketch-maps, map projections and time zones. Throughout the text are photographs, maps and diagrams.

Refer also

John N H Britton: *Regional analysis and economic geography: a case study of manufacturing in the Bristol region* (Bell, 1967).

J L Fisher and Neal Potter: *World prospects for natural resources: some projections of demand and indicators of supply to the year 2000* (Johns Hopkins Press, 1964).

Norton Ginsburg, *ed*: *Essays in geography and economic development* (University of Chicago Department of Geography, Research paper no 62, 1960).

Oswald A Hull: *A geography of production* (Macmillan; New York: St Martin's Press, 1968).

C F Jones and G G Darkenwald: *Economic geography* (New York: Macmillan: Collier-Macmillan, third edition, 1965).

H H McCarty and J B Lindberg: *A preface to economic geography* (Prentice-Hall, 1966).

J U Nef: *The conquest of the material world* (Chicago University Press, 1964).

J H Paterson: *Land, work and resources: an introduction to economic geography* (Arnold, 1972).

George Pierre: *Précis de géographie économique* (Paris: PUF, third edition, 1962).

N J G Pounds: *An introduction to economic geography* (Murray, fourth edition).

M J Wise and E M Rawston, *ed*: *R O Buchanan and economic geography* (Bell, 1973).

Resources and man: a study and recommendation by the Committee on Resources and Man (Freeman, 1969, for the National Academy of Sciences, National Research Council).

535 Gallois, Lucien (1857–1941) was one of the leading figures in the French school of regional geography after the death of Paul Vidal de la Blache, following him at the Sorbonne. He carried out the great project, *Géographie universelle* (*qv*) envisaged by Blache, and himself published a number of regional monographs, among the best known being *Les géographies allemands de la Renaissance*, 1890 and *Régions naturelles et noms de pays*, 1908.

536 'Gazetteer of the Persian Gulf, Oman and Central Asia', by John

Gordon Lorimer, was published in two volumes; volume II was issued in 1908 and volume I, in three parts, with introduction and table of contents, was completed by L Birdwood, in 1915, after Lorimer's death. The Irish University Press reprinted the work in 1970 in six parts, two volumes. In the first are twelve chapters geographically arranged, each of the chapters being sub-divided according to chronological periods, plus a number of appendices. The second volume is a geographical dictionary, presenting, in a series of alphabetically arranged articles, a detailed account of the physical and political conditions of the Persian Gulf and the surrounding countries, including also information concerning natural products and agriculture, livestock, population, communications and trade, internal and external.

537 Geddes, Sir Patrick (1854–1932) was a pioneer thinker in planning and sociology, whose ideas have exerted considerable influence on geographers interested in urban geography. His association with French ideas and, in particular, with the 'place-folk-work' concept of Frédéric Le Play led to the foundation of the Le Play Society (*qv*). Arthur Geddes, son of Sir Patrick, who died in 1969, was also a scholar, specialising in geography, population problems in relation to environment and France.

> *Refer also*
> Jacqueline Tyrwhitt, *ed: Patrick Geddes in India* (Lund Humphreys, 1947).

538 Geikie, Sir Archibald (1835–1924) was one of the great scholar geologists and director-general of the Geological Survey of Great Britain. Of his publications, *Outlines of field geology*, 1876. *Earth sculpture and the origin of land forms*, 1898, reprinted 1904, second edition, 1909; *Landscape in history and other essays*, 1905; *Textbook of geology*, in two volumes, 1903, and *Structure and field geology for students of pure and applied science*, 1905, have remained the most useful. He also wrote *Founders of geology*, 1905 (Dover Editions, second edition, 1963).

539 'Geo Abstracts' developed from *Geographical abstracts*, which in turn began as *Geomorphological abstracts* (*qv*). In the latest series of *Geographical abstracts*, compiled by a team of experts under the direction of K M Clayton, six issues a year were produced as follows: A, Geomorphology; B, Biography, hydrology and water resources, meteorology and climatology, oceanography, pedology; C, Economic geography; D, Social geography, cartography. In 1972, the title became *Geo abstracts*, based on the University of East Anglia, and the work was then divided into six main sections: A, Landforms and the Quaternary; B, Biogeography and Climatology; C, Economic geography; D, Social geography; E, Sedimentology and F, Regional and Community Planning, demonstrating the changed emphases in geographical thinking.

540 'Geoderma', *quarterly* 1967–, 'international journal of soil science' (Elsevier Publishing Company), covers all aspects of soil research; text is in English, French and German, with English summaries.

541 'Geo-ecology of the mountainous regions of the tropical Americas', edited by Carl Troll (Bonn: Ferd Dümmlers Verlag, 1968), is, in effect, the proceedings of the symposium organised by Unesco in conjunction with the Latin American Regional Conference of the International Geographical Union, held in Mexico City, August 1966. The symposium may be considered the result of the lifetime involvement of Professor Troll and his far-encompassing interest in the tropical mountains throughout the world, a subject in which his publications have attracted international acclaim. Professor Troll himself contributed the introductory paper on climatic, phytogeographical and agrarian ecology of tropical American mountains. The whole volume must surely remain a basic reference work for those interested in this group of subjects.

542 'Geoforum', 1970–, quarterly journal of physical, human and regional geosciences, is devoted exclusively to the complex problems of man-land relationships and provides an effective platform of international stature on which to build an efficient system for the close evaluation and dissemination of knowledge of our geographical environment. Published by Vieweg and Sohn of Braunschweig, it aims to offer close evaluation of research in the earth sciences, methodology and application.

543 'Geografia dell' Africa', the first known atlas of Africa, by Livio Sanuto, published in Venice, 1588, has been reprinted in facsimile by Theatrum Orbis Terrarum Limited. This, Sanuto's main work, was left incomplete at the time of his death; the three indices were made by Giovan Carlo Saraceni and the bibliographical note was contributed by R A Skelton.

544 'The geographer and urban studies', by David Thorpe (Department of Geography, University of Durham, 1966), is number 8 in the *Occasional papers* series, consisting of thirty-five pages, illustrated with sketchmaps, plans, diagrams and including a bibliography. 'The main text is a broad statement of the role of the geographer in urban studies, which has as its aim an outlining of the most profitable approach which he can adopt to the study of towns. The major conclusions of this statement are considered to be of significance to the methods and content of geographical teaching at all levels . . .'. An Appendix deals with some specific aspects, under the headings 'Urban field studies: some suggestions', 'The growth of urban areas', 'Shopping centres', 'Housing estates' and 'Functioning regions', each section having a select bibliography of British works.

545 'The geographer as scientist: *essays on the scope and nature of geography*', by S W Wooldridge (Nelson, 1956), brings together a number of papers written during twenty-five years of active teaching and research, each a classic of its kind, revealing Dr Wooldridge's systematic methods in studying places—the physical study of landforms, geomorphology and soil science and their significance in determining the patterns of settlement and farming, in addition to wide reading and understanding. Other topics include 'Geographical science in education', 'On taking the "Ge" out of geography', 'The status of geography and the role of field work', 'The role and relations of geomorphology', 'The changing physical landscapes of Britain' and further studies of Britain, and 'The conservation of natural resources'. Sketchmaps and diagrams illustrate the text.

546 'The geographer's craft', by T W Freeman (Manchester University Press; New York: Barnes and Noble, 1967), deals with the work of a selected number of geographers who have adopted distinctive approaches to the field of geographical research: Francis Galton, Paul Vidal de la Blache, Johan Cvijić, Ellsworth Huntington, Sten de Geer, P M Roxby and A G Ogilvie.

Refer also

J Beaujeu-Garnier: *La géographie : méthodes et perspectives* (Paris: Masson, 1971).

547 'A geographer's reference book', edited by C H Saxelby, was prepared and published by the Geographical Handbook Committee in 1955. The work presents a mixture of source material and factual information for use in teaching and draws attention to some new developments in world resources. References are given under broad subject groupings.

548 'Geographia' of London have published a great variety of maps and atlases, mostly for quick-reference, commercial or tourist use. Many maps, for different purposes, have covered the London area, including the famous *Atlas of London and suburbs*. A series of world maps, both general and special, are frequently revised; more recent ventures include marketing and sales maps of Europe and various marketing and industrial survey maps of Great Britain. The Geographia marketing maps of the conurbations, published in association with the London Press Exchange, began with that for the West Midlands, followed by a similar survey of Liverpool and Merseyside, both prepared in conjunction with the Department of Geography, University of Birmingham; a similar survey of Glasgow and Clydeside was made with the Department of Geography, University of Glasgow. A wide range of plans of towns in all parts of Britain is available and the *Commercial gazetteer of Great Britain* is a useful guide. The firm is also agent for a number of European cartographic houses.

549 'Geographia', the first atlas known to be printed in the Italian language, by Francesco Berlinghieri (Florence, 1482), was reprinted by Theatrum Orbis Terrarum in 1966, with an introduction by R A Skelton. The atlas consisted of thirty-one copper engraved maps, the only edition known to be prepared on the original Ptolemaic projection, with equidistant parallels.

550 'Geographia Polonica', a journal published by the Polish Academy of Sciences, Institute of Geography, in English, French and Russian, is intended to inform foreign geographers on the achievements of Polish geographers. It contains translations or summaries of comprehensive studies published originally in Polish, as well as specially commissioned articles. There is an emphasis on methodology; and the journal includes also reports prepared by Polish geographers for international meetings and conferences held in Poland.
    Refer also

Polish cartographical review, 1969–
Václav L Beneš and N J G Pounds: *Poland* (Benn, 1970).

551 'Geographical analysis: *an international journal of theoretical geography*' began quarterly publication by the Ohio State University Press in January 1969, edited by Professor L J King in the Department of Geography. The concept of the periodical is to encourage 'significant research aimed at the formulation and verification of geographical theory through model development and mathematical and statistical analysis'.

552 The Geographical Association is one of the two organisations of professional geographers in England, founded in 1893 to further the study and teaching of geography in all categories of educational institutions in the United Kingdom and abroad. Conferences and courses are arranged throughout the year and the annual meeting has become an event of geographical consequence, based on a main theme chosen each year; a valuable exhibition is also staged, which brings together the work of all kinds of organisations and of commercial publishers interested in geographical subjects. The annual report, including the activities of the Branches, appears in the January issue of *Geography*, together with the financial and publication reports. The Spring conference, held at different centres, also takes a special theme of current importance as its point of central interest, talks, discussions and field excursions being related to it. Local branches and sections exist at a number of provincial centres, each of which conducts its own programme of meetings, discussions, lectures, excursions and field work. There are also the Standing Committee for Teaching Aids, the Standing Committee for Field Studies and the Standing Committee for Sixth Form/University Geography. The quarterly journal of the Association is *Geography* (*qv*). Other publications include *Geography in secondary schools*, revised in 1960 by E W H Briault and D W Shave and several pamphlets, handbooks and reprints on many aspects of school teaching and the equipment of geography rooms; a completely new handbook, by Dr N J Graves, was issued in the Autumn of 1971. A valuable series is *British landscapes through maps*, designed for use with Ordnance Survey maps and with the *Exercises on OS maps* series prepared by the Secondary Schools Section Committee; there are also the *Sample studies, Asian sample studies, The geography room, Geography in primary schools, Air photographs—man and the land*, reprints, air photo packs and

L Dudley Stamp: *Hugh Robert Mill: an autobiography with intro-duction*. Beginning in January, 1972, a terminal bulletin, *Resources for geography*, provided details of new textbooks, wall-charts, film-strips and other materials sent to the Association's library; also a new publication, 1972, was *Geography in education: a bibliography of British sources 1870–1970*, compiled and edited by Clare T Luke-hurst and N J Graves, to mark the twenty-second International Geo-graphical Congress, Montreal. Some 1400 entries were listed. A history of the Association was published on the occasion of the Dia-mond Jubilee, *The Geographical Association 1893–1953* . . . A library of more than ten thousand volumes is maintained, including British and foreign geographical periodicals, atlases and maps and mono-graphs of all kinds. The library catalogue is available in parts, Asia, Africa, North and Latin America, Australia and New Zealand, and the oceans. The special classification scheme devised for the library uses a numeral notation for regional placings and a literal one for subject placings, each notation being capable of detailed subdivision. Regional placing takes precedence, with added entries in the cata-logue as required.

See also
'Teaching geography'.

553 'Geographical data handling', edited by R F Tomlinson (Inter-national Geographical Union Commission on Geographical Data Sensing and Processing for the Unesco/IGU Second Symposium on Geographical Information Systems, Ottawa, 1972, in two volumes), considered the problems of gathering environmental data, giving de-scriptions and critical appraisal of the contributions of all remote sensing techniques and reviewing special hardware and equipment systems for handling such data. A list of manufacturers is included. Methods and algarithms for the manipulation and analysis of spatial data are presented, together with explanations, illustrated, of exist-ing types of graphic output for handling geographical data. The design criteria and economics of such systems are discussed. A model is provided for the assessment of the effectiveness of existing systems of geographical data handling and case studies are examined.

554 'Geographical digest', an annual publication first issued as an experiment by the Research Department of George Philip, under the editorship of Harold Fullard, in 1963, has amply justified the initial aim 'to provide, in a concise form, information on recent changes in the world of interest to geographers and especially to provide such information as is difficult to obtain without consulting many sources'. The eighth edition, 1970, was enlarged to include a detailed analysis of United States trade. Other sections deal with significant political changes, new place-names, population and census details, world production statistics, new sources of raw materials, United Kingdom imports and exports, world trade figures, new projects in progress, communications, developments in exploration, discovery and surveying, including space and major geographical catastrophes in 1969. In addition to previous features, the enlarged tenth edition, 1972, included detailed census figures for the United Kingdom and Ireland, based on the 1971 Census of Population; a special examination of overseas trade figures for Italy and metric measures was also introduced.

555 'Geographical essays', by William Morris Davis, 1909 edition, was republished unabridged in the main in 1954 by Dover Publications, edited by D W Johnson. Selections of Professor Davis' most important geographical essays are brought together in this production, representative of his contributions to the science of geography. Minor alterations have been made to the original text, but the originals may be found by consulting the citations given in the Table of Contents. The essays are in two groups—Educational and Physiographic. Within each part, the essays are grouped together according to subject matter rather than in the order of original publication. A few figures have been retained in the text, but most of the original illustrations have not been reproduced.

556 'Geographical essays in honour of K C Edwards', edited by R H Osborne and others, was published by the Department of Geography, University of Nottingham. Twenty-seven papers fall into two groups: those on the East Midlands, which were included simultaneously in *The East Midlands geographer*, 1970; and others dealing with a wide variety of subjects and places—New Zealand, the Soviet Far East, Wales, African pre-history, British seaweeds. In a Foreword, Professor Edwards' career and the influence he has had on geography, particularly in Nottingham and the East Midlands, are described, including a list of his published work.

557 'Geographical essays in memory of Alan G Ogilvie', edited by R Miller and J W Watson (Edinburgh: Nelson, 1959), contains ten contributions by former students and colleagues on the American Geographical Society of New York, on human geography, and on regions such as Scotland, Canada, South Africa and Spain. The volume was originally planned as a festschrift to mark his retirement, but was converted, by his death in 1953, into a posthumous tribute.

558 'Geographical essays on British tropical lands', edited by R W Steel and C A Fisher (Philip, 1956), makes a useful introduction to the problems involved. Factual material is dated up to 1949–1950. Chapters by six eminent geographers, in addition to the editors themselves, are concerned with 'Geography and the tropics: the geographer's contribution to tropical studies'; 'Some problems of population in British West Africa'; 'The transport pattern of British West Africa'; 'Soil erosion in Nigeria'; 'The trade of Lake Victoria and its marginal lands'; 'Land-use and settlement in Jamaica'; 'Rainfall and water-supply in the dry zone of Ceylon' and 'The problem of Malayan unity in its geographical setting'. The sketchmaps, figures, notes and references in the text are valuable additions, but there is no index.

559 Geographical Field Group owed its origin in the inter-war years to the Student Group of the former Le Play Society, which, in turn, developed from the Le Play Society (*qv*). The Group has been outstanding in the promotion of field studies both at home and abroad. The headquarters are at the Department of Geography, University of Nottingham, where an annual conference and meeting are held.
Refer also
P T Wheeler: 'The development and role of the Geographical Field Group', *East Midland geographer*, 1967, part 3.

560 'Geographical fieldwork: a handbook', edited by K S Wheeler and M Harding for Blond Educational, comprises the work of practising teachers in the exchange and demonstration of their experience in taking classes out to look at, enjoy and understand various types of landscapes. Among the specific topics are 'Geography teaching and fieldwork'; 'Fieldwork with schoolchildren'; 'Fieldwork and maps'; 'The visual recording of fieldwork'; 'A farm study'; 'The traverse'; 'Fieldwork in an urban area'; 'Making a study of communications'; 'A parish study'; 'The study of a river'; 'A study of coastal features'; 'The study of a mountain area' and 'Studying a quarry'. Appendices give information on fieldwork preparation and fieldwork centres. There is a bibliography.

Refer also

J E Archer and T H Dolton: *Fieldwork in geography* (Batsford, 1968).

M F Cross and P A Daniel: *Fieldwork for geography classes* (McGraw-Hill, 1968).

Field studies for schools series, edited by Margaret S Dilke (Evans).

561 'Geographical handbook' series was compiled by the Geographical Section, Naval Intelligence Division of the Admiralty, for information during the first world war and was therefore of restricted circulation. Recognising their value, Kegan Paul, Trench, Trubner issued a second series in fifty-eight volumes, 1942–, which comprised entirely new works prepared by the Naval Intelligence Division sub-centres at Oxford and Cambridge by trained geographers and scholars in other relevant fields, under the direction of Lt General K Mason and H C Darby. The bibliographies and maps are particularly valuable. Among the especially useful volumes are those for *China proper*, in three volumes, 1944–45; *Jugoslavia*, in three volumes, 1944–45; and *Spain and Portugal*, in four volumes, 1941–45.

562 'Geographical interpretation of historical sources: *readings in historical geography'*, edited by Alan R H Baker, John D Hamshere and John Langton (Newton Abbot: David and Charles, 1970), brings together twenty papers of fundamental significance to the study of historical geography. In the preface, the editors state that the choice of papers 'is organised around the theme of source materials and their interpretation. The primary criteria used in making the selection were that the essays should illustrate the range of historical source material that exists, the types of problems that these present to geographical analysis and some of the methods that have been employed to overcome these problems.' The sample studies cover England and the Welsh borderland; Domesday woodland; population trends and agricultural development shown in the Warwickshire Hundred Rolls of 1279; the market area of Preston in the sixteenth and seventeenth century; the combination and rotation of crops in East Worcestershire; family limitation in pre-industrial England; agricultural changes in the Welsh borderland; locational change in the Kentish hop industry and the analysis of land use patterns; the Lancashire cotton industry in 1840; the population of Liverpool in the mid-nineteenth century and moated settlements in England. There are illustrations, sketchmaps and diagrams in the text; also notes and references.

Refer also

Journal of historical geography (Academic Press, 1975–).

A R H Baker, *ed: Progress in historical geography* (Newton Abbot: David and Charles, 1972).

563 'A geographical introduction to history', by Lucien Febvre, in collaboration with Lionel Bataillon (Routledge and Kegan Paul, 1924, 1949, fourth impression, 1966), was translated into English by E G Mountford and J H Paxton. In the foreword, by Henri Berr, the effect of environment on man and man's exploitation of the earth are discussed, stating Professor Febvre's opinions thus—'Lucien Febvre has set definite limits to his subject out of regard for scientific accuracy. He does not deny the direct action of the environment on the physical and psychical nature of man; but he holds no brief for it, and leaves the subject severely alone.' The book rouses a wealth of ideas; it is at once objective and personal, revealing an enthusiasm for his predecessors in this field, Paul Vidal de la Blache, F Rauh and J Michelet. The plan of the book was complete in 1912–13, but the work on it was interrupted by the First World War; taken up again in 1919, much had to be revised and it was not until 1924 that the first edition appeared. An interesting bibliography is arranged under headings related to the body of the text.

564 'The geographical journal', the quarterly organ of the Royal Geographical Society (*qv*), began publication in 1893, successor to the *Journal of the Royal Geographical Society*, 1830–1880. The articles are varied in content and international in scope, including accounts of recent exploration and travel, original contributions to geographical research and papers read at the meetings of the Society. From time to time, assessments of developments are most valuable, such as, in the issue for June 1964, 'British geography in the twentieth century', 'The RGS and British exploration: a review of recent trends' and 'British maps and charts: a survey of development'; and the annual presidential addresses are invaluable as summaries of work in progress. Folded maps and maps in the text are usually original, frequently drawn from an author's survey by the draughtsmen of the Society. Plates and text figures also add to the value of the articles.

An extensive review section, usually preceded by one or two review articles, includes the most significant works in all aspects of geography, also the best of travel literature, with a high proportion of overseas publications, arranged by broad regional and systematic headings. These reviews are contributed by experts and are frequently in themselves scholarly contributions to their subjects; a 'Books received' section has recently been added, arranged regionally by continent, also an 'Expedition reports' section and notes on university journals. The feature 'Cartographical survey' ('Cartographical progress' until 1967) is a valuable contribution to the scattered information on maps available; off prints of this section are bound and are available from the Society. In addition, shorter notices and news items, 'The Society's news', 'University news' and 'The record' are all essential sources of current information. The obituary paragraphs have through the years accumulated much biographical information. In the journal for January 1943 is contained the article 'The first hundred volumes'. The annual index is included with the December issue and cumulative indexes are prepared approximately every ten years. The seventh general index covers volumes 121 (1955) to 130 (1964), and includes personal, topographical and subject references to all papers, articles, reviews and notes.

565 'Geographical location codes', produced by the US Department of Health, Education and Welfare, Office of the Assistant Secretary, Comptroller; Data Management Center, 1972, is arranged in four parts: Part I, Locations in the United States with States listed alphabetically, and within each State the city names, in alphabetical sequence and having their county, name and codes for county, city, congressional district, Metropolitan statistical area, with the 1970 population; II, an alphabetical listing of each county and the three digit county code within each State; III, locations in outlying areas of the United States in alphabetical sequence with their respective area code and city code; IV, locations in foreign countries listed in alphabetical sequence followed by the continent, city and county codes.

566 'The geographical lore of the time of the Crusades: *a study in the history of medieval science and tradition in Western Europe*', by John Kirtland Wright (American Geographical Society of New York, 1925; new unabridged edition, with introduction by Clarence J Glacken, Dover Publications; Constable, 1965), remains a classic of scholarly thought and geographical application. Two sentences from the preface seem to summarise Dr Wright's approach to his life's work; referring to 'geographical concepts', he writes, 'they have also sprung from the accumulated learning and lore of preceding ages and to no small extent from unfettered flights of the imagination. The history of geography, therefore, leads its students into many fields, affording them a key by means of which they may gain a sounder understanding of the extensive ranges of human activity and of the evolution of important phases of intellectual life.' This work was an enlargement of the thesis offered to Harvard University, 1922. The thirteen main sections, in two parts, are concerned with 'The contribution of the ancient world', 'The contribution of Western Christendom before 1100 AD', 'The contribution of the Moslems', 'The sciences from the period 1100–1250 AD', 'The place of geography in the medieval classification of knowledge'—and secondly, under the main heading 'The substance and character of the geographical lore of the time of the Crusades', 'Cosmogony, cosmology and cosmography', 'The atmosphere', 'The waters', 'The lands', 'The astronomical geography of the known world', 'Cartography', 'Regional geography', Conclusion', followed by extensive notes, a bibliographical note and a bibliography. There are some illustrations, mainly of early maps.

567 'The geographical magazine' was launched in 1935 on the initiative of Michael Huxley, as an independent illustrated magazine presenting the geography of the modern world and its relation to history, politics and economics. Editorial policy has changed from time to time; some special issues remain in the memory for their particular usefulness, such as the April 1960 'Atlases and map-making' number and the superbly illustrated issue for October 1969, devoted to 'Cartography for the 1970s'. Another innovation has been the occasional issue of map supplements. The features 'World news' and 'Current affairs', illustrated with sketchmaps and diagrams, and 'Shorter news', as well as 'Notes by Ptolemy' have been recently introduced and are particularly useful in drawing attention to new developments and topical issues in all parts of the world. A recent trend has been the more frequent reports on maps, both early and current and 'A geographical bibliography . . . selective list . . . ' is included annually; the file is now available on microfilm. The book reviews section, 'The world in books', is a short feature, but of high standard, followed by 'Short reviews', notes of new periodicals and a classified 'Book list'. As Spring approaches, advertisements and notes about travel, guides, youth hostels, etc, are particularly relevant.

568 'The geographical review' has been the chief periodical publication of the American Geographical Society since 1916. Original studies in depth cover a broad range. Especially useful is the 'Geographical record' section, in which are noted new developments, particularly important monographs, surveys, reports, new periodicals and personal news concerning the world's leading geographers; followed by a section devoted to 'Geographical reviews'. The journal is one of the most reliable sources of information about new maps and atlases, especially those prepared in the United States. A recent feature has been the inclusion of brief abstracts of the articles. A cumulative index is prepared every ten years. With the September 1970 issue, a list of new books was added, arranged alphabetically by author, with prices when available.

569 The Geographical Society of Ireland was founded in 1934 for the promotion of geographical studies in Ireland. *Irish geography*, published once a year, concentrates on Irish material; specialist articles are usually illustrated by text maps and are well documented. A section of practical book reviews is included and 'Geographical literature relating to Ireland' is to be an annual feature. The Society's library is housed in the Geography Department of Trinity College, Dublin, and consists mainly of periodicals obtained in exchange for *Irish geography*, review copies of books, and bequests. The Society's collection of film-strips was recently donated to the Association of Geography Teachers of Ireland.

570 'Géographie de la population' is a unique work on this subject, in two volumes, by Mme Jacqueline Beaujeu-Garnier of the Sorbonne (Paris: Librairie de Médicis, 1956, 1958). Volume I includes general considerations, West and Southern Europe, the United States of America, Canada, Australia and New Zealand, and Latin America; volume II covers Africa, the Middle East, Monsoon Asia and socialist lands. Translated by S H Beaver (Longmans, 1966), it forms one of the *Geographies for Advanced Study* series. The illustrations, maps and diagrams and the bibliography are component parts of the work.
Refer also
   W D Borrie: *The growth and control of world population* (Weidenfeld and Nicolson, 1970).
   J O M Broek and J W Webb: *A geography of mankind*

(McGraw-Hill, second edition, 1973).

Max Derruau: *Nouveau précis de géographie humaine* (Paris: Colin, 1969).

Pierre George: *Introduction à l'étude géographique de la population du monde* (Paris: PUF, 1951).

Pierre George: *Questions de géographie de la population* (Paris: Institut National d'Études Démographiques, 1959).

G A Harrison and A J Boyce, ed: *The structure of human populations* (Oxford: Clarendon Press, 1972).

A J Hunt: 'Problems of population mapping', *Transactions*, Institute of British Geographers, 1968.

G T Trewartha: *A geography of population: world patterns* (Wiley, 1969).

——*The less developed realm: a geography of its population* (Wiley, 1972).

571 'Géographie d'Israel', by Efraim Orni and Elisha Efrat (Israel Universities Press, 1970), is one of the volumes in the Israel Program for Scientific Translations Limited. The text is in French, including many photographs, maps and diagrams; there is a bibliography and a folded map in a pocket.

Refer also

J Ben-David: *Agricultural planning and village community in Israel: studies on the human implications of settlements in the arid zone* (Unesco, 1964).

Yehuda Karmon: *Israel: a regional geography* (Wiley, 1971).

572 'La géographie française au milieu du XXe siècle', edited by G Chabot, R Clozier and Mme J Beaujeu-Garnier (Paris: L'Information Géographique et J-B Baillière, 1957), is a collection of forty-two essays on bibliographical and theoretical topics concerning the development and organisation of French geography, including some brilliant new studies on the leading interests of French geographers. It is one of a growing number of scholarly analyses by geographers of the state of the subject in their respective countries.

573 'La géographie humaine', a pioneer work of Jean Brunhes (*qv*), 1910, had a profound influence and so continued an interest that its publishing history has been complex. Among the most interesting of subsequent editions have been a fourth edition, revised by M Jean-Brunhes Delamarre and Pierre Deffontaines, published by the

Librairie Félix Alcan in 1934, in two volumes, with a third volume of plates and maps; an abridged and edited translation by E C Le Compte, Isaiah Bowman and R E Dodge, under the title, *Human geography*, in 1920; and a new translation and abridgement by E F Row (Rand McNally; Harrap, 1952; third edition, 1956).

Refer also

M Chisholm: *Research in human geography: Social Science Research Council reviews of current research* (Heinemann Educational Books, 1971).

Paul Claval: *Essai sur l'évolution de la géographie humaine* (Cahiers de géographie de Bésancon, 1964, no 12).

K R Cox: *Man, location and behavior: introduction to human geography* (Wiley, 1972).

D C Money: *Patterns of settlement: human geography in colour* (Evans, 1972).

A V Perpillou: *Human geography* (Longmans, 1966).

Peter Toyne and Peter T Newby: *Techniques in human geography* (Macmillan, 1971).

574 'Géographie régionale de la France', by Georges Chabot (Paris: Masson, 1966; revised edition, 1969), is not only a factual examination of France, but an outstanding example of the methodology of regional geography. Arrangement is straightforward and double page maps accompany the description of each region, in addition to some sketchmaps in the text.

575 'Géographie universelle' (Paris: Colin, 1927–1955), the vast project to produce a world regional geography at a uniformly high standard, was conceived by Paul Vidal de la Blache before the first world war. After his death in 1918, Lucien Gallois renewed the project and the first volumes appeared in 1927; all except the volumes for France were finished before 1939, but the second war slowed production again and the last French volume did not appear until 1955, completing a work of twenty-three volumes and the *Atlas historique et géographique* by the leading French geographers; each volume is illustrated with plates, maps, text-maps, figures and bibliographies, and has its own index.

576 'Géographie universelle des transports', in four volumes, runs as follows: 1, French railways, including those of North Africa and French colonies; 2, European railways, excluding France and the

USSR, in four parts; 3, America, Africa and Asia and the land areas of Oceania; 4, Road, sea and air transport. Illustrations, maps and text-maps are generously provided.

577 'Géographie universelle Larousse', under the direction of M Jean-Brunhes Delamarre and P Deffontaines (Paris; Larousse, 1958–60), is in three volumes on a plan which groups together countries touching the same ocean; *L'Europe péninsulaire,* 1958; *Afrique, Asie péninsulaire, Océanie,* 1959; *Extrême Orient, Plaines Eurasiatiques, Amériques,* 1960. Within these groupings, the unit of treatment is political. The production is sumptuous, with superb illustrations; there are short bibliographies and an index of place-names for the whole work is in the third volume. An English edition was planned, of which the volume for Europe was published by Paul Hamlyn in 1961.

578 'Die geographischen Fragmente des Eratosthenes Neu gesammelt, geordnet und besprocken', 1880, 'the best commentary and critical edition of the fragmentary geographical work of Eratosthenes (275–195 BC)', was reproduced in 1964 by N Israel, Meridian Press and Theatrum Orbis Terrarum.

579 'Geographisches Jahrbuch' is a remarkable bibliographical series produced since 1866 by various publishers, mainly by Perthes series produced since 1866 by various publishers, mainly by Perthes of Gotha and later by VEB Hermann Haack, Geo-periodical articles covering a different geographical area, preceded by an introductory survey. Indexes for the period 1866 to 1936 are included in volumes 40 and 52; a guide to contents up to volume 58, part 1, is given in *Aids to geographical research (qv);* and in A J Walford: *Guide to reference material,* the subjects covered in volumes 60 and 61 are summarised.

580 'Geographisches Taschenbuch and Jahrweiser für Landeskunde', an annual or bi-annual begun by Franz Steiner Verlag in 1949, presents a guide to German regional geography and considerable information also regarding geographical documentation in the rest of the world, under the present editorship of Professor E Meynen. Articles, bibliographies, lists of organisations and institutes responsible for the promotion of geographical and related work in Germany, geographical societies and their publications, statistical sections, notes on methodology and cartographical techniques, reviews of new official map publications and a complete bibliography of works on German geography make this a most substantial and helpful work. An index includes references to previous as well as to the current issue and, on occasion, to other bibliographical publications also. A special supplement to the 1960/61 volume constituted the 1960 *Orbis geographicus* (*qv*), covering the International Geographical Union and cartographical societies, university professorships and institutions, with lists of geographers from eighty-eight countries.

581 **'Geographisches Zeitschrift'** was launched by Alfred Hettner in 1895. Publication ceased with the second world war, but revived in 1963, now continued quarterly by Franz Steiner Verlag. Original studies, extensive reviews and detailed discussions of important works are included, on an editorial policy which still closely follows the ideals of Hettner, his belief in the unity of geographical studies, in the importance of methodology and the relevance of the subject to everyday life. A cumulated index to volumes 1 to 50 is in preparation.

582 **'Geography',** the quarterly journal of the Geographical Association (*qv*), was begun in 1901 as *The geographical teacher*, changing the name in 1927. Illustrated articles of geographical and topical interest and on aspects of the teaching of geography are followed by the 'This changing world' feature, which draws attention to current developments of interest to geography teachers; this feature was redesigned and increased in size in 1971. The articles are preceded by abstracts and the latest feature, indicative of adaptation to automation, is the 'Key words to articles in this issue for information retrieval systems'. Announcements concerned with the status of the subject, new teaching methods, materials and aids, an extensive section of informative reviews and 'Geographical articles listed from periodicals received in the library', together with 'books and publications received', both arranged under broad subject groupings, make this an invaluable publication for checking either subjects of bibliographical knowledge, particularly from the teaching angle. The index is included with the November issue.

583 **'Geography: an outline for the intending student',** edited by W G V Balchin (Routledge and Kegan Paul, 1970), begins with a Preface and first chapter by the editor—'The nature and content of geography', an Appendix at the end gives details of relevant organisations and publishers. Between are four sections: 'The basic skills of geography'; 'The organisation of geographical material'; 'Pure and applied geography'; and 'Information for the intending geographer', within which specialist geographers have contributed the individual chapters. Short lists of 'further reading' are appended to each chapter and there is a brief index.

Refer also

Ronald Abler *et al: Spatial organisation: the geographer's view of the world* (Prentice-Hall, 1971).

E A Ackerman: *Geography as a fundamental research discipline* (University of Chicago Department of Geography, Research paper no 53, 1958).

E A Ackerman: *ed: The science of geography* (Washington, D C: National Academy of Sciences, National Research Council, 1965).

J M Blaut and David Stea: 'Studies of geographic learning', *Annals* of the Association of American Geographers, 1971.

Fred E Dohrs and Lawrence M Sommers, *ed: Introduction to geography: selected readings* (New York: Crowell, 1967).

Olivier Dollfus: *L'analyse géographique* (Paris: PUF, 1971).

T W Freeman: *The writing of geography* (Manchester University Press, 1971, written for the geography student.

P Haggett: *Geography: a modern synthesis* (Harper and Row, 1972).

Q H Stanford and W Moran: *Geography: a study of its elements* (Toronto University Press, 1969).

L J Wood: 'Perception studies in geography', *Transactions*, Institute of British Geographers, July 1970.

D Whittlesey: 'The horizon of geography', *Annals* of the Association of American Geographers, 1947.

584 'Geography and education', Ministry of Education pamphlet no 39 (HMSO, 1960), is a key document, summarising 'The heritage of geography'; 'The nature of geography'; 'The development of geography as a school subject'; and various aspects of geography teaching at successive standards. The following are included as appendices: 'Letter of the Royal Geographical Society to the universities of Oxford and Cambridge, 1871'; 'Memorial of the Royal Geographical Society to the universities of Oxford and Cambridge, 1874'; 'Geography rooms and their accommodation and equipment'.

585 'Geography and man: *a practical survey of the life and work of man in relation to his natural environment*', edited by W G V Balchin, in three volumes (New Era Publishing Company, second edition, 1955), 'The heritage of man: Europe', 'The British Isles, Asia, Africa' and 'The Americas, Australasia, Man's work in industry', which includes agriculture and fisheries, is a most readable as well as evocative work. The preface deals with general matters, exploration and maps.

Refer also

E J Taafe, *ed: Geography:* report of the geographical panel of the Behavioural and Social Sciences Survey of 1967–9, under the auspices of the National Academy of Sciences and the Social Science Research Council of the USA (Prentice-Hall, 1970).

586 'Geography and planning', by T W Freeman (Hutchinson University Library, fourth edition, 1974), considers planning at local, regional and national levels—'The planner and the geographer'; 'The physical landscape'; 'Climate and weather'; 'Rural land use'; 'Aspects of town geography'; 'Some problems of industrial location'; 'National parks'; 'The changing scene'. Notes and references for each chapter are grouped at the end and there are some figures in the text.

Refer also

G H J Daysh and A C O'Dell: 'Geography and planning'; paper read at the Royal Geographical Society, 15 April, 1946, published in *The geographical journal*, July 1947 (January–March, 1947).

H J De Blij: *Geography: regions and concepts* (Wiley, 1971).

T W Freeman: *Geography and regional administration: England and Wales 1830–1968* (Hutchinson University Library, 1968).

John Friedmann and William Alonso, *ed: Regional development and planning: a reader* (Cambridge, Mass.: MIT Press, 1964).

Walter Isard and J H Cumberland, *ed: Regional and economic planning: techniques and analysis for less developed areas* (Paris: European Productivity Agency of the OEEC, 1961).

D M Smith: *Industrial location: an economic geographical analysis* (Wiley, 1971).

E C Willats: 'Planning and geography in the last three decades', the Eva G R Taylor Lecture, 1971, printed in *The geo-*

graphical journal, September 1971.

Department of Environment: *Atlas of planning maps*, two volumes, 1970.

587 'Geography as human ecology: *methodology by example*', edited by S R Eyre and G R J Jones (Arnold, 1966), 'is defined in this volume as the interaction between human activity and natural circumstances'. The book comprises the essays of eleven scholars, writing with geography teachers particularly in mind.

Refer also

Michael Graham: *A natural ecology* (Manchester University Press, 1973).

588 'Geography at Aberystwyth: *essays written on the occasion of the Department Jubilee, 1917–18—1967–68*', edited by E G Bowen, Harold Carter and James A Taylor (Cardiff: University of Wales Press, 1968), comprises a series specially commissioned and dedicated to Professor H J Fleure. The evolution of geographical studies at Aberystwyth is traced, following which are seventeen chapters by individual scholars on a variety of topics, especially physical and human, illustrated with sketchmaps, figures and with end of chapter references. Subjects covered include 'The role of the sea in the evolution of the British landscape'; 'Raised shore platforms of the western islands of Scotland'; 'The periglacial landscape of the Aberystwyth region'; 'Climatology and the geographer'; 'Scale problems in hydrology'; 'Reconnaissance vegetation surveys and maps'; 'Factors in soil formation in Wales'; 'Surveying techniques in coastal geomorphology'; 'Photogrammetric techniques in geography'; 'The seas of Western Britain: studies in historical geography'; 'Mid-Wales: prospects and policies for a problem area'; 'Geography and political problems'; 'The rural community in Central Wales: a study in social geography'; 'Urban systems and town morphology'; 'New techniques in urban analysis'; 'A multivariate grouping scheme: association analysis of East Anglian towns' and 'Regional geography at Aberystwyth'.

589 'The geography behind history', by W Gordon East (Nelson, 1938; revised edition, 1965), aims to show how the majority of events and developments are caused or conditioned by geographical factors. The outline runs as follows: 'Geography as an historical document'; 'Geographical position'; 'Climate and history'; 'Routes';

'Towns'; 'Frontiers and boundaries'; 'Habitat and economy'; 'The dawn of civilisation'; 'The dawn of civilisation in the Americas'; 'Europe and China'; 'International politics'. Sketchmaps and diagrams figure in the text and there is a brief reading list, subdivided according to the chapter topics.

590 'Geography from the air', by F Walker (Methuen, 1953), was written when the use of aerial photographs as an aid in geographical studies was a comparatively new technique. Beginning with a general explanation, the text proceeds to examine 'Geological information on air photographs'; 'The study of erosion on air photographs'; 'Minor relief features and soils'; 'Coasts and shorelines'; 'Human geography' and 'Economic conditions and the formation of settlements'. A number of excellent aerial photographs are included, also some diagrams, and there is a short technical explanation of photogrammetry.

Refer also

T E Avery: *Interpretation of aerial photographs: an introductory college textbook and self-instruction manual* (Minneapolis: Burgess, 1962).

D R Harris and R U Cooke: 'The landscape revealed by aerial sensors', *The geographical magazine*, October 1969.

Jean Hurault: *L'Exam stereoscopique des photographies aériennes* (Paris: Inst. Géog. Nat, two volumes, 1960, including box of photographs and box of maps and diagrams).

A I Shersen: *Aerial photography* (Jerusalem: Israel Program for Scientific Translations, 1961).

591 'Geography in education': *a report prepared by the Education Committee of the Royal Geographical Society,* 1955, and *Geography and technical education: a memorandum prepared by the Education Committee of the Royal Geographical Society,* published with the approval of the Council of the RGS and the Executive Committee of the Geographical Association, 1958, were documents of central importance in the establishment of geographical studies in the context of contemporary education; in the words of the members responsible for the second report, 'to place on record what they regard as the important place which geography should have in such developments'.

592 'Geography in the field', by K S Wheeler (Blond Educational, *Teachers' handbook* series, second edition, 1970), is a revised edition of *Geographical fieldwork: a handbook*, by K S Wheeler and M Harding, which evolved from the work of a group of Surrey teachers, who, under the auspices of the County Inspectorate, formed the Surrey Fieldwork Society in 1958. It is one of the most helpful texts in the methodology of fieldwork, dealing with many different aspects and amply illustrated with sketchmaps and diagrams. The work ends with 'A selected list of fieldwork centres and bibliography' and an 'Index of fieldwork techniques'.

593 '**Geography in the secondary school,** *with special reference to the secondary modern school*', a report by E W H Briault and D W Shave (Geographical Association, 1952; second revised edition, 1955), stresses the importance of geography in the balanced education of all children, both in the systematic and regional approaches.

594 '**Geography in the twentieth century:** *a study of growth, fields, techniques, aims and trends*' (New York: Philosophical Library; Methuen, 1951; second revised and enlarged edition, 1953; third enlarged edition, 1957; in Methuen's *Advanced geographies* series) is the work of twenty-two specialist authors, under the editorship of Griffith Taylor. Chapters are grouped in three main sections: 'Evolution of geography and its philosophical basis'; 'The environment as a factor'; and 'Special fields of geography'. 'A concise glossary of geographical terms' is appended.

595 '**Geography in the United Kingdom . . .**' *See* the *Reports* prepared on behalf of the British National Committee for Geography, submitted to the International Geographical Congresses; these are usually reprinted in *The geographical journal*.
    Refer also
        G R Crone: 'British geography in the twentieth century', *The geographical journal*, June 1964.
        Robert W Steel and J Wreford Watson: *Geography in the United Kingdom 1968–1972*.

596 '**Geography in world society:** *a conceptual approach*' is a monumental work by Alfred H Meyer and John H Strietelmeier (*Lippincott geography* series, 1963). In six parts, with subdivisions—'The nature of the discipline of Geography'; 'Man's planetary domain';

'The geographic aspects of technology and ethics in societal and national life'; 'The life of man as viewed in its areal setting'; 'The regional and resource factors of nation-states'; and 'Summary observations on man's relations to space in time'—the text was in preparation at the time when exploration of space and the planets was beginning to become a reality. It was designed as an introduction to university geographical studies and to develop intelligent awareness of the critical role of geography in the world. There are photographs, maps and diagrams throughout and references at the ends of chapters. A folding plate depicts the climates of the earth and an appendix considers the 'significance of climate identification—classification and its application to geographic understandings'.

Refer also

Wayne K D Davies, *ed*: *The conceptual revolution in geography* (ULP, 1972).

597 'The geography of the British Isles' series, edited by A V Hardy (CUP, 1972–), is concerned with the total environment landforms, industrial output, town and country planning and social problems. Published or in preparation, including illustrations and maps, are H J Savory: *South-east England*, 1972; W S Dancer and A V Hardy: *Greater London*; H J Savory: *Wales*; W E Marsden: *North-west England*; H Tolley and K Orrell: *Yorkshire; Northern Ireland, The Midlands* and *South-west England*.

598 'The geography of economic activity', by Richard S Thoman, Edgar C Conkling and Maurice H Yeats (McGraw-Hill, 1962, 1968), is intended to be an introduction to economic geography: 'The human being and his economies'; 'The natural environment'; 'Patterns and theories of production and exchange'; 'The sources and application of energy'; and, particularly detailed, 'The roles of selected commodities'. Throughout the text are photographs and diagrams and, as an appendix are special red and blue maps pertaining to agriculture designed from the latest United States Census of Agriculture and on manufacturing, using data from the 1963 United States Census of Manufactures. Endpaper maps show 'Density of world population' and 'The world's political units'.

Refer also

Gunnar Alexandersson: *Geography of manufacturing* (Prentice-Hall, 1967).

Hans Boesch: *A geography of world economy* (Van Nostrand,

1964).

Joel Darmstadter *et al*: *Energy in the world economy: a statistical review* . . . (Johns Hopkins University Press, 1971).

Gerald Garvey: *Energy, ecology, economy* (New York: Norton, 1972).

G J Karaska and David F Bramhall, *ed*: *Locational analysis for manufacturing: a selection of readings* (MIT Press, 1969).

E W Miller: *A geography of manufacturing* (Prentice-Hall International, 1962).

D M Smith: *Industrial location: an economic geographical analysis* (Wiley, 1971).

James E Vance, *jr*.: *The merchant's world: the geography of wholesaling* (Prentice-Hall, 1970).

Richard J Ward, *ed*: *The challenge of development: theory and practice: a sourcebook* (Chicago: Aldine, 1967).

599 'A geography of Europe', by Jean Gottmann (Holt, Rinehart and Winston, fourth edition, 1969), as in the previous editions, reviews geography as 'dedicated to the description and analysis of constantly changing facts and situations'. The opening chapters view Europe as a whole, the following revised sections concern the changes in the geography and economy of Western Europe, the rapid evolution of the Mediterranean countries and their ties with the West, Central Europe, the marginal Soviet Republics and the USSR. Special emphasis is placed on such organisations as the Common Market, urban growth and its consequences, the use of resources and the need for planning. In conclusion, 'The diversity and unity of Europe' is discussed; there is a bibliography.

Refer also

Lewis M Alexander: *Offshore geography of northwestern Europe: the political and economic problems of delimitation and control* (The Association of American Geographers, 1963; Murray, 1966).

James R Coull: *The fisheries of Europe: an economic geography* (Bell, 1972).

Harry Garms: *The natural history of Europe*, *ed*: by A Melderis and Joyce Pope (Hamlyn, 1967).

George W Hoffman, *ed*: *Eastern Europe: essays in geographical problems* (New York: Praeger, 1971).

L A Kośinski: *The population of Europe: a geographical perspective* (Longmans, 1970).

F J Monkhouse: *A regional geography of Western Europe* (Longman, fourth edition, 1974).

Jacqueline Murray: *The first European agriculture, a study of the osteological and botanical evidence until 2000 BC* (Edinburgh University Press, 1970).

F A Mutton: *Central Europe* (Longmans, second edition, 1967).

Norman Pounds: *Eastern Europe* (Longmans, 1968).

600 '**The geography of greater London:** *a source book for teacher and student*', prepared by the Standing Sub-Committee in Geography of the Institute of Education, University of London, under the general editorship of R Clayton (Philip, 1964), was conceived as a joint enterprise, bringing together the results of recent research by university teachers and the knowledge and experience of teachers of the Institute engaged in the training of geography teachers for schools, to provide for all teachers interested in urban geography up-to-date information and guidance. Authoritative sections are included on all aspects, such as 'Maps of Greater London', 'Museums, libraries, record offices, and other sources of information', 'Some statistical sources on Greater London', 'Teaching aids'. An extensive bibliography by P M Wilkins comprises entries, annotated as necessary, under the following headings: A 'Main section': Physical aspects and the land; Topographical-historical surveys; London's growth and history; The face of London; The government of London; London's economy; The demographic background; The metropolitan community: its geographical character; Planning: problems and administration; B 'Local reference section'; C 'Books of general interest'; D 'Books for the junior library'.

601 '**Geography of international trade**', by Richard S Thoman and Edgar C Conkling (Prentice-Hall, 1967, *Foundations of economic geography* series), examines trade data, interpreting the pattern and structure of international trade in terms of current monetary and economic blocs. The result provides one of the first analyses of the basic types of international relations. The series as a whole is designed so that each volume focuses on a major aspect of economic geography. A number of sketchmaps and diagrams are included in the text, which contains also a glossary of terms and a short bibliography.

Refer also

Gunnar Alexandersson and Göran Norström: *World shipping: an economic geography of ports and seaborne trade* (Wiley, 1963).

B J L Berry: *Geography of market centres and retail distribution* (Prentice-Hall, 1967).

Direction of international trade (UN Statistical Office, International Monetary Fund and International Bank for Reconstruction and Development, New York, monthly).

World trade annual

602 'The geography of modern Africa', a major work by W A Hance (Columbia University Press, 1964, 1965), has as its purpose the presentation of the chief features of the economy, the handicaps and some of the potentialities that affect the future of economic growth. With this aim in mind, the arrangement of material is regional—featuring an introduction, 'Northern Africa', 'West Africa', 'Equatorial Africa', 'Eastern Africa', 'South Central Africa', 'Southern Africa', 'Madagascar and the Mascarenes'. Illustrations and sketchmaps accompany the text and there is a regionally arranged bibliography.

Refer also

R Battistini and G Richard-Vindard, *ed*: *Biogeography and ecology in Madagascar* (The Hagues: W Junk, 1972).

Christopher Lloyd: *The search for the Niger* (Collins, 1973).

R B Ogendo: *Industrial geography of Kenya: with special emphasis on the agricultural processing and fabricating industries* (Nairobi: East African Publishing House, 1972).

J D Pearson and R Jones: *The bibliography of Africa*: proceedings and papers of the International Conference on African Bibliography, Nairobi, December 1967 (Cass, 1970).

Stefan von Gnielinski, *ed*: *Liberia in maps* (ULP, 1972).

603 'The geography of Norden: *Denmark, Finland, Iceland, Norway, Sweden*', edited by Axel Sømme (Oslo: F W Cappelens for the Norwegian National Committee of Geography, 1960; Heinemann, 1961 second edition, 1968), was prepared for the Nineteenth International Geographical Congress, Stockholm, 1960, by thirteen eminent geographers from the leading universities and colleges of the five countries. It is an excellent example of co-operation in such work, skilfully co-ordinated and produced. There are fine plates of aerial and ground photography and a section at the end of coloured general and thematic maps, in addition to maps and diagrams in the text.

604 'The geography of recreation and leisure', by Isobel Cosgrove and Richard Jackson (Hutchinson University Library, 1972), asks the question 'Does leisure, as another economic activity, have a spatial expression? Can it affect other forms of economic activity and do they in their turn affect patterns of leisure activity? The study continues by studying the growth of spa and seaside towns and the 'inland tour'. North American and European leisure patterns are analysed, examples being drawn from other countries also. Problems of land-use planning for leisure in rural and coastal areas in Britain arise, which involve questions such as the changing role of rural Britain and the closer ties coming into existence between urban and non-urban areas. Sketch-maps are included and there are end of chapter references.

605 'The geography of religion in England', by John D Gay (Duckworth, 1971), begins with an examination of the approaches adopted by other geographers of religion in a comprehensive survey of research in this topic already completed, following with an analysis of the source material available, attaching special importance to the 1851 Census. The remaining chapters discuss in detail 'The Church of England'; 'The Roman Catholics'; 'The Nonconformists', 'The Baptists, the Presbyterians and the Congregationalists'; 'The Methodists'; 'The smaller Christian groups'; 'Quasi-Christian groups and Eastern religions' and 'The Jews'. Appendices are given to tables, chapter by chapter references and bibliography, with a section of explanatory maps.

Refer also

H J Fleure: 'The geographical distribution of the major religions', *The bulletin of the Egyptian Royal Society of Geography*.

606 'The geography of Romania', by Dr Tiberiu Moraru and others (Bucharest: Meridiane, 1966), concentrates particularly on physical and economic aspects. There are a number of photographs and sketchmaps throughout the text and a folding physical map in a pocket.

607 'The geography of sea transport', by A D Couper (Hutchinson University Library, 1972), 'takes a broad view of the sea as a link

317

between places. The main theme is technological change in sea transport and the impact of this on the character and distribution of economic activities in the world' (Introduction). Under ten major divisions—'Shipping and civilisation'; 'Medieval world-links'; 'British shipping and economic growth'; 'World shipping routes'; 'Trends in modern shipping'; 'Conventional dry cargo shipping'; 'Oil tankers'; 'Bulk carrier and unitised shipping'; 'Coastal and short sea shipping'; 'Shipping and the developing countries', many aspects of the role and value of shipping are discussed. The text is accompanied by explanatory figures and diagrams, a brief glossary and end of chapter references.

608 'The geography of towns', by Arthur E Smailes (Hutchinson University Library, 1953; fifth edition, 1966, paperback edition), traces the origin and bases of towns, the setting of towns and their cultures, their morphology, urban regions and the development of the town structure. There are maps and town plans throughout the text to demonstrate points and suggestions are included for further reading, mostly in English.

Refer also

M Ash: *Regions of tomorrow: towards the open city* (Evelyn, Adams and Mackay, 1969).

W G V Balchin, *ed*: *Swansea and its region* (University College of Swansea on behalf of the Local Executive Committee of the British Association, 1971).

M W Beresford and G R J Jones, *ed*: *Leeds and its region* (Leeds Local Executive Committee of the British Association, 1967).

D B Clark and M B Gleave, *ed*: *Social patterns in cities* (Institute of British Geographers, Urban Geography Study Group, 1973).

D J Dwyer, *ed*: *The city in the third world* (Macmillan, 1974).

Brian Goodall: *The economics of urban areas* (Oxford: Pergamon Press, 1972).

Jean Gottmann: 'The dynamics of large cities', *The geographical journal*, June 1974.

Peter Hall: 'The containment of urban England', *The geographical journal*, October 1974.

Peter Hall *et al*: *The containment of urban England* (Allen and Unwin, two volumes, 1973).

David Herbert: *Urban geography: a social perspective*

(Newton Abbot: David and Charles, 1973).

F S Hudson: *A geography of settlements* (Macdonald and Evans, 1970).

Leslie Martin and Lionel March, *ed: Urban space and structures* (CUP, 1972).

R G Putnam *et al: A geography of urban places: selected readings* (Toronto: Methuen Publications, 1970).

Milton Santos: *Les villes du tiers monde* (Paris: Editions M.-Th. Génin, 1971).

A E Smailes: *Urban systems* (Transactions, Institute of British Geographers, 1972).

D W G Timms: *The urban mosaic: towards a theory of residential differentiation* (CUP, 1971).

609 'A geography of the USSR: *the background to a planned economy'*, by J P Cole and F C German (Butterworth, second edition, 1970), presents much information necessary to the study of recent economic developments and policies in the USSR. The second edition was completely re-written, taking into account the 1966–70 Five Year Plan and the increasing influence of Comecon. Tables and maps pin-point details in the text.

Refer also

A Lavrishchev: *Economic geography of the USSR: general information, geography of the industry, agriculture and transport* (Moscow: Progress Publications, translated by David Myshne, 1969).

Phillip R Pryde: *Conservation in the Soviet Union* (CUP, 1972).

610 'Geography regions and concepts', by Harm J de Blij (Wiley, 1971); the author has 'attempted to place approximately one hundred concepts and ideas in a regional perspective. Many of these concepts are truly geographical; others are ideas, about which . . . students of geography should have some knowledge.' The ideas are worked into fifteen main chapters—'Regions of the world', 'The growth of Europe', 'Regions of Europe', 'Eastern Europe—the shatter zone', 'The Soviet Union—region and realm', 'North America', by S S Birdsall, 'Middle America and the legacy of Mesoamerica', 'Latin 'South America', 'Africa forms the key', 'North Africa and Southwest Asia', 'India and the Indian perimeter', 'China and its sphere', 'Southeast Asia: between the giants', 'Prodigious Japan: the aftermath of Empire', 'Australia and the islands'. Cartography is by

Hans J Stoce. The book is well indexed, so that individual 'concepts' may be identified; it is also very much a book in which to browse and is illustrated by numerous black and white photographs.

611 'Geo-Katalog' (Munich: The Geo Center, Internationales Landkartenhaus GmbH, 1972–) replaces the *R V-Katalog* and the *Zumstein-Katalog*, formerly published by Zumstein and Reise-und Verkehrs-verlag, 1964–. The volume for 1972 contained 622 pages of catalogue, with additional sections of information, as on globes, publishers and map sellers, in German, English and French, in a plastic binding. The catalogue is in two main sections: maps, atlases and handbooks on all parts of the world, space and the Moon; and a Thematical Appendix containing geological maps and atlases, travellers' guides, school atlases, globes and various other items. Thumb-index tabs mark the chapters and other quick reference devices have been used.

612 Geological Society of London, founded in 1807 for the investigation of the mineral structure of the earth, has become one of the great geological organisations of the world, the *Quarterly journal*, 1845–, being of central importance. Annual *Proceedings* and occasional *Memoirs* are also published. The library, holding some hundred thousand volumes and over three thousand geological maps, is available to Fellows and on the introduction of a Fellow.

613 Geological Survey of Canada, founded in 1841, has been responsible for much of the exploration of Canadian territory, especially in the west and, during this century, detailed mapping has been systematically carried out, together with studies of mineral resources. The publication programme includes *Annual reports, Memoirs, Bulletins,* the *Economic geology series* and *Geophysical papers*. In addition to the map-making division, the Survey maintains a museum, library and laboratories.

614 Geological Survey of Great Britain, instituted as the Geological Ordnance Survey in 1935, was foreshadowed in 1832, when De la Beche, secretary of the Geological Society, was authorised to add geological colouring to the one inch ordnance maps of Devon, with adjoining Somerset, Dorset and Cornwall. Since that time, a national programme of mapping and publication has been gradually formulated, comprising the map series, *Palaeontological memoirs,*

Mineral statistics, Iron ore memoirs, Stratigraphical monographs, Water supply memoirs and special reports and memoirs. Memoirs accompany the sheet maps. The geological maps of the British Isles are now in five main series: the twenty-five miles to one inch, 1:1,584,000, fourth edition, 1957; the ten miles to one inch, 1:625,000, second edition, 1957; the quarter-inch to one mile, 1:253,440, in various editions; the one inch to one mile, 1:63,360, new series reprints with the national grid; and the six inches to one mile, 1:10,560. There are also special maps of the coalfields and other areas of significance. The Survey is now within the Institute of Geological Sciences.

Refer also

Sir Edward Bailey: *Geological Survey of Great Britain* (Allen and Unwin, 1952).

Sir J S Flett: *The first hundred years of the Geological Survey of Great Britain* (HMSO, 1937), which includes a bibliography.

George M Bennison and Alan E Wright: *The geological history of the British Isles* (Arnold, 1969).

A K Wells and J F Kirkaldy: *Outline of historical geology* (Allen and Unwin, sixth edition, 1968).

See also under Institute of Geological Sciences.

615 The Geologists' Association was formed in 1858 to encourage interest and research in geology and allied subjects through discussion, visits and field work. More recently, the Association has directed most of its work to the discovery and demonstration of new geological knowledge, whilst still providing facilities for students and amateurs to gain practical knowledge of the subject. Individual groups have developed in north-east Lancashire, the Midlands, North Staffordshire and South Wales. The *Proceedings*, issued in four parts each year, contain papers embodying the research of members, reports of the geology demonstrated at the field meetings and in museums and, from time to time, résumés of current knowledge of particular subjects; the volumes are fully indexed, with ten-yearly cumulated indexes, and form an important source of reference in geological literature, well illustrated by plates, maps and text figures. *Monthly circulars* contain announcements of meetings and papers to be read, with full particulars and lists of maps, books or other source material suggested for consultation; they form excellent guides to the geological features of the districts. In addition, there are special publications, descriptive geological pamphlets and the *Geologists' Association guides* concerning individual areas. The library, incorporated with that of University College, London, contains most of the standard geological works of reference, the publications of the leading geological and natural history societies at home and abroad and of the British and colonial geological surveys.

Refer also

G S Sweeting: *The Geologists' Association 1858–1958. a history of the first hundred years* (The Association, 1958).

616 '**The geometrical seaman:** *a book of early nautical instruments*', by E G R Taylor and M W Richey (Hollis and Carter, 1962), provides a unique, illustrated monograph on the instruments available to early seamen and therefore of interest to the geographer specialising in the progress of exploration and discovery. Following an introduction and a fascinating chapter on 'the old instrument-maker's shop', the apparatus described includes lead and line, the azimuth compass, the cross-staff, quadrant, mariner's astrolabe and the 'kamal', the back-staff, Hadley's quadrant, sextant, the reflecting circle, the helmsman's traverse board, the sinical quadrant and traverse board, marine chronometer, Gunter's scale and sliding gunters, the vernier, bubble level, station pointer, telescopes, globes, the marine chair, rutter and pilot books, tide-tables, nautical tables and catalogues of nautical instruments.

617 '**Geomorphological abstracts**' has been published by the Department of Geography, London School of Economics, since 1960, first in four issues a year, then in six issues yearly from 1964, when the scope was enlarged. Coverage is international; abstracts are mostly informative, arranged by a broad subject grouping. Author and regional indexes have been prepared and a cumulative index is available covering 1960–1965; from 1966, an author index and subject index of more than 22,000 entries was prepared on a computer. In 1966, the service formed the basis of a fully developed abstracting service, *Geo Abstracts* (*qv*).

Refer also

Martin H P Bott: *The interior of the earth* (Arnold, 1971).

D Brunsden, *ed*: *Slopes: form and process* (Institute of British Geographers, 1971).

R B Bunnett: *Physical geography in diagrams* (Longmans, third impression, 1966).

M A Carson and M J Kirby: *Hillslope form and process* (CUP,

1972).

Richard J Chorley: 'The role and relations of physical geography', *Progress in geography*, 1971.

Richard J Chorley ed: *Spatial analysis in geomorphology* (Methuen, for the British Geomorphological Research Group, 1972).

Richard J Chorley and Barbara A Kennedy: *Physical geography: a systems approach* (Prentice-Hall, 1971).

Sir Charles Cotton: *Geomorphology: an introduction to the study of landforms* (Whitcombe and Tombs, seventh edition, 1968).

J L Davies: *Geographical variation in coastal development* (Oliver and Boyd, 1972).

M Derruau: *Précis de géomorphologie* (Paris: Masson, fifth edition, 1967).

John C Doornkamp and C A M King: *Numerical analysis in geomorphology: an introduction* (Arnold, 1971).

Carl O Dunbar: *The earth* (Weidenfeld and Nicolson, 1966).

D J Easterbrook: *Principles of geomorphology* (McGraw-Hill, 1969).

T F Gaskell, *ed*: *The earth's mantle* (Academic Press, 1967).

Physics of the earth (Thames and Hudson, 1970).

K J Gregory and E H Brown: 'Data processing and the study of landforms', *Annals of geomorphology*, 1966.

M Herak and V T Stringfield, *ed*: *Karst: important karst regions of the northern hemisphere* (Amsterdam: Elsevier, 1972).

Alfred Hettner: *The surface features of the land: problems and methods of geomorphology* (Macmillan, translated from the second edition by Philip Tilley, 1972).

Pascual Jordan: *The expanding earth: some consequences of Dirac's Gravitation Hypothesis* (Oxford: Pergamon, translated and edited by Arthur Beer *et al*, 1971).

F Machatschek: *Geomorphologie*, translated into English from the ninth edition by D J Davis, edited by K M Clayton (Oliver and Boyd, 1969); a standard text in Germany.

K F Mather, *ed*: *Source book in geology, 1900–1950* (OUP; Harvard University Press, 1967).

Cliff Ollier: *Weathering* (Oliver and Boyd, edited by K M Clayton, 1969).

C P Patton and F L Kramer: *Physical geography* (Belmont, California: Wadsworth Publishing Company, 1970).

C P Patton and F L Kramer *et al: Physical geography* (Belmont, California: Wadsworth, 1970).

Marton Pécsi, *ed: Problems of relief planation: studies in geography in Hungary* (Budapest: Akadémiai Kiadó, 1970).

A F Pitty: *Introduction to geomorphology* (Methuen, 1971).

Adrian E Scheidegger: *Theoretical geomorphology* (Allen and Unwin, 1970).

S J Shand: *The study of rocks* (Allen and Unwin, third edition, 1951).

R J Small: *The study of landforms: a textbook of geomorphology* (CUP, 1972).

B W Sparks: *Rocks and relief* (Longmans, 1971).

J A Steers: *The unstable earth: some recent views in geomorphology* (Methuen, fifth edition, reprinted, 1963).

David R Stoddart: 'Climatic geomorphology: review and reassessment', *Progress in geography*, 1969.

A N Strahler: *Planet earth: its physical systems through geologic time* (New York: Harper and Row, 1972).

A N Strahler: *Introduction to physical geography* (Wiley, 1970).

A N Strahler *et al*: 'Some results and applications of karst hydrology: a symposium', *The geographical journal*, June 1973.

M M Sweeting: *Karst landforms* (Macmillan, 1972).

W D Thornbury: *Principles of geomorphology* (Wiley, second edition, 1969).

Jean Tricart: *L'epiderme de la terre: esquisse d'une géomorphologie appliquée* (Paris: Masson, 1962).

Jean Tricart: *Précis de géomorphologie* (Paris: SEDES, 1968–).

Jean Tricart: *Principes et méthodes de la géomorphologie* (Paris: Masson, 1965).

C R Twidale: *Structural landforms: landforms associated with granitic rocks, faults and folded strata* (Cambridge, Mass: MIT Press, 1971).

Peter J Wyllie: *The dynamic earth: textbook in geosciences* (Wiley, 1971).

B Zakrzewska: 'Trends and methods in land form geography', *Annals* of the Association of American Geographers, 1967).

618 'Geomorphology of cold environments', by Jean Tricart, translated into English by Edward Watson (Macmillan, 1969, 1970), presents in a condensed form the material contained in the two volumes of *Traité de géomorphologie* (SEDES, Paris, 1963), with a revision of text and bibliography by Professor Tricart. While the treatment is original, the outline and approach are traditional enough—'Extent of frost climate phenomena'; 'Periglacial processes and landforms'; 'Glacial processes and landforms'. The few photographs are superb.

Compare A M Harvey, *ed*: *Geomorphology in a tropical environment* (Occasional Paper no 5, British Geomorphological Research Group, May 1968).

619 'Geophysikalische Bibliographie von Nord-und Ostsee', a comprehensive work by Fritz Model, published for the Deutsches Hydrographisches Institut of Hamburg by the firm of Gebrüder Borntraeger, Berlin, 1966, covers a clearly defined area between the west coast of Ireland and the eastern limit of the Baltic, in two parts, to 1961. Books and articles are included, in a wide range of languages, including Russian. The second part consists of an alphabetical list of authors and of periodicals, plus other sections designed to facilitate the use of the bibliography; the introductory matter to the first part is in English as well as in German.

620 The Geoscience Information Society, United States of America, organised as an independent non-profit professional body in 1965, aims to promote the exchange of information in the earth sciences through the mutual co-operation of its members. Literature guides and bibliographies are planned, including a *Bibliography of theses in the United States and Canada*. The annual meeting is held in conjunction with the annual convention of the Geological Society of America.

621 GeoServices, of London and Alberta, a current awareness service for all interested in the earth sciences, prepares three periodicals (published by Lea Associates, 1968–). *Geotitles weekly* lists in English the titles of all new publications within the field; publications scanned include journals, trade magazines, books, theses, patents and standards, conference announcements, trade literature and broadcasts. Searching is done in London and by correspondents in different parts of the world and the time-lag between publication and inclusion in the index is claimed to be no more than ten to fourteen days, distribution being by air mail. Titles are arranged by what is called a UDC-linkable GeoServices Decimal Classification and they are also available on library catalogue cards. The weekly editorial draws attention to significant trends. *Geoscience documentation,* 1970–, consists of a world list of current serial publications, giving details of frequency, publisher and changes in publication; new serials will be added, as will analyses of geoscience literature, bibliographic news and information on data handling projects. The monthly *Geocom bulletin*, 1968–, concentrates on news of research methodology and exploration, with emphasis on mathematical and computer studies. Regular cumulative indexes are planned.

622 The Geo-stat system for geographical statistics, which includes transparent map overlays, so that items can be placed and identified according to geographical location as well as by other factors, uses national grid co-ordinates. Geo-stat works with any metric scale and a map can contain one or a hundred national grid squares; different scales can be used for different jobs, so long as the scale gives a reasonable spread of holes.

623 'A German and English glossary of geographical terms', compiled by E Fischer and F E Elliott (American Geographical Society, 1950), includes those terms which are of central importance to the subject.

624 The German Copper Institute, Berlin, founded in 1927 for the purposes of research, industry and scientific studies in copper, is mainly concerned with the dissemination of information on copper to a wide public. A library is maintained, in which a comprehensive card index is kept. The Institute works closely with the New York Copper and Brass Research Association and with the British Copper Institute. A monthly *Kupfer-Mitteilungen* contains essays and articles on German and foreign publications in the field of copper research and about ninety technical journals are regularly evaluated. In 1961, the Institute introduced a teaching service including lectures, demonstrations and film presentations for technical colleges and private firms.

625 'Geschichte der Kartographie' was completed in 1943 by Leo Bagrow and published by Safari-Verlag, Berlin, in 1951; an English edition, with some rearrangement of the text, was undertaken by R A Skelton, with the title *History of cartography* (Watts, 1964). This erudite work is concerned with maps as 'craft products', presenting an account of the principal groups of maps to the mid eighteenth century, especially in their aesthetic and cultural aspects. The majority of the illustrations, line and half-tone, are printed from the original blocks. A useful 'List of cartographers to 1750' and a 'Select bibliography', together with references throughout the text, make this the most definitive English-language history of the period to date.

Refer also
A Libault: *Histoire de la cartographie* (Paris: Chaix, 1959).

626 Gesellschaft für Erdkunde zu Berlin, founded in 1828, is one of the great geographical societies of the world. Particularly important is the quarterly journal *Erde*, 1839–, which contains abstracts, bibliographies and detailed reviews, in addition to original articles of consistent scholarship. Another important bibliographical work is the *Bibliotheca geographica: jahres-bibliographie der geographischen literatur*, edited by Otto Baschin, which covers the years 1891–1912 in nineteen volumes (Berlin: Kühl, 1895–1917).

627 'Glacial and periglacial geomorphology', by Clifford Embleton and Cuchlaine A M King (Arnold, 1968), emphasises particularly the landforms and the processes of erosion and deposition; features actively being created by ice today are considered alongside features relict from the Pleistocene, which combine to form the present environment. The first section of the book describes the characteristics of contemporary ice-sheets and glaciers, including their physical nature, régimes and mode of flow, the causes and effects of glaciation on other land features. The second part deals with the erosional work of glacier ice and meltwater, with chapters on cirques and U-shaped valleys, followed, in part three, by studies of special forms, including till fabrics, moraines, drumlins and glacial lakes. Finally, such topics as weathering processes and permafrost are discussed. The whole work is well documented and there are 125 maps and diagrams, as well as thirty plates, illustrating the text.

Note Stanford University has a Permafrost Library
Refer also
I Cornwall: *Ice Ages: their nature and effects* (John Baker, 1970).
J Ross Mackay: 'The world of underground ice', *Annals* of the Association of American Geographers, March 1972.
R J Price: *Glacial and fluvioglacial landforms* (Edinburgh:

Oliver and Boyd, 1973).

B W Sparks and R G West: *The ice age in Britain* (Methuen, 1972).

J R Williams: *Ground water in the permafrost regions of Alaska* (us Government Printing Office, 1970, for the Geological Survey).

Glaciers, Proceedings of Workshop Seminar held at the University of New Brunswick, September, 1970.

628 'Glacier sounding in the Polar regions' was the title of a Symposium held at the Royal Geographical Society on the afternoon of 17 February, 1969. The papers, subsequently published in the December 1969 issue of *The geographical journal*, consisted of five specialist reports: 'The vhf radio echo technique', by Dr S Evans; 'Airborne radio echo sounding of the Greenland ice sheet', by P Gudmandsen; 'Airborne radio echo sounding by the British Antarctic Survey', by Dr Charles Swithinbank; 'Results of radio echo sounding in Northern Ellesmere Island, 1966', by Dr G Hattersley-Smith; 'Long-range echo flights over the Antarctic ice sheet', by Dr G De Q Robin. The discussions are reproduced, as well as some magnificent plates, maps and figures in the text, and references follow each section.

629 Globes: The oldest extant globe is probably that in the Royal Museum at Naples, the *Atlante Farnesiano*, which is thought to date from about 300 bc. Both celestial and terrestrial globes were used by Greek scholars and many are the references to the use of celestial globes and armillary spheres by Persian and Arab astronomers. Crates, the Greek philosopher (*c* 150 bc), asserted that the only way of portraying accurately the true shape of the various parts of the world was to show them on a globe; he built a globe on which were shown three imaginary land masses in the regions of the Americas and Australasia, to balance the land masses he knew.

The earliest known modern terrestrial globe is that made by Martin Behaim (*qv*), which is richly coloured and decorated and based probably on a map by Henricus Martellus of about 1490. During the following years, many more were built, some of great size, elaborate and fairly accurate for those parts of the earth which were at all well known. In 1507, Martin Waldseemüller began to make gores, lens-shaped flat sections, which could be pasted on a globe with a minimum loss of accuracy. This made possible the 'mass production' of globes and they continued to be used in conjunction with the increasing variety of maps and charts by explorers, cosmographers and liberal scholars alike. The earliest examples of English globes are known by reference only or by their presence in portraits, as in the picture of Sebastian Cabot when an old man and in the Holbein painting 'The ambassadors'. From about the 1540s, the globes of Gemma Frisius were held in the greatest esteem in England; John Dee, for instance, who studied under Gemma Frisius and another of his pupils, Gerard Mercator, in 1547 brought back to Cambridge 'two great globes of Gerardus Mercator's making'. The Frisius globes were gradually superseded by those of Mercator, whose 1541 terrestrial globe and 1551 celestial globe had a very wide circulation. There are many references in the literature of the time, also in records of acquisitions in such libraries as the Bodleian. Several of the Mercator engraved gores have survived, still in sheet form. Jodocus Hondius and Willem Blaeu also made globes as well as maps. In the Netherlands, the Van Langrens (or Florentius) family established a famous globe-making business. Through the seventeenth century, globes became even more fantastic. The great cartographer, P Vincenzo Maria Coronelli (1650–1718), made a globe fifteen feet in diameter for Louis XIV, which could actually be climbed into; in 1688, he produced engraved gores for globes three feet six inches in diameter, the largest engraved gores to that time, and in 1696, he made one also for William III, to show the expanding world. A modern globe featured by Georama reproduces the original Coronelli stand. Fine globes were made also by Gerhard Valck and his son between 1700 and 1750, and in England, by John Senex, publisher of atlases, maps and globes. The Adams family, also, in their Fleet Street publishing house, set a high standard for English globe-making, with their well-known eighteen inch diameter globes. With the globes of William and John Cary and such European globe-makers as Rigobert Bonne and Joseph Jérôme le Français Lalande in France and Giovanni Maria Cassini in Italy, the great period of decorative globes came to an end.

A facsimile of the rare second edition of *Libro dei Globi*, 1693–1701, volume X of Coronelli's thirteen-volume *Atlante Veneto*, 1693, was issued by TOT, 1969, together with a portrait of Coronelli and a bibliographical note by Dr Helen Wallis; included are the gores of Coronelli's largest pair of engraved globes, $3\frac{1}{2}$ feet in diameter. There is a Coronelli World League of Friends of the Globe; a third international conference was held in September 1969, for the first time together with the International Conference on the History of Cartography.

The present-day renewed interest in globes has resulted in considerable experiment in printing, finishing and mounting, and a number of magnificent examples are available, though expensive. For teaching purposes at various levels, Philip and Georama offer perhaps the most interesting range, from the six inch 'London' Library Globe to the seventy-two inch Pilkington-Jackson Orographical Globe. Between the two is a great variety of political, physical and special-purpose models. The latest developments include relief model globes, plastic inflatable globes and illuminated globes. The Istituto Geografico de Agostini, Novara, has specialised in globes of all kinds, for which full, often illustrated, catalogues are available. There are now several important collections of globes in various parts of the world, of which the Jagellonian University Museum, Cracow, holds one of the finest; a special catalogue of the collection was prepared in connection with the XIth International Congress of the History of Science, 1965.

A catalogue of early globes, made prior to 1850 and conserved in the United States, compiled by Ena L Yonge (American Geographical Society of New York, 1968; *Library series* no 6), includes armillary spheres, planetariums, orreries and astronomical clocks, also globe gores. The items are grouped by types, thereafter alphabetically by name of maker. A list of globemakers is a useful feature.

Refer also

D R McGregor: 'Geographical globes', *The cartographic journal*, June 1966.

E L Stevenson: *Terrestrial and celestial globes: their history and construction including a consideration of their value as aids in the study of geography and astronomy*, in two volumes (Yale University Press for the Hispanic Society of America, 1921).

George Goodall: *The globe and its uses* (Philip, second edition, 1948).

W Bonacker: *Das Schrifttum zur Globenkunde* (Leiden: Brill, 1960).

Oswald Muris and Gert Saarmann: *Der globus im Wandel der Zeiten: eine Geschichte der Globen* (Berlin: Columbus Verlag Paul Oestergaard KG, 1961).

Raymond Lister: *How to identify old maps and globes: with a list of cartographers, engravers, publishers and printers concerned with printed maps and globes from c1500 to c1850* (Bell, 1965) (*qv*).

Helen Wallis: 'A contemporary handbook to the Molyneux globes', *British Museum quarterly*, 1953.

Helen M Wallis: 'The first English globe: a recent discovery', *The geographical journal*, September 1951.

Helen M Wallis: 'Further light on the Molyneux globes', *The geographical journal*, September 1955.

R M Fisher: 'William Crashawe and the Middle Temple globes 1605–15', *The geographical journal*, February 1974.

H Fullard: 'The construction of globes', *The cartographic journal*, June 1964.

Der Globusfreund (Vienna, 1952–).

630 'Glossary of geographical names in six languages, *English, French, Italian, Spanish, German and Dutch*', compiled and arranged by Gabriella Lana, Liliana Isabez and Lidia Meak (Elsevier, 1967), forms one of the series *Glossaria interpretum*, supervised and co-ordinated by M Jean Herbert and sponsored by many of the world's linguistic organisations. The languages chosen were according to the frequency of their use at international conferences on the subject.

631 'A glossary of geographical terms' was prepared by a committee of the British Association for the Advancement of Science (Longmans, 1961) under the editorship of Sir Dudley Stamp. Definitions are drawn, with acknowledgements, from leading authoritative works, covering physical, human, economic and political geography. A second edition appeared in 1966.

632 'The golden encyclopaedia of geography' was adapted and edited by Theodore Shabad and P M Stern from the *Westermann Bildkarten Welt-Lexikon* (Macdonald, 1960). An introduction dealing with physical, economic and climatic features is followed by a series of articles, alphabetically arranged, on the main regions and towns, typical plants and animals and economic products, the whole being profusely illustrated.

633 'Goode's world atlas', previously *Goode's school atlas*, went into a twelfth revised edition by E B Espenshade, jr (Rand McNally, 1966), using improved cartographic and reproduction techniques. A pronouncing index of more than thirty thousand entries is included.

634 'Gough map of Britain', by an unknown cartographer, probably between 1347 and 1366, was first noticed by Richard Gough in his *British topography*, 1780, and the map itself was bequeathed with his collection to the Bodleian Library in 1809. The Bodleian has made a reproduction, with a matching transparent overlay showing the corresponding modern locations.

635 'Gran atlas Aguilar' is an outstanding atlas in three volumes, produced in Madrid in 1969. The method of relief representation is particularly fine, showing contours and clear layer colouring; a full blue is used for hydrographic features and the continental shelves and ocean troughs are well depicted. The town plans are another feature to note.

636 'Le grand atlas ou cosmographie Blaviane', the work of Johan Blaeu (Amsterdam, 1663), has received revived notice through the reproduction in 1967–68 of all the twelve volumes by N Israel, Meridian and TOT, with an introduction by Professor Dr Ir C Koeman in a separate volume. It is difficult to over-praise this exciting atlas and the words of the facsimile publishers may be taken literally—'The complete facsimile in twelve volumes of the most splendid atlas ever published. Extensive historical, geographical and cartographical descriptions of Europe, Africa, Asia and America . . . The engraved maps are not only surprisingly accurate, they are also wonderful works of art. The complete work is printed on specially made paper. The maps are mounted on guards.' All the frontispieces are included in the reproduction.

637 'Grande atlante geografico' is a beautiful atlas, edited by L Visintin (Istituto Geografico de Agostini, Novara, in a fifth revised edition, 1957). 232 plates of maps on astronomy, geology, physical, economic and political geography, climate and population are on scales varying from 1:50M to 1:1,500,000. Numerous city plans are most useful. Special features include fine distribution diagrams and block diagrams and the clear, varied symbols used throughout. Brief text notes accompany the maps and there is an index of about one hundred thousand entries.

638 'Great airports of the world', by Roy Allen (Ian Allan, second edition, 1968), describes forty-one airports, each entry giving basic facts and an account of particular characteristics, with runway diagram and photographs. The Introduction mentions outstanding events in the development of airports, especially in London, and sections at the end concern 'Helicopters of the world', 'Aids and services at the airport' and 'Airliners that use the world's airports', all illustrated.

639 Gresswell, Dr Ronald Kay (1905–1969) specialised in the study of coastlines and glaciation in Britain and Scandinavia, his work being recognised not only by his colleagues, but by Lancashire CC, the Nature Conservancy and by various government ministries. In his fine teaching work, he emphasised the value of field work and his interest in the training of young geographers is shown in his school textbooks: *The physical geography of glaciers and glaciation*, 1958; *The physical geography of rivers and valleys,* 1958; *Geology for geographers*, 1963; *Physical geography*, 1967; in addition to a number of articles for periodicals, notably the *Transactions* of the Institute of British Geographers.

640 'The Griffin', journal of the Department of Geography, North-Western Polytechnic, London, began in April 1970; in form, it is mimeographed, otherwise it is a typical example of the numbers of excellent journals which are prepared now by almost every Geography Department in the country. It covers a wide range of subjects, the articles being contributed by students, past and present, and by staff.

641 'Der Grosse Bertelsmann Weltatlas', compiled by Dr W Bormann at the Cartographical Institute, Bertelsmann Verlag, 1961, 1963 and 1964, is an excellently produced atlas, the result of a significant publishing venture. A special cartographic institute was established for the purpose, official information was gathered from all over the world and editions were published simultaneously in Denmark, Finland, Germany, the Netherlands and Sweden. Subsequently, French and Spanish editions were published and the *McGraw-Hill international atlas* (*qv*) was based on it. In the original, a valuable preface in German and English discusses 'The atlas—its development and possibilities', followed by a detailed introduction explaining the plan of this atlas itself, the scales employed, projections, contents and principles of nomenclature adopted.

642 'Der Grosse Brockhaus atlas', accompanying the sixteenth edition of *Der Grosse Brockhaus* and *Der Neue Brockhaus* 1960, is a useful reference atlas, including nearly four hundred coloured maps, town plans and statistical data. The index-gazetteer comprises some sixty thousand entries.

643 'Das Grosse Duden-Lexikon, Band 10: Weltatlas', prepared at the Geographisch-Kartographischen Institut Meyer, under the direction of Dr Adolf Hanle (Bibliographisches Institut Mannheim/Wien/Zurich, 1969), includes double-page spreads or folded sheets, with location maps and/or diagrams on the reverse. Moon surface photographs are a feature.

644 'Ground water year book', the first, 1964–66, prepared by the Water Resources Board (HMSO), contains ground water statistics for aguifers in England and Wales, together with related rainfall, evaporation and soil moisture deficits for the period January 1 1964 to December 31 1966. The index of observation wells and table of selected ground water level observations are prefaced by introduction, explanatory notes, other specialised notes and a few references. Folded diagrammatic maps are grouped at the end. The Water Resources Act 1963 requires the publication, inter alia, of information relating to ground water resources.
Refer also
> *Groundwater studies: an international guide for research and practice* (Unesco, 1972).
> F van der Leedon: *Ground water: a selected bibliography* (Port Washington: Water Information Center).

645 'The growth of world industry', published by the United Nations in two volumes, provides a comprehensive international review of statistics on the production of industrial commodities. The first volume contains the basic national data for each country in the form of separate country chapters and the second gives a selection of indicators, showing global and regional trends in industrial activities. The selection of commodities is based on a list of products and materials prepared by the Statistical Office of the United Nations.

646 'Guide bibliographique d'hydrogéologie', compiled by Jean Margat (Paris: Bureau de Recherches Géologiques et Minières, 1964), contains references to the more important and most recent books and articles in the French language, mainly later than 1950. It is planned to produce a companion guide to the more important works in other foreign languages.

647 'A guide to historical cartography: *a selected annotated list of references on the history of maps and mapmaking*', by W W Ristow and Clara E LeGear (Library of Congress, Map Division, Reference Department, 1960, second revised edition, 1961), is an important contribution to the definitive documentation of this subject; in addition to all usual reference sources, map catalogues are included, also such comprehensive monographs as those of Beazley and Bunbury.

648 'A guide to Irish bibliographical material, *being a bibliography of Irish bibliographies and some sources of information*', by Alan R Eager (The Library Association, 1964), was compiled as 'an exploratory volume' to make a beginning in the indexing of Irish enumerative bibliography and to serve as a quick reference guide for those interested in Irish studies. The arrangement of entries is based generally on the DC, with author and subject indexes; no annotations are included.

649 'A guide to Latin American studies', by M H Sable (Los Angeles: University of California, Latin American Center, 1967), was intended mainly for undergraduate and graduate students in all fields relevant to Latin America; all aspects of Latin American civilisation and all disciplines in the humanities, natural, applied and social sciences are covered. About five thousand entries, annotated in English, include monographs and reference books, pamphlets, periodical articles, government documents and conference proceedings, mainly in English and Spanish, but also in French, German and Portuguese.

Refer also

Irene Zimmerman: *Current national bibliographies of Latin America: a state of the art study* (University of Florida Press).

650 'A guide to literature on Iraq's natural resources', by Abu Ghraib of Baghdad, 1969, was prepared by A P Srivastava within the framework of the Unesco/Special Fund Project, Iraq 12; the work lists studies and reports from 1833 to 1968 broadly grouped under hydrology and allied areas, plants, climate, irrigation, soil and drainage.

Refer also

Iraq, semi-annual, 1934—(British School of Archaeology in Iraq).

K M Langley: *The industrialisation of Iraq* (Harvard University Press, 1961).

651 'Guide to London excursions', edited by K M Clayton, was prepared for the 20th International Geographical Congress, London, 1964. Usefully collected in this publication is a vast amount of information on the geographical features of interest as far distant as the radius of Oxford, with effective maps and diagrams. Chapters are included on the Meteorological Office Headquarters, the Ordnance Survey, the Royal Greenwich Observatory and other centres of advanced work of interest to geographers.

652 'A guide to manuscripts relating to America in Great Britain and Ireland', edited by B R Crick and others, was published for the British Association for American Studies by the Oxford University Press, 1961. It is comprehensive, giving annotations and locations, dealing by counties with England, Wales and Monmouthshire, Scotland, Northern Ireland and the Republic of Ireland.

653 'Guide to New Zealand reference material and other sources of information', compiled by John Harris (New Zealand Library Association, 1946; second edition, 1950), includes all subjects in their application to New Zealand to be found in monographs, official publications, serials and journals of societies and listing library collections. The sections are numbered and classified according to subject, following generally the classification of the Otago University Library, which uses the Bliss Bibliographic Classification. The first supplement appeared in June 1951 and the second in 1957, both prepared by A G Bagnall. Items are printed on one side of the page only, so that libraries may cut out and mount, if desired, the numbers referring to place in the main work.

654 'Guide to Russian reference books' in six volumes, of which the second deals with history, auxiliary historical sciences, ethnography and geography, has been published by the Hoover Institution on War, Revolution and Peace (Stanford University, 1962–). It lists and annotates 1,560 reference tools relating to Soviet and Russian history in general as well as to the histories of various specific events or geographical areas. Each section is preceded by an introductory survey.

655 'Guide to South African reference books', compiled by Reuben Musiker (Cape Town; Amsterdam: Balkema, fourth edition, 1965), arranges the items cited according to broad category headings or subject groupings, such as Bibliographies, Periodicals, Statistics, Economics, Commerce and trade, Agriculture, Geography. Brief annotations are appended as considered desirable.

Refer also

Reuben Musiker: *South African bibliography* (Crosby Lockwood, 1970).

656 Guides. *Note*: A short article on *Guides* was included in the first edition; the items named as examples need updating, otherwise the only comment that requires mention here is to emphasise the increasing numbers and variety of this genre of publication.

Refer also

John Vaughan: *The English guide book c. 1780–1870: an illustrated history* (Newton Abbot: David and Charles).

657 Gutkind, Dr Erwin E (1896–1968) directed his chief scholarship to the study of urban planning and rural settlement. Of his many written works, the one most interesting to the geographer is *Our world from the air: an international survey of man and his environment*, 1952. In 1956, he was appointed by the University of Philadelphia to undertake the project 'International History of City Development' under the auspices of the Institute for Environmental Studies; the work was planned in ten volumes and was completed by his daughter, a research associate at the University.

658 Gyldendal of Copenhagen produce from time to time works of great interest to geographers. Perhaps their most significant recent innovation has been the introduction of graded series of atlases for systematic study; *Atlas 1, Atlas 2* and *Atlas 3* were designed for progressive use in Danish schools. The idea was continued in the UK by Collins and Longmans.

659 'Habitat', the illustrated journal published bi-monthly by the Central Mortgage and Housing Corporation, is now mainly concerned with urban centres and the problems of city life, on an international scale.

660 Hakluyt, Richard (*c* 1552–1616) graduated at Oxford in 1574 and lectured for a while on maps, globes and geography generally. He travelled widely, making exhaustive notes concerning

geographical exploration and travels, which he subsequently prepared for publication. Notable among his writings were *Divers
voyages* . . ., 1582, reprinted by TOT in 1967, with *A shorte and briefe
narration of the two navigations to newe Fraunce*, 1580, edited, with
introduction by David B Quinn; and the *Principall navigations* . . .'
1589, which was enlarged to three volumes, 1598, 1599 and 1600. The
best complete modern edition is that published by the Hakluyt Society and MacLehose, Glasgow, in twelve volumes, 1903–5, with the
'Essay on the life and work of Hakluyt' by Professor Sir Walter
Raleigh. A considerable literature has grown on the Hakluyts and on
the Society (*see* below) which bears their name; especially interesting
is *The original writings and correspondence of the two Richard Hakluyts*, published by the Hakluyt Society in 1935, with introduction
and notes by E G R Taylor.

661 Hakluyt Society, founded in 1846, is a publishing society only,
having for its object the publication of original narratives of important voyages, travels, expeditions and other geographical records.
Many of them, especially the accounts and translations of the Elizabethan and Stuart periods, are admirable examples of contemporary
prose styles. In the case of a foreign original, the work is rendered in
English, either in a new translation, or in an earlier translation, unabridged, providing that this is accurate and suitable. Two volumes
are published annually, each edited by an expert, including notes,
maps, portraits and other illustrations, and facsimile reproductions,
whenever possible, of original plates, woodcuts or drawings. In the
first series, a hundred volumes were issued between 1847 and 1898;
the second series began in 1899. Indexes of the Society's publications
are included in *Richard Hakluyt and his successors*, edited by Edward
Lynam, published to mark the centenary of the Society in 1946.
Reprints of the original volumes have been made, by arrangement
with the Cambridge University Press, by Kraus Reprint Corporation, New York.

    Refer also

      Alison M Quinn: 'The modern index to Richard Hakluyt's
Principall Navigations', *The indexer*, Spring, 1967.

      David B Quinn: *Richard Hakluyt, editor: introduction to the
complete facsimiles of Divers voyages* (1582) and 'A shorte and
briefe narration of the two navigations to neue Fraunce' (1580)
(TOT, 1967, *Mundes novus* series, translated by John Florio),
introduced by a survey of the sources and bibliography of the

books, with a modern index.

George B Parks: *Richard Hakluyt and the English voyages* (New York: American Geographical Society, 1928; Frederich Ungar Publishing Company, second edition, with introduction by James A Williamson, 1961); the author refers to the younger Hakluyt as 'the first professional geographer in England's history' and to the *English voyages* as 'the flower of his career, the planned and purposeful career of the geographer'. An appendix sets out 'A list of English books of travel overseas and geographical description to 1600, from 1496', arranged chronologically. Another appendix brings together Hakluyt's writings, letters, *mss* and published works, also studies about him.

Janet Hampden: *Richard Hakluyt: voyages and documents: selected with an introduction and a glossary* (OUP, 1958).

662 Hallwag maps are a familiar feature of contemporary life. The political maps are fully coloured to show de facto boundaries, relief is shown by hill shading, with spot heights, and such features as railways and shipping routes, roads, pipelines, ruins and oases are depicted with the clarity demanded for road and tourist users. Town stamps are graded according to size of population.

663 'Handbook for geography teachers' was first edited by Miss D M Forsaith and produced by Goldsmith's College in 1932. A new edition was prepared by G J Cons, chairman of the University of London Institute of Education Standing Sub-Committee in Geography, published by the Committee in 1955; a third edition followed in 1957 and a fourth, edited by R C Honeybone, in 1960. A fifth edition by M Long, in 1964, was reprinted in 1965. Sections deal with geography in schools of various kinds; geography both out of doors and indoors; geographical societies. Booklists are included for successive levels of study and for teachers.

Compare

Robert E Gabler, *ed*: *A handbook for geography teachers* (Normal, Ill.: National Council for Geographic Education, Publication Center, 1966).

664 'Handbook of American resources for African studies', prepared by Peter Duignan (Stanford, California: Hoover Institution on War, Revolution and Peace, 1967), mentions ninety five manuscript and library collections, also missionary and church, ethnographic and business archives.

665 'Handbook of Hispanic source materials and research organizations in the United States', edited by Ronald Hilton (Stanford University Press, second edition, 1956) was first issued in 1942 by the University of Toronto Press, under the title *Handbook of Hispanic source materials,* compiled by the same editor. This is a comprehensive work, covering Spain, Portugal and Latin America of the pre- and post-Columbian periods; Florida, Texas and California until their annexation by the United States. Arrangement is regionally, then alphabetically. An index map and a list of published sheets of 'The Map of Hispanic America' 1:1M are included.

666 'Handbook of Latin American studies' has been published approximately annually by Harvard University Press since 1936; arrangement is by subject, subdivided according to country or region.
  Refer also
    to the works of George Pendle, the acknowledged expert on Latin American countries, including *Argentina* and *Paraguay: a riverside nation* (OUP for The Royal Institute of International Affairs, 1955, 1961, 1963; and 1954, 1956, 1967, respectively); *The land and people of Peru* (Black, 1966).

667 'Handbook on the principles of hydrology': in 1966, the Canadian National Committee for the International Hydrological Decade began to sponsor the first of a series of familiarisation seminars on the 'Principles of Hydrology' at the University of Saskatchewan, to provide an opportunity for workers trained in diverse disciplines to gain a common understanding of the science; voluntary contributions have since been included in the resulting publications. The aim is to supply, to a certain extent, the requirements for the teaching and training of students in hydrology, both at the advanced undergraduate and first-year graduate levels; and to provide a handbook from which individuals active in the practical aspects of hydrology may gain some appreciation of the basic hydrological principles and also have access to Canadian data useful to them. The text is in French and English.

668 'Handbooks to the modern world' series, published by Blond, London, provide essential information and comment about every country, by means of essays, statistical tables, maps and half-tone illustrations, compiled by a panel of experts. *Western Europe . . .,* edited by John Calmann, covers the area from Iceland to Turkey; part I provides basic information on each country, part II deals with important questions affecting all or much of Western Europe and part III with the Common Market and various aspects of European integration. *Africa . . .,* edited by Colin Legum, went into a second, enlarged edition to include the developments of the new states; *Asia . . .,* edited by Guy Wint, is in four main parts—the usual basic information by country, surveys of the history and development of each country, essays on all aspects concerning the continent as a whole and an appendix giving selected texts of important treaties and agreements. *Latin America and the Caribbean . . .,* edited by Claudio Véliz, 1967, follows the general pattern; volumes on Australia and New Zealand, the Soviet Union and North America complete the series.

669 'The haven-finding art: *a history of navigation from Odysseus to Captain Cook',* by E G R Taylor, with a foreword by Commodore K St B Collins, Hydrographer of the Navy (Hollis and Carter, 1956), sets out in a readable narrative that wears its scholarship easily, the gradual improvements in apparatus and instruments that made accurate navigation possible. In five parts, the first is devoted to a general introduction, followed by 'Navigation without magnetic compass or chart'; 'With compass and chart'; 'Instruments and tables'; 'Towards mathematical navigation'. A number of reproductions and figures are included throughout the text and there is a select bibliography of original documents and secondary works. A new augmented edition, published in association with the Institute of Navigation, contains an appendix on Chinese Medieval Navigation based on the research of Joseph Needham.

Refer also

J B Hewson: *A history of the practice of navigation* (Glasgow: Brown, Son and Ferguson, 1951).

David Lewis: *We, the navigators: the ancient art of landfinding in the Pacific* (University Press of Hawaii, 1972).

W E May: *A history of marine navigation* (Henley-on-Thames: Foulis, 1973).

D W Waters: *The art of navigation in England in Elizabethan and early Stuart times* (Hollis and Carter, 1958).

670 'The heart of the Antarctic: *being the story of the British Antarctic Expedition 1907–1909, with an introduction by H R Mill',* by

Sir E H Shackleton, is in two volumes, with maps in a pocket. Shackleton and his scientific helpers were the first to establish the position of the South Magnetic Pole; quite apart from the discoveries and important scientific results of his expeditions. Shackleton left his influence on Antarctic exploration by his adoption of a new technique in sledge travelling and the abandonment of many of the older traditions of polar exploration.

See also
Edward Shackleton: *Arctic journeys: the story of the Oxford University Ellesmere Land Expedition 1934–5* (Hodder and Stoughton, 1937).

671 W Heffer and Sons Limited, Cambridge, new and secondhand booksellers, hold stocks of publications on all general subjects; a journal and periodical subscription service and a reasonable search service are maintained and recently developed have been the individual services. Heffer's Paperback Shop, Heffer's Penguin Shop, Heffer's Children's Bookshop, Heffer's Stationery Shop and Printing Works. *The book news* is circulated every other month. Of special interest to geographers are the individual catalogues issued from time to time, including, for example, 'Geographical and earth sciences', with entries grouped under the headings 'Geography', 'Planning and urbanisation', 'Atlases and cartography', 'Polar', 'Oceanography', 'Geology', 'Meteorology and Climatology', 'Periodicals'. Other catalogues have been compiled on 'Latin America', 'India and Pakistan', 'Africa and Asia', 'Oriental and African Studies', 'Modern Europe' and 'Soviet Union'.

672 Herbertson, Andrew John (1865–1915) was one of the scholar-geographers who helped to lay the foundations of modern academic geography. He studied in Germany and France, developing theories over a broad field, his early work being in physical geography, especially meteorology and oceanography, from which he proceeded to the study of botany and worked as demonstrator in botany under Sir Patrick Geddes at Dundee. In 1899 he was appointed lecturer in regional geography at Oxford as assistant to H J Mackinder, to whom he succeeded as reader and director of the School of Geography in 1905. He introduced the theory of the major natural regions of the world, based on structure, relief and climate; his paper to the Royal Geographical Society in 1905 on 'The major natural regions' was not greeted with enthusiasm at the time, but many of his ideas now seem surprisingly up-to-date. *Man and his work: an introduction to human geography*, written with F D Herbertson, also reveals his modern outlook. Herbertson's meteorological knowledge is shown particularly in his contribution to the *Atlas of meteorology* (*qv*), the third volume of *Bartholomew's physical atlas*. He was a founder-member of the Geographical Association, which has established a Herbertson Memorial Lecture in his honour. In a special issue of *Geography*, November 1965, an appreciation of his life and work is given, with lists of his published works, both books and periodical articles, together with an outline of his editorial activities.

Refer also

E W Gilbert: 'Andrew John Herbertson 1865–1915', *The geographical journal*, December, 1965, which includes a bibliography.

673 'Hereford mappa mundi', now in Hereford Cathedral, was probably made between 1285 and 1295. Cartographically, it is of the greatest interest; it reveals also considerable evidence concerning secular life in the Middle Ages. *The world map of Richard Haldingham in Hereford Cathedral* was reproduced by The Royal Geographical Society in 1954, with a memoir by G R Crone (Reproductions of early manuscript maps, III), in nine overlapping sheets, with a sheet of diagrams, at a scale of about nine-tenths the original. Richard Gough said of the map in 1780—'In the library of Hereford Cathedral is preserved a very curious map of the world, inclosed in a case with folding doors, on which are painted the Virgin and the Angel. It is drawn with a pen on vellum, fastened on boards, and is six feet four inches high to the pediment and five feet four inches wide.'

Refer also

'Key to the Photographs of the Ancient Map of the World preserved in Hereford Cathedral', available at the Cathedral.

W L Bevan and H W Philliott: *Mediaeval geography: an essay in illustration of the Hereford Mappa Mundi*, 1873, reprinted by TOT, 1969.

A L Moir: *The world map in Hereford Cathedral*, a paper read to the Woolhope Naturalists' Field Club, Hereford, on 25th November, 1954; Malcolm Letts: 'The pictures in the Hereford mappa mundi', *Notes and queries*, January, 1955; both reprinted as a pamphlet available from the Cathedral, Hereford.

G R Crone: 'New light on the Hereford map', *The Geographical journal*, December, 1965.

674 Herodotus (5th century BC), Greek author of a history of the Persian Wars, travelled widely, hence his interest for geographers, for throughout his writing he indicates the extent of geographical knowledge and opinion in his time. He distinguished between his sources of information as 'eyewitness' and 'hearsay'; and his remarks concerning contemporary trading, occupations and home 'crafts', the people and physical conditions he encountered are valuable evidence, making due allowance for error or misinterpretation.

Refer also

J Kenrick: *The Egypt of Herodotus*, 1841.

John L Myres: *Herodotus: father of history* (Oxford: Clarendon Press, 1953; Loeb translation, in four volumes).

W Rennell: *The geography of Herodotus* (1800, second edition, 1830).

J Talboys Wheeler: *The geography of Herodotus* . . . (Longmans, Brown, Green and Longmans, 1854).

675 Hettner, Alfred (1859–1941) was a physical and regional geographer and one of the founders of modern German geography. He travelled widely and his influence reached into many spheres, but his main work was achieved as professor at Heidelberg. One of his chief published works was *Die Geographie: ihre geschichte, ihre Wesen und ihre Methoden*, 1927; and his ideals and geographical theories were embodied in the great journal *Geographisches Zeitschrift (qv)* which he founded. Hettner's *Surface features of the earth*, a key work in geomorphology first published in 1921, has been translated into English by Philip Tilley and published by Macmillan.

676 'The Heyden new world atlas' (New York and London: Heyden, 1970) is an atlas for general reference rather than for more advanced use. Arrangement is by continent, each being introduced by a physical and a political map. The majority, sectional maps, show river patterns, settlements in five grades, main communications and political and administrative boundaries. The fifty thousand or so names included in the gazetteer refer to relevant map plates and there are a glossary of geographical terms and notes on pronunciation.

344

677 Hinks, Arthur Robert (1873–1945) exerted a widespread influence through his many geographical activities. He was a meticulous scholar, particularly in astronomy, mathematics and all aspects of surveying and cartography, and a stimulating lecturer, communicating his formidable knowledge with an infectious energy. He also wrote many articles and books on maps and surveying, which have proved constantly valuable to students. His other main contribution to the status of geography arose from his appointment to the staff of the Royal Geographical Society in 1912; he improved the production, especially the typography, of *The geographical journal*, revised the *Hints to travellers* series and initiated the *Technical* series. Between 1914 and 1918, he directed the production of more than a hundred sheets of the provisional 1:1M Map of the world and some sheets of the 1:2M Map of Africa; and from 1919, as secretary to the Permanent Committee on Geographical Names, he added greatly to the success of the project.

Refer also
    T S Blakeney: 'A R Hinks and the first Everest Expedition 1921', *The geographical journal*, September, 1970.

678 Hipparchus (*c* 160–125 BC), the most celebrated astronomer of the ancient world, evolved the concept of map projections. His power of thought was in advance of technical developments, but he divided the great circle into three hundred degrees and greatly improved the spherical astrolabe.

Refer also
    H Berger: *Die Geographischen Fragmente des Hipparch*, 1869.
    The geographical fragments of Hipparchus, edited, with introduction, by D R Dicks (Athlone Press, 1960).

679 'Histoire des villes de France avec une introduction général pour chaque province', in six volumes by M Aristide Guilbert and others (Paris: Furne et Cie, Perrotin, H Fournier, 1845), is a magnificent work, including superb steel engravings.

680 'A historical atlas of Canada', edited by D G G Kerr was sponsored by the Canadian Historical Association (Nelson, Second edition, 1966). Cartography is by Major C C J Bond and the maps were drawn by Ellsworth M Walsh and others. The maps are mainly in two colours, with brief textual entries, beginning with 'Environment and prehistory', and there is a selected bibliography.

681 'An historical atlas of China', in the new edition, is based on the *Historical and commercial atlas of China*, compiled by Albert Harrmann and published by the Harvard-Yenching Institute in 1925 (Monograph series, volume 1). A new edition was first published in 1966 by the Aldine Publishing Company, Chicago; Edinburgh University Press were agents for Great Britain and the Commonwealth. The work has now been extended and re-drawn under the supervision of Professor Norton S Ginsburg, with a prefatory essay by Paul Wheatley (Djambatan/Morton). Ten new maps have been added on the main characteristics of Chinese agricultural land use, density and patterns of population, distribution of minerals and industries and of the transportation network. Endpapers present a physical map of modern China and one of the political and administrative divisions, making altogether seventy five six-colour maps and town plans. The bibliography has been updated; a list of Chinese characters has been included and there are two indexes of geographical and proper names.

682 'The historical atlas of the holy land', edited by E G Kraeling (Rand McNally, 1959), is one of the many works of scholarship inspired by modern archaeological discoveries. The atlas comprises a brief outline of the historical geography by maps, photographs and text, which begins with an account of the finding of the Dead Sea Scrolls.

683 'Historical atlas of Latin America: *political, geographic, economic, cultural*', edited by A Curtis Wilgus (New York: Cooper Square Publishing, Inc, 1943; new edition, enlarged, 1967), consists of sketchmaps, with facing commentary, on the following topics: 'The geographical background'; 'The ethnological background'; 'The European background'; 'The colonial period'; 'The revolutions for independence'; 'The national period'; 'Latin American boundary controversies'; and 'Latin American relations with the United States and Europe'.

684 'An historical geography of the Ottoman Empire from earliest times to the end of the sixteenth century, *with detailed maps to illustrate the expansion of the Sultanate*', prepared by Donald Edgar Pitcher (Brill, 1972, released 1973), deals principally with facts gleaned from many sources and arranged to present a coherent picture of the progress of Ottoman expansion. The emphasis is on political geography. Of the thirty-six coloured maps, some are large-scale surveys on the whole of the Balkans, Anatolia or the Middle East, others concentrate on historically important smaller areas. With two exceptions, they are original, freshly constructed from available evidence. The index lists all names, giving the equivalents in Turkish, Greek, Rumanian and Hungarian.

685 'The history and use of diamond', by S Tolansky, published by Methuen, examines the strange and scientific characteristics of diamonds, together with their history from Biblical times, their folklore and anecdotes connected with them and the techniques of mining and cutting. The final chapters cover the importance of diamonds in contemporary industry and their synthetic production in large quantities. A bibliography is included.

686 'A history of ancient geography among the Greeks and Romans from the earliest ages till the fall of the Roman empire' is a classic study in two volumes by E H Bunbury (Murray, 1879; second edition, 1883). Dover Publications issued an edition in 1932, with a second edition in 1959.
> *Refer also*
> *Atlas of the classical world* (Nelson, 1959).
> *Shorter atlas of the classical world* (Nelson, 1962).
> E H Warmington: *Greek geography* (Dent, 1934).

687 'A history of cartography: *2,500 years of maps and mapmakers'* (Elsevier, 1968; Thames and Hudson, 1969) is a fine display of the art of the cartographer, of 'those old maps that fascinate collectors'. The maps were chosen by R V Tooley, the text contributed by Charles Bricker and the preface by G R Crone. An introduction discusses the mapmaker's skills, following which each section deals with the history of cartography in each continent—'Europe: the rise of map publishing'; 'Asia: seaway to the Indies'; 'Africa: the mysterious continent'; 'The Americas: a new world'; 'Australia: the southern land'. Throughout are illustrations of instruments and other engravings. In some cases, the detail of the maps is reproduced, in others the whole of a sheet or plate in colour—'The New Description of America, or the New World', for example, from Ortelius's *Theatrum Orbis Terrarum* and the enchanting plan of seventeenth century Goude from Jan Blaeu's *Stedenboek*. There is a short bibliography 'for further reading'.

Refer also

G Alinhac: *Cartographie historique et descriptive* (Paris: Institut Géographique National, 1965).

688 **'A history of geographical discovery in the seventeenth and eighteenth centuries',** by Edward Heawood (CUP, 1912; reprinted New York: Cass; Octagon Books, 1965), was one of the *Cambridge geographical* series; it dealt with a period of discoveries which has 'met with less attention, perhaps, than it deserves', using primary sources of information as much as possible, from the Arctic, 1550–, through Oceania, 1605–, Africa, 1600–, Russian discoveries in the North-East from 1700 and all areas to 1800. A brief, neat summary concludes the text, with supplementary notes and a really useful index. Folding maps and illustrations are in the text.

689 **'The history of geography:** *papers by J N L Baker'* (Oxford: Blackwell, 1963) comprises eighteen papers selected by his former students to mark his retirement; they are prefaced by an appreciation of his achievements in geographical studies, a list of his published works and a portrait. The subjects of the papers are mainly historical, some of the most interesting and valuable drawing attention to individual contributions of earlier, some little-known writers—'Nathanael Carpenter and English geography in the seventeenth century'; 'Mary Somerville and geography in England'; 'The geography of Bernhard Varenius'; 'The history of geography in Oxford'; 'Major James Rennell and his place in the history of geography'; 'The geography of Daniel Defoe'; 'Geography in the Essays of Elia'; 'The earliest maps of H Moll'; and 'Some geographical factors in the campaigns of Assaye and Argaon'.

Refer also

D R Stoddart: 'Growth and structure of geography', *Transactions*, Institute of British Geographers, June 1967.

690 **'A history of land use in arid regions',** a composite work edited by Sir L Dudley Stamp (Unesco: Arid Zone Research, 1961), was prepared with the practical aim of the improvement of arid and semi-arid lands. Following an introduction by Sir Dudley Stamp, a number of sections, each by an expert, deal with 'Climatic change in arid regions since the Pliocene'; 'Evolution of irrigation agriculture in

Egypt'; 'The arid zone of India and Pakistan'; 'Land use development in the arid regions of the Russian plain, the Caucasus and Central Asia'; 'Development of land use in northern Africa (with references to Spain)'; 'Land use in the Sahara-Sahel region'; 'Land use in pre-Columbian America'; 'Post-Columbian development in the arid regions of the United States of America'; 'Land utilization in the arid regions of Southern Africa and South West Africa'; 'The problems of arid Australia'—and ending with a consideration of health problems, to which Jacques M May contributed. There are a number of sketchmaps in the text and end-of-chapter bibliographies.

691 '**The history of the study of landforms:** or the development of geomorphology', planned in four volumes, by R J Chorley and others, will when completed, be a definitive work. Volume I, *Geomorphology before Davis* (Methuen, 1964) was a work of exact scholarship, including many excerpts from original sources, well documented with references and bibliographies. II *The life and work of William Morris Davis* followed in 1973).

Refer also

R A Phinney, *ed: The history of the earth's crust: a symposium* (Princeton University Press; OUP, 1969).

692 '**The Holt world atlas**' (Holt, Rinehart and Winston, 1966) was edited by Jean de Varennes and Jean Lavallée especially for use in Canadian schools. The Atlas is in six sections: 'The world', consisting of twenty-four maps portraying various aspects such as physical features, population and economy; 'The continents', presenting in sixty-nine pages all the continents except Antarctica, having a small-scale map depicting the area covered followed by larger-scale regional and thematic maps; 'Canada', in particular detail, occupying thirty-six pages, including as a special feature land-use maps of the Montreal, Toronto, Edmonton and Vancouver areas; 'The United States', covered in sixteen pages of physical, regional and thematic maps and a land-use map of New York City; 'Resources', comprising six commodity distribution maps per page, together with statistical analyses showing the major world producers of each commodity; 'Statistics', provided for 124 countries on such topics as land area, population, land use, exports and standard of living. Graphs show a comparison of Canada with various aspects of other countries. Details of presentation throughout the Atlas have been carefully planned; for example, the uses of type faces and sizes.

693 'How to find out in geography: *a guide to current books in English',* by C S Minto (Oxford: Pergamon Press, 1966), includes principally books published within the previous five years. The author states 'This book is not regarded as a bibliography: its purpose is limited to assisting the undergraduate student and the adult general reader in selecting books on general and special aspects of geography. It is further limited in scope by being concerned with books in English readily available in bookshops and libraries.' For these reasons also the entries are arranged according to the Dewey Decimal classification, that most used in British public libraries; with this arrangement, the index should really be more detailed to be helpful. There are some reproductions of map extracts, title pages or covers, some being too much reduced for clarity.

Refer also

J Gordon Brewer: *The literature of geography: a guide to its organisation and use* (Bingley, 1973, Hamden, Conn, Linnet).

694 'How to identify old maps and globes, *with a list of cartographers, engravers, publishers and printers concerned with printed maps and globes from about 1500 to c1850',* by Raymond Lister (Bell, 1965), is illustrated by fifty nine plates of reproductions. Following 'An outline history of maps and charts', 'Celestial maps and charts' are considered—'Methods of map reproduction', 'Decoration and conventional signs', 'Terrestrial and celestial globes and armillary spheres'. The appendices give information otherwise scattered: 'The use of watermarks in dating old maps and documents', a 'select bibliography' and 'A list of cartographers, engravers . . . etc'. A second book on early maps by Raymond Lister was published by Bell in 1970: *Antique maps and their cartographers (qv).*

695 Hudson's Bay Record Society, London, was constituted in 1938 for the purpose of issuing in book form the unique records of the Hudson's Bay Company; the intention was to select for publication material of various dates between 1670 and 1870 rather than to print in historical sequence. The aim is two-fold—to make available to members of the Society those records in which public interest already exists, such as Ogden's journals, Rae's letters and Isham's 'Observations'; secondly, to direct attention to less well known topics or regions to the study of which the Company's archives seem able to make a worthwhile contribution; for example, with volume XXIV, 1963, Labrador and Northern Quebec are concerned, about which few records of any kind had previously been published. Each document chosen for publication has covered a vital topic in the history of the Company, of the fur trade and of Canada. Each has been published in full, accompanied by an introduction by a chosen scholar and supported by extracts from other documents. The total archives comprise more than thirty thousand documents, covering every branch of the Company's activities throughout the years. The *History of the Hudson's Bay Company*, by E Rich, in two volumes dealing with the periods 1670–1763 and 1763–1870 respectively are numbered volumes XXI and XXII.

696 **'Human geography from the air'**, by R M Minshull, published by Macmillan, provides practice in the interpretation of types of air photographs, based on a carefully chosen selection of oblique aerial photographs illustrating the major aspects of human geography in Britain. Each photograph is followed by a set of exercises and questions constructed to encourage students to find out as much as possible for themselves by the study and analysis of each picture. A variety of work is involved, such as tracing, sketching, the drawing of sketchmaps and cross-sections.

697 **'Human nature in geography:** *fourteen papers, 1925–1965'*, by John Kirtland Wright (Harvard UP; OUP, 1966) represents a 'selection from the professional papers of a lifelong student of the history of geography'. The papers, some of which have been previously published, others not, are concerned with many periods and personalities. The book is without doubt important in itself and it is also significant of a growing number of works embodying the reflections of mature geographers, revealing deep knowledge of and devotion to their subject.

698 **Humboldt, Friedrich Wilhelm Karl Heinrich Alexander, Baron von** (1769–1859) brought a scientific inspiration to modern geography. Educated at Göttingen and for several years a mining geologist, he travelled widely and on his first-hand observation and experience many of his published works are based. During his lifetime, he became noted as a scholar in social and political as well as in scientific fields. His major work, *Kosmos: a sketch of a physical* *description of the universe*, in five volumes, 1845–62, is an attempt at a physical description of the earth, a work of superb scholarship and stylistic excellence; in it, Humboldt attempted to demonstrate the inter-relation of all creation, dominated by physical geography. He made a notable contribution to geographical methodology, and emphasised the importance of maps, inspiring Berghaus (*qv*) and Justus Perthes. The Humboldt University of Berlin, Institute of Political and Economical Geography, founded in 1906 and reconstructed in 1950, stands as a monument to his influence on academic geography. His many-sided activities and his publications are examined in *Alexander von Humboldt: Studien zu seiner universalen Geisteshaltung*, a volume of essays published under the editorship of Professor J H Schultze, by the Berlin Geographical Society in 1959, as part of the commemoration of his death.

A vast literature has grown up around him and his work. In addition to the above, Hanna Beck, in *Alexander von Humboldt*, 1959, completed the first full length study of his work and his American journeys; and published an anthology of his work on the American tropics, in 1969. A special exhibition, 'Alexander von Humboldt and his world 1769–1859' was held in Berlin to mark the two hundredth anniversary of his birth and a film, 'Alexander von Humboldt—from his life and work', was made under the auspices of Inter Nationes. The Humboldt Foundation, established in 1860 and reorganised in 1953, awards scholarships to young teachers at universities, research and other academic institutes abroad for study at universities and institutes in the Federal Republic. Each year approximately three hundred such scholarships are awarded.

Refer also

Douglas Botting: *Humboldt and the cosmos* (Michael Joseph, 1973).

L Kellner: *Alexander von Humboldt* (OUP, 1963), which contains a bibliography both of Humboldt's own works and of works contributing to his biography.

A H Robinson and Helen M Wallis: 'Humboldt's map of isothermal lines: a milestone in thematic cartography', *The cartographic journal*, December, 1967.

699 **'A hundred years of geography'**, by T W Freeman (Duckworth, 1961, in *The 'Hundred years'* series), traces progress during this period under broad headings; useful 'Notes and references' and 'Short biographies of geographers' sections are included.

700 'Hungarica' contains references to English books, prints, maps and periodicals relating to Hungary, collected by Béla Iványi-Grünwald and published by Mrs Jocelyn Iványi (Bures, Suffolk, 1967); entries are arranged alphabetically by author's name, and are numbered, with a subject index referring to the numbers.

Refer also

Abstracts of Hungarian economic literature (Budapest: Scientific Information Service of the Hungarian Scientific Council for World Economy, 1971–).

Gyula Miklós, *ed: Studies in Hungarian geographical sciences* (Budapest: Hungarian Academy of Sciences, 1960).

Marton Pécsi: *Applied geography in Hungary* (Budapest: Hungarian Academy of Sciences, 1964).

Marian Pécsi *et al: Ten years of physico-geographical research in Hungary* (Budapest: Hungarian Academy of Sciences, 1964).

Marian Pécsi and B Sárfalvi: *The geography of Hungary* (Budapest: Corvina Press; Collet's, 1964).

701 The Hunting Survey Companies comprise Hunting Surveys Limited, Hunting Geology and Geophysics Limited and Hunting Technical Services Limited, for which the holding and management company is Hunting Surveys and Consultants Limited, Boreham Wood, Hertfordshire. Hunting Surveys Limited carries out panchromatic and colour photography for surveys and interpretation; auxiliary aids include airborne profile recorder, Doppler navigator, statoscope and horizon camera. Laboratory photography includes the making of photo mosaics, rectified enlargements, electronic printing and precision mapping and holds a record library of worldwide photographic cover. Topographic and planimetric mapping by photogrammetry are carried out, including profiles, cross-sections and capacity tables, electronic computations and alignment programmes for road and engineering calculations. Land surveys and models are also undertaken. Hunting Technical Services Limited maintain a group of scientists providing a consultancy service in the land use and agricultural aspects of natural resources development, specialising in regional and project planning, land use and land capability studies, soil surveys and land classification, irrigation and drainage studies, watershed management and forestry, and agricultural and project economics. Hunting Geology and Geophysics Limited provides all forms of airborne geophysical survey, overland and offshore for mineral and oil exploration and for regional geological studies; geology, geophysics and geochemistry applied to groundwater, mineral and construction material resources evaluation and to civil engineering projects; sea, lake, harbour and river bottom and sub-bottom surveys for mining, construction materials and civil engineering work. Aerofilms Limited and Hunting Photographic Limited are associated companies. Hunting Surveys Limited and Hunting Geology, and Geophysics Limited both issue *Information sheets*. The *Hunting Survey review* contains descriptions of new projects, illustrated by photographs, and individual booklets are produced from time to time on specific topics, for example 'A modern approach to road design' and the more comprehensive and finely produced 'In a changing world'. Hunting Technical Services also publishes illustrated booklets showing the wide range of services in the 'investigation and development of natural resources'. The quarterly *Hunting Group review* is the trade journal.

702 Huntington, Ellsworth (1876–1947) made a unique contribution to geographical thought with his challenging theories, which stimulated much thought and discussion. From geological studies, he turned to climatology, heredity and eugenics, striving increasingly in his publications to analyse the influences of biological inheritance and physical environment in shaping the course of history. He published nearly thirty books, parts of a number of other books and innumerable articles, notably *The pulse of Asia*, 1907; *Palestine and its transformation*, 1911; *Civilization and climate*, 1915 (Archon Press, third edition, 1972); *Character of races*, 1924; *The human habitat*, 1927; and *Mainsprings of civilization*, 1945.

Refer also

Geoffrey J Martin: *Ellsworth Huntington: his life and thought* (Hamden, Conn.: Archon Books, Shoestring Press, 1973).

703 Hutchinson university library series includes a sub-series devoted to geographical subjects, notably G R Crone: *Maps and their makers* ... (*qv*); S W Wooldridge and W G East: *The spirit and purpose of geography* (*qv*); F W Morgan: *Ports and harbours;* Norman J G Pounds: *The geography of iron and steel;* James Bird: *The geography of the Port of London*. The policy of publishing in hard cover and paperback simultaneously began with the new edition of G R Crone: *Maps and their makers*.

354

704 Hydrographic Department of the Admiralty, founded in 1795, has the duty of publishing and distributing Admiralty charts to the Merchant Navy, the Fleet and the general public. Publications are world-wide in geographical scope and constantly under revision; many special charts are also prepared. Other nautical publications are concerned with the safety of navigation, such as the *Admiralty list of lights*, the *Admiralty list of radio signals* and the *Admiralty notes to mariners*. The *Annual reports* are central documents; also the *Admiralty manual of hydrographic surveying* and the *Admiralty manual of tides*. *British Admiralty charts and other hydrographic publications: their use and correction* lists every chart and includes at the back a series of maps showing the limits of each available chart. An annual *Catalogue of Admiralty charts and other hydrographic publications* is issued.

705 Ibn Battuta (1304–1378) is undoubtedly one of the most outstanding of all land travellers who have recorded their experiences. Samuel Lee first translated the *Travels* into English, from an abridged text, in 1829. Professor Hamilton Gibb translated selections for the *Broadway travellers* series, 1929, and the full text for the Hakluyt Society in 1958.

706 'Ice', the news bulletin of the International Glaciological Society, has been issued twice a year since 1958. General information is published here, of more personal interest than in the *Journal of glaciology* (*qv*), concerning expeditions and the activities of members; also reviews and short articles of less enduring value.

707 'The Icefields Ranges Research Project' scientific results began publication in 1969. The first volume, edited by Vivian C Bushnell and Richard H Ragle (published jointly by the American Geographical Society of New York and the Arctic Institute of America), consists of nineteen papers on natural, climatic, glaciological and quaternary studies, illustrated, and with figures and maps.
  Refer also
  Ian Cornwall: *Ice ages, their nature and effects* (John Baker; New York: Humanities Press, 1970).
  W D Kingery, *ed*: *Ice and snow, properties, processes and applications* (Cambridge, Mass., M I T Press, 1963).

708 Idrisi *see* Al-Idrisi.

709 'Imago mundi: *a review of early cartography'* was founded by Leo Bagrow in 1935 to serve as a vehicle for the publication of scholarly work on early maps and mapmakers and as a forum for discussion and exchange of information in this field. It is the only international review covering the early history of cartography, of the highest scholarship and superbly produced. The journal's publishing history has been complex. Bagrow himself edited thirteen volumes before his death; Edward Lynam was co-editor for the second and third volumes, which were published in London. At one time, the journal was sponsored by the trust 'Humanistiska Fonden', thereafter under the patronage of King Gustav of Sweden; then it was produced under the direction of an editorial committee by N Israel of Amsterdam, with Professor E M J Campbell as editor. Future volumes will be issued as the annual publication of a newly formed Society, operating under the aegis of the Board of *Imago mundi*. With this change, the opportunity is being taken both to broaden the coverage of the subject and, also, to improve the standard of the publication in purely material terms. *Imago mundi* sets out to communicate the results of original research, to inform those interested by comment, reviews of recent publications, correspondence and an annual bibliography. Each issue contains a number of superb map reproductions. A series of supplements, published from time to time, under separate subscription arrangements, present larger facsimiles and studies of early maps too extensive for the regular issues; Bagrow's own *Anecdota cartographica* was the first. Volume XXII contains the papers read at the symposium on the History of Cartography held in London at the time of the 20th Congress of the IGU (1967). Cumulative indexes were published in volumes X and XX.

710 'Impingement of man on the oceans', edited by Donald W Hood (Wiley Interscience, 1971), begins with an introduction on man and the ocean environment, followed by six sections: 'Transport processes and reservoirs'; 'Chemical models of the ocean'; 'Artifacts of man'; 'Man's alteration of coastal environment'; 'Models for studying future alterations of the oceans by input of non-indigenous substances'; 'Implications of man's activities on ocean research development'. Diagrams and sketch-maps accompany the text, there are chapter references and the whole work is excellently produced.

711 'Index India' began publication with the January to March 1967 issue, from the Rajasthan University Library, Jaipur. Articles, editorials, notes and letters deal with India and Indian matters, selected from periodicals and newspapers published in English throughout the world; about 375 periodicals are scanned for each issue.

712 India Office Library and Records: after 1947, when the India Office Library and Records passed into the custody of the new Commonwealth Relations Office, the printed, manuscript and other resources grew rapidly, the use of the material for research purposes expanded, much additional space was needed for an enlarged staff and for modern technical facilities such as photocopying and conservation. The Library and Records Conservation Departments were amalgamated at the end of 1967 and at about the same time the India Office Library moved to Blackfriars Road, London, following one hundred years residence in the India Office building in King Charles Street, Whitehall. The East India Company's archives, now included within the India Office Records, accumulated steadily from 1600 and the Library was founded by the Company in 1801 in the East India House in Leadenhall Street. The Official Publications amount to more than 100,000 volumes and the Map Collection of maps, plans and drawings, includes topographical, subject and archival material. The only printed catalogue of the latter was published in 1878.

Refer also

Sir William Foster: *Guide to the India Office Records*, 1600 to 1858 (London, 1919), reprinted in 1961 and again in 1966.

India Office Records, Report for the years 1947–1967.

Annual Report of the India Office Library and Records.

713 'India: regional studies', edited by Dr R L Singh, was published by the Indian National Committee for Geography in 1968 on the occasion of the 21st International Geographical Congress. The contributors, all academic geographers, analyse the geography of thirteen regions of India, including some photographs and a number of small maps, drawings and tables. End of chapter references are included.

Refer also

Q Ahmad: *Indian cities: characteristics and correlates* (University of Chicago, Department of Geography, Research paper no. 102, 1965).

Norman Brown, *ed*: *India, Pakistan, Ceylon* (University of

Pennsylvania Press, 1960, revised edition, 1965).

T Durand-Dastès: *Géographie de l'Inde* (Paris: PUF, 1965).

A K Dutt, *ed*: *India: resources, potentialities and planning* (Dubuque, Iowa: Kendall/Hunt Publishing Co., revised edition, 1973).

T Scarlett Epstein: *South India: yesterday, today and tomorrow. Mysore villages revisited* (Macmillan, 1973).

Hiroshi Ishida: *A cultural geography of the Great Plains of India: essays, techniques and interim report-cum-methods* (University of Hiroshima, Department of Geography, 1972).

A T A Learmonth: 'Medical geography in India and Pakistan', *The geographical journal*, March 1961.

J Michael Mahar: *India: a critical bibliography* (University of Arizona Press, 1964).

Philip Mason, *ed*: *India and Ceylon: unity and diversity: a symposium* (OUP for the Institute of Race Relations, 1967).

R C Sharma: *Settlement geography of the Indian desert* (New Delhi: Kumar Brothers, 1972).

R L Singh, *ed*: *India: a regional geography* (National Geographical Society of India, 1971).

B N Sinha: *Industrial geography of India* (Calcutta: World Press Private, 1972).

O H K Spate: *India and Pakistan: a general and regional geography* (Methuen, third edition, 1967).

714 **'Industrial activity and economic geography:** *a study of the forces behind the geographical location of productive activity in manufacturing industry'*, by R C Estall and R O Buchanan (Hutchinson University Library, second edition, 1966), is a succinct text working out the detailed title ideas, illustrated by sketchmaps and including references.

Refer also

B F Hoselitz and W E Moore, *ed*: *Industralization and society* (Unesco: Mouton, 1963).

715 **'Industrial archaeologists' guide',** illustrated with photographs, figures and diagrams in the text, is published by David and Charles of Newton Abbot; it contains information on such as the National Record of Industrial Monuments, scientific and technological museums, science and technology collections, individual sites, the use of photography in industrial archaeology, relevant local societies, journals and newsletters.

716 'Industrial archaeology: *the journal of the history of industry and technology',* 1964–, published quarterly by David and Charles, aims, by original papers, comprehensive reviews of new projects, notes, news and readers' correspondence, to keep industrial archaeologists informed of new developments; the journal is illustrated with plates and drawings in the text.

717 Industrial Diamond Information Bureau, London, publishes the monthly *Industrial diamond abstracts,* which covers current scientific and technical literature, including patents, on industrial diamonds and associated subjects, frequently illustrated with diagrams; also *Industrial diamond review.* A library is maintained, which acquires world literature in this field, especially technical and scientific pamphlets. The *Industrial diamond trade name index,* 1961–, includes an Index of Manufacturers, Agents and Sales Organisations, an Index of Proprietary and Trade Names and an Index of Available Products, together with much information on diamonds and diamond tools. Selected bibliographies are prepared, as are specialist monographs, such as 'Diamonds in industry', 1961, in English, French, German, Dutch and Italian and 'Industrial diamonds made in South Africa', 1962.

718 'Industrial minerals', published monthly by Metal Bulletins Limited, London, is an illustrated journal having world coverage. Usually, one long article deals with one mineral in detail throughout the world or with the mineral industries of a certain country, followed by a section 'World of minerals', which contains news of developments, usually accompanied by statistical tables. Current topics are expertly noted and the 'Company news' section and advertisements are equally useful to those concerned with current markets.

Refer also

Cornelius S Hurlbut, *jr: Minerals and man* (Thames and Hudson, 1969).

Kenneth Warren: *Mineral resources* (Newton Abbot: David and Charles, 1973).

Herbert Wöhlbier, *ed: Worldwide directory of mineral industries.*

719 'Influences of geographic environment on the basis of Ratzel's

system of anthropo-geography', by Ellen Churchill Semple (Constable, 1932), was an attempt to interpret and explain Ratzel's theories to the English-speaking world. The work, which was meticulously documented and detailed, caused considerable discussion at the time and opinions still ebb and flow on the whole subject. Harriet Wanklyn in *Friedrich Ratzel: a bibliographical memoir and bibliography* (CUP, 1961) makes some comments on Miss Semple's work; and in J K Wright: *Human nature in geography* (*qv*), section 12 is 'Miss Semple's *Influences of geographic environment*: notes toward a bibliography'.

720 'Information bulletin of the Soviet Antarctic Expedition', 1958–, was published, in three volumes, by Elsevier, 1964–65; from 1964, a bi-monthly translation, illustrated with maps and charts, was issued by Dr M M Somov of the Russian Arctic and Antarctic Scientific Research Institute, sponsored by the Geophysical and Polar Research Center of the University of Wisconsin with support from the National Science Foundation, with the intention of bringing together all the data obtained from the Expedition, especially in glaciology and meteorology. Russian work in the Antarctic programme of the International Geophysical Year and during the years following, has been particularly valuable.

721 'L'information géographique: *revue illustrée paraissant tous les deux mois pendant la période scolaire'*, is an excellent service for schools, compiled by educationists in Paris and circulated by Baillière five times a year since 1936. Included are articles, well illustrated by sketch-maps, diagrams and graphs; notes and statistical information; selected abstracts; bibliographies; and notes of developments and projects useful for teachers to know about. Practical notes on new publications are usually included.

722 'Information Hungary', edited by Ferenc Erdei and others (Oxford: Pergamon Press, 1968–, 'Countries of the world information series'), is arranged according to broad subject groupings, beginning with 'Land and people'. It is a monumental work, in which two other sections of particular interest to geographers are 'Atlases and maps' and 'Historical maps'. There are photographs in the text.

723 'Information USSR: *an authoritative encyclopaedia about the Union of Soviet Socialist Republics'*, edited by Robert Maxwell

(Oxford: Pergamon Press, 1962), is an expanded and updated English-language version of the Soviet official handbook, in its second edition, 1957. Four appendices have been added: 'Statistical data to 1960'; a directory of establishments of higher learning in the USSR; a select bibliography of recent books in English on the USSR; and 'Data on trade with the Soviet Union'.

724 Institut Français d'Afrique at Dakar is noted for scholarly research work and for informative, frequently erudite, publications. The *Bulletin d'IFAN*, 1939–, has been divided into two series since 1954, of which series A is devoted to 'sciences naturelles' and series B to 'sciences humaines'; this bulletin replaced the former *Bulletin* of the Comité d'Etudes Historiques et Scientifiques de l'Afrique Occidentale Française. *Mémoires* have been issued since 1940; also *Notes africaines* and a number of issues of *Catalogues et documents*.

725 Institut Géographique National, founded in Paris in 1940, is the civilian body which replaced the Service Géographique de l'Armée and is the national agency responsible for the topographic maps at scales of 1:10,000 or smaller. The central task of the Institute is the preparation of the 1:20,000 base map of France. The majority of maps are prepared by the stereo-plotting of aerial photographs, the Photogrammetric Department of the IGN being one of the largest in the world. Mechanographic punched-card equipment is used for geodetic documentation, capable of undertaking a wide range of search and classification functions. *Exposé des travaux de l'IGN* and the catalogue *Cartes en service*, comprising 'cartes terrestres', 'cartes en relief' and 'cartes aéronautiques' are annual publications. The *Lexique anglais-français des termes appartenant aux techniques en usage à l'Institut Géographique National* was published in three volumes, 1956–58.

726 The Institute of Agricultural Economics, University of Oxford, publishes the *Farm economist* and the *Digest of agricultural economics and marketing*, now incorporated in *World agricultural economics and rural sociology abstracts*, published by the Commonwealth Agricultural Bureaux, Farnham Royal, Buckinghamshire (Amsterdam: North Holland Publishing Company). Books published by the Institute have included—K E Hunt and K R Clark: *Poultry and eggs in Britain . . .*, 1963; and by the same authors, *Poultry and eggs . . .*, 1967; H Frankel: *Economic changes in British agriculture 1959/64*

(The Agricultural Register), 1964; G T Jones: *Analysis of Census data for pigs*, 1964; D Wood: *Economic aspects of pigmeat marketing*, 1965; K E Hunt and K R Clark: *The state of British agriculture . . .*, 1966; K S Woods: *The development of country towns in the south-west Midlands during the 1960s*, 1968; E Neville-Rolfe: *Economic aspects of agricultural developments in Africa*, for the US Department of Agriculture, 1969, and so on.

727 Institute of Australian Geographers was established in 1959 at the Department of Geography, University of Sydney, as a result of a growing conviction among professional geographers that a national organisation was necessary to promote the study of geography in Australia. *Australian geographical studies* has been issued twice a year since 1963; the original contributions concentrate mainly on Australia and neighbouring regions, but include wider geographical studies from time to time, and the reviewing service is world-wide in scope.

728 The Institute of British Geographers, a graduate body, was formed in 1933 for the study, discussion and advancement of geography, primarily at academic level. From 1965, the secretariat has been centred on the Royal Geographical Society headquarters. The annual conferences, held at different university centres, and the summer field meetings, promote valuable research and discussion. The Institute now issues three publications each year, incorporating papers by leading geographers on all aspects of geography. The *Transactions* include the results of members' research, 1935–; abstracts are now appended. *Area* (*qv*) is published four times a year and the first volume of the Institute's Special Series of Publications was *Land use and resources: a memorial volume to Sir Dudley Stamp* (*qv*). Among the separately published works, two of the most notable have been S W Woolridge and D L Linton: *Structure, surface and drainage in south-east England*, 1939 (Philip, revised edition, 1955), and Henri Baulig: *The changing sea-level*, 1935, re-issued 1956. Lists of publications are available from the Institute.

729 Institute of Documentation Studies was established on a new site in Frankfurt, in 1969, together with the Automatic Documentation Centre. The Institute forms part of the Max Planck Society and will, with the newly founded branch office in the United

362

States, help in the co-ordination and promotion of state, scientific or industrial information and documentation projects, act in an advisory capacity and assist in the training of documentation specialists. The Automatic Documentation Centre is concerned with the application of computers in documentation, possessing initially a fully equipped IBM 1460 computer and an IBM 113 for computer typesetting.

730 The Institute of Geological Sciences is responsible both for the geological survey of Great Britain and for the programmes of British Technical Aid in geology in developing countries, as arranged by the Overseas Development Administration of the Foreign and Commonwealth Office and the United Nations and its agencies.

731 The Institute of Marine Engineers, founded at the London Docks in 1889, encompasses specialist sections—Marine Electrical Engineering; Education; Materials; Ocean Engineering, among others. Each section arranges its own meetings and reports of these meetings are published in the *Transactions*. The library is one of the most complete in the world in marine engineering and associated subjects. A punched card information retrieval system, operated in conjunction with Lloyd's Register of Shipping, enables the library to provide advice about published material on a wide range of marine developments. The *Transactions* are available in paper or microfiche editions. *Marine and shipbuilding abstracts*, formerly included in the *Marine engineers review,* is now a quarterly information service covering more than seventy journals, also available in paper or microfiche editions, as is the *Marine engineers review*, which presents a monthly survey of developments throughout the world. A news sheet, conference papers and some half-dozen textbooks are also among the Institute's publications.

732 The Institute of Pacific Relations, an unofficial international organisation founded for the study of the social, economic and political relations of the Pacific area, is composed of independent National Councils in a number of countries, including the Royal Institute of International Affairs and the University of British Columbia.

733 The Institute of Transport, London, founded in 1919, was incorporated by Royal Charter in 1926 'to promote, encourage and coordinate the study and advancement of the science and art of transport in all its branches'. Meetings, lectures and discussions are held during the winter in London and at branches throughout Great Britain and Ireland, Australia, New Zealand, Nigeria and South Africa. There are graduate and student societies, separately constituted but working closely with the parent body. The principal papers presented to the Institute are reprinted in the *Institute of Transport journal*, published every other month. The library at headquarters contains a substantial collection of books, periodicals and reports on transport and allied subjects; some of the branches hold smaller collections. A biennial handbook sets out all information concerning the Institute.

734 The Institute of World Economics (Kiel) Library is one of the largest of its kind in the world. The German Research Association has passed a resolution that its holdings shall be increased still further and it will have special information retrieval services in its fields of coverage.

735 The Institution of the Rubber Industry was founded in 1921 and now has many active sections in Great Britain and other parts of the world. Its main purpose is to further technical training and to provide a means of communication between those engaged in various parts of the industry, to promote the dissemination of knowledge of rubber science and technology by meetings and the publication of *Transactions* and other literature. The *Transactions and proceedings* are published six times a year; the *Annual report on the progress of rubber technology*, the *Proceedings of international conferences* are key documents and also published are monographs on specialised subjects from time to time. No separate library is maintained; the Library of the Rubber and Plastics Research Association is available for use by courtesy.

Refer also

The *International rubber digest*, published monthly by the Secretariat of the International Rubber Study Group, a comprehensive listing of statistics and news items concerning rubber production throughout the world.

736 Intergovernmental Oceanographic Commission, under the sponsorship of Unesco, co-ordinates the activities of regional and national research in marine sciences. The *Five years of work* (Unesco,

364

1966) contains the history and description of current operations, international expeditions and co-operating groups; a list of documents pertaining to oceanographic activities; and the 'Radio communication requirements for oceanography: a short outline for oceanographers' needs for radio frequencies to be used for oceanographic data transmission', appended, 1967. The *Manual on international oceanographic data exchange*, second edition, 1967, assembles data in a convenient form for the instruction of practising oceanographers; the various documents concerned with the exchange of oceanographic data; and a list of national oceanographic data centres with information concerning their mode of operation. *Perspectives in oceanography* was published in 1968, 1969 and there are also various monographs on specific methodology. The *International marine science* series comprises a quarterly newsletter, published jointly by Unesco and FAO, 1963–; collected reprints, such as the reports on the International Indian Ocean Expedition, published by Unesco in three volumes to 1966 and continuing as desirable; the Technical Series, 1965–; reports of sessions, 1961–, and special publications, including the reports of individual symposia and the reports from the Japanese Oceanographic Data Center, Hydrographic Division, among others, in four or five issues a year, 1965–, and *A manual of sea-water analysis*, by J D H Strickland and T R Parsons, published by the Commission and the Unesco Office of Oceanography, 1965.

737 'International African bibliography', published by the International African Institute, London, from 1971, has incorporated the bibliographical section from the journal *Africa*. With the expansion of Africanist literature, it has doubled in size over the past few years and the number of titles of books and articles from periodicals has now reached an annual level of about three thousand, making the separate publication necessary. The scope of the bibliography remains as before.

Refer also

Bibliography of African bibliographies (South African Library', *South African libraries*, April 1971.

International conference on African bibliography, *Papers*, 1967.

J M D Crossley: 'Notes on Africana in the Yale University Library', *soudh African libraries*, April 1971.

Reuben Musiker: 'The bibliographical scene in South Africa', *South African libraries*, April 1971.

Hans E Panofsky: 'The African Studies Library of Northwestern University', *South African libraries*, April 1971.

738 International African Institute was established in 1926 primarily to promote the serious study of Africa and its peoples through research, publication and information services. The Institute's official organ, *Africa*, quarterly since 1931, is an erudite journal containing articles of wide interest, notes of publications, careful book reviews and until 1971 a 'Bibliography of current publications' prepared in co-operation with other organisations interested in African studies. *African abstracts*, published quarterly, contains abstracts of all significant articles in European languages on ethnographic and social aspects, in the widest sense. Two further series of publications are *The handbook of African languages* and *The ethnographic survey of Africa*, begun in 1945, which present a conspectus of up-to-date information, with comprehensive bibliographies. The value of all this work for the geographer lies particularly in reports and reviews of agriculture and land use, population analysis, distribution and migration. The Institute's library holds some five thousand books and a large collection of pamphlets, manuscripts, periodicals and government reports; a classified bibliographical card index is maintained.

739 International Association of Physical Oceanography was founded in 1919, based on Göteborg, Sweden, as the Oceanographic Section of the International Union of Geodesy and Geophysics, to promote the study of scientific problems relating to the oceans, to initiate and co-ordinate research and to provide for discussion and publication. *Publications scientifiques* have been issued since 1931, usually annually; *Procès-verbaux* of the General Assemblies appear every third year.

740 International Association of Quaternary Research was founded in Copenhagen in 1928 as the International Association for the Study of the European Quaternary Period; the scope of the work was enlarged and the present name adopted in 1932. Congresses are held every four years and the papers relating to them are included in the *Transactions*.

741 International Association of Scientific Hydrology is a constituent association of the International Union of Geodesy and Geophysics, formed to promote the study of hydrology, to encourage and facilitate research necessitating international co-operation and to ensure the dissemination of information. Separate commissions have been set up on continental erosion, surface waters, subterranean waters, snow and glacier study. The annual *Bibliographie hydrologique* and the *Bulletin* are central publications; in addition, irregular bibliographies are prepared on specific topics and reports of research are issued from time to time.

742 International Association of Sedimentology, founded in 1952, is based on the Geological Institute, Wageningen. The *Annual reports* are valuable records and in 1959 the *Bibliographie internationale* began publication.

> *Refer also*
> F J Pettijohn and P E Potter: *Atlas and glossary of primary sedimentary structures*, 1964.

743 International Association of Seismology and Physics of the Earth's Interior was established in 1901 to develop studies in the economic, social and scientific aspects of seismology. Among its important published works are the *Travaux scientifiques, Bulletin mensuel* and the *International seismological summary.*

744 'The international atlas' (Philip, 1969), not to be confused with Philip's international atlas of 1931–1951, is one of the few new major world atlases to be published during the past fifty or so years; the product of co-operation between Rand McNally, George Philip, Cartographia, Esselte and Teikoku-Shoin of Tokyo, under the leadership of Russell Voison of Rand McNally. The editorial board was chosen from thirteen countries and cartographers from six countries were responsible for the maps; glossaries are in four languages, English, French, German and Spanish, as are the Preface and Table of contents. The work reflects the knowledge now available by means of new tools in mathematics, electronics, photography, radar and under-sea sounding. Five distinctive series of maps give a balanced coverage of the world, with particular attention given to areas of growing importance. Six principal scales, 1:24M, 1:12M, 1:6M, 1:3M, 1:1M, and 1:300,000 are followed through with different styles of cartography and colouring. Twenty nine pages of large scale plans enable comparison of sixty of the most important cities in the world. Hill shading is the most outstanding relief feature; all signs and symbols are standardised; placenames and physical features have been given in national spelling and every map page carries its own glossary in addition to the complete glossary preceding the index. A lavishly illustrated essay by Marvin W Mikesell, 'Patterns and imprints of mankind', deals with population, settlement, land use, urbanisation and resources and several extra factual features add to the reference value of the work. Although the atlas was so long in planning and creation, continuous revision kept all information as accurate as possible. Smyth sewn binding enables the double pages to lie flat and provides extra strength.

745 **'International atlas of West Africa',** prepared under the auspices of the Organisation of African Unity, Scientific, Technical and Research Commission, and with the assistance of the Ford Foundation, began its appearance in 1969–, with eight of the total intended forty-two plates. In the main, scales range between 1:10M and 1:20M, with four maps on smaller scales and a two-page spread at 1:5M, showing administrative and political boundaries. Layer colouring or shading is used to show relief and symbols are mostly those in standard use. Twenty-three pages of text are in French and English and sources used are quoted. A second edition is in progress.

746 **International Bank for Reconstruction and Development** sponsored much high-level enquiry of interest to geographers. In particular, the economic development series, published by Johns Hopkins Press, furnished basic surveys, frequently of the lesser-known regions of the world; typical were those for Colombia, 1950; British Guiana, 1953; Venezuela, 1961.

747 **'International bibliography of vegetation maps',** edited by A W Küchler (University of Kansas Libraries, Library series, 1965–1970, sponsored by the National Science Foundation), was agreed at the International Colloquium on Vegetation Mapping held at Toulouse in 1960. In four volumes, the first covers all of North America, compiled by Dr Jack McCormick and A W Küchler; the second, 1966, covers Europe; the third, 1969, the USSR, Asia and Australia; and the fourth, 1970, Africa, South America and world maps generally. Entries are arranged geographically, grouped in regions, sub-regions and countries. World maps at scales down to 1:20M are included. Detailed definitions and plan of the Bibliography are set out in the Introduction, which explains the individual entries and their arrangement of information.

748 International Cartographic Association had its origin in a meeting of cartographers from both national and commercial mapping organisations, near Stockholm, in 1956, under the sponsorship of the Swedish Esselte organisation. A small committee of representatives from France, Germany, Great Britain, Sweden, Switzerland and the United States of America was formed to examine possibilities, and in 1958 a second international conference was held, based on the house of Rand McNally and Company, Chicago. The German Cartographic Society organised a conference at Mainz in 1958, at which the name of the International Cartographic Association was adopted and an Executive Committee appointed. At the IGU Congress, Stockholm, 1960, a Special Commission on Cartography was set up to study the affiliation of the ICA to the IGU; the first General Assembly of the Association was held in Paris in 1961, the second in London in 1964, arranged to coincide with the meetings of the XX International Geographical Congress in the hope of facilitating liaison between the two organisations. The objects of the ICA are the advancement of the study of cartography and its problems, the encouragement and coordination of cartographic research, the exchange of ideas and documents, the furtherance of training in cartography and the dissemination of cartographic knowledge. 'Cartography' is understood to include not only the design and study of maps but also their evaluation, and the compilation, drafting and all stages of reproduction.

Refer also

International yearbook of cartography, 1965, which contains a selection of papers and discussions from the 1964 technical conference.

The cartographic journal, December 1964, for an outline of the progress and objects of the ICA.

749 'International catalogue of scientific literature 1901–1914', originally published in 238 volumes, has been reprinted by the Scarecrow Press in 32 volumes, of which Section F is concerned with Meteorology; H, Geology; J, Geography, mathematical and physical and P, Anthropology, each in one volume. The index is comprehensive for the subjects covered of books and articles published throughout the world during the period.

750 International Civil Aviation Organisation developed in 1947 from the provisional ICAO founded at San Francisco in 1944. At successive conferences, the convention on international civil aviation has been established. The sixth World Map Conference of the ICAO was particularly important, when proposals were made for new chart requirements and also modifications for the geographical map series. In 1960, at the Stockholm International Geographical Congress, proposals were discussed for the production of a common base map from which both the 1:1M International map of the world and the ICAO charts might be derived. The standard air charts and maps· are produced at scales of 1:1M, 1:500,000 and 1:250,000. An *Aeronautical chart catalogue* was begun in 1951, presenting a world list of charts conforming to the ICAO standards, with details of price and how they may be obtained; supplements keep this catalogue up-to-date.

751 International Commission for Aeronautical Charts was founded in 1907 at the Third Congress of the Fédération Aéronautique Internationale and was responsible for the first practical air maps, in 1909, on a scale of 300,000.
Refer also
   W W Ristow: *Aviation cartography: a historico-bibliographic study of aeronautical charts* (Library of Congress, Map Division, Reference Department, second edition, 1960).

752 International Commission for the Northwest Atlantic Fisheries was established during the years 1949–50, with a membership of twelve countries. The *Annual reports*, issued from 1951, trace the work of the Commission. Other publications include an annual abstracting service covering statistical and technical articles, and annotated papers and newsletters from time to time. A small reference library is maintained at the secretariat at Halifax, Nova Scotia, and here are collected scientific and statistical works, research reports and maps relating to the fisheries and all documents bearing on the commission's work.

753 International Commission for the Scientific Exploration of the Mediterranean Sea was founded in 1919. *Annual reports* and other irregularly timed documents are issued reporting on the work of the Commission; one of the most important publications undertaken has been the *Fiches, faune et flore de la Méditerranée*.
Refer also
   Richard Carrington: *The Mediterranean* (Weidenfeld and

Nicolson, 1971).

L G Pine: *The Middle Sea: a short history of the Mediterranean* (Newton Abbot: David and Charles, 1973).

754 International Council for the Exploration of the Sea was established in 1902 as a result of the discussions at the First International Conference of the Study of the Sea, held in Stockholm in 1899, and the Second Conference at Oslo in 1901. A vast publishing programme is undertaken, including the *Journal du conseil, Rapports et procès-verbaux*, the *Bulletin hydrographique*, the *Bulletin statistique* and the *Annales biologiques*. A *Herring atlas*, edited by W C Hodgson, was published in 1951. The library holds some fifteen thousand volumes and a hydrographic card index is maintained.

755 International Demographic Symposium held in Zakopane in 1964 was especially important; the *Proceedings* were published by the Polish Academy of Sciences, Committee for Demographic Sciences, in English, French, German and Russian, illustrated and including drawings. The papers deal with the regularity of population development in socialist countries, with changes in population structure from several aspects; the discussions and the conclusions reached at each session are included.

756 'International dictionary of stratigraphy', recommended at the International Geological Congress in Mexico, 1956, was undertaken jointly by the Comité Français de Stratigraphie and the Centre National de la Recherche Scientifique. A collection of about 120 fascicules, containing contributions from some hundred specialists, covers nearly all countries, grouped according to continent—Europe, USSR, Asia, Africa, Latin America, Oceania, North America, with a final section, 'Major stratigraphic terms'. Each fascicule contains in alphabetical order the different stratigraphical terms used, description of section type and bibliographical references. Maps show locations and the whole is indexed. In addition, in each of the fascicules in the eighth section, the special significance of a term, for example, 'Pennsylvanian', in any one country, can be studied, with the description of the formations attributed to each continent; this section was published in collaboration with the Commission on Stratigraphy of the IUGS, Sub-Commission on Stratigraphic Terminology, complementing the previous series by giving a synthesis on a world scale for each major stratigraphic term.

Refer also

L Dudley Stamp: *An introduction to stratigraphy* (Allen and Unwin, third edition, fifth impression, 1963).

757 The International Federation of Library Associations recognised the special interests of map librarianship in August 1969 when a new Sub-section for Geography and Map Libraries was incorporated with Dr Walter R Ristow, of the Library of Congress, as its first chairman. The compilation of a world directory of map collections was agreed as a first priority. Papers presented at meetings (alternate years) are to be published in *INSPEL*, the journal of the Special Libraries Section, edited by Dr Baer. Dr Helen Wallis became secretary of the new section.

758 International Geographical Congress, the assembly of world geographers, which has been held every three or four years since the first was inaugurated in Antwerp in 1871, has been now established at four-yearly intervals. A complete list of the congresses is to be found in *Orbis geographicus (qv)*. Since 1922, the International Geographical Union *(qv)* has provided the Executive, the organising committee of the Congress, which was previously the function of each of the host countries. The details of the programmes and overall organisation are carried out by the hosts; individual sections participate in lectures, symposia and study tours. English and French are now the working languages. The body of publications prepared for each Congress is invaluable and *Abstracts of papers* are published, systematically arranged according to appropriate subject content and subdivided as necessary. In the 1964 volume, additional sections for political geography, teaching of geography, methodology and bibliography were added to bring together abstracts of papers submitted for symposia not covered by sections of the Congress. *Proceedings of Congress meetings and symposia* have been published since 1871. Full details of Congress history and procedure are to be found in *Orbis geographicus* and in the issues of the *IGU newsletter*.

759 International Geographical Union was founded in 1923 to encourage the study of geographical problems, to initiate and co-ordinate researches requiring international co-operation and to provide for their scientific discussion and publication, to provide for meetings of the International Geographical Congress and to appoint Commissions for the study of special matters during the intervals between congresses. Each of the countries belonging to the union establishes a national committee formed on the initiative of the principal academy of the country or through its national research council or some similar institution or scientific society. Full details concerning the Union are to be found in *Orbis geographicus (qv)* and in the issues of the *IGU newsletter*, published in English and French once or twice a year since 1950. Publications, mainly bibliographical, are numerous, issued from the headquarters office or from the various Commissions.

At each General Assembly, Reports are presented from all Commissions and Commissions approved for the forthcoming four year period. The twenty Commissions for 1972–1976 are as follows: National and Regional Atlases; Applied Geography; World Land-Use Survey; Medical Geography; History of Geographical Thought; International Geographical Terminology; Geography in Education; Geographical Data Sensing and Processing; Quantitive Methods; Man and Environment; Geomorphological Survey and Mapping; Present-day Geomorphological Processes; International Hydrological Decade; High-altitude Geoecology; Regional Aspects of Development; Geography of Transport; Population Geography; Agricultural Typology; Rural Settlement in Monsoon Lands; Processes and Patterns of Urbanization—reflecting current subjects of preoccupation. Working Groups are concerned with Geography of Tourism and Recreation, Impact of Contemporary Urbanization on Rural Areas, Rural Planning and Development, IGU Committee of Co-ordination of Periglacial Research, Dynamics of Shoreline Erosion, Desertification in and around Arid Lands and Industrial Geography.

Refer also
   La géographie à travers un siècle de congrès internationaux (IGU, 1972).

760 International Geological Congress, held every three or four years in different countries, was established in 1878. It is the occasion for conferences and meetings of many related bodies and much bibliographical work is produced. *Congress proceedings and papers* are published, while irregular *Circulars* make known the details of work in progress. Special Commissions sponsor specific projects, such as the International geological map of the world, 1:5M, the International geological map of Europe (*see* over) and the Geological map of Africa.

761 'The international geological map of Europe' is one of the oldest examples of international scientific co-operation; the idea was first promoted at the Second International Geological Congress at Bologna in 1881, when the Commission for the project was created. At the Third International Congress at Berlin in 1885, the editorial work was entrusted to the Preussische Geologische Landesanstalt in Berlin and the first edition was published between 1893 and 1913. Work began on the second edition in 1933 and was delayed by the second world war. The map will be complete in forty-nine sheets, on a scale of 1:1,500,000, the work jointly of the Bundesanstalt für Bodenforschung and UNESCO.

762 International Geophysical Year 1957–58 was the occasion for co-ordinated scientific research by many countries under the aegis of the International Union of Geodesy and Geophysics. A vast literature is accumulating on the researches and all the analyses arising from them; the IGY collection of Arctic and Antarctic research in the IGY at the National Academy of Sciences, for example, has already reached some ten thousand books, articles, reports, conference proceedings, manuscripts and memoranda. The *Annals of the IGY* have been published, 1957–, by Pergamon Press, Oxford. The IGY organisation includes an Artifical Satellite Sub-Committee.

Refer also

The United Kingdom contribution to the International Geophysical Year, 1957–58 (Royal Society, 1957).

Werner Buedeler: *The International Geophysical Year* (Unesco, 1957).

Sir Archibald Day: *Guide to IGY World Data Centres.*

A Hayter: *The year of the Quiet Sun* (1968).

D C Martin: 'The International Geophysical Year', *The geographical journal*, March 1958.

Walter Sullivan: *Assault on the unknown: the International Geophysical Year* (1961).

763 International Glaciological Society, so named since 1972, was founded as the Glaciological Society in 1936 to encourage research on and to stimulate interest in the practical and scientific problems of snow and ice. Membership is open to all who have a scientific, practical or general interest in any aspect of the subject. *See* under *Journal of glaciology* and *Ice. Note* that literature on polar expeditions and applied aspects of glaciology is quoted in each issue of the *Polar Record* (*qv*).

764 International Hydrographic Bureau, now the International Hydrographic Organisation, was founded by Prince Albert I of Monaco in 1921 following the Hydrographic Conference of 1919, to establish close association between national hydrographic offices, to encourage co-ordination and uniformity in research and to ensure publication. The *Annual reports*, issued since the Bureau's inception, trace the development of its work; a *Yearbook*, published since 1928, forms a guide to the hydrographic services of the world. *The international hydrographic review*, including a continuing bibliography, has been published twice a year since 1923, and the *International hydrographic bulletin* monthly since 1928. The library collects all hydrographic reports, periodicals, standard technical and scientific works, hydrographic catalogues and index charts published throughout the world and maintains a documentation service. Of the mapping programme, one of the most important achievements has been the *General bathymetric chart of the oceans*, published in 1903 and 1912, with subsequent revisions.

Refer also

J R Dean: 'The International Hydrographic Bureau', *The geographical journal*, December 1963.

D W Newson: 'The General Bathymetric Chart of the Oceans—seventy years of international cartographic co-operation', *The cartographic journal*, June 1971.

Note The first Hydrographic Society in Great Britain was inaugurated in March 1972 at the headquarters of the British Petroleum Company, with the aim of furthering the science of surveying at sea and related activities. With Rear Admiral G S Ritchie as its first President, the Society will represent marine interests on an international basis, membership embracing all branches and levels of experience.

765 The International Hydrological Decade came into being in 1965, following endorsement by the Unesco General Conference two months previously; within a short time, some seventy committees had been set up throughout the world to carry out relevant research projects. A quarterly periodical, *Nature and resources*, replaced the *Unesco Arid Zone newsletter*, which finished in December 1964. This new journal, considered as the *Bulletin* of the

International Hydrological Decade, covers all the different aspects of the programme of the Division of Natural Resources Research, in the fields of hydrology, geology, soil sciences, ecology, conservation of nature and arid zone research. Extracts from the resolutions adopted by the General Conference are included in the first issue, 1/2 combined issue, June 1965. In addition to articles and news items, the journal is invaluable for the information it imparts concerning national and international meetings and conferences, new research projects, United Nations and Unesco sponsored publications; the feature 'Publications received' contains annotated references.

Refer also

Canadian National Committee, International Hydrological Decade: *Hydrological mapping.* Proceedings of Workshop Seminar held at the University of Saskatchewan, 1969.

766 **'International journal of comparative sociology'** was founded in 1960 by the editor, K Ishwaran (Brill of Leiden), appearing at first biennially, every second issue being devoted to a special theme; since 1968, the journal has become a quarterly. Each issue contains usually at least one article of direct interest to geographers, the others providing desirable background reading.

767 **'International library of sociology and social reconstruction'**, a series published by Routledge and Kegan Paul, contains many regional economic studies of direct interest to geographers, also, for example, R E Dickinson: *City, region and regionalism: geographical contribution to human ecology*, 1947, followed by his *City and region: a geographical interpretation*, 1964.

768 **'International list of geographical serials'**, edited by C D Harris and J D Fellmann (University of Chicago, Department of Geography, research paper no 63, 1960), included both current and retrospective titles. This work followed *A union list of geographical serials*, by C D Harris and others (second edition, 1950), and *A comprehensive checklist of serials of geographic value*, by Harris and Fellmann, 1959. Over a thousand numbered titles were listed and arranged first internationally, then by region and country. Complete holdings are noted for the Library of Congress, the American Geographical Society, the University of Chicago and the Royal Geographical Society. The revised edition, expanded and updated, by Harris and Fellman, with the assistance of Jack A Licate, combines some eight hundred new titles and all entries were checked. Careful notes on the purpose, scope, compilation and content of the entries are set out in the introduction. Chauncy Harris has also compiled *Major foreign language geographical periodicals with English summaries of articles.*

See also
An annotated world list of selected current geographical serials in English . . .

Refer also
W O Aiyepeku: 'The periodical literature of geography', *Libri*, 1972.

Emmett F Stallings: 'The research character of selected American geographical serials', *Bulletin*, Special Libraries Association, Geography and Map Division, March 1971.

769 **'International map of the world on the millionth scale',** first proposed by Professor Albrecht Penck in 1891, became a reality during the course of successive discussions. At a meeting of the VIIth Assembly of the International Geographical Union in Lisbon, 1949, a new Commission on the IMW was established and fresh terms of reference were adopted; and at the UN Technical Conference on the IMW in Bonn, 1962, the specifications were again revised. For details of the history of the map and the complete recommendations, Professor Penck's article 'Construction of a map of the world on a scale of 1:1 million' (*The geographical journal*, 1893) should be consulted; also the *Report of the Commission on the International Map of the World 1:1,000,000* (American Geographical Society, 1952) and the *Report* of the Bonn Conference, 1962. During the early years, the Central Bureau was centred on the Royal Geographical Society, but was transferred to the Cartographic Office of the United Nations in 1953, as part of the programme for co-ordinating cartographic services. The Central Bureau has published progress reports since 1921 and *Annual reports* have been issued from 1954– by the Department of Economic and Social Affairs, New York. Bibliographies of selected official documents covering the IMW appeared with the 1954 *Report* in *World cartography*, volume IV, 1954, and a first supplement to the bibliography appeared with the *Report* for 1961. An *International bibliography of the 'Carte internationale du monde au millionième'* was compiled by E Meynen as a special publication of *Bibliotheca cartographica*, no 1, on the occasion of the Bonn Conference, 1962; this included titles of all books, papers and reports since 1891, together with an abstract of the history of the map series, a register of all published sheets and several index maps showing the different issues of the IMW and their derived and related editions. New sheets are noted in the 'Recent maps' section of *The cartographic journal*.

Refer also

The International map of the world on the millionth scale in the field of cartography', *World cartography*, no 13, 1955.

R A Gardiner: 'A re-appraisal of the International map of the world (IMW) on the millionth scale', *International yearbook of cartography*, I, 1961.

G R Crone: 'The future of the International million map of the world', *The geographical journal*, March 1962.

770 'International marine science', a newsletter prepared jointly by Unesco and FAO, is designed to help marine scientists, administrators and government officials to be better informed on international, regional and national activities of significance to marine science. It contains information on organisations, national oceanographic programmes, international projects, meetings, training facilities, miscellanous news items and publications.

771 International Nickel comprises The International Nickel Company of Canada, Limited, Copper Cliff and Toronto; the International Nickel Company Inc, New York; and The International Nickel Company (Mond) Limited and Henry Wiggin and Company Limited, in London. From the publicity departments of these companies issues a continuous stream of information of general and educational importance. Two regular publications are the *Nickel bulletin*, a monthly abstracting service of current information on nickel and nickel alloys; and *Inco-Mond nickel*, an illustrated journal featuring applications of nickel-containing materials. The *Annual report* is naturally a central source of information. Technical films, filmstrips, specimens, samples and photographs are available on loan, and educational publications, including many of considerable length and erudition, may be had free, covering aspects of the steel industry, non-ferrous alloys, nickel-iron alloys, cast irons, corrosion-resisting materials, nickel plating, precious metals, Mond chemical products and iron powders.

772 The International Road Federation, a non-profit service organisation established in 1948 to encourage the development and improvement of highways and highway transportation, has offices in London, Paris and Washington, co-ordinated by a joint committee. Each office holds a library and archives. Technical, economic and statistical information and documents are distributed and the Federation's own publishing programme is extensive. The *Annual reports* provide the body of current information, illustrated with photographs and maps concerning road developments in all parts of the world; the excellently produced quarterly *Road international* (*qv*) is the chief journal of the Federation, but there is also the *World highways* newsheet, 1950–, circulated monthly in English, German and Spanish; the *World directory of highway officials* has been issued annually since 1954 and *World road statistics* from 1950 in English and French. *Proceedings*, 1952– and *Reports*, 1951– are published as necessary.

773 The International Road Research Documentation Scheme, 1965–, began as a regular international exchange of abstracts of published and unpublished literature, sponsored by the OECD. The abstracts, in English, French and German, are distributed through the Road Research Laboratory, United Kingdom, the Laboratoire des Ponts et Chaussées, France and the Forschungsgesellschaft für das Strassenwesen, in the Federal Republic of Germany.

774 International Society for Photogrammetry has, since 1910, provided an important forum for the discussion of the latest developments; there are seven autonomous technical commissions and an International Congress of Photogrammetry is organised every four years under the direction of the committee of the Society. Publications, which are nearly all in English, French and German, include *Photogrammetria*, from 1938; each volume of four quarterly parts contains the Proceedings of the Conferences, national reports, reports of the technical commissions and original papers.

775 The International Society of Soil Science, located at the Royal Tropical Institute, Amsterdam, dates back in effect to 1911, when the *Internationale Mitteilungen* was initiated; in 1924, the Society was reconstituted under its present title and its journal became the *Proceedings of the International Society of Soil Science*. The Society meets at intervals for discussion at various centres and its findings are published as *Congress transactions*, in English and French, usually including bibliographies.

776 International Soil Museum, joint project of Unesco and the International Society of Soil Science, was established in January 1966 under the direction of F A van Baren, Professor of Soils at the State University of Utrecht and Secretary General of the International Society of Soil Science, the first meeting of the Advisory Panel taking place at The Hague in September 1967. Contacts are maintained with FAO and with institutions and soil scientists in all parts of the world.

777 'International studies', quarterly journal of the Indian School of International Studies, New Delhi, published by the Asia Publishing House, usually concentrates in each issue on one country. Original articles, notes and memoranda, bibliographies and book reviews are included.

778 The International Tin Research Council, founded in 1932, with the object of developing the consumption of tin, was financed by the major tin producers of the world. With headquarters at Greenford, Middlesex, the Council controls organisations for the technical development of tin in other countries, centred on the Centre d'Information de l'Etain, Brussels; Technical Service Centre for Tin, Montreal; Centre d'Information de l'Etain, Paris; Zinn-Informationsbüro, Düsseldorf; Technisch Informatie Centrum voor Tin, The Hague; Centro d'Informazioni dello Stagno, Milan and the Tin Research Institute Inc, Columbus, Ohio. The whole group is active in the documentation of tin throughout the world; research findings are published in the journals of scientific societies, in the technical and trade press, in practical handbooks and in *Tin and its uses*, quarterly journal of the Tin Research Institute. Library facilities are maintained at each centre, including reference, bibliographic, loan, translating, photocopying and abstracting services.

779 International Union for Conservation of Nature and Natural Resources was founded in 1948 to facilitate international co-operation, to promote scientific research, to disseminate information and to conduct programmes of conservation education, especially in Africa and the Middle East. The maintenance of a documentation centre is also important. A quarterly *Bulletin* and *Annual report* are published, also special technical reports from time to time.

780 International Union of Geodesy and Geophysics, founded in

1919, is a member of the International Council of Scientific Unions, its function being to promote the study of problems relative to the figure and physics of the earth, to initiate, facilitate and co-ordinate research and to provide for discussion and publication. The Union consists of seven international associations: the International Association of Geodesy, the International Association of Geomagnetism and Aeronomy, the International Association of Meteorology and Atmospheric Physics, the International Association of Oceanography, the International Association of Scientific Hydrology, the International Association of Volcanology and the International Association of Seismology and Physics of the Earth's Interior. It is thus one of the great co-ordinating world organisations and the publishing programme, both of the main body and of the constituent associations, is vast. *Procès-verbaux* of meetings have been published since 1922, in English and French; the initial quarterly *Bulletin d'information de l'UGGI* was superseded by *Chronique* from 1957, issued monthly in English, German, French and Russian, with bibliographical supplements on geodesy, hydrology and oceanography from 1958.

Refer also

The International Union of Geodesy and Geophysics, its scientific role, its international character and its organization (Paris, 1960).

A description of the Union and its constituent associations and commissions with an account of their scientific activities (Bureau of the IUGG, Richmond, Surrey, 1947; revised edition, 1961).

781 'International vegetation map 1:1M' is in progress under the direction of Henri Gaussen. The first sheet, of Tunisia, by Gaussen and A Vernet, was completed in 1958; some sheets of India began to appear from 1961. Gaussen's system for the 1:1M map, first shown in the vegetation map in the *Atlas de France*, is being used.

782 The International Wool Secretariat, London, is a non-governmental, non-profitmaking concern, dating from 1937. The Library, established in 1947, holds books, pamphlets, periodicals, films and filmstrips relating to the economics, history, science and technology of wool. Official publications and statistical bulletins from Australia, New Zealand, South Africa and Canada, in addition to other material relating to wool producing and manufacture in those countries and in the United Kingdom, India and Pakistan, are received; loan is made to other libraries, but photocopies are readily supplied to individual enquirers. The classification used is a modified UDC; periodical articles are indexed and issued, arranged by UDC. Quarterly accessions lists are issued, also subject bibliographies, lists of periodical holdings, the *IWS news service*, 1946–; semi-monthly, *Wool knowledge*, the journal of wool education, 1948–, which includes bibliographic references; *Wool science review*, irregularly from 1948; *The world of wool;* an *Annual review of IWS and the Wool Bureau; World wool digest*, 1950–, semi-monthly, and numerous other handouts and visual aids.

Refer also

The wool trade directory of the world (Skinner, London).

H S Bell: *Wool: an introduction to wool production and marketing* (Pitman, 1970).

783 'International yearbook of cartography' has resulted from an imaginative and valuable international partnership, beginning in 1961, between some of the leading cartographical agencies, first under the editorship of Professor Eduard Imhof of Zurich, in collaboration with experts from Austria, Great Britain, Italy, Germany, Sweden, the Netherlands, France and the USA, published by George Philip, together with Armand Colin, C Bertelsmann Verlag, the Esselte Map Service, Freytag-Berndt und Artaria, the Istituto Geografico de Agostini, Art Institut Orell Füssli AG and Rand McNally. Articles are in German, French or English, with synopses in the two languages not used. A variety of topics is covered in each volume regarding the compilation, design and methodology of maps and on new productions. The reproductions of map sheets are particularly valuable. The volume for 1965 contained a selection of papers and discussions from the 1964 Technical Conference of the International Cartographic Association. There is so far no index, but each volume contains contents lists for the previous volumes.

784 'Introduction to biogeography', by Brian Seddon (Duckworth, 1971): 'This book is an attempt to explain in ordinary language the forces that have shaped the territories of living things and the problems that are posed by their geographical distribution' (Preface). This is achieved under the following headings: 'Mapping distributions'; 'Distribution as a geographical quantity'; 'The influence of local factors on distribution'; 'Climatic control of plant distribution'; 'Vegetation: methods of description'; 'Vegetation: the question of adaptation'; 'Vegetation: classification and correlation'; 'Migration and dispersal'; 'Relicts and refugia'; 'Changes in distribution with time'; 'Intercontinental migration'. More attention is given to plant geography than to animal geography. Maps demonstrating mapping methods and diagrams occur throughout the text and there are end-of-chapter lists of sources. Information data and survey methods are discussed at the beginning of the first section.

Refer also

Leo Aario and Joachim Illies: *Biogéographie* (Westermann, fourth edition, 1971).

D J de Laubenfels: *A geography of plants and animals* (Iowa: Brown, 1970).

K C Edwards: 'The importance of biogeography', Address to the Geographical Association, printed in *Geography*, April 1964.

R Hesse *et al*: *Ecological animal geography* (Wiley, second edition, 1951).

G Lemée: *Précis de biogéographie* (Paris: Masson, 1967).

J Tivy: *Biogeography: a study of plants in the ecosphere* (Oliver and Boyd, 1971).

D Watts: *Principles of biogeography: an introduction to the functional mechanisms of ecosystems* (McGraw-Hill, 1971).

785 'Introduction to climatic geomorphology', by J Tricart and A Cailleux (translated by Conrad J Kiewiet de Jonge, Longman, 1972), was first published by the Société d'Edition d'Enseignement Supérieur, Paris, in 1965. In the Foreword to the English edition, Professor Tricart challenges the concepts of William Morris Davis and states 'Climatic geomorphology and the study of the morphogenic processes are therefore at the origin of a new approach to geomorphology. They also help to mitigate the disadvantages of a growing specilisation. Besides a more and more detailed analysis of the mechanisms, they create new links between different disciplines. Climatic geomorphology, indeed, must examine the interactions between all the factors influencing the processes: not only the geologic structure, which is a comparatively stable entity, but also the climate, which makes itself felt through its direct and, more important, its indirect influence on the vegetation and on the soils which, finally, are more immediately exposed to the external forces than the rocks'. Following an Introduction, five subdivided sections develop these ideas: 'Normal erosion or climatic geomorphology?';

'Morphoclimatic mechanisms'; 'Criteria for a morphoclimatic division of the earth'; 'Morphoclimatic equilibrium' and 'The major morphoclimatic zones of the earth'. Included are a valuable 'Consolidated bibliography' covering a wide range of books and articles, a brief biographical sketch of the author and his printed works and a collection of folded maps, in addition to photographs and diagrams in the text.

786 'An introduction to human geography', by J H G Lebon (Hutchinson University Library, 1952; sixth edition revised, 1969), defines his purpose as 'the comparative study of major societies in the areas of their characterisation', proceeding, in the first chapter, to justify this definition 'and to examine its connections both with the ideas of earlier authorities and with modern doctrine on the nature of geography'. Further chapters are devoted to 'Climate and man'; 'The foundations of the human economy'; 'The major human societies'; and 'Civilisations in confrontation'. Bibliographies are appended to each chapter and there are a few clear sketchmaps and figures in the text. A folding chart—'Centres of origin of the chief cultivated plants' follows the text. The book is available in both hard cover and paperback editions.

> *Refer also*
>
> K R Cox: *Man, location and behavior: an introduction to human geography* (Wiley, 1972).
>
> John Langton: 'Potentialities and problems of adapting a systems approach to the study of change in human geography', *Progress in geography*, 1972.

787 'An introduction to quantitative analysis in economic geography', by Maurice H Yeates (McGraw-Hill, 1968), was prepared to demonstrate the use of new techniques in the study of economic geography. With the aid of graphs, figures and tables, individual theories are explained, including some regional examples. A selected bibliography is included.

788 'An introduction to the study of map projections', by J A Steers (ULP, 1948; fourteenth edition, 1965), has remained a 'standard' work for students, being not so technically presented as A R Hinks: *Map projections*. The text includes explanations of latitude and longitude, scale and the nomenclature of projections, followed by chapters on the main groups of conventional projections, interrupted and

orthoapsidal projections, with final chapters on the Ordnance
Survey map projection and grids, the choice of projection and notes
on the history of projections. Appendices set out relevant tables and
a short list of references. Explanatory diagrams and figures accompany the text.

Refer also

R E Dahlberg: 'Evolution of interrupted map projections',
International yearbook of cartography, 1962.

A R Hinks: *Map projections* (CUP, 1924; standard work for
many years).

A R Hinks: *Maps and survey* (CUP, fifth edition, 1947).

G P Kellaway: *Map projections* (Methuen, second edition,
1958).

D H Maling: *Coordinate systems and map projections* (Philip,
1973).

H S Roblin: *Map projections* (Arnold, 1969).

789 'Irish forestry', journal of the Society of Irish Foresters, is published twice a year. Articles, notes, reviews and miscellaneous news
items are the main features; in the Autumn issue is included a report
of the Society's activities during the previous year. The Autumn 1963
issue is especially useful for the article by T Clear: 'A review of
twenty-one years of Irish forestry'.

790 'Irish geographical studies', edited by N Stephens and R E
Glasscock, was produced by the Department of Geography, The
Queen's University of Belfast, in honour of Professor E Estyn Evans,
following his forty years of teaching, 1928–1968. Twenty-three
essays representative of recent geographical research, with the geography of Ireland as a common theme, are grouped in three parts—
the evolution of the physical landscape, historical aspects of the cultural landscape and contemporary geographical problems. There are
twenty plates and numerous line drawings in the text.

Refer also

E Estyn Evans: *The personality of Ireland: habitat, heritage
and history* (CUP, 1973).

Sir Robert Matthew: *Belfast regional survey and plan* (Bell,
1964).

Daphne P Mould: *Ireland from the air* (Newton Abbot: David
and Charles, 1972).

Patrick O'Malley: *Irish industry: structure and performance*

(Dublin: Gill and Macmillan; New York: Barnes and Noble, 1971).

Leslie Symons, *ed*: *Land use in Northern Ireland* . . . (University of London Press, 1963).

791 Irish University Press (International) Limited, London, is to be noted by geographers for its planned series of Area Studies—USA (*qv*), China and Japan (*qv*), Russia, Central and South America, Australia, New Zealand, being reprints of British Parliamentary Papers, each multi-volume sets for which detailed catalogues are available. Many other regional sets have been issued, also some based on some special subject, for example, *Mining districts, Shipping, The Industrial Revolution, Factories* and *Agriculture*. T P O'Neill wrote *British Parliamentary Papers*, a monograph, in 1969. The Irish UP issues a *Bulletin*, check lists and announcements, either as leaflets or single sheets. The *Bibliotheca Hibernicana* catalogue, compiled by William Shaw Mason, originally published in 1823, is one of the most important of the reprints (1970).

792 'The Isle of Man: *a study in economic geography'*, by J W Birch, published by CUP for the University of Bristol, 1964, considers all aspects of the economy and life of the island, accompanied by photographs, sketchmaps and figures. 'The fascination of the Isle of Man is that you can study everything in miniature there—history, geography, climatology, economics, political evaluation . . .' can stand as the keynote of the book; there is a selected bibliography.

793 Istituto Geografico de Agostini of Novara was founded in Rome in 1901 and has become one of the great cartographic agencies of the world. Staff are trained at the Institute in all the techniques of modern cartography. Atlases, road maps and special-purpose maps of all kinds are planned, constructed and printed. Most famous is the *Grande atlante geografico* (*qv*); other fine atlases include the *Atlante mondiale*, the *Nuovo atlante geografico moderno* and many regional atlases, mostly under the direction of L Visintin. Plastic relief maps and globes are also specialities, and wall maps for school use are produced in effective new relief styles.

Refer also

Umberto Bonapace: 'La production cartographique de l'Institut Géographique de Agostini: buts et problèmes actuels', *International yearbook of cartography*, 1963.

794 'The Jacaranda atlas', edited by V G Honour and others (Queensland: Jacaranda Press, revised edition, 1972), is an interesting world atlas, incorporating much useful information and distinguished especially by many experimental and contemporary ideas. In the second edition, there are some new maps and the rest have been up-dated. Particularly interesting are the maps showing the functional zoning of cities, maps of atmospheric fall-out and some infra-red and aerial photographs. Computer print-outs are more or less successful from the point of view of interpretation.

Refer also

The Jacaranda social studies resource atlas for New Zealand, edited by E R Bloomfield and C A Watson (Port Moresby: Niugini Press, 1972), which includes references to Australia and the Pacific.

795 'James Cook: the opening of the Pacific', written by Basil Greenhill, Director of the National Maritime Museum (HMSO, 1970), is a useful record of Cook's life and achievements, illustrated with photographs, maps and engravings. Illustrations include contemporary instruments and a plan of the Britannia Otaheite war canoe.

796 'Japanese geography: *a guide to Japanese reference and research materials',* compiled by Robert B Hall and Toshio Noh (University of Michigan Press, 1956; Center for Japanese Studies, Bibliographical series, no 6), is concerned with twentieth century sources—bibliographies, encyclopedias, etc, yearbooks, collections of statistics and censuses, sets and collections, the history of Japanese geography, physical geography, historical and cultural geography, economic geography and regional descriptive geography—followed by a list of publishers with a special interest in Japanese affairs.

Refer also

Prue Dempster: *Japan advances: a geographical study* (Methuen, second edition, 1969).

Max Derruau: *Le Japon* (Paris: PUF, 1967).

J W Hall and R K Beardsley: *Twelve doors to Japan* (McGraw-Hill, 1965).

J Pezeu-Massabuau: *Géographie du Japon* (Paris: PUF, 1968).

Martin Schwind: *Das Japanische Inselreich* . . . (Walter de Gruyter, three volumes, 1967–).

Richard Storry: *Japan* (OUP, 1965).

G T Trewartha: *Japan: a physical, cultural and regional geography* (Wisconsin University Press, 1960; Methuen, second edition, 1965).

Problems of the human environment in Japan (Public Information Bureau, Ministry of Foreign Affairs, 1971: Report submitted to the UN by Japan as part of its contribution to the preparatory work for the United Nations Conference on the Human Environment, 1972).

797 **'Japanese studies on Japan and the Far East:** *a short biographical and bibliographical introduction*', prepared by Teng Ssu-Yü and others (Hong Kong University Press, 1961), includes, among other more general topics, Eastern anthropology and ethnology, economics and economic development, Far Eastern and Southeast Asian geography and geology. Items are numbered, titles are given in Japanese, usually with English translations and annotations are in English; there is an index to subject matter and authors.

Refer also

Japanese geography, 1966: its recent trends (Special paper, no 1, The Association of Japanese Geographers, Tokyo).

Nippon, 1936– (Tsuneta Yano Memorial Society).

Japanese cities: a geographical approach (Special paper, no 2, The Association of Japanese Geographers, Tokyo, 1970).

Journal of the Japan Cartographic Association, Tokyo, 1963–, having contents list in English.

Materials informations Japan (Tokyo: JRDI Laboratory, 1969–).

Frank J Shulman, *ed: Japan and Korea: an annotated bibliography of doctoral dissertations in western languages 1877–1969* (American Library Association, 1970).

798 **'Jena review',** the bi-monthly journal of VEB Carl Zeiss Jena, is finely produced, including excellent technical articles and notes, with illustrations, on new equipment; a work of central importance in practical geography.

799 **'Jerusalem studies in geography',** a new journal published 1970– by the Department of Geography, The Hebrew University of Jerusalem; the aim is to publish the results of research both in Israel and abroad. The journal was first cyclostyled, including illustrations,

388

maps and diagrams.

800 'Jewish history atlas', compiled under the direction of Martin
Gilbert, with cartography by Arthur Banks (Weidenfeld, 1969),
traces the history, world-wide migrations, achievements and life of
Jewish people from the civilisation in ancient Mesopotamia to the
present day. Maps portray early Jewish migrations, the Promised
Land, the kingdom of David and Solomon, the destruction of Jewish
independence, the rise of the Roman empire, Palestine at the time of
Jesus Christ, European Jewry from 500 to the emancipation of European Jewry 1789–1918; Zionism 1860–1939; and modern movements
which have affected the Jews.

 Refer also
  *Atlas of Mesopotamia: a survey of the history and civilisation of
  Mesopotamia from the Stone Age to the fall of Babylon, comp.* M
  A Beek, translated by D R Welsh, and edited by H H Rowley
  (Nelson, 1962).

801 'John Speed's atlas of Wales', Part II of 'The Theatre of Great
Britaine', published in 1676, has been reproduced in facsimile, with a
bibliographic introduction, by SR Publishers Limited, East Ardsley.

 Compare modern atlases, e.g. *An historical atlas of Wales
 from early to modern times* (Faber, 1951, 1959; second edition,
 1972).
 An historical atlas of Wales and *A geographical atlas of Wales*,
 both compiled by J I Jones (Hughes and Son, Wrexham, 1956).

802 Johnston, Alexander Keith (1804–1872), a great cartographer
and a scholar much in sympathy with the work of leading continental
geographers, whose ideas he helped introduce into Britain, founded
the firm of W and A K Johnston, which still operates in Edinburgh.
His *Physical atlas* (second edition, 1856) was inspired by the *Physikalischer Atlas* of Berghaus (*qv*). Another notable atlas was the *Royal
atlas*, 1859.

803 Jones, Llewellyn Rodwell (1881–1947) was one of the generation
of geographers following Sir Halford Mackinder who, by their scholarship and energy, established British academic geography; his chief
academic work was at the London School of Economics, where he
contributed greatly to the new Joint School of Geography of King's
College and the LSE between 1921 and 1945. His regional studies on

Northern England, North America and East Africa have become established texts; he had a great interest in port geography and his *Geography of London River*, 1931, in particular, became a classic. *London essays in geography, the Rodwell Jones Memorial Volume*, was published in 1951.

804 '**Journal of Asian and African Studies**' is issued from the Department of Sociology, York University, Toronto; there are editors in twenty-four countries, including Great Britain, and a Board of scholars representing many parts of the world (Brill, Leiden). It is an interdisciplinary journal covering the whole area and is described as 'the first attempt to answer a need in the relevant field, in that it unites contributions from anthropology, sociology and related social sciences into a concerted emphasis upon building up systematic knowledge and using the knowledge derived from pure research for the reconstruction of societies entering a phase of advanced technology'.

805 '**The journal of Christopher Columbus**', translated by Cecil Jane, was published by Blond in 1968, including ninety illustrations from prints and maps of the period, notes and a bibliography. Particularly informative is the chapter by R A Skelton, 'The cartography of Columbus' first voyage', and the 'Letter of Columbus describing the results of his first voyage'; there are extensive notes on both the Journal and the letter.

806 '**The journal of economic abstracts**', an international journal published quarterly by the contributing journals under the auspices of The American Economic Association, which acts as agent, has, since 1963, aimed to assist economists around the world to become acquainted with methods and conclusions currently being reported in the general economic periodicals. In most cases, abstracts are prepared by the author of the original article.

807 '**Journal of the economic and social history of the Orient**' was founded by N W Posthumus in 1957 and is now edited by Claude Cahen and W F Leemans, with the help of an international board of Orientalists. The *Journal* has proved a forum for all kinds of studies on the economic and social conditions of Asia and North Africa from the earliest times to the nineteenth century. Originally designed to supplement the thirty-volume *Economic and social history of the Orient*, the *Journal* has developed independently, published by Brill of Leiden; three issues make a volume.

808 'The journal of geography' has been published since 1902, in nine issues a year, by the National Council for Geographic Education; edited by A J Nystrom, it has been devoted primarily to the place of geography in education, but includes also substantive geographical articles.

809 'Journal of glaciology', published three times a year from 1947, contains the papers read at meetings of the International Glaciological Society (*qv*), together with specially submitted papers and discussions, articles and short notes of current interest, review articles, abstracts and a bibliography of recent glaciological work. The longer articles are preceded by abstracts in German and French.

Refer also

L Lliboutry: *Traité de glaciologie* (Paris: Masson, two volumes, 1965).

810 'Journal of hydrology', first issued in March 1963, marked the need for a journal devoted exclusively to the subject; published quarterly by the North Holland Publishing Company, Amsterdam, its scope has from the beginning been international, including surface and ground waters, agro-hydrology, the hydrology of arid zones, hydraulic engineering, meteorology and climatology.

Another journal with the same title was begun by the Hydrological Survey, New Zealand Hydrological Society, Ministry of Works in 1968; there is also the *Annuaire hydrologique,* Québec, Ministère des Richesses Naturelles du Québec, 1965—and similar works in many other countries, initiated during the past decade.

811 'Journal of Latin American studies' (CUP, 1970) has been sponsored by the centres and institutes of Latin American studies in or attached to universities, covering the continent from the point of view of all the social sciences.

Refer also

H Blakemore and C T Smith, *ed: Latin America: geographical perspectives* (Methuen, 1971).

C Furtado: *Economic development of Latin America: a survey from Colonial times to the Cuban Revolution* (CUP, 1970, Cambridge Latin American studies, no 8).

812 'Journal of Nigerian studies', a monthly periodical published by the African Book Company Limited, aims to disseminate knowledge of all aspects of the life of the country by means of articles, news items, bibliographical assessments and information on collections of Nigerian literature.

Refer also

S W Skinner: *The agricultural economy of Nigeria* (Washington: US Department of Agriculture, Economic Research Service, 1972).

R K Udo: *Geographical regions of Nigeria* (Heinemann Educational Books, 1970).

813 'Journal of Pacific history' (OUP, 1966–) is an annual publication, its scope extending beyond history in all its aspects to anthropology, archaeology, geography, economics and bibliographical features concerning documents and archives. It is sponsored by the Research School of Pacific Studies of the Australian National University, though not to be considered a journal of the School.

814 'Journal of regional science', published by the Regional Science Research Institute in co-operation with the Department of Regional Science of the Wharton School, University of Pennsylvania, in April, August and December, contains articles, usually with appended references and including maps and diagrams as necessary, also reviews and a 'Books received' feature.

815 'Journal of South-East Asia and the Far East', published twice a year since 1967 by the Institut de Sociologie de l'Université de Bruxelles, contains articles on a wide range of topics, with special studies in English and French on the current social, economic and political problems of India, Pakistan, Indonesia and the Philippines, China, Japan and Korea.

Refer also

George Allen and Unwin, 'Books on Asian Studies' catalogue, 1971.

Barry Cohen: *Monsoon Asia: a map geography* (Heinemann, 1971).

K Ishwaran *ed: Contributions to Asian studies* (Brill, 1971).

816 'The journal of transport history', published twice yearly by

Leicester University Press, 1953–, is the only British journal to be devoted to the history of transport as a whole, in all its branches, ancient and modern. The scope of the articles is wide-ranging. The *Journal* is also very much concerned with the literature of the subject, a continuing feature, 'Sources of transport history' being particularly useful. In each May issue appears a list of the articles on transport in British periodicals during the preceding year. Book reviews are a regular feature, normally including some overseas publications.

817 'Journal of tropical geography', semi-annual from 1953, is the publication of the Departments of Geography, University of Singapore and the University of Malaya, Kuala Lumpur. Useful bibliographies are included.

818 'Journal of West Midlands regional studies', published annually since December 1967 by the Wolverhampton College of Technology, to provide information on research being done in the College and to encourage the preparation of material in a form suitable for publication. The foreword states—'The emergence of the journal is a natural development stemming from the work of interested people from many professional fields who, whether natives of the West Midlands or not, find this region a rich source of study. Originally concerned with certain aspects of West Midlands industrial archaeology, investigations led inevitably to projects about the lives and conditions of the people. The studies therefore cover fields such as economic and political history, geology, geography, sociology, as well as the scientific and technical aspects of industrial developments.' There are photographs occasionally and sketchmaps and figures in the text.

819 'Kansas geographer' has been revived following a seven-year suspension, published by the Kansas Council for Geographic Education, in co-operation with the Division of Geography at Kansas State Library.

Refer also

Kansas in maps, prepared by R W Baughman for the Kansas State Historical Society (McCormick-Armstrong, 1960).

820 'Kartographie: Kartenaufnahme, Netzentwürfe, Gestaltungsmerkmale, Topographische Karten', by V Heissler and G Hake (Berlin: Walter de Gruyter, 1970) is a most comprehensive and technical book on all aspects of cartography. There are diagrams in the text and eight map sections in a cover pocket.

821 'Kartographische Geländedarstellung', by Eduard Imhof (Berlin: Walter de Gruyter, 1965), a major work on relief representation, is in German, but the illustrations would in any case be intelligible. The whole process of portraying the geographic landscape is considered, from the topographic, artistic and technical points of view.

822 'Kartographische Nachrichten', prepared by the Deutsche Gesellschaft für Kartographie, 1951, first quarterly then bi-monthly (Bertelsmann Verlag), contains erudite articles, reviews and bibliographies.

823 Keltie, Sir John Scott (1840–1927) had a varied career in publishing before joining the staff of the Royal Geographical Society in 1883. His life's work lay in his administration of the Society, as librarian between 1885 and 1892, then as secretary until 1915; but he is chiefly remembered for his research into geographical education on the continent and in America, which he described in the influential report of 1885 which bears his name and which led directly, in conjunction with the work of Sir Halford Mackinder, to the establishment of modern academic geography in Britain and the foundation of the Oxford School of Geography.

Refer also

'Geographical education. Report to the Council of the Royal Geographical Society' (RGS *Proceedings*, Supplementary Papers, volume 1, part IV, 1882–1885).

824 Kendrew, Wilfred George (1885–1962) was an outstanding influence in British geography, especially at Oxford, and a pioneer in climate geography, as director of the Radcliffe Meteorological Station and subsequently reader in climatology. His *Climates of the continents (qv)* in its successive editions became known throughout the world; *Climate*, 1930, which later became *Climatology*, 1949, went into a second edition in 1957; *Weather: an introductory meteorology for airmen*, 1942, and *The climate of central Canada*, with B W Currie, 1955, are among his other most interesting works, in addition to innumerable contributions to books and periodicals.

Refer also

R E Huschke, *ed: Glossary of meteorology* (American Meteorological Society, 1959).

825 'Kinship and geographical mobility', edited by Ralph Piddington (Leiden: Brill, 1965), in the 'International studies in sociology and social anthropology' series, examines the effects of migration, urbanisation, industrialisation and acculturation on a system of closely-knit kinship bonds outside the 'primitive' or 'folk' societies with which social anthropologists were in the past largely concerned. Experts have as yet not reached agreement and further observations over a long period will be necessary.

826 Kinvig, R H (1893–1969), a much travelled geographer, will be remembered especially for his great achievement in founding the Department of Geography at the University of Birmingham, which established a Chair of Geography in 1948. His interests lay in human geography, in the development of geography and in maps. In 1930, he published an essay on the North West Midlands and encouraged local study in the Department, particularly land use and physical planning. He also studied the Atlantic side of Britain and wrote a *History of the Isle of Man*; also, works on Eastern Europe and Latin America. The Geographical Society of the Department was named the Kinvig Geographical Society in 1958, as a mark of esteem, on his retirement.

827 Köppen, Vladimir Peter (1846–1940) developed an early interest in climate and vegetation. His first version of the world climatic regions, in 1900, was based largely on plants as indicators; in 1918, this was modified to make it freer from botanical geography. He edited the great *Handbuch der Klimatologie* and wrote many papers, also the climatic section of *Die Klimat der Geologischen Vorzeit* with his son-in-law, Alfred Wegener. The Köppen climatic regions were used by A J Herbertson and J G Bartholomew in the *Atlas of meteorology* (*qv*).

828 'Kultura' *see* Cartactual.

829 'Kulturgeografisk atlas', compiled by J Humlum (Copenhagen: Gyldendal, 1955), is a re-issue in two volumes of Humlum's well-known atlas of economic geography. In this publication, with maps and text separated, the length of text has been increased, also the number and variety of the maps. All maps are in red and black and one of the features of the work is the skill with which symbols have been used to such effect; notes on the map plates are in Danish, German, French and English. The maps on population, crops, mineral production and trade are especially well conceived. The text volume is in Danish, lavishly illustrated by photographs and diagrams. The whole work emphasises the trends in world affairs, especially in production and trade.

830 Laborde, Edward Dalrymple (1909–1962) exerted a great influence on the teaching of geography in British public schools, especially through his work at Harrow. He edited many texts and, in particular, his translations made a number of French geographical works available in English, notably Georges Jorré: *The Soviet Union: the land and its people* and A V Perpillou: *Human geography.*

831 Lafreri, Antonio is noted particularly for the collections of maps he is known to have made up into 'atlas' form, as required by his customers. For one such collection, about 1570, he engraved an elaborate title-page, using the figure of Atlas, and this is the first occasion known when this figure was used. Later, it was adapted by Rumold Mercator and thereafter gave the name to such a collection of maps brought together according to some unifying principle.

832 'The Lancashire textile industry in the sixteenth century', by N Lowe (Manchester University Press, 1972), is a study of the Lancashire woollen and linen industries, based, to a great extent on the wills and inventories of workers and merchants in east and southeast Lancashire and on the reports of law cases. Included are chapters on the sources of raw materials, trade and markets, government regulation and control and on the internal organisation of both industries. In an appendix a number of inventories are given in full, together with a glossary.

833 'Land and water', by Patrick Thornhill (Methuen, 1968), forms the first of a series of transparency atlases intended for use with a particular overhead projector, either as base maps or as a means of highlighting specific data. The maps are made of durable plastic, enclosed in a binder. A political map is included, also the base map on which the whole map is built. The land maps contain data such as relief features, rock formations, glaciation and drainage; the Polar regions and oceans are treated separately.

834 'Land evaluation' was the collective title given to the thirty-two papers of a CSIRO Symposium organised in co-operation with Unesco, at Canberra, August 1968; they were edited by G A Stewart, Chief of the CSIRO Division of Land Research (Macmillan, 1969). The papers include some general comments on land evaluation, by G A Stewart, followed by papers on the 'Principles of land classification', 'Land evaluation reviews and case studies', 'Data handling and interpretation', 'Land parameters' and 'Sensors for land parameters', illustrated in half-tone and line.

835 'Land from the air: *a photographic geography'*, by G Dury and J A Morris, published by Harrap, has the intention of explaining the reading and interpretation of geographical aerial photographs showing a wide variety of topographical types, illustrated with twenty-one half-tone plates and a number of figures in the text. Scope is limited to the British Isles and each photograph demonstrates a specific theme—'A Welsh mining valley', 'Orchard and marsh in North Kent', among others. A section 'Books for further reading' is appended.

Refer also

    J B Bird and A Morrison: 'Space photography and its geographical applications', *The geographical review*, October 1964.

836 'Land of the 500 million: *a geography of China'*, by George B Cressey (McGraw-Hill series in geography, 1955) has remained a recommended book for background reading, dealing with the people, physical features, especially climate, crops and resources, commerce and industry, followed by regional assessments and a chapter on 'China's prospects'. There are photographs, sketchmaps and figures throughout the text and an extensive bibliography, grouped under subject headings.

Refer also

    G B Cressey: *China's geographic foundations* and *Asia's lands and peoples*.

    The Times atlas of China, edited by Professor D C Twitchett and P J M Geelan (Times Books, 1974).

    Audrey Donnithorne: *China's economic system* (New York: Praeger, 1967).

    C P FitzGerald: *The southern expansion of the Chinese people*

(New York: Praeger, 1972).

Owen Lattimore: *Inner Asian frontiers of China* (New York: American Geographical Society, Research series no 21, second edition, 1951).

Andrew March: *The idea of China: myth and theory in geographic thought* (Newton Abbot: David and Charles, 1974).

T Shabad: *China's changing map: national and regional development, 1949–71* (New York: Praeger; Methuen, revised edition, 1972).

837 'Land use and resources: *studies in applied geography'* was created by the Institute of British Geographers in 1968 as a memorial volume to Sir Dudley Stamp, forming the first of the Institute's series of *Special publications*. Chapters were contributed by a number of leading geographers in this country and abroad, including 'The man and his work', which contains a bibliography of his publications; 'The land of Britain'; 'The developing world'; and 'Sir Dudley Stamp and his life and times', by M J Wise.

Refer also

M Chisholm: *Rural settlement and land use* (Hutchinson, 1962).

Colin Clark: *Population growth and land use* (Macmillan, 1967).

William C Found: *A theoretical approach to rural land-use patterns* (Arnold, 1971).

J H Paterson: *Land work and resources: an introduction to economic geography* (Arnold, 1972).

Polish Academy of Sciences: *Problems of applied geography* (*Proceedings* of the Anglo-Polish Seminar, 1959; Warsaw: PWN, 1961).

Resources and man: a study and recommendations by the Committee on Resources and Man of the Division of Earth Sciences, National Academy of Sciences, National Research Council (Freeman, 1969).

838 'Land use information: *a critical survey of US statistics, including possibilities for greater uniformity'* was prepared by Marion Clawson and Charles L Stewart and published by The Johns Hopkins Press and OUP. The title is self-explanatory; the authors point out that United States data have developed each in isolation and the purposes of this work are to present information and ideas and to develop a general overall system for handling land-use data, suggesting the establishment of an organisation that would assist in tabulating, cross-referencing and collating the gathered data.

839 'Land utilisation survey of Great Britain' was initiated in 1930 by L Dudley Stamp. The field work was carried out mainly between 1931 and 1933 by teams of voluntary workers, every acre of land in England, Wales, Scotland, the Isle of Man and the Channel Islands being recorded on six inch Ordnance Survey maps. The results were reduced to the scale of one inch to the mile and published in 150 sheets for England and Wales and the more populous parts of Scotland. The work was organised on a county basis and the findings were eventually co-ordinated and published in a series of *Reports*, one for each county, under the title of *The land of Britain*. The whole undertaking was summarised by Dudley Stamp in *The land of Britain: its use and misuse* (Longmans, 1948); a shorter summary had been issued for the British Council in the previous year, with the title *The land of Britain and how it is used*. This monumental work represented Britain's land use at the time of the second world war. A *Second Land Use Survey of Britain* on the scale of 1:25,000 was begun in 1960 by the Isle of Thanet Geographical Association under the direction of Alice Coleman of King's College, London. Full details are to be found in the *Land Use Survey handbook*, by Alice Coleman and K R A Maggs and in 'The first twenty-four published land use maps', a special issue of *Panorama* (Isle of Thanet Geographical Association, 1964).

> *Refer also*
>
> Alice Coleman: 'The Second Land Use Survey: progress and prospect', *Geographical journal*, June 1961.
>
> Alice Coleman: 'Land use survey—the next step', *The geographical magazine*, October 1969.
>
> R H Best and J T Coppock: *The changing use of land in Britain* (Faber, 1962).
>
> J T Coppock and Alice M Coleman: 'Land use and conservation', *The geographical journal*, July 1970).
>
> H C Darby: 'Domesday Book—the first land utilization survey', *The geographical magazine*, March 1970.

840 'Landforms and life: *short studies on topographical maps'*, by C C Carter (Christophers, 1931, reprinted 1933, 1936, 1938), made a great impression on geographical thought when it first appeared, a

pioneer work and the forerunner of many similar texts. In the introduction, the author could still say what is now taken for
granted—'The power of the topographical map, as an essential tool,
is being increasingly recognised . . .' The text is divided into parts,
each including several sub-sections: 'The map'; 'The surface expression of denudation'; 'The surface expression of structure';
'Land-forms and life'; 'Coast forms'; 'Coast life', giving examples
taken from the relevant parts of Britain. Throughout the text are
photographs, sketchmaps and diagrams, showing some surprisingly
'modern' concepts, such as the effect of industrial conurbations on
natural life.

Refer also

J L Davies: *Landforms of cold climates* (MIT Press, 1969; The
Australian National Press, 'An introduction to systematic geomorphology' series, 3).

I Douglas: *Humid landforms* (MIT Press, 1971).

Roy Millward and Adrian Robinson: 'Landscapes of Britain'
series (Macmillan, 1971–).

841 'Landscape', published three times a year from 1951 in Santa
Fe, New Mexico, covers all aspects of landscape forms—cultural
geography, human ecology, urban geography, planning and conservation. It is well illustrated; there are articles, brief notes and comments, and book reviews.

842 'Landscape studies: *an introduction to geomorphology'*, by K E
Sawyer (Arnold, 1970), deals with the study of the processes of
landscape formation and precise quantitative measurement in field
work, discussing actual land forms with the aid of specially
adapted Ordnance Survey map sections and of photographs and
line diagrams. The standard of the work has been designed for students in college of education or first year university.

Refer also

Dorothy Sylvester: *The rural landscape of the Welsh Borderland* (Macmillan, 1969).

843 'The large scale county maps of the British Isles 1596–1850: *a
union list'*, compiled in the Map Section of the Bodleian Library
by Elizabeth M Rodger (The Library, 1960), includes all printed
county maps issued separately during the period specified on a
scale between half an inch and three inches to one mile, with a few

exceptions. Arrangement of entries is first by county alphabetically, within the four divisions, England, Wales, Scotland and Ireland, then by date of publication of the first edition, each entry bearing a running number. Details include the existence of index maps or gazetteers. An introduction explains the approach to the work and the characteristics of each map are given in the entries.

844 **'Larousse agricole:** *encyclopédie de l'agriculture'* is a monumental work prepared under the direction of Raymond Braconnier and Jacques Glandard, consisting of entries of varying length on all aspects of agriculture, domestic plants and animals, forestry, modern agricultural techniques and a comparison of French agriculture with that in other countries. More than a thousand photographs, diagrams and figures illustrate the text and there are fifty-six separate plates, many in colour.

845 **'Larousse encyclopedia of the earth'**, translated by R Bradshaw and M M Owen from *La terre, nôtre planète*, was published by Paul Hamlyn in 1961, with a second edition, 1965. The *Larousse encyclopedia of world geography* (*qv*) was adapted from *Géographie universelle Larousse* (*qv*). Both are lavishly illustrated.

The *New Larousse Encyclopedia of the Earth*, edited by Leon Bertin, from a revised text prepared by a panel of British and American consultants, was specially adapted for English-speaking readers and many examples on particularly relevant environments were introduced (Hamlyn, 1972).

846 **'Larousse encyclopedia of world geography'**, adapted from *Géographie universelle Larousse*, edited by Pierre Deffontaines, was first published in three volumes in France by Augé, Gillon, Hollier-Larousse, Moreau et Cie (Librairie Larousse, Paris) and Paul Hamlyn, 1964; The Western Publishing Company published the work in one volume in 1965. Arrangement of the text is by regional grouping of countries and there are illustrations and maps throughout.

847 **'Late Tudor and early Stuart geography 1583–1650:** *a sequel to Tudor geography, 1485–1583'*, by E G R Taylor (Methuen, 1934; New York: Octagon Press, 1968), comprises a 'Bibliography of English geographical literature 1583–1650', first arranged under authors' names, with running numbers, then grouped chronologically, prefaced by explanatory chapters setting out the geographical features of the period under review—'Richard Hakluyt the younger'; 'The first edition of the *Principal voyages*,1589'; 'The second edition of the *Principal voyages*, 1598–1600'; 'Regional geography, or chorography: 1583–1625'; 'Samuel Purchas: 1612–26'; 'Mathematical geography, navigation and surveying'; 'The realm of nature'; 'Economic geography; 1625–50'; 'The urbane traveller', and 'Colonial geography'. Some reproductions are included and the text is rich in quotations and notes.

848 'Latin America: *an introduction to modern books in English concerning the countries of Latin America'* was prepared by The Hispanic and Luzo-Brazilian Councils in 1960, with a second edition, revised, by the Library Association in 1966. The later edition incorporates works published in the previous five years, placing greater emphasis on economic and social conditions and omitting guide books and children's books. A section on 'General books' is followed by the body of the work, which deals with the literature on individual countries, arranged alphabetically. Brief annotations are added to the entries as necessary and there is an author index. A useful list of British-Latin American organisations in London is appended.

Refer also

Joel Bergman: *Brazil* . . . (OUP for the Development Centre of the Organization for Economic Co-operation and Developments 1970).

Catalog of the Latin American Collection of the University of Texas Library (G K Hall, thirty-one volumes, 1969).

Irish University Press Area Studies series: *Central and South America*, reprints in fifty volumes, 1971.

D G Browning: *El Salvador: landscape and society* (OUP, 1971).

G M Dorn, *comp*: *Latin America: an annotated bibliography of paperback books* (Library of Congress, 1967).

P E James: *Latin America* (Cassell, third edition, 1959).

George Pendle: *South America, a reader's guide* (National Book League, 1957).

Irmgard Pohl and Josef Zepp: *Latin America: a geographical commentary*, edited by Kempton E Webb (Murray, translation of one of the volumes of *Harms Erdkunde*).

Alice Taylor, *ed*: *South America* (Newton Abbot: David and Charles, 1973).

849 'The Latin American markets: *a descriptive and statistical survey of 30 markets made up of almost 173 million people*' was compiled by J Walter Thompson Company and published by McGraw-Hill in 1956, with maps and a bibliography. For most of the countries information is provided under the following headings: the land and its climate; population and characteristics; mineral and vegetation sources; energy and power; agriculture, livestock and fisheries; manufacturing; transport and communications; imports and exports; income and standard of living; market classification by administrative division.

Refer also

Celso Furtado: *Economic development of Latin America: a survey from colonial times to the Cuban Revolution* (CUP, 1970).

Social aspects of economic development in Latin America (Unesco, two volumes, 1963, 1967).

850 'Latin American Publications Fund handbook' was first published in London under the auspices of the Fund, in 1969. Papers include 'Cities in a changing Latin America: two studies of urban growth in the development of Mexico and Venezuela' and 'Urbanization and economic development in Mexico', by David J Fox; and 'The city as centre of change in modern Venezuela', by D J Robinson.

851 'Laxton: the last English open field village', by J D Chambers (HMSO, 1964) is a well-produced brochure illustrated with reproductions, photographs, figures and sketchmaps. The text deals with the village, farming system, the Manorial Court and other aspects of the Manor, of interest to historical geographers and those interested in agricultural or settlement geography; an Appendix sets out 'Rules and regulations for the grazing of the open fields, Laxton Estate in the County of Nottingham'.

852 Le Play, Frédéric (1806–1882) exercised a continuing influence on British geography, largely through Professor Herbertson, Sir Patrick Geddes and other geographers who contributed to the work of the Le Play Society. His insistence on the importance of fieldwork and the relation of communities to environment led the way to the acceptance of this aspect of geographical studies and to the founding of such organisations as The Geographical Field Group.

Refer also

　M Z Brooke: *Le Play, engineer and social scientist: the life and work of Frédéric Le Play* (Longman, 1970).

853 Le Play Society was founded in 1930 by Sir Patrick Geddes, Professor C B Fawcett and Miss M Tatton for the promotion of international studies involving field work in geography and geology by groups visiting various countries. Pioneer work was accomplished before the Society ceased in 1960. The studies of 'place, work, folk' had followed closely the methods of the French sociologist, P G F Le Play and linked the work of geographers, historians and sociologists.
Refer also

　S H Beaver: 'The Le Play Society and field work', *Geography*, 1962, part 3.

854 Lebon, Dr J H G (1909–1969) was an outstanding geographer who, during his academic career, passed on his inspiration to generations of students in this country and abroad. His chief interests lay in physical, particularly in climatological, geography and in regional work in the Middle East and Sudan, but he was learned and experienced in many facets of the subject and stressed always the essential unity of geographical studies. He wrote *An introduction to human geography*, 1952, which made new contributions to the subject, also many articles and *Land use in the Sudan*, no 4 in the *World Land Use Survey*; at the time of his death he had almost completed a new geography of the Middle East. A bibliography of his writings is included in the *Transactions of the Institute of British Geographers*, November 1970.

855 'Lehrbuch der Allgemeinen Geographie' is a comprehensive survey of world geography, published by Walter de Gruyter, Berlin, in ten volumes, of which the first appeared in 1961. Unlike the *Géographie universelle* (*qv*), the approach is thematic, the plan of the complete work being as follows: Herbert Louis: *Allgemeine Geomorphologie*; Joachim Blüthgen: *Allgemeine Klimageographie*; Fritz Wilhelm: *Allgemeine Hydrogeographie*; Josef Schmithüsen: *Allgemeine Vegetationsgeographie*; Hans Bobek: *Allgemeine Sozial-und Bevölkerungsgeographie*; Gabriele Schwarz: *Allgemeine Siedlungsgeographie*; Erich Obst: *Allgemeine Wirtschafts-und Verkehrsgeographie*; Martin Schwind: *Geographie der Staaten*; Josef Schmithüsen: *Allgemeine Landschaftskunde*; Eduard Imhof and others: *Karte und Luftbild: als Arbeitsmittel des Geographen*. Individual volumes have already run into more than one edition.

856 **'Leicestershire landscapes:** *case studies in local geography for the CSE pupil'*, prepared by the Leicestershire Association for Local Geographical Studies (Blond Educational, 1970), is a particularly successful, well illustrated example of many such studies that have recently appeared, demonstrating the renewed interest of geographers in field work and local geography. Thirteen contributors consider the characteristics of the Soar Valley, Charnwood Forest, the City of Leicester, Market Harborough, East and West Leicestershire, the Vale of Belvoir and farming in the county, with a foreword by Professor J F Kerr.

857 **'Leland's itinerary in England'** was reprinted in 1964 from the version based on Hearne's second edition (1744 and 1745) with a foreword by Thomas Kendrick (Centaur Press Limited, five volumes), edited by Lucy Toulmin Smith first in 1907. The reprint is now available in paperback.

858 **'Let me enjoy: essays, partly geographical',** by O H K Spate (Methuen, 1966), reflects the maturity of one of Britain's leading geographers. First, as he states in the Preface—'to attempt some reflection of the joy . . . in . . . the inconsequential variety of human experience . . .', secondly, 'to explain what it is that the craft of the geographer can bring to the understanding and generalizing of this experience . . .' and thirdly 'to assert that it is not necessary to be always solemn to be serious . . .'. These preliminary remarks put forward a promise, which is eminently fulfilled in the thought-provoking and always entertaining (in the best sense) text. The essays are grouped under four headings: 'People and places', 'The compass of geography', 'Toynbeeana' and 'Southwards the course'. Some references are listed at the end for the further exploration of the more serious reader.

> *Compare*, for example, D W Meinig, *ed: On geography: selected writings of Preston E James* (Syracuse University Press, 1971); and Ronald Abler *et al: Spatial organization: the geographer's view of the world* (Prentice-Hall, 1971).

859 **'The library atlas',** by Harold Fullard and H C Darby (Philip, 1938; eighth edition, 1965) is in two parts, general and economic. The general section, on scales ranging from 1:2½M to 1:8M, was published previously as *The university atlas*. Thirty-two pages of economic maps and diagrams include distribution maps of major products throughout the world; diagrams and maps of world occupations, transport, imports and exports; economic development and production, land use and agriculture, minerals and industry for Great Britain and for other selected areas. Climatic graphs are included for more than two hundred representative stations throughout the world. The index comprises over fifty thousand entries, conforming in general with the rules of the Permanent Committee on Geographical Names and the US Board on Geographic Names.

860 'The Library catalogue of the School of Oriental and African Studies' was printed by G K Hall in twenty-eight volumes, 1963; entries dealing with the whole of Asia, Oceania and Africa are available in the complete set or in fourteen sections. The author index and title index are followed by the subject index—General, Africa, Middle East, South Asia, South-East Asia and Pacific Islands and the Far East. Manuscripts and microfilms are included, also periodicals and serials; there are also entries in Chinese and Japanese.

861 'Library guide for Brazilian studies', compiled by William Vernon Jackson (Pittsburgh: University of Pittsburgh Book Center, 1964), is a guide to the major United States research collections of Brazilian materials; the holdings of seventy-four libraries are described and evaluated. Summary chapters analyse particular collections as a whole and sketch co-operative projects for collecting current materials. Appendices form important parts of the book, comprising an annotated list of ninety-eight Brazilian periodicals in the humanities and social sciences, and a breakdown of the Library of Congress classification numbers for Brazilian history and literature. Emphasis throughout is on materials for advanced study and research.

Note Most of the country's bibliographic activities emanate from the Instituto Brasileiro de Bibliografia e Documentaçao. Subject bibliographies have been issued on agriculture, botany, zoology and social sciences.

Refer also

Atlas pluviométrico do Brasil (Hydrological Bureau of the 'Divisao de Aguas'; maps by the Serviço Gráfico do Instituto Brasileiro de Geografia e Estatística).

862 Library of Congress Map Division aims to keep at least one copy of each edition of every map, atlas, globe and other form of cartographic publication with any reference value. The basic collection to date amounts to some three million maps and more than twenty thousand atlases, and the collections are growing at the rate of some ninety thousand to a hundred thousand maps and up to fifteen hundred atlases a year. A *Bibliography of cartography* has been maintained, of which microfilm copies are available. The library has issued printed cards for maps and atlases from the beginning of the card printing programme; a more comprehensive cataloguing of maps began in 1946, though still on a selective basis. Cards for maps and atlases printed before 1953 were included in the *Library of Congress author catalog*; from 1950, entries were included also in the *Subject catalog*. With the re-organisation of the catalogue in 1953, a separate part, *Maps and atlases*, was issued and this policy continued until 1955 (1956), when entries were again included in the main sequences, *Books: authors* and *Books: subjects*. Bibliographical publications of central interest to geographers are frequently published, notably the *List of geographical atlases* . . . below-mentioned.

Refer also
Donald A Wise: 'Sources of cartographic acquisition in the Library of Congress', *Bulletin*, Special Libraries Association, Geography and Map Division, December 1971.

863 'Lighthouse of the skies: *The Smithsonian Astrophysical Observatory: background and history 1846–1955'*, written by Bessie Zaban Jones and published by David and Charles, presents an analysis of its contributions in the study of solar radiation, long-range weather forecasting, etc, including a list of publications issued by the Institution.

See also
The Smithsonian Institution . . .

864 The Linmap system of Line-printer Mapping, the first commercial British computer mapping system, was originally developed by Computation Research and Development for the Ministry of Housing and Local Government; in its version 1 form it has the ability to process up to forty-two data items for each map produced and a capacity of four thousand points of information per map. These capacities will be increased as the scope of the system is enlarged. Linmap has been designed to accept magnetic tape input and to work for the Co-ordinate Reference System of data identification which uses Ordnance Survey National Grid Co-ordinates. 'Colmap' is a colour map system based on Linmap. Symap (*qv*) has been developed at Harvard University and Mapit is another programme for the production of flow maps, dot maps and graduated symbols; and a new design by CalComp is a high-speed, high-resolution computer-output-microfilm system.

Refer to recent issues of *The cartographic journal*, especially that for December 1971; the Oxford system of automatic cartography (*qv*) and, from recent monographs,

F Hackman: 'Scaling the heights', *The geographical magazine*, August 1972.

Gillian A Hackman *et al*: 'Instant maps for planners', *The geographical magazine*, August 1972.

R Kern and G Rushton: 'Mapit: a computer program for production of flow maps, dot maps and graduated symbol maps', *Cartographical journal*, December 1969.

G R P Lawrence: *Cartographic methods* (Methuen, 1971), which includes notes on computer-produced maps.

865 Linton, David Leslie (1906–1971), a notable scholar and teacher, was particularly interested in geomorphology. In association with S W Wooldridge, he wrote *Structure and surface drainage in South-East England*; and he passed on his knowledge and inspiration to generations of students in numerous addresses, papers and edited works. He was Chairman of the British Geomorphological Research Group, editor of *Zeitschrift für Geomorphologie* and, for some years, editor of *Geography*.

866 'A list of American doctoral dissertations on Africa' is compiled and published by the Library of Congress. A comparable work published by SCOLMA is *Theses on Africa accepted by universities in the United Kingdom and Ireland*, kept up to date by annual volumes of *United Kingdom publications and theses on Africa*.

See also next item

867 'List of French doctoral dissertations on Africa, 1884–1961', compiled by Marion Dinstel, former librarian of the African Document Center, Boston University, was sponsored by the Boston University Libraries and reproduced in 1966 by G K Hall. The work is

408

arranged by country and/or area, and alphabetically within each area by author; each title is numbered and there is an author index, also a limited subject index. Forty African states are represented, as well as material on the continent in general, amounting in all to nearly three thousand entries.

Refer also

B C Bloomfield *et al, ed: Theses on Africa accepted by Universities in the United Kingdom: a list* (Heffer, 1964).

868 '**List of geographical atlases in the Library of Congress**', the only extensive bibliography of atlases and an indispensable reference work, is especially useful to the student of early cartography. The basic work was in four volumes, 1909–1920, by Philip Lee Phillips; a fifth volume, with bibliographical notes, was compiled by Clara Egli LeGear, 1958, containing references to over two thousand world atlases acquired by the library between 1920 and 1955; a further supplement by the same compiler, 1963, on the same plan, contained also some eight hundred oriental atlases and a valuable list of the contents of Yousuf Kamal's *Monumenta cartographica Africae et Aegypti*. A seventh volume comprises a consolidated author list and the eighth volume an index. Author lists and topographical lists are also included in the first four volumes. Theatrum Orbis Terrarum Limited published a reprint in 1970, with bibliographical notes.

869 '**A list of maps of America in the Library of Congress** *preceded by a list of works relating to cartography'*, compiled by Philip L Phillips, published in Washington, 1901, was reprinted in 1967 by Theatrum Orbis Terrarum Limited. About fifteen thousand maps of America are arranged chronologically, then according to subject and the bibliography on cartography lists some 1,200 books on mapmaking and its history.

Refer also

John A Wolter: 'Source materials for the history of American cartography', *Bulletin*, Special Libraries Association, Geography and Map Division, June 1972.

870 '**Die Literatur über die Polar-Regionen der Erde bis 1875**', prepared by J Chavanne, A Karpf and F Le Monnier (1878), comprises more than six thousand items, including works on adjacent regions; it was reprinted in 1962 by N Israel, Meridian and Theatrum Orbis Terrarum Limited.

871 'Lithofacies maps: *an atlas of the United States and Southern Canada*' was the work of graduate students at Northwestern University engaged in regional stratigraphic studies under the editorship of L L Sloss, E C Dapples and W C Krumbein (Wiley, 1960). Together with the accompanying text, it presents a unique source of information concerning the thickness and lithology of the sedimentary rocks of the USA.

872 'Liverpool essays in geography: *a jubilee collection*', edited by Robert W Steel and Richard Lawton (Longmans, 1967), contains contributions from 'over thirty authors who, between them, span successive generations of Liverpool-trained geographers from the 1920s to the 1960s'; a festschrift, not to a single scholar, but to a Department of Geography. Each author has written on his own speciality, within the unity which shows the compass of geographical studies at Liverpool University. There are maps and figures throughout the text and appendices present the staff of the Department of Geography at Liverpool from 1902 and graduates of the Department; but there is no index.

Refer also

F E Hyde: *Liverpool and the Mersey: the development of a port 1700–1970* (Newton Abbot: David and Charles, 1971).

873 'Locational analysis in human geography', by Peter Haggett (Arnold, 1965), was based on a series of lectures given at Cambridge. Part I, 'Models of locational structure', discusses the geographically significant aspects of the main theoretical models—both classical (Thünen, Weber, Christaller and Lösch) and modern (Isard, Garrison, Berry and Hägerstrand), attempting to weld them around the theme of the geometrical symmetry detectable within regional systems. Part II, 'Methods in locational analysis', includes a particularly interesting section on 'Region-building'. There are numerous diagrams throughout the text, references and a bibliography.

874 'London in maps' (The Connoisseur, 1972), with text by Philippa Glanville, brings together reproductions of decorative and informative maps of the City dating from the sixteenth to the twentieth century. This outstanding production, which will surely become a collector's piece, shows the continuing development of the London topography and the increasing complexity of social life, trade and transport, also the vast increase in population in the Greater London area during the past two centuries.

875 'London 2000', by Peter Hall (Faber, 1963; second edition, 1969, 1971), is, to quote the author, 'an exercise in academic polemic'. In the second edition, the text remained unchanged, but postscripts were added to each chapter setting out such facts as were necessary to bring the content up to date. The five main parts: 'Posing the problem', 'Guiding growth', 'Building the new London', 'Running the new London', 'Living in it' are subdivided into chapters, and an appendix to chapter VI is 'Twenty-five new towns for London' arranged alphabetically by name and giving the basic facts concerning each. Sketchmaps and photographs illustrate the text.

> *Refer also*
> Greater London Development Plan: three reports, 1969.
> *London under stress*: a study of the planning policies proposed for London and its region (Town and Country Planning Association, 1970).
> Peter Self: *Metropolitan planning*—The Planning System of Greater London (Greater London Paper 14, 1971).
> Peter Self: *Town planning in Greater London* (Greater London Paper 7, 1962).
> Christopher Trent: *Greater London: its growth and development through two thousand years* (Phoenex House, 1965).

876 Longmans, Green and Company Limited, founded in 1724, has published many serious monographs and bibliographical works in geographical subjects, such as the UNESCO *source book for geography teaching* (*qv*), *Longman's dictionary of geography* (*qv*) and *A glossary of geographical terms* (*qv*). The *Geographies for advanced study* series, edited by Professor S H Beaver, is a reliable series of monographs on individual countries or regions, including, for example, Georges Jorré: *The Soviet Union: the land and its people*; F J Monkhouse: *Western Europe*; R J Harrison Church: *West Africa*; C O'Dell: *The Scandinavian world*; and thematic studies such as B W Sparks: *Geomorphology*, all well produced and illustrated by photographs and sketch-maps. For school work, there are *Europe in maps*, 1969; the *Concepts in geography* series, 1969–; *Longman's geography paperbacks; Sketchmap geographies; First lessons in human geography;* and *New geography in the classroom*, edited by Rex Walford. Longman's loops in geography, produced by Halas and Batchelor Animation

Limited, are edited under the supervision of H J Clarke and W J Allen; a new series of 8 mm film loops uses colour and animation to elucidate and interpret some of the more complex topics in meteorology, edited by Dr R G Barry.

877 'Longman's dictionary of geography', 1966, edited by L Dudley Stamp, brings together in one alphabetical sequence information on societies and their awards, brief explanations of geographical terms and physical features and notes on countries and cities of the world, commodities and international trade. Biographical entries are quoted from the *Dictionary of national biography*. A 'Selected bibliography of geographical books published in Britain' is included, based on one prepared by the editor for the National Book League in 1964, with later additions, intended as a guide in the setting up of a school or college library; books published in North America are also included, but limited to those in the English language.

878 'The look of our land—an airphoto atlas of the rural United States' (US Department of Agriculture, Economic Research Service: Agricultural handbooks nos 384, 406, 409 and 419, 1970–1971) consists of paperbacked groups of air photographs: *The Far West, North Central, The East and South, The Mountain and deserts* and *The Plains and Prairies*, covering together the 156 land resource areas delimited in Handbook no 296, 1965, *Land resource regions and major land resource areas of the United States*. Each region is briefly described, accompanied by simple outline maps. A complementary volume is *Aerial photographs in geologic interpretation and mapping* (United States Geological Survey, Professional Paper no 373, 1960).

879 'Lost leviathan: whales and whaling', by F D Ommanney (Hutchinson, 1971), provides, in the author's eminently readable style, a vast amount of information on the various types of whales, the history of the whaling industry and the different uses to which whale products are put. Dr Ommanney served as a member of the *Discovery* team which investigated Antarctic whaling. Some black and white photographs, diagrams and figures are included in the text, also a useful list of references to reports, books and articles.

880 'The lost villages of England', by Maurice Beresford (Lutterworth Press, 1954), remains a classic work, well documented, including a county index to lost village sites mentioned in the text, notes and a list of works frequently cited. There are pertinent sketchmaps and illustrations.

881 'The Lower Swansea Valley project', edited by K J Hilton (Longmans, 1967), presents a comprehensive survey of the area made by members of the University College of Swansea, with support from the Nuffield Foundation; it provides also an excellent example of a recent case study of an area, isolating the factors that have been inhibiting the social, physical and economic use of the land and estimating its potential. The text, as it stands, including several sketchmaps and diagrams, is based on twelve reports—'The human ecology of the Lower Swansea Valley', by Margaret Stacey; 'Report on transportation and physical planning in the Lower Swansea Valley', by R D Worrall; 'Report on the hydrology of the Lower Swansea Valley', by D C Ledger; 'Report on the geology of the Lower Swansea Valley', by W F G Cardy; 'The soil mechanics and foundation engineering survey of the Lower Swansea Valley project area', by H G Clapham and others; 'The prospects for industrial use of the Lower Swansea Valley: a study of land use in a regional context', by Susanne H Spence; 'Lower Swansea Valley: housing report' and 'Lower Swansea Valley: open space report', by Margaret Stacey; 'Plant ecology of the Lower Swansea Valley'; 'Soil biology of the Lower Swansea Valley', by P D Gadgil; 'Afforestation of the Lower Swansea Valley', by B R Salter and 'Tips and tip working in the Lower Swansea Valley', by G Holt.

882 Lundqvist, Gösta, who died in 1968, was one of Sweden's foremost cartographers, working especially with the Esselte Company in Stockholm and the Generalstabens Litografiska Anstalt. Many original atlases and map series owe their existence to him. In 1962, he became head of all the map production departments in Esselte. His wide travel enabled his reference atlases, wall maps and tourist maps to be really practical and helpful as well as of cartographical excellence.

883 Lyell, Sir Charles (1797–1875) became the first professor of geology at King's College, London, where the Lyell Club is named after him. His influence on geological thought in academic circles was very great, also in the Geological Society, of which he was president 1835 to 1837 and 1848 to 1850; his publications have perhaps been even more influential. The *Principles of geology* was published in 1830, having a second edition in 1832; a third edition, in four volumes, followed in 1834, of which the fourth volume, rewritten as *Elements of geology*, 1838, went into six editions and was followed by *The student's elements of geology*.

Refer also

Sir Edward Bailey: *Charles Lyell*, 1962.

T G Bonney: *Charles Lyell and modern geology* (Macmillan, 1895).

F J North: *Sir Charles Lyell: interpreter of the principles of geology, 1965*.

L G Wilson, *ed: Sir Charles Lyell's scientific journals on the species question* (1970, one of the Yale *Studies in the history of science and medicine*).

884 **'McGraw-Hill encyclopedia of Russia and the Soviet Union'**, edited by Michael T Florinsky and others (Donat Publishing Company, 1961), contains a mass of useful information on the principal developments in Russia before and after the revolution of 1917, presented in alphabetical order; some entries are single or two-line or longer, for example 'Agriculture'. There are maps and diagrams throughout the text, also small black and white portraits. References are given at the ends of articles.

885 **'McGraw-Hill international atlas'** was based on *Der Grosse Bertelsmann Weltatlas* (*qv*) edited, in English, French and German, under the direction of Dr W Bormann, 1964 (dated 1965). Information gained during the IGY researches is incorporated, as well as other recent developments in roads, railways, water and power projects.

886 **McGraw-Hill Publishing Company Limited** is particularly interesting to geographers for the *McGraw-Hill series in geography*, which includes such standard works as V C Finch and others: *Elements of geography, Physical elements of geography* and *The earth and its resources*; O W Freeman and H F Raup: *Essentials of geography*; G B Cressey: *Asia's lands and peoples, Land of the 500 million: a geography of China* and *China's geographic foundations*; Erwin Raisz: *General cartography* and *Principles of cartography*; G T Trewartha: *An introduction to climate*. The *McGraw-Hill illustrated world geography*, edited by Frank Debenham and W A Burns, was published in 1960. *See* also *The McGraw-Hill international atlas*, and the *McGraw-Hill*

414

encyclopedia of Russia . . . Other series include the 'Biological sciences', 'Population biology', 'Agricultural sciences', 'American forestry', 'International development' and a 'Field guide series'. A complete catalogue is issued annually, with information sheets and handouts as necessary. The House of Grant publications were acquired a few years ago.

887 'Mackenzie Delta bibliography', edited by Mary Jane Jones, was sponsored by the Northern Science Research Group, Department of Indian Affairs and Northern Development (Queen's Printer, 1969). The bibliography brings together references to monographs and articles showing academic and other interests in the project since 1964.

888 Mackinder, Sir Halford John (1861–1947) is notable particularly for his achievements in establishing academic geography in England. In many ways, he was foremost among British scholar-geographers, exerting the greatest influence not only on those aspects of the subject in which he was specially interested, such as regional and political geography, but on succeeding generations of geographers. His academic work was centred on Reading, London and Oxford, but his theories and geographical beliefs reached a wider public through his papers to the Royal Geographical Society, his lectures given throughout the country and his British Association address of 1905. Among the highlights of his career was his address to the 1895 International Geographical Congress and his presidential address to the Geographical Association on the theme 'Modern geography: German and English', which led to the foundation of the first School of Geography in Oxford in 1889, with himself as director and A J Herbertson as his second. Two papers to the Royal Geographical Society which achieved far-reaching results were 'The scope and methods of geography' and 'The geographical pivot of history', reprinted separately by the society in 1951, with an introduction by E W Gilbert. Among his published books, *Britain and the British seas (qv)* and *The Rhine: its valley and history* (Chatto and Windus, 1908) are probably the most remarkable.

Refer also

E W Gilbert: 'The Right Honourable Sir Halford J Mackinder, PC 1861–1947', *Geographical journal*, March 1961, which includes a bibliography.

E W Gilbert and W H Parker: 'Mackinder's democratic ideals and reality after fifty years', *The geographical journal*, June

1969.

J F Unstead: 'H J Mackinder and the new geography', *The geographical journal*, June 1949.

889 Macmillan and Company Limited, London, issues monographs, booklets and visual aid materials of great use to geography students and teachers. The *Landscapes of Britain* series, for example, 1970–, beginning with *The South-West peninsula, The West Midlands* and *South-East England*, describes and discusses in each volume the physical, economic and historical elements of the landscape of the area, lavishly illustrated with photographs, maps and diagrams. Frequent catalogues are issued of both books and non-book materials. Since the overhead projector became universally accepted as a teaching aid, Macmillan, with many other publishers, have been increasingly preparing transparencies; the geographical series cover the world, with an emphasis on the British Isles. Macmillan Educational include geography as one of their lines—new titles being *Topics in geography, London* and *Transport* by Oswald Hull, *Towns*, by M Turner, *Food, clothing and shelter*, by L W Steven, *A map book of the Benelux countries*, by A J B Tussler and A J L Alden and *Beginning practical geography*, by Arthur Bray.

890 Mair Geographical Publishing House, Stuttgart, founded in 1950, specialises in road maps; also, since 1960, a number of road atlases of European countries has been issued. The Deutsche Generalkarte 1:200,000 was published between 1952 and 1957, in a map series of uniform size, based on a new survey. The *Grosse Shell-Atlas of Germany and Europe*, 1960–, revised annually, aims at supplying, for any given need, the proper map at the most convenient scale. Arranged in systematic order, the maps are at scales of 1:4,500,000, 1:1,500,000, 1:500,000 and 1:200,000, in addition to a number of maps at larger scales. Brief comments below the map faces provide compact sources of information.

Refer also

Volkmar Mair: 'Strassenkarten aus Mairs Geographischen Verlag', *International yearbook of cartography*. 1963.

891 'The major seaports of the United Kingdom', by James Bird (Hutchinson, 1963), describes the history, layout and development of the chief groups of British ports, illustrated by fine aerial photographs, sketchmaps and diagrammatic plans. Following an introduction, 'Industrial and commercial estuaries' includes New-castle, Glasgow and Clydeside, Belfast, Hull and other Humber ports, Southampton and Southampton Water and the Bristol complex. South Wales ports are considered separately, especially Swansea; 'Packet ports', Dover, Harwich and Holyhead; 'The inland port', such as Manchester; 'General cargo giants', Liverpool, Merseyside, the Thames and the Port of London. A final section is headed 'Ports in perspective', dealing with port hinterlands and the port of the future; an appendix comments on the Report of the Rochdale Committee. Notes and references are given at the end of each section and there is a short list of 'selected further references' published since 1953.

Refer also

James Bird: 'Of central places, cities and seaports', *Geography*, April 1973.

892 **'The makers of modern geography'**, by Robert E Dickinson (Routledge and Kegan Paul, 1969), was an endeavour 'to trace the development of modern geography as an organised body of knowledge in the light of the works of its foremost German and French contributors', with a first chapter entitled 'From Strabo to Kant'. Leading names are Alexander von Humboldt, Carl Ritter, Friedrich Ratzel, Ferdinand von Richthofen, Albrecht Penck, Alfred Hettner, Otto Schlüter, Frédéric Le Play and Vidal de la Blache.

893 **'The making of the Dutch landscape: an historical geography of the Netherlands'**, by Audrey M Lambert (Seminar Press, 1971), the first comprehensive work in English on the subject, is particularly interesting, for nowhere has man's formative influence on the landscape been more apparent; without his efforts, nearly half the country would be beneath the flood level. Dr Lambert describes the struggle to reclaim the coastal and riverine marshlands and the problems involved in the colonisation and cultivation of the higher and largely infertile sands of the east and south. Rural settlement and the growth of towns and trade are traced, for the position of the Netherlands at the mouth of Western European waterways stimulated trade, culminating in Holland's 'Golden age'. Striking contrasts and comparisons are found with developments in England. A short bibliography is included.

894 **'Man and his world'**, the Noranda Lectures, Expo 67 (Toronto University Press, 1968), with an introduction by Helen S Hogg, comprises essays by scholars from many countries. 'The development of earth science', by Dr J Tuzo Wilson, is of special interest to geographers, illustrated with photographs, sketchmaps and diagrams; references are included.

895 **'Man and the land: a cultural geography'**, by George F Carter (Holt, Rinehart and Winston, 1964; second edition, 1968), was conceived as an introduction to geography, especially to the question why people in different lands live differently from one another. Beginning with 'The origin of man and the problem of race', the author continues to explore the characteristics of peoples living in arid environments, wet tropics, Mediterranean settings, forests and grasslands, mountains and polar regions, concluding with 'The role of physical environment and culture'. There are plenty of photographs, diagrams and maps in the text and suggestions for further reading at the end of each part.

Refer also

A S Boughey: *Man and the environment: an introduction to human ecology and evolution* (New York: Macmillan; Collier-Macmillan, 1971).

Pierre George: *Sociologie et géographie* (Paris: PUF, 1966).

J B Hoyt: *Man and the earth* (Prentice-Hall, second edition, 1967).

J C Robertson: 'Man's place in the ecological pattern', *The geographical magazine*, January 1970.

J E Spencer and W L Thomas, *jr: Introducing cultural geography* (Wiley, 1973).

896 **'Man and nature:** *or physical geography as modified by human action'*, by George Perkins Marsh, originally published in 1864, is an acknowledged classic, forward-looking work, republished from the first edition by the Belknap Press of Harvard University Press, 1965, edited by David Lowenthal (second printing, 1967) for The John Harvard Library series. Referred to by Lewis Mumford as 'the fountainhead of the conservation movement', Marsh attempted to reveal the menace of man's waste of the earth's resources, showing how man has changed the earth, suggesting means of conservation and reform. The second chapter deals with the 'Transfer, modification, and extirpation of vegetable and of animal species', the third, fourth and fifth successively with 'The woods', 'The waters', 'The sands' and ending in chapter six with 'Projected or possible geographical changes by man'. The style is discursive, deeply sincere and revealing an intensive study of the subject as well as powerful vision.

897 'Man and society in Iran', by A Reza Arasteh, in collaboration with Josephine Arasteh, first published in 1964, was reprinted, with some corrections, in 1970. The authors' main preoccupation in this study was to evolve a comprehensive frame of reference with which to analyse man and culture in Iran, which might also serve as a model for the study of other countries. To suit the various topics, a variety of methods have been used, essentially those of historical, statistical, descriptive and speculative analysis. The three main aspects chosen were 'Man in traditional Iranian society'; 'Man in contemporary Iranian society' and 'A measure for the future', each being sub-divided.

Refer also

Acta Iranica (Bibliothèque Pahlavi, Téhéran-Liège).

Peter Beaumont: *River regimes in Iran* (University of Durham, Department of Geography, 1973).

R N Frye: *Iran* (Allen and Unwin, second edition, 1960).

Jean Hureau: *Iran today* (Paris: Arthaud, 1974).

D N Wilber: *Iran past and present* (Princeton University Press, sixth edition, 1967).

898 'Man and wildlife', by Dr C A W Guggisberg (Evans, 1970), an account of the relationship between man and animals, examines the progressive destruction that man the hunter, the farmer and the industrialist have wrought on his environment. Photographs, many in colour, are included, also maps. There is a comprehensive survey of national parks throughout the world.

899 'Manitoba historical atlas: *a selection of facsimile maps, plans and sketches from 1612 to 1969'*, edited, with introduction and annotations, by John Warkentin and Richard Ruggles (The Historical and Scientific Society of Manitoba, Winnipeg, 1970), was prepared for the centenary of the province. The first part includes exploration and mapping 1612 to 1800 and the imaginative mapping of Manitoba to 1731, followed by the first stage of scientific mapping, to 1681, and the second stage from 1681 to 1731 and onwards in greater detail to the French mapping and the English maps of the remaining years of the century. Part II deals with early European settlement and scientific exploration 1801 to 1869, early settlement maps and scientific surveys. In part III, geographical patterns begin to appear, 1870 to 1969, land surveys, topography and hydrography representation, land settlement and rural settlement patterns, village, town and city plans, the portrayal of resources, cultural features and economic and population changes. Reproductions and maps are in black and white, using appropriate techniques; there are facing notes throughout, extensive text between the topics and a bibliography.

900 '**Man's rôle in changing the face of the earth:** *an international symposium'* under the Chairmanship of C O Sauer, Marston Bates and Lewis Mumford (University of Chicago Press for the Wenner-Gren Foundation for Anthropological Research and the National Science Foundation, 1956), in two volumes, edited by W L Thomas and others, is a monumental presentation of all aspects of conservation and regional planning from antiquity to modern concepts, illustrated with maps in the text. There is a bibliography. The work is prefaced by an essay contributed by E A Gutkind: 'Our world from the air: conflict and adaptation'. Some of the main themes concern 'Man's tenure of the earth', 'Through the corridors of time', 'Man's efforts on the seas and waters of the land', 'Alterations of climatic elements', 'Slope and soil changes through human use', 'Modifications of biotic communities', 'Ecology of wastes', 'Urban-industrial demands upon the land', 'Limits of man and the earth' and 'The rôle of man'. The symposium discussions and summary remarks are included and many interesting photographs, sketch-maps and figures add force to the text.

Refer also

Marston Bates: *Man in nature* (Prentice-Hall, second edition, 1964).

C O Sauer: *Land and life: a selection from the writings of Carl Ortwin Sauer*, edited by John Leighly (University of California Press, 1963; CUP, 1967).

901 '**Manual of map reproduction techniques**', by E D Baldock, published by the Surveys and Mapping Branch, Mines and Technical Surveys, Ottawa, describes in methodical detail the procedures that make it possible to print any number of copies of maps, each sharply precise and delicately coloured. Illustrated with photographs, diagrams and map specimens, the manual considers 'Drawing techniques', 'Negative scribing', 'Subsequent colour tints', 'Positive scribing', 'Photo colour proof', 'Map editing' and 'Lithography'.

Refer also

L Scott: 'Early experience in the photomapping technique',
The cartographic journal, December 1969.

L van Zuylen: 'Production of photomaps', *The cartographic
journal*, December 1969.

902 'Map collections in the United States and Canada: a directory',
edited by Marie C Goodman (Special Libraries Association, Geography and Map Division, 1954, second edition by David K Carrington, 1970), includes 527 collections, excepting the following, because
of their comprehensiveness: the American Geographical Society, the
University of California at Los Angeles, Canada Department of
Mines and Technical Surveys, Geographical Branch, the University
of Chicago; Harvard College Library; New York Public Library; the
Free Library of Philadelphia; Stanford University; Yale University
and the US government departments. Arrangement is by state. There
is an appendix listing United States Government repositories and a
folding map is attached to the inside back cover. Changes and additions are noted in the *Bulletin*, Special Libraries Association, Geography and Map Division.

Refer also

Betty May and Karen Lochhead: 'The national map collection of Canada', *Bulletin*, Special Libraries Association, Geography and Map Division, September 1971.

Joan Wineals and Yves Tessier, *comp*: *Directory of Canadian
map collections* (Association of Canadian Map Libraries, 1969).

903 Map Collectors' Circle was formed in 1963 to stimulate interest
in and publish material on early maps and atlases and on cartographers and map publishers. The *Map collectors'* series, edited by
R V Tooley, is issued on a present programme of ten works in every
two years; these are available only to subscribers in the first instance,
some of the more comprehensive works being subsequently reproduced in book form. Each volume contains an introductory essay,
carto-bibliographical descriptions and full-page or double-spread
plates of maps, many of which have not previously been reproduced.
While every work is of specific interest, two in particular are of outstanding importance. *County atlases of the British Isles, 1579–1850: a
new bibliography*, by R A Skelton, in co-operation with the staff of
the British Museum Map Room (part I, no 9, part II, no 14), includes
full descriptions of every county map in atlases, beginning with

Christopher Saxton, and the complete set will largely supersede Chubb's monumental work. *A dictionary of mapmakers*, by R V Tooley, is also being issued in parts, beginning with no 16, 'A to Callan'; the concept of the work is comprehensive, including cartographers, engravers, geographers and publishers from the earliest times to 1900. Reports of meetings are included in *The cartographic journal*.

904 'Map interpretation', by G H Dury (Pitman, fourth edition, 1972) emphasises the importance of knowledge of the physical and human aspects of geography in the use of maps—'It is an hieroglyphical and shadowed lesson of the whole world', he quotes from Sir Thomas Browne. Following some general introductory remarks, the work is divided into three main parts: 'Physical interpretation', 'The features of occupance' and 'Special topics', each sub-divided. A valuable final chapter on 'Cartographical appreciation', by Dr H C Brookfield and Dr Dury, also makes comparison between a few selected map series and 'Notes and references' complete the work. A few photographs and sketch-maps illustrate the text.

905 Map librarianship
IT IS SURPRISING that, although the value of maps has so long been recognised in Britain and in many British libraries, the fundamentals of map librarianship are only beginning to be considered on any but a local basis. In Britain, there is little professional training in map librarianship or substantial literature on the subject, as there is for other specialities, such as music, medicine or government publications. Some map curators have during the past few years admitted that their collections could be improved in acquisition policy, arrangement or maintenance and have expressed the wish for some authoritative training. The third meeting of the British Cartographic Society, held at Swansea in 1965, discussed as a matter of priority, 'Problems of maintenance, storage, classification and procurement for map libraries'. The *Papers* presented, together with the ensuing discussion, were printed in *The cartographic journal* for June 1966. A Map Curators' Group of the British Cartographic Society, convened by Dr Helen Wallis, held its first meeting at the Royal Geographical Society in December 1966. Meetings are to be held twice a year and a *Newsletter* is being published.

The major map collections have grown and have been organised empirically; they are in the charge of scholars, many of whom are among the leading authorities in their subject. But in the public libraries, there is rarely such knowledge and, even in school, college and special libraries, acquisition, arrangement, storage and maintenance frequently leave much to be desired.

ACQUISITION

The increased use of maps for various purposes has led to a corresponding increase in the literature concerning them, but it is still far from easy to find definitive information about current output on specific regions or subjects. Librarians in the great national geographical libraries and in the libraries of university departments must be knowledgeable on the state of world mapping. Of great value here is the *Bulletin* of the International Cartographic Association, 1962–.

The *Bulletin* is published usually twice a year; the main language is German, although verbatim reports appear in the language in which they were originally presented.

World cartography, issued irregularly since 1951 by the Cartographic Office, Department of Social Affairs of the United Nations, New York, provides another mine of information on activities, progress and plans in the field of cartography throughout the world. In English and French, the fascicules include longer or shorter articles, reports, notes and valuable bibliographies. Also, for example, index maps of the state of publication of the IMW 1:1M and other co-operative undertakings are to be found from time to time. Fascicule VII 1962 reports on activities, plans and progress in the various branches of cartography, taking into account present needs in all countries. This issue reiterates one of the main purposes of this journal, the stimulation of the dissemination of information among scientists, technicians and cartographic agencies, on an international basis. After a longer interval than usual, Fascicule VIII 1967 appeared, containing the *Reports* on cartographic activities submitted by the participants in the United Nations Inter-regional Seminar on the Application of Cartography for Economic Development, held at Elsinore in October 1965.

The United Nations Regional Cartographic Conferences for Asia and the Far East, of which the first was held in 1955 at Mussoorie, are also reported in *Proceedings* and *Technical papers*, which are invaluable for informed discussion on current topics and for reviews of achievement in individual areas, not entirely confined to the Far East.

Numerous organisations throughout the world issue publications on the subject, the importance of which to any individual library depends on the extent and depth of its work; among organisations making regular contributions to the literature of mapping, at research level, are the International Association of Geodesy, the International Society for Photogrammetry, the Centre de Documentation Cartographique et Géographique, the Institute of Geodesy, Photogrammetry and Cartography of Ohio State University, the Ontario Institute of Chartered Cartographers, the Commission on Cartography of the Pan-American Institute of Geography and History and the British Cartographic Society. In 1941, the American Congress on Surveying and Mapping was founded, with headquarters in Washington, DC, having sub-divisions for cartography; control surveys; property surveys; topography; instruments and education. The publications arising from these congresses, as from all other similar meetings, are of essential importance. Librarians in university departments specialising in particular parts of the world need to scan specific publications, such as *Canadian cartography* and the *Acta geodetica et cartographica Sinica*, Peking.

The International Association of Geodesy co-ordinates documentation in the field of geodesy and organises international geodetic studies and investigations. The Central Bureau in Paris is responsible for an index containing analyses of all published articles on geodesy; this appears in the *International geodetic bibliography* (Butterworths Scientific Publications, 1928–30–). *Papers* and *Reports* are published in the Association's *Bulletin géodésique*, quarterly from 1924, with a new series beginning in 1946.

All librarians in charge of map libraries will find the *International yearbook of cartography* (*qv*), annual since 1961, both informative and interesting. The languages used are German, French and English, with summaries in the two languages not used. So far, there has been no index and enquiries have produced no evidence of a plan for indexing, but, beginning with the 1963 issue, the titles of the articles in preceding yearbooks have been cited in each volume. The first volume dealt mainly with thematic maps, the second, enlarged issue stressed topographic maps, with sections also on the United Nations Bangkok conference and new atlases, illustrated by maps and diagrams. The third, 1963, featured a number of articles on the compilation and design of topographic and thematic maps and editorial policy widened to include pictorial and plastic representations of the earth's surface. The fourth issue took atlas production as its specific theme. The fifth contained *Papers* read at the 1964 Technical Conference of the International Cartographic Association. A variety of topics were treated in the sixth volume, which contained also the statutes of the International Cartographic Association, in English, French and German, with the aim of making its work more widely known to organisations not yet members. In 1967, Professor Dr Konrad Frenzel took over the chief editorship; the volumes again increased in size and a great variety of articles have since been included, especially on thematic maps and the mapping of statistics. Brief sections giving current information and reports are included at the end of each volume and a feature of the greatest value is the inclusion of specimen plates of various map services which might not otherwise be easily seen in Britain.

The first systematic attempt to list French maps was made by the Cartographic Department of the Bibliothèque Nationale in 1936. Following this venture, the establishment of an annual international bibliography was proposed in 1938. Impeded by the war, however, the first issue of the *Bibliographie cartographique internationale* (*qv*) did not appear until 1949, published by Armand Colin for the Comité National Français de Géographie and the International Geographical Union, with the support of UNESCO and the Centre National de la Recherche Scientifique. Editing is done at the Bibliothèque National from lists submitted by participating countries. Minor or unreliable maps are excluded and the 'secret document' classification, which is still frequently applied to maps, also limits its completeness; each entry is accompanied by a brief annotation, and it is no doubt the best 'check list' yet available, bearing in mind the time lag in production. All kinds of thematic maps, plans and surveys are included and, at the end of the volume, a separate section is devoted to recent catalogues of maps issued by each country. The whole work is extensively indexed.

The *Bibliographie géographique internationale* also includes maps, but much more selectively.

The *Bibliotheca cartographica* was planned by a working group, the Arbeitskreis Bibliographie des Kartographischen Schrifttums, set up in 1956 by the Deutsche Gesellschaft für Kartographie, as an international bibliography to cover all new publications relating to all aspects of the theory and practice of cartography. It is published twice a year, more than 520 publications being examined for each issue by more than fifty experts and international organisations throughout the world. Editing is done at the Institut

425

für Landeskunde within the Bundesanstalt für Landeskunde und Raumforschung, together with the Deutsche Gesellschaft für Kartographie, and publication is based at the Institute for Cartography and Topography, University of Bonn. Two issues have usually appeared each year since 1957, comprising some twenty thousand references; publication languages are German, English, French and Russian. References appear under the following headings: bibliography, map collections, documentation, general publications, history of cartography, institutes and organisations, topographic and landscape cartography, thematic maps and cartograms, atlas cartography, use and application of maps, special purpose maps, relief and relief maps, block diagrams, globes. A *General catalogue of cartographic literature*, the first volume covering the period from 1900, is also in preparation.

A basic research tool and acquisition check list is the *Annotated index of aerial photographic coverage and mapping of topography and natural resources undertaken in the Latin American member countries of the OAS*, prepared by the Pan-American Union, Department of Economic Affairs, in nineteen volumes (Washington, 1964–65). This work is an exhaustive country by country inventory of all known photographic, topographic and planimetric mapping and maps of geology, soils and land capability, vegetation, ecology, land use and forests. The maps are located on index diagrams and full bibliographic citation is given for each item.

Limited in extent but more quickly available are the accessions lists of the great map collections, reviews in relevant journals and the (usually) annual catalogues compiled by map publishers.

New geographical literature and maps, the classified list of accessions to the library and map room of the Royal Geographical Society, was begun by the Society in 1951 and is now issued twice a year, in June and December. All new maps and atlases acquired are included and, from 1958, the scope was widened to include all articles contained in twenty of the most important geographical periodicals in English, French and German; a selection is made from 150 others. An annual list of completed theses has been included since 1960. From 1967, the map information provided in the issues has been extended to include details of individual map sheets for all except the large-scale series and, for the first time, details of maps published in *The geographical journal* have been included.

Maps and atlases are also included in *Current geographical publications*, the record of additions to the Research Catalogue of the

American Geographical Society of New York, begun in 1938 by Elizabeth Platt and still the responsibility of the librarian and library staff. Ten issues a year are published, in which references to periodical articles as well as books are arranged according to the classification used in the Research Catalogue, regional placing taking preference over thematic. The scale, issuing body and the subject of the maps are cited in each entry. An index to maps in books and periodicals is maintained in the Map Department of the society; this was reproduced in ten volumes in 1967 by G K Hall, forming an invaluable reference work.

All map librarians need to scan these two last mentioned lists for new items relevant to their collections. Essential also is the section 'Cartographical survey', previously 'Cartographical progress', in *The geographical journal*, in which attention is drawn to new or completed mapping projects in all parts of the world; this is in addition to the full reviews included in the 'Review section', on the appearance of a new atlas or major map. At the end of the year, the four issues are issued as a separate publication. *The geographical review*, main organ of the American Geographical Society, also includes reviews of new maps and atlases and, from time to time, a major article surveys recent production of new atlases throughout the world. Reviews of major cartographical works of particular interest in Britain are included in *Geography*, and in *The Scottish geographical magazine* section 'Reviews of maps'.

The British Museum *Accession lists* for maps is printed as a supplement to the *Catalogue of printed maps . . .*; an essential reference and acquisitions source available is *The photo-lithographic edition of the catalogue of printed maps, charts and plans*, which records the holdings of the British Museum map room to the end of 1964, in fifteen volumes (1967). The *Accessions lists* published by the Bodleian map room and of other university departments are also essential tools for the librarians of map collections in Britain. The librarians of research collections need also to scan some of the other notable *Accessions lists* and indexes circulated by the great map collections throughout the world, e.g. those of the Département des Cartes et Plans, Bibliothèque Nationale and the *Catalogue des cartes* of the Institut Géographique National; the *Geographical bulletin*, bibliographical series and the Accessions lists of the Canada, Department of Mines and Technical Surveys, Geographical Branch; the *Catalogo delle Pubblicazioni*, Istituto Geografico Militare, Florence; the *Katalog över landkart*, Norges Geografiske Oppmåling, Oslo; the

Catalogo de cartas e publicaçoes Instituto Geografico é Cadastral, Lisbon; the *Kartor, atlaser, böcher* published by the Generalstabens Litografiska Anstalt, Stockholm; the *Karttalvettelo* of the Maanmittaushallitus, Helsinki; the *Index to printed maps* of the Bancroft Library, University of California, Berkeley; the *Catalogue* of maps of the Geodaetisk Institut, Copenhagen, and many others. The *Generalkatalog der Deutschen landeskunde*, Institut für Landeskunde, Bad Godesberg, is one of the most complete individual catalogues. Russian mapping output is particularly well documented within the country; in addition to the central journals, each state is responsible for its own catalogues. To give one example, the national output of maps and atlases of the Byelorussian Soviet Socialist Republic has been listed since 1925 in the *Annals* of the publications of the BSSR, issued monthly by the Chamber of Literature of the BSSR, attached to the V I Lenin State Library of the BSSR.

The Map Division of the Library of Congress (*qv*) aims to keep at least one copy of each edition of every map, atlas, globe and other form of cartographic publication having any reference value. The bibliographical work which is constantly being undertaken by the Division is therefore particularly comprehensive; notable is the *List of geographical atlases in the Library of Congress*, which is the most extensive bibliography of atlases available and an indispensable reference work. The basic work was in four volumes, 1909–20, by Philip Lee Phillips; a fifth volume, with bibliographical notes, was completed by Clara Egli Le Gear in 1958, containing references to over two thousand world atlases acquired by the library between 1920 and 1955; a further supplement was completed by the same compiler in 1963, on the same plan. A seventh volume comprises a consolidated *Author list* and the eighth volume is the index. *Author* and *Topographical lists* are also included in the first four volumes. Naturally, these volumes contain a vast amount of information on early atlases as well as on the modern.

The Special Libraries Association of New York has devoted much thought to geographical collections and maps. The Geography and Maps Division was organised as a unit of the Washington Chapter in 1941 and the first number of the *Bulletin* appeared in November 1947, thereafter twice a year until 1953, when it became quarterly. Its articles, notes and news items, lists of new maps, books and bibliographies are of the greatest practical use to librarians in charge of map collections; from time to time the findings of surveys and recommendations are included. One of the most important of these was the

Final report on the cataloguing and classification practices of the larger American map libraries, in the issue for April 1956. *Surveying and mapping*, quarterly from 1941, is another journal that should be scanned by the map librarian, especially in an academic institution requiring to keep up to date with current technical developments. The organ of the Congress on Survey and Mapping, Washington, it was created 'to advance the sciences of surveying and mapping and to contribute to public interest in the use of maps'. It covers all aspects of mapping, both military and civil. *The cartographer*, issued twice a year by the Ontario Institute of Chartered Cartographers, and *Cartography*, from the Australian Institute of Cartographers, Melbourne, are both essential for their notices and reviews and, in the latter, the section 'Cartographic abstracts'. *The cartographer* stresses particularly cartography as a graphic art and aims to provide a forum for the exchange of information and ideas.

Kartographische nachrichten, in six issues a year 1951–, by the Deutsche Gesellschaft für Kartographie, is an erudite and essential source of information, published by Bertelsmann Verlag, Gütersloh; another journal of the greatest scholarship, the *Referativnyi zhurnal—geografiya*, bi-monthly from 1951, monthly since 1956, by the Akademiya Nauk SSSR, Moscow, includes abstracts and references to articles on cartography, maps and atlases.

Information covering new British maps must be culled from many sources. *British books* includes the most notable publications. The Ordnance Survey issues a monthly *Publications report* and a frequently revised sales list; information on other maps covering Britain is to be found in the *Publications lists* of the Geological Survey, Second Land Use Survey, Soil Survey, etc, and the relevant sections of the catalogues of private firms. The co-ordination of British cartographical activity was strengthened in 1960 when the Council of the Royal Society approved the formation of a Sub-committee for Cartography which could devote itself entirely to cartographic matters, previously discussed by the National Committee for Geography, appointed in 1961. The Sub-committee advises the National Committee for Geography on all cartographic matters, with the particular purpose of formulating British policy in international proceedings, encouraging the exchange of ideas and experiences and the advancement of cartographic knowledge in this country. In the *Bulletin* of the Society of University Cartographers for December 1966 is an article, by G S Holland, which outlines the chief cartographic productions of the Royal Geographical Society during the past thirty years. The Royal Scottish Geographical Society, during the 1960–61 session, set up a Cartographic Committee to establish a separate Cartographic Section of the Society. The first independent cartographic body to come into existence was, however, the British Cartographic Society, which was created as the result of discussions at the University of Edinburgh in September 1962 and at the University of Leicester in 1963. A *List* of holdings of the Society's library, which is housed in Edinburgh Public Library, is issued and will become progressively valuable as the library grows. Most important for acquisition purposes is the bi-annual *Journal*, June 1964–; in the first issue were included an account of cartographic activity in Britain and five papers from the Cartographic Symposium held at the University of Leicester. In addition to the articles and the notes and news sections, which enable the librarian to be knowledgeable concerning contemporary developments in the subject, the 'Recent maps' section, sub-divided by country, and the 'Recent literature' section will be of permanent usefulness to all concerned with the maintenance of a cartographic collection. New sheets of the IMW 1:1M and of the ICAO charts, for example, are announced and important new atlases and other major works are extensively reviewed. A cumulative index to the first four volumes is to be issued with the fifth volume.

National and research map collections are usually as comprehensive as possible in coverage of the home country and representative of the map output of other countries. Legal deposit and exchange account for much of this stock. University collections must be determined by any special regional or thematic commitments undertaken by the departments concerned. Political difficulties, either temporary or more permanent, may limit acquisition from some parts of the world; for example, the export of Survey of India maps has been much restricted and it is usually difficult to obtain maps from South American countries or from Russia. Collet's Russian Bookshop can assist in obtaining those cartographical works from the USSR which are published for general export and their periodic *Newsletters* are invaluable for obtaining information concerning Russian publications which would otherwise be missed.

All map librarians need also to consult *Geo Abstracts* (*qv*) which covers cartography. A considerable amount of information of cartographic interest is included also in the annual volumes of *The geographical digest*, edited by Harold Fullard (Philip, 1964–). For any map librarian wishing to contact the national cartographical agency of any country a list, with addresses, is given in *Orbis Geographicus*, volume I.

Die Kartographie, 1943–1954: eine bibliographische übersicht, compiled by H G Kosack and K-H Meine (Lahr, Schwarzwald, Astra Verlag, 1955) provides a general bibliography of references relating to cartography for the period stated, with a section on historical cartography.

A useful check list to its date is *Map collections in the United States and Canada: a directory* (*qv*). Another American handy list is *Whyte's atlas guide* (*qv*). Its principal use is as a guide to specialist maps covering such features as airways, bridges, dams, minerals, etc. *Maps*, by P M de Paris, was the first in the series 'Library resources in the Greater London area' (Library Association, Reference and Special Libraries Section, South Eastern Group, 1953).

The many excellent catalogues issued by private cartographical organisations usually include a mixture of maps of the home country and other world or regional series, according to their publishing policy. The Clarendon Press, Oxford, Bartholomew and Philip in Britain, Esselte of Stockholm, Westermann of Braunschweig, all issue annually revised, well-produced catalogues, annotated and illustrated. Edward Stanford, London, now acts as a clearing house for maps and maintains a bibliographical service. The *International map bulletin: a list of maps and atlas publications by many official overseas surveys* contains entries for over one thousand map series; individual maps and catalogues are entered from more than 180 countries. These, with the *RV-katalog*, first published in 1964 by Zumsteins Landkartenhaus, Munich, are probably the most comprehensive map catalogues available. The latter, which is intended as an annual publication, is proving one of the most important sources of information on world maps, atlases and globes; the inclusion of specimen maps increases its value.

Opportunities for actually seeing maps and atlases on or even before publication have increased in recent years. The host country of the International Geographical Congress every four years stages exhibitions of materials of interest to geographers, many of them specially published for this event, and any exhibitions involving the interest of publishers and various academics, such as the International Printing Machinery and Allied Trades Exhibition and other familiar Book Fairs provide the opportunity of handling maps and atlases not hitherto seen outside the home country. International cartographic exhibitions have taken place in many countries, as, for example, in Hungary annually since 1962, sponsored by the State

Office of Geodesy and Cartography (National Office of Lands and Mapping, 1967–), specialising each year in one particular category; national atlases, automobile maps, tourist maps, wall maps for schools, geographical atlases and globes for schools and, in December 1967, city maps under the title 'Cities of the world today and tomorrow'. Hundreds of maps and other cartographical materials from many countries are gathered together on these occasions. National exhibitions, similar in character on a more restricted scale, are frequent. In Britain, for example, the annual conference of the Geographical Association is the occasion for a publishers' exhibition; here again, emphasis is usually on one special theme, but there is also great variety, including displays of Ordnance Survey maps, land use survey maps, relevant government publications, sometimes FAO and other United Nations productions, representative maps, atlases and monographs from all the map-making firms and publishers interested in geographical subjects. Frequently, prepublication copies are on display and it is the occasion for special catalogues and other publicity material.

ARRANGEMENT

It is convenient for geography students at all levels if the map collections can be stored in or near the geographical library, but there may be some conflict of interests here, as students of other disciplines also require to use maps of various types. Location of materials naturally depends on the subject priorities of individual institutions and the accommodation available; experience has shown, however, how frustrating for the worker it can be to have books, periodicals and atlases, perhaps, in one place and the collections of sheet maps in another department, even in a separate building.

In the case of closed stacks, arrangement according to acquisition order or by size, using a location number, has proved more practical in many libraries, because better use is made of the stack space available. Whatever the system adopted for shelving books and maps, however, the catalogue entries must organise all holdings in an arrangement that satisfies the requirements of users. The system adopted has depended in most cases upon the time when the library collections were started and recorded.

The published general bibliographical schemes of classification have taken Geography into consideration inadequately or not at all. In most general libraries using the Dewey Decimal Classification, 'Geography' is represented by regional descriptions, frequently

432

mixed with light travel literature and history; while material concerned with climate, vegetation, industries, transport, etc is not recognised as having any geographical interest at all. The basic eccentricities of the Dewey Decimal Classification with regard to Geography are only too well known to geographers who try to use a library thus classified, the position being often aggravated by misconceptions on the part of the classifiers themselves. To quote Dr Meynen on this point: 'Unless he has done some work in Geography himself, the librarian will be unable to recognise at once the specific geographic character of a book or an article'. This applies, of course, to the application of all general bibliographical schemes. Further, the use of the DDC in the arrangement of entries in a bibliographical reference work limits the value of such works for geographers.

In the seventeenth edition of the Dewey Decimal Classification, greater thought has been given to the placings for geography and some options are allowed. The basic division 'General geography' is still allocated the 910–919 placing:

911   Historical geography
912   Graphic representations of the earth's surface: atlases, maps, charts, etc (but 'map projections' are still at 526.8)
913   Geography of the ancient world
914   Geography of modern Europe
915   Geography of modern Asia
916   Geography of modern Africa
917   Geography of North America
918   Geography of South America
919   Geography of the rest of the world.

'General geography of specific continents, countries, localities is placed by editors' preference in 913–919, but, optionally may be placed in 930–999, with "general history of these areas",' says the Preface; and, again, 'Traditionally, DDC has placed the various branches of geography under the specific topics that are areally considered, for example, Economic geography, 330.9; Phytogeography, 581.9; Medical geography, 614.42. However, with the growing academic and lay interest in geographical matters, some general libraries have come to prefer an arrangement that brings all Geography together. This is supplied optionally, at 910.1, Topical geography, which is divided by subject, for example, Economic geography, 910.133; Phytogeography, 910.158; Medical geography at 910.161.4. Earth sciences are still, however, at 550. But, under 910 is 'Areal differentiation and traveller's observation of the earth

(Physical geography, formerly 551.4) and man's civilisation upon it. Use 910.001–910.008 for standard subdivisions; but class charts and plans in 912.'

910.02   The earth (Physical geography)

Add notations 14–16 to 910.02

.03   Man and his civilisation

Add area notation 1–910.03

.09   Historical and regional treatment

.091 Geography of regions limited by continent, country, locality

Add area notation 1–910.09

.093–009 Discovery, exploration, growth of geographic knowledge

Add area notations

Class geography of specific continents, countries, localities in 913–919

.1   Topical geography

.2–.3 Miscellany and dictionaries, encyclopedias, concordances of travel

.4   Accounts of travel

.5–.9 Other standard subdivisions of travel'.

H E Bliss was the great theoretician, but he did not take into account the definition, especially during the past two decades, of the subject discipline Geography. Bliss attempted close analysis of the inter-relation of geographical subjects, but it must be remembered that his thinking was basically that of the early years of the century, although it was perpetuated in the second edition of *The bibliographic classification*, 1952. In the introduction to the latter are to be found some curiously involuted concepts: 'Geography, especially Physical geography, or Physiography, as mainly the descriptive science of the Earth's *surface*, is more special than Geology, merging into Physical geology and more particularly into division, Physiographical geology. But Geography, as comprising Biogeography and Human geography, extends beyond Geology, and in this aspect it may be regarded as co-ordinate with Geology and with Biology. Meterorology is regarded as subordinate to Geography and co-ordinate with Physiography'. Human geography is separated from Physical geography and Biogeography. DQ, Geography in general, is only part of the whole subject; regional geography is included under Physical geography, following this reasoning: 'Regional geography, the study of regions and zones

434

with regard to ecological-geographical conditions and distribution, may be regarded either as subordinate to Physical geography or as co-ordinate with it, and therefore with Biogeography. It is distinct from this last and from Political and Historical geography, in that it does not describe habitats, countries and peoples, or races' (Volume I, 1940, pp 90–91). Bliss quite failed to understand the purposes and methods of regional geography; further, he allocated 'Human geography to Ethnography and Social-political history, Political and Historical geography being ancillary to the latter'. Further again, Bliss follows through a contorted argument—'Economic geography is to be distinguished from Commercial geography, from Human geography and from Historical geography. Briefly, Economic geography comprises more of the physical, mineral and biological, while Commercial geography is less physiographic than the Economic and less theoretical than the Anthropogeographic, which is more biologic, ecologic and ethnologic'. But Economic *geology* was with *Geology*!

The Library of Congress prepared new schedules for geographical works: 'to meet the needs of special collections the library is now proposing an alternative schedule which will collocate all of these works in class G', to quote the Head of the Subject Cataloging Division. This class embraced Geography, anthropology, folklore, manners and customs, recreation (third edition, Washington, Superintendent of Documents 1954). In the Colon classification, Geography is placed in chapter U, having the following main divisions: mathematical geography; physical; geomorphology; oceanography; meteorology; biogeography; anthropogeography; political geography; economic geography; travel, expeditions and voyages.

In Geography, to a greater extent than in other subjects, any scheme must cater for all aspects of the subject and be capable of satisfactory revision as required. It is the wide scope of this dynamic subject that has necessitated special treatment; previous schemes have been devised theoretically, in isolation from the subject.

The hospitality of the Universal Decimal Classification in coping with special subjects has made it the most used of the general bibliographical schemes in those libraries which have not devised their own schemes. It was therefore to the UDC that geographers looked when considering a scheme that would be internationally acceptable. The Commission on Classification of Geographical Books and Maps in Libraries was constituted during the International Geographical Congress, Washington, 1952; a group of specialists under

435

the chairmanship of Professor André Libault, with a number of correspondent members, including Mr G R Crone, then librarian and map curator of the Royal Geographical Society, conducted discussions on this vital problem, revealing similar difficulties and similar empirical methods of dealing with them throughout the world. The Commission's brief was to promote interest in the classification of geographical literature, to stimulate the formation of geographical sections in general libraries and to co-ordinate the work of organisation concerned with the indexing of geographical literature.

An interim explanatory brochure was published for the 1956 Congress at Rio de Janeiro which soon became o p. The greatest difficulties were inherent in the age of the great collections, whose curators began to organise them not only before the systematic approach to the 'organisation of knowledge', but before the concept of 'Geography' was fully developed.

In his introduction to the *Final report on the classification of geographical books and maps*, 1964, Professor Libault pays tribute to the skill and devotion of Professor Dr E Meynen, on whose work the final proposals largely rested. He managed to create an internationally acceptable scheme, embodying such combinations as should make possible the application of the scheme, in general or particular, to any geographical library. The scheme has been recognised by the International Federation for Documentation, which has since issued papers incorporating further points of improvement and updating. The British Standards Institution is engaged upon the preparation of an English full edition of the extended UDC for publication by the end of 1969.

Since experience has shown that the 1956 *Report* and the *Final Report* . . . are not as widely known as they should be among either British documentalists or British geographers, a brief analysis of their content may be helpful here, quoting, in particular, some of the basic tenets of Professor Meynen's concept of Geography. The *Final report* . . . was presented to the Twentieth International Geographical Congress, London, 1964, by the International Geographical Union Commission on the Classification of Geographical Books and Maps in Libraries (Institut für Landeskunde, Bad Godesberg, 1964). Part I is a most lucid account by Dr Meynen 'On the classification of geographical books and maps and the application of the Universal Decimal Classification (UDC) in the field of geography'; part II is a 'Draft of a regional classification according to physiogeographical areas of the earth for application in the Universal Decimal Classification (UDC)' by E Meynen, B Winid and M Bürgener; and part III is a 'Draft of a regional classification of the oceans and seas for application in the Universal Decimal Classification (UDC)' by Dr Meynen. Four appendices are included: 'Regional classification on physio-geographical areas of the earth for application in the UDC—common auxiliaries of the main units' (Proposal); 'Regional classification on physio-geographical areas of the earth for application in the UDC—common auxiliaries of the main units and further subdivision' (Proposal); 'Regional classification of the oceans and seas for application in the UDC—common auxiliaries of the main units and further subdivision' (Proposal). The whole text is presented in English, French and German and fixed inside the back cover are a series of maps, showing the proposed notations for classification of the world, Europe, Asia, Africa, North and Central America, South America, Oceania, Arctic (north polar regions), Antarctica (south polar regions), oceans and seas.

As Dr Meynen points out in his 'On the classification of geographical books and maps . . .', 'A carefully constructed, clear-cut classification and a systematization uniformly used for references and bibliography would mean enormous progress for our method of work.' The general system outlined is based upon the concept of geography as leading 'from the natural elements of a land to biological life, and finally to the creation of its cultural landscape', thus:

Physical geography
    Geological structure and relief forms
    Weather and climate
    Water and water management
Biological life
    Vegetation
    Fauna
    Human race
Human geography
    Economy
    Settlement
    Government and Administration

It determines not only the work of the individual geographer, but also the organization of many bibliographies.' In addition, further concepts must be considered. 'Geography as a scientific doctrine presupposes a theory of the doctrine of landscape. It comprises problems of terms, problems of logic and methodology. Literature on the

437

history of geography, the biographies of great scholars and teachers, the literature on the development of research institutes or organizations form a group of their own . . . Formerly, literature on journeys very often was the primary source of geographical knowledge; therefore, in older bibliographies, they form part of regional literature. Today, we are of the opinion that this literature forms a special group of systematic geography that precedes the regional geography of our times. It must be mentioned here that present-day reports of journeys and study tours are generally no longer a means of promoting geographical knowledge. They are rather reports on the techniques and organization of journeys and research . . . The work of the geographer presupposes some knowledge of research techniques and presentation as well as of the results of other disciplines . . . mathematical knowledge of the earth, mathematical geography (today only partly carried on by geographers), cartography, technique of taking and evaluating photographs, geographical nomenclature, statistics, etc . . . Last not least, the topic "geography and teaching (didactics of geography)" forms a large group of literature of its own'. A comparative schedule is included in this first part of the *Final report* . . . 'Comparative schedule of classification systems used by geographical bibliographies and reference periodicals', that is, the UDC 91 Geography, *Bibliographie géographique internationale, Current geographical publications, Generalkatalog der deutschen landeskunde* and the *Referativnyi zhurnal—geografiya*.

Professor Meynen's analysis continues with detailed comments on the history of the UDC, the place of Geography in the UDC and the organisation of the UDC, with an accompanying table 'Example of subdivision of the UDC main tables 91—Geography' which lead directly to the tabulation of the revised UDC 91—Geography, based on the proposals of the International Geographical Union Commission on Classification of Geographical Books and Maps in Libraries cumulated in 1962. The *Final report* . . . 'sets out proposals for a regional classification as an auxiliary'. A working group is continuing the Commission's work with the aim of establishing an international centre of geographical and cartographical intelligence, in co-operation with national centres, using a uniform system of classification based on the Commission's proposals. The Commission envisaged the storage of all such information in a form compatible with modern developments in the use of electronic computers, using perhaps magnetic tape, and foresaw the possibility of using these techniques for the reproduction of maps for scanning by the reader, so that he can choose which he needs to study.

An information retrieval system for maps was being operated already in the University of California, Los Angeles, map library, described in the UNESCO *Bulletin for libraries*, January–February 1966. The whole collection of some two hundred thousand maps at this time was classified by the Library of Congress classification and useful comments were made in this article on the application of the scheme to map classification.

The classification used for the arrangement of the *Bibliographie géographique internationale* dates back to the system established by Raveneau in 1891, revised to a certain extent in recent years by Professor Libault; while the other most familiar individual classification, adopted by the American Geographical Society of New York for its *Research catalogue*, was devised by S W Boggs for the Council of the Association of American Geographers, published in 1907 as *Library classification and cataloging of geographical materials*. This is a very detailed classification, able to cope with the classification of articles and pamphlets as well as larger documents.

The classification compiled by G R Crone, when he was librarian and map curator of the Royal Geographical Society, is interesting in that it has a philosophical, truly 'geographical' approach. In the foreword to 'A classification for Geography', published by the Society in 1961 (Library series no 6), Mr Crone explains that 'it is the result in part of the experiences of the library staff and of an attempt to produce a scheme related to the requirements of Geography today. The ruling idea has been to move from the separate subjects in which the geographer may be interested through their interrelations and on to the final synthesis.' In this scheme, the main classes are 'Exploration of the environment'; 'the Physical environment'; 'the Biological environment'; 'Integration and relationships'; 'Geographical synthesis'; 'Geographical studies: the end-product'; 'Aids to geographical studies'. Each of these classes contains at least two subdivisions, each again sub-divided into several sections. The individual nature of the collection for which the classification was devised is revealed in the sub-division 'Organisation of expeditions', with sections 'Hints to travellers', 'Equipment', etc, and in the detailed treatment of the sub-division 'Geodesy, survey, cartography'. The level of practice and use is also implicit. In the hands of less knowledgeable classifiers, the scheme would allow of some cross-classification between, for example, the 'Geographical synthesis' class, which includes Human geography, the social environment, city regions, regional planning, etc, and 'Geographical studies: the end-product', where regional studies proper are found, including regional description and cultural landscape (Landeschaftskunde). The class 'Aids to geographical studies' includes almanacs, epheme-rides, bibliographies, biography, catalogues, dictionaries, direc-tories, encyclopedias, gazetteers, place names, glossaries, guides, maps and atlases, periodicals, readers' guides, statistical methods, world history and yearbooks.

In accord with the Oxford approach to geographical studies, the emphasis in the classification adopted by the department library is regional, with the systematic aspect subsidiary. The classification of the Association of American Geographers is used for a classified index of periodical articles, for which a really detailed scheme is needed. In the Oxford scheme itself, numerals are used for the regional schedule, for example, 200—British Isles; 220—England and Wales; 230—Wales; 300—Europe; 340—France ... 800—Australia. Letters, A–Z, with some omissions, are used for systematic sub-divisions; A—Educational geography; B—Mathematical geo-graphy ... H—Climatology and meteorology ... T—Terminology; Y—Atlases. Precise shelf arrangement is achieved by adding a run-ning number to the class number, so that a book on the climate of France might bear the number 340.H.23. The number of pamphlets is preceded by the letter P, which is not used in the schedules.

Another detailed scheme devised for a particular purpose and working admirably in that context, is the War Office classification, which demonstrates most of the points to be taken into consideration in the organisation of a large map collection. 'Provision is made for all maps available and for those which may become available in the future'. Letters of the alphabet are allocated to the main divisions:

A   The Universe (astronomic charts, etc)
B   The world
C   Europe
D   Asia
E   Africa
F   North America
G   Central America
H   South America
I   Australasia
J   Pacific Ocean (and islands not adjacent to continents)
K   Atlantic Ocean (and islands . . .)
L   Indian Ocean (and islands . . .)

M Arctic regions
N Antarctic regions.

Each division is then sub-divided, each being given an arabic number. In the continental divisions, the sub-divisions are allocated to countries which are arranged in alphabetical order and numbered consecutively, for example: c1—Europe general; c2—Europe, seas, gulfs, channels, etc; c4—Austria; c5—Balkans . . . A mnemonic feature is included, since the sub-division '1' is always 'seas, gulfs, channels, etc'. Further sub-division is achieved by means of a colon, for example, c1:1—northern Europe. Town plans are placed within the relevant classification, with the name of the town added. The scheme is intended to be operated always in conjunction with a standard atlas and gazetteer for definition. Other general rules govern niceties of placing. A sequence number in brackets is added to the class number to complete the reference; for example, the first and second maps to be acquired of a province of Norway would be c36:13(1) and c36:13(2), so that each sheet has a unique reference number. The staff record is the *Handlist*, in which the entry is abbreviated title, scale, date and number of sheets, for identification. The complete *Handlist* forms an inventory of the whole collection, arranged in the same order as maps are housed in the map presses. 'It should be borne in mind that the handlist is the most valuable of all library records and great care should be exercised in its maintenance and use.' (Parsons: *see* reference at end of entry.) Finally, sequence numbers are allotted to map series within the classification divisions, for example, 1–10 denotes series larger than 1:250,000; 11–20, series of 1:250,000 and larger than 1:500,000, etc. Small letters, (a) (b), etc are used to indicate reproductions and variants. The handlisting of atlases and guide-books follows a similar pattern.

The Geographical Association has given much thought to the whole problem of the arrangement of geographical materials. A classification scheme for the Association's library was evolved, having taken into account the individual systems used in other comparable collections. All material is classified by region or by subject, using a numerical notation 100 to 900 for the former and a literal one, a–p, for the latter, both notations being capable of detailed sub-division. In the subject hierarchy, for example, the letter 'g' identifies works on economic geography, 'gc' distinguishes material relating to agricultural products and manufactures based on agriculture, and 'gct' refers specifically to documents of information concerning textile manufactures. Within each final sub-division, thus distinguished

441

by a combination of numerals or letters or both, items are arranged alphabetically according to the names of the authors. The regional factor is given preference in placing, with added entries in the catalogue for related regions or subjects as necessary.

In the scheme drawn up for school use by the Cheltenham Ladies' College (second edition 1958), a separate class P was allocated to Geology and geography. It is a numerical scheme, in three main divisions, 'Geology', 'Geography' and 'Geography by countries'. All are sub-divided. The Geology section includes meteorology and climate. 'Geography' includes Map-making and reading, Surveying, Travel and exploration, as well as the other usual aspects. Sub-divisions, such as English counties or American states, are intended to be arranged alphabetically, but geographers are invited to make their own decisions for the sub-divisions, possibly using a decimal point after the main number. A simplified version of the extension of the UDC 91 classification, described above, was made available for school use in 1965.

Much of all this theorising on the potentials of various classification schemes is, however, rapidly assuming only historical interest, as increasing numbers of the world's great library and map collections move towards the use of computerised catalogues. Full cataloguing remains the essential process. The cataloguing of early maps involves very specialised knowledge and, even in the case of modern maps, considerable experience is desirable. The majority of modern maps do bear a title, but, if no title is given on the sheet, it may be necessary to provide one, as definite as possible. Precise regional entry is the practice of the Royal Geographical Society; the British Museum rules state 'the main entry of every atlas, map, etc, is placed under the generally accepted name of the geographical or topographical area which the work delineates'. The rules of the Library of Congress, however, state that the regional heading of the entry is to be referred to the widest possible geographical unit in which it occurs. Effective use of mechanical aids such as computers does, however, require very great precision in the use of the terms in which concepts are expressed, otherwise much of the vast potential economy of the retrieval system will be vitiated. At national and international level geographers are making great efforts to secure agreement on terminology in the interests of universal understanding of research, and the published glossaries embodying the results of their discussions will be valuable also if required for computer programming.

For modern maps, the government department, survey office or private publisher is, in the majority of cases, stated on the map sheet. Even now, however, the date is not always given and this should be established as nearly as possible. Indication of scale is essential; this should be given as stated on the map, but it is helpful to reduce it also to a uniform fraction or proportion. All other relevant information should be noted; most important are the projection used, series status, including revision dates, names of cartographer and printer, method of relief representation and/or of subject data shown, inset maps and plans. It is important to state the exact limits of the map and its size and physical format. It may be monochrome or in several colours. If the map concerned has been produced in connection with some special research or has any other particular qualities, the annotation should include this information; also reference to any other maps or documents which may have special bearing on the map or assist in its full interpretation. Index diagrams to map series should be available for use in conjunction with the catalogue and added entries need to be made for all significant features. With regard to place names, the principles adopted by the Permanent Committee on Geographical Names or other recognised lists should be used.

Frequently, separate sections of the catalogue or individual indexes are made for 'Series', 'Place', 'Scale', etc. The map collection of the American Geographical Society of New York is particularly fully catalogued; items are filed under detailed subject headings, based on the principles of Samuel Boggs. A completely revised edition of *Cataloging and filing rules for maps and atlases in the Society's collection* was issued in 1964. The most useful manual on the subject is S W Boggs and Dorothy Cornwell Lewis: *The classification and cataloging of maps and atlases*, first published in 1932, with a second edition, published by the Special Libraries Association 1945. In the introduction, the main features and problems of map classification and cataloguing are stressed, beginning with the general assertion that, 'The differences between maps and books are numerous and fundamental. In approaching the problem of map cataloging, it is therefore not in the interest either of specialists in library science or of the map users who are to be the catalog's beneficiaries to begin with the assumption that maps are to be regarded as if they were simply books in another format'. Much of the poor cataloguing of maps and atlases in general libraries arises from just this assumption.

A committee of the Geography and Map Division of the Special Libraries Association also made a special study of the cataloguing of

443

maps, atlases, globes and relief models, of which the first report was published in the *Bulletin* of the division, no 3, December 1948. The committee continued to investigate practice in the large American libraries and a second report appeared in *Bulletin* no 13, October 1953. The committee's final report, with comments by Charles W Buffum, Map Division, Library of Congress, and B M Woods, was issued in *Bulletin* no 24, April 1956.

Many map curators have compiled their own rules for guidance, some of which have been published; notable examples include *Rules for descriptive cataloging in the Library of Congress* (relevant section), 1949, and *Règles adoptées par le Département des Cartes et Plans pour la conservation des collections et la rédaction des catalogues*, 1951, Bibliothèque Nationale.

STORAGE AND MAINTENANCE

The basic document for English readers is *The storage and conservation of maps: a report prepared by a committee of the Royal Geographical Society*, 1954, which was published separately and in the June 1955 issue of *The geographical journal*. The committee concerned with the drafting of the *Report* was the Library and Map Committee of the RGS, composed of members representing the RGS, the British Museum map room, the Ordnance Survey, the Directorate of Military Survey, the Library Association, the British Records Association, the Society of Local Archivists, the British Standards Institute, the Hydrographic Department of the Admiralty, the Bodleian map room, the University of Cambridge Department of Geography and the University College, Swansea, Geography Department. Other brief, but useful, sources are included in the list of references at the end of this section.

The method of storing sheet maps depends on the size and purpose of the collection. The aim should be to preserve them in the state in which they came from the publisher; equally important is it to protect them from the effects of atmosphere, dirt and handling. If they are to be handled constantly, as in a public library local collection, for example, one set may be kept freely accessible in the library for general use; the most used are usually the Ordnance Survey six inch series in British local collections and these may be bound around the edges with suitable material and kept in suitably sized boxes. The most constant demand for maps for loan is usually for the one inch series; here again, a duplicate set of dissected and folded linen-backed maps may be acquired which may be inserted in manilla pockets made to size, along the spine of each being marked the location number used and the area covered by the map.

The most used method in academic and research libraries of storing sheet maps is flat in large-sized shallow drawers; too many should not be piled on top of one another, otherwise it will be difficult to pull any one sheet out. The whole contents of each drawer may be kept in a manilla portfolio, or they may be sub-divided into a suitable number of folders; the main point being that no attempt should be made to pull out individual map sheets. It is axiomatic that both the outside of the drawer and each individual folder should be clearly labelled. The drawers must not be overloaded. In some cases, an additional fold of cloth or other suitable material has been inserted in each drawer, to protect the contents from dust. The front of the drawers should be hinged so that it falls out of the way when opened. The number of drawers in a unit depends on use; if storage only is the objective, then the cabinets may be built to any required height, but if the room is to be used for study purposes also, then the top of the cabinets should be at a convenient height for consultation of the maps required. In any case, some flat space must be allowed for staff use. The choice between wood or steel cabinets is largely a matter of opinion and cost. From experience, it has been proved that well-constructed wooden cabinets wear just as well as steel, which tends to chip and the locking devices tend to be less co-operative than in wooden ones. The argument previously put forward in favour of steel cabinets in case of fire was disproved during the war, when it was found that paper in wooden cabinets was only charred, whereas the steel had generated so great a heat inside the drawers that a much greater proportion of the contents was destroyed. Steel drawers lined with asbestos may provide the perfect solution. In tropical countries, of course, steel would be the obvious choice. Steel was the choice of the Royal Scottish Geographical Society, when the map room was reorganised and refurnished in 1958 and experiments were made in design; map cases in a darker shade of blue against pale blue walls were installed. Two large tables were provided for readers, one including a tracing panel. No windows were made, but an oval lay-light almost fills the ceiling area, above which is the fluorescent lighting. The map room of the National Library of Wales at Aberystwyth is equipped with rows of wooden cabinets so placed that their combined tops make for ample working surface.

Vertical filing methods take various forms. Generally speaking, this method is preferable for smaller maps; it is also convenient in the case of modern map series having the index number at the top of the sheet. According to contents, suitable forms of folder should be used to contain maps in short series, maps on a particular subject, or, in a long series, a sufficient number of sheets that can be handled easily. One or two permanent divisions should be placed in the drawers, otherwise the folders of maps become unmanageable when any number of them have been withdrawn for use. At the same time, the total contents of each drawer should not be packed too tightly or the folders at the back tend to become damaged. Maps should not be stored vertically loose, without folders; even with the protection of the folder, the lower edge may become crumpled if care is not taken. There are various forms of vertical or horizontal suspension filing. If this method is adopted, the side by which each map is suspended must be reinforced. The Roneo Flushline Vertical Planfile has been designed to store plans, maps or charts freely without the necessity for suspension bars or folders. The principle lies in the form of the half-dozen or so vertical 'divides', which are slightly curving in formation instead of being straight; the slight friction caused by the curve holds the sheets firm and avoids the danger of crumpling the bottom edge. Closed, the cabinet is free-standing and neat, with the top providing a working surface. It opens by a hinge at the front, so that the desired partition can be pulled forward by hand and the sheets lifted out. In the closed position, the 'divides' close up to hold all the sheets steady. The standard model holds fifteen hundred sheets, but takes up less room in depth than a cabinet in which the drawers must frequently be pulled out to their fullest extent. The Stanford Planfile, designed specially for Ordnance Surveys maps and plans, can accommodate up to two hundred sheets by a method of suspension filing and an index to the contents can be mounted on the inside of the lid.

Wall maps and all maps on rollers should be handled carefully; when rolled, they should be tied firmly by the tapes provided and either hung vertically from hooks or, preferably, be kept horizontally in racks or troughs. The Olympia map stand and Rigid Map Hook have been designed by Westermann for the compact storage and display of wall maps in a small space. George Philip and Son offer a wide range of apparatus for holding and suspending wall maps. Aluminium is being widely used for a variety of fittings; a light-weight rail of aluminium and plastic, for example, is available for holding sheet maps firmly for display without damaging the edge, at the same time giving edge to edge vision of the map sheet.

446

Small- to medium-sized public libraries holding perhaps a few authoritative 'handy' atlases, *The Times atlas of the world* and *The atlas of Britain and Northern Ireland*, can easily shelve these works in the normal oversize sequence or, preferably, in one atlas stand. Holdings of sheet maps may comprise the one inch Ordnance Survey, seventh series, which can be housed in a stout looseleaf binder made for the purpose; the local collection should contain at least the six inch and the twenty five inch maps for the area, requiring a cabinet, folder or box made to size for the former and a cabinet for the latter. The larger public libraries are in the same position as the academic and special libraries, except in the sheer bulk of map stock. The New York Public Library map collection, for example, is among the largest in the world. The time is long overdue for British public libraries to take as much care in the acquisition and exploitation of their map collections as they do of their music and other special materials. Complete sets of current Ordnance Survey editions should be acquired, plus a representative selection of the most interesting of foreign map production; local collections should be much more systematic than they frequently are in building up and making known their map collections concerning the area. Such a policy requires, of course, knowledgeable staff, proper equipment and full documentation, but the resulting public service would be well worth the effort.

Small atlases may often be kept on normal quarto or folio shelves. The larger world or national atlases should be stored on special atlas stands, of which there are various designs, single or double sided, and usually having a slightly sloping top, with a ridged edge to prevent the volume slipping when it is in use. One or at most two atlases should be kept on each shelf. Some of the largest atlases, especially the looseleaf variety in boxes, for example, the *Atlas van Nederland*, present special problems and usually require specially constructed shelving. If large atlases are stored vertically, care must be taken that they do not slant sideways, thus damaging their pages, even when they are specially guarded. Plenty of flat working space is essential when maps and atlases are being used, for each reader will need three or four times the space normally allotted in a library.

When maps taken from monographs, periodicals, directories, guidebooks and the town guides issued by local authorities are kept for information purposes, either vertical filing or a series of suitably sized pamphlet boxes may be most serviceable, according to use. Most of these categories of maps may have only one year of active life and therefore require no other protection. If such maps are to be used

447

for a longer time, it may be necessary to dissect them and mount them on linen; the paper surfaces will crack if they are not dissected. In all cases, ease of access and protection from dust, damp or undue warmth, as from radiators, must be the chief considerations.

Opinions differ widely on the desirability of using lamination processes to protect the surfaces of maps; as these processes are improving all the time, the original objections are to a large extent met, but in any case only a minority of maps in a collection are suitable for this kind of protection.

Repair of modern maps largely consists of mending tears or damage due to friction at the edges of folds. Cellophane should not be used, unless it can effectively mend the tear from the back; it is usually better to mount the whole map, taking extra care to press the torn edges exactly together.

Microfilming of duplicate copies of maps is a useful way of saving space in a working library. Modern colour film exposed through a 35mm camera can produce reasonably good copies of coloured maps, though the difficulties are greater than in letterpress reproduction. Careful selection must be made of the microfilm reader provided, for not all of them are suitable for map scansion. One successful viewer is the Recordak Archival Viewer, manufactured by Williamsons and marketed by Kodak; it provides two scales of viewing, projecting downwards to an inclined surface on which tracing can be made. Further research is still needed in this kind of equipment.

The map library should contain a tracing table and should be equipped to provide photostat copies of maps, subject to the usual copyright limitations.

Refer also

Robert I Boak: 'Restoration and preservation of maps', *Bulletin*, Special Libraries Association, Geography and Map Division, September 1970.

S W Boggs and D C Lewis: *The classification and cataloging of maps and atlases* (Special Libraries Association, second edition 1945).

J Burkett: *Special library and information services in the United Kingdom*: section 8 on map libraries by G R Crone (*Library Association record*, 1936, 98–104).

G R Crone: 'The cataloguing and arrangement of maps', *Library Association record*, 1936, 98–104.

G R Crone: *Existing classification systems*. Report of the

Commission for the Classification of Books and Maps in Libraries (IGU Eighteenth International Geographical Congress, Rio de Janeiro, 1956).

G R Crone: 'Notes on the classification, arrangement and cataloguing of a large map collection', *The Indian archives*, VII, 1, 1953, 8–13.

G R Crone and E T Day: 'The Map Room of the Royal Geographical Society', *The geographical journal*, March 1960.

Român Drazniowsky: 'Bibliographies as tools for map acquisition and map compilation', *Cartographer*, III, 2, 1966, bibliog.

Român Drazniowsky: *Cataloguing and filing rules for maps and atlases in the Society's collection* (American Geographical Society of New York, 1964, mimeographed and offset publication no 4).

L Dufresnov: *Catalogue des meilleures cartes géographiques générales et particulières* (Amsterdam, Meridian, 1965).

A M Ferrar: 'The management of map collections and libraries in university geography departments', *Library Association record*, May 1962, 161–165.

John G Fetros: 'Developing the map collection in smaller libraries', *Bulletin*, Special Libraries Association, Geography and Map Division, September 1971.

M E Fink: 'A comparison of map cataloging systems', *Bulletin*, Special Libraries Association, Geography and Map Division, December 1962.

M Foncin: 'Some observations on the organisation of a large map library', *World cartography*, III, 1953, 33–40.

G H Fowler: 'Maps', *Bulletin* of the Technical Section, British Records Association, no 16, 1946.

A C Gerlach: 'Geography and map cataloging and classification in libraries', *Bulletin*, Special Libraries Association, Geography and Map Division, May–June 1961.

C B Hagen: 'Maps, copyright and fair use', *Bulletin*, Special Libraries Association, Geography and Map Division, December 1966.

C B Hagen: 'Map libraries and automation: a bibliography', *Bulletin*, Special Libraries Association, Geography and Map Division, December 1966.

Clara E Le Gear: *Maps, their care, repair and preservation in libraries* (Library of Congress, Reference Department, Division of Maps, Washington DC, 1949; revised edition 1956). Includes an extensive bibliography of predominantly American works.

R J Lee: *English county maps: the identification, cataloguing and physical care of a collection* (Library Association, 1955). Mainly concerning earlier maps, but some useful comments applicable to modern ones.

D C Lewis: 'Maps: problem children in libraries', *Special libraries*, March 1944.

D H Maling: 'Some thoughts about miniaturisation of map library contents', *The cartographic journal*, June 1966.

Emil Meynen: 'A geographic classification of geography material as based upon the Dewey decimal classification', *Annals* of the Association of American Geographers, XXXVI, 1947, 209–222.

Emil Meynen: *UDC 91—Geography*. Proposal for a revision of the group UDC 91—Geography. (International Geographical Union Commission on the Classification of Books and Maps in Libraries; Ninth General Assembly and Eighteenth International Geographical Congress, Rio de Janeiro, 1956.)

Emil Meynen: 'Die wissenschaftliche kartensammlung grundsätzliches und hinweise', *International yearbook of cartography*, III, 1963. Includes some sketches of equipment and a bibliography.

I Mumford: 'What is a map library?' *The cartographic journal*, June 1966.

E J S Parsons: *Manual of map classification and cataloguing prepared for use in the Directorate of Military Survey* (War Office, 1946).

P L Phillips: *Notes on the cataloging, care and classification of maps and atlases, including a list of publications compiled in the Division of Maps* (Washington DC, Government Printing Office, revised edition 1921).

R T Porter: 'The library classification of geography', *The geographical journal*, March 1964.

W W Ristow: 'The emergence of maps in libraries', *Special Libraries*, July–August 1967).

R A Skelton: 'The conservation of maps', *Bulletin of the Society of Local Archivists*, no 14, October 1954. A discussion of map storage and use problems in general and the British Museum plans and practices in particular.

D M Smith: 'Cartographic indexing', *The indexer*, April 1974.

Special Libraries Association, Geography and Map Division:

Cartographic research guide, Part IV: The catalogue library and the map librarian (New York, SLA, 1957).

Lawrence E Spellman: 'Value of maps as reference tools', *Bulletin*, Special Libraries Association, Geography and Map Division, September 1970.

Stanley D Stevens: 'Planning a map library? create a master plan', *Special libraries*, April 1972.

United States Department of the Interior, Geological Survey: Federal Map Users' Conference, October 1964, *Proceedings*.

Helen Wallis: 'The rôle of a national map library', *The cartographic journal*, June 1966.

Ernst Winkler: 'Das system der geographie und die dezimalklassifikation', *Geogr Helv*, 1946, 1, 337–349.

M L Wise: 'Geography in the public library', *Library Association record*, December 1954.

B M Woods: 'Map cataloging', *Library resources and technical services*, Autumn 1959.

'Conference on maps and map librarianship', *Bulletin*, Special Libraries Association, Geography and Map Division, December 1971.

'A survey of the usage of a large map library', *Bulletin*, Special Libraries Association, Geography and Map Division, June 1970.

906 Maps The development of map-making in the countries of the world constitutes a record of man's increasing knowledge, both of the world around him and of the scientific skills that have enabled him to plot its features more accurately. From the earliest times, all peoples have been able to make rough plans, on bark, cane and other materials, to help them in moving from place to place, adding descriptive directions from their own observations. In the British Museum may be seen clay tablets from Babylonia containing cadastral surveys made before 2000 BC for taxation purposes, and the cadastral plans of the ancient Egyptians are famous. The first maps to attempt to show relief features were perhaps those made by the Incas in the twelfth century BC. Anaximander, in the sixth century BC, is credited with producing the first map of the 'world,' which, to him, was circular and bounded by a river. The oldest surviving rectangular map of the world is contained in *Christian Topography* by Cosmas, an Alexandrian monk, *c.* AD 535. Thereafter, such great names come to mind as Eratosthenes, Hipparchus, Posidonius, Artemidorus, Strabo,

Ptolemy and Marinus of Tyre, who was the first to use rough parallels and meridians. Increasingly detailed charts were drawn by seamen navigating the shores of the Indian Ocean and the Mediterranean. (*See* Portolan charts.)

Scientific cartography developed rapidly, speeded up, as time went on, by the interchange of knowledge and ideas, accurately or otherwise. With the development of wood-block printing, maps became more widely known and not infrequently reproduced errors and misleading features as well as new facts. The first known printed map of the world was one used as an illustration to St Isidore's *Etymologiae*, printed in Augsburg in 1472, and the earliest engraved maps were in the edition of Ptolemy's 'Geographia' printed from copper plates at Bologna in about 1477. The great centres of geographical knowledge in Europe in the fifteenth century were Nuremburg, Augsburg, Strasbourg and Basle, which were also centres of printing and wood engraving. It was not until sheet maps became common in the sixteenth century that intaglio printing was widely used in map production. During the sixteenth century, the two methods continued side by side. In 1500, Juan de la Cosa, who was with Columbus, produced a chart of the world, the first known to include the New World discoveries. In 1570, the *Theatrum Orbis Terrarum* of Abraham Ortelius was the first well-edited collection of the best maps to be made available to the public.

Rapid development in the mathematical principles of mapmaking culminated in the achievement of Gerhard Mercator, whose Atlas was published after his death in 1595. From then on, until the eighteenth century, Amsterdam and Antwerp were the centres of cartographic production. Only eight of the thirty-five maps in Saxton's Atlas (1574–79) were engraved by English craftsmen, and Speed's *Theatre of the Empire & Great Britaine* (1611–12) was entirely engraved in Amsterdam. Great work was done in France in the eighteenth century, notably by Guillaume Delisle and B d'Anville.

Of the modern systematic surveys, the Ordnance Survey of Great Britain was founded in 1791, beginning its work with the 1 in to the mile series (now in seven editions) and continuing with the $\frac{1}{4}$ in, $\frac{1}{2}$ in, 6 in and 25 in. The 1:25,000 has been a recent development and the introduction of the National Grid has made for uniformity of reference. The discovery of lithography in 1799 revolutionised the production of maps and to-day practically all conventionally produced maps are printed by rotary offset-litho. A contribution of the Ordnance Survey to the history of reproduction methods was the invention of photo-zincography in 1859, first used in 1860. The Carte de France de l'Etat Major, copper-engraved on a scale of 1:80,000 and later photo-lithographed, was carried out between 1817 and 1880. The Survey of Ireland, 6 in to the mile, was begun in 1824. Other noteworthy national surveys have been undertaken in Switzerland, India, Japan, the USA, Canada and parts of Northern Africa and Egypt. The International Map of the World, 'one in a million,' is now a world undertaking, having been proposed at the Berne Geographical Congress in 1891 and discussed at successive Conferences in 1895, 1899, 1904, 1908, 1909 and 1913. The projection is a modified polyconic, so that adjoining sheets can be fitted together. It inspired the Million Map of Hispanic America.

Mention should also be made of the special purpose maps such as those of the Land Use Survey of Great Britain, the Geological Survey, the Period Maps of Britain and those devoted to climate, agriculture, political or economical features, and so on. Hydrographic charts are a study in themselves. Each maritime nation is considered responsible for charting its own coastal waters and there is now a free interchange of information between nations. British Admiralty Charts are prepared by the hydrographic department and published by the Lords Commissioners of the Admiralty. Of five kinds, ocean, general, coastal, harbour and physical, they are constructed on either mercator or gnomonic projection and are engraved on copper plates.

Maps are made by only a few firms and there are few specialist map publishers in Britain. Until the nineteenth century, maps were coloured by hand, but to-day, because of the high costs of production and the need for perfect register, the number of colours used is often limited to three plus black. At the same time, striking new representations of relief have appeared, notably from the Cartographic Department of the Clarendon Press; these include relief maps photographed from plastic models, thus giving a three-dimensional effect to the map, plastic relief model maps, and the Oxford System of Automatic Cartography using magnetic tape and punched cards. Of private map-publishers, notable are George Philip and Son, Ltd, and Edward Stanford: John Bartholomew and Son, Ltd, especially noted for the $\frac{1}{2}$ in series of Great Britain and for a tradition of high quality cartography in map and atlas design since 1784, including editions of *The Times atlas of the world*: W and A K Johnston, Ltd and G W Bacon and Co. Aerial surveys and

453

photography in its application to printing have led to further developments and new scientific discoveries have made possible the production of maps whose legibility is not impaired by crumpling or immersion in water, which will not easily tear or which can be made fluorescent in the dark.

907 '**Maps and air photographs**', by G C Dickinson (Arnold, 1969), is divided into four sections: 'Thinking about maps' considers their development in all parts of the world, the evolution of national map series, including the Ordnance Survey; 'Working with maps' examines all the practical aspects of the making of maps; 'Looking at maps' describes the interpretation of various landscapes from maps and 'Air photographs' completes the text, which is generously illustrated by photographs, sketchmaps and diagrams.

> *Refer also*
>
> Felipe Guerra Peña: 'The selection of scales for aerial photography to be used in geographic interpretations', *International yearbook of cartography*, 1970.

908 '**Maps and charts published in America before 1800:** *a bibliography*', compiled by James Clements Wheat and Christian F Brun (Yale University Press, 1969), a major contribution to the bibliography of early American cartography, describes 915 maps, from the crude wood-cut map of New England, 'White Hills', 1677 to 1799, by which time forty-one maps had been recorded. It is an exhaustive annotated text covering the territory which is now the USA, also parts of Latin America, Europe, Africa, the West Indies and Asia. The contents are arranged geographically with the world maps first, followed by those of the continents and oceans, with a natural emphasis on America. Eighteen reduced facsimiles of the more important maps are included and there is a comprehensive bibliography. Date of publication is noted, together with description, size and scale and place of publication.

> *Refer also*
>
> John A Wolter: 'Source materials for the history of American cartography', *Bulletin*, Special Libraries Association, Geography and Map Division, June 1972.

909 '**Maps and diagrams:** *their compilation and construction*', by F J Monkhouse and H R Wilkinson (Methuen, 1952, in a 'University paperback', 1963; third edition, 1971; *Methuen's advanced* *geographies* series), is a comprehensive summary of the materials and techniques employed in plotting data relating to relief, climate, economics and population. An appendix by R G Barry deals with numerical and mechanical techniques.

Refer also

J M Adams: 'Mapping with a third dimension', *The geographical magazine*, October 1969.

V Balasubramanyan: 'Application of information theory to maps', *International yearbook of cartography*, 1971.

D K Bassett: 'Numerical methods for map analysis', *Progress in geography*, 1972.

Jacques Bertin: 'Les constantes de la cartographie', *International yearbook of cartography*, 1971.

F G H Blyth: *Geological maps and their interpretation* (Arnold, 1965).

Rolf Böhme: 'International co-operation in recording information for revision of small-scale general maps', *International yearbook of cartography*, 1970.

H Bosse: *Kartographische Generalisierung* (Mannheim: Bibliographisches Institut, 1967).

L M Buychguens and Yu G Kelner: 'Generalisation en cartographie complexe des grandes régions naturelles', *International yearbook of cartography*, 1970.

L D Carmichael: 'Cartographic depiction of land resources information', *The cartographic journal*, June 1972.

H W Castner and A H Robinson: 'Dot area symbols in cartography: the influence of pattern on their perception', American Congress on Surveying and Mapping, Washington, DC, 1969.

R J Chorley and P Haggett: 'Trend surface mapping in geographical research', *Transactions*, Institute of British Geographers, 1965.

Michael Cobb: 'Changing map scales by automation', *The geographical magazine*, August, 1971.

M M Datta: 'Base maps for development', *International yearbook of cartography*, 1970.

O M Dixon: 'Methods and progress in choropleth mapping of population density', *The cartographic journal*, June 1972.

Roger Downs and David Stea, *ed: Image and environment: essays on cognitive mapping* (Arnold, 1974).

J J Foster and W Kirkland: 'Experimental studies of map

typography', *Bulletin* of the Society of University Cartographers, Summer 1971.

Vincenzo Franzitta: 'Les dernières méthodes d'organisation du travail de cartographie', *International yearbook of cartography*, 1972.

Kristian Gleditsch and Peter Vold: 'The utility map', *International yearbook of cartography*, 1970.

Gillian A Hackman *et al*: 'Instant maps for planners', *The geographical magazine*, August 1972.

Fernand Joly: 'Normalization of symbols in thematic cartography', *International yearbook of cartography*, 1971.

Naftali Kadmon: 'Comparing economic maps with the aid of distribution—parameter graphics', *International yearbook of cartography*, 1971.

J S Keates: *Cartographic design and production* (Longman, 1974).

J S Keates: 'Symbols and meaning in topographic maps', *International yearbook of cartography*, 1972.

Rudolf Knöpeli: 'Map revision', *International yearbook of cartography*, 1970.

Cornelis Koeman: 'The impact of photography from space on small-scale—and atlas—cartography', *International yearbook of cartography*, 1970.

Cornelis Koeman: 'The principle of communication in cartography', *International yearbook of cartography*, 1971.

A Koláčný: 'Cartographic information—a fundamental concept and term in modern cartography', *The cartographic journal*, June 1969.

A Koláčný: 'The importance of cartographic information for the comprehending of messages spread by the mass communication media', *International yearbook of cartography*, 1971.

A M Komkou: 'The international language of geographical maps', *International yearbook of cartography*, 1971.

Edgar Lehmann: 'Symbol systems in thematic cartography', *International yearbook of cartography*, 1972.

C I M O'Brien: 'The place of large scale mapping in the cartographic programmes of developing countries', *International yearbook of cartography*, 1970.

Sándor Radó and Tibor Dudar: 'Some problems of standardization of transportation map symbols in thematic mapping', *International yearbook of cartography*, 1971.

456

Lech Ratajski: 'The methodical basis of the standardization of signs on economic maps', *International yearbook of cartography*, 1971.

S Rimbert: *Leçons de cartographie thématique* (Société d'Edition d'Enseignment Supérieur, 1968).

K A Salichtchev: 'Present-day thematic cartography and the tasks of international collaboration', *International yearbook of cartography*, 1969.

K A Salichtchev: 'The subject and method of cartography: contemporary views', *Canadian cartographer*, December 1970.

K A Salichtchev *et al*: 'Synthetic social-economic maps', *International yearbook of cartography*, 1971.

Victor Sochava: 'About the structure of national reviews of the condition and perspectives in thematic cartography', *International yearbook of cartography*, 1972.

P Speak and A H C Carter: *Map reading and interpretation* (Longman, 1970).

Ernst Spiess: 'The need for efficient base maps in thematic mapping', *International yearbook of cartography*, 1971.

V I Sukhov: 'Application of information theory in generalisation of map contents', *International yearbook of cartography*, 1970.

Brigadier D E O Thackwell: 'The importance of cartography to modern states', *The cartographical journal*, June 1969.

Judith Tyner: *The world of maps and mapping* (McGraw-Hill, 1973).

W B Upton, *jr*: *Land forms and topographic maps* (Wiley, 1970).

Russell L Voisin: 'The international atlas as an expression of the value of international cartographic participation', *International yearbook of cartography*, 1971.

William Craig Watson: 'A study of the generalisation of a small-scale map series', *International yearbook of cartography*, 1970.

A W White: 'Problems of map production in small quantity and frequent editions', *International yearbook of cartography*, 1970.

W Witt: *Thematische Kartographie* (Hanover: Akademie für Raumforschung, 1967).

W Witt: 'Ungelöste probleme in der thematischen kartographie', *International yearbook of cartography*, 1972.

Michael Wood: 'Human factors in cartographic communication', *The cartographic journal*, December 1972.

910 'Maps and map-makers', by R V Tooley (Batsford, 1949; third edition, 1971), in hardback and paperback, is one of the most comprehensive studies, in English, of the development of map-making from the earliest times to the mid-nineteenth century, excellently illustrated with reproductions. The second edition incorporated additions to the chapter bibliographies, and a new chapter on the maps of Scandinavia. In the third edition, a new bibliography was prepared, the lists of authorities at the ends of chapters was extended and numerous minor corrections and additions were made.
Refer also
Norman J Thrower: *Maps and man: an examination of cartography in relation to culture and civilisation* (Prentice-Hall, 1972).

910a 'My head is a map', a festschrift for R V Tooley on his seventy-fifth birthday, edited by Helen Wallis and Sarah Tyache (Francis Edwards and Carta Press, 1973), contains an article on the map collections in the British Museum Library, notes on cartographers, the map trade and an appreciation of R V Tooley by Robert Stockwell.

911 'Maps and their makers: *an introduction to the history of cartography'*, by G R Crone (Hutchinson University Library, 1953; second revised edition, 1962, reprinted 1964; third edition, in hard cover and paper-back simultaneously, 1966; fourth edition, 1970), provides a most useful succinct account. Lists of general works on cartography and of reproductions of early maps and charts are given in appendices. Considerable re-arrangement and additions of material were made in the fourth edition.
Refer also
A Carson Clark: 'Some early cartographers and their maps', *Bulletin* of the Society of University Cartographers, Summer 1971.

912 'Maps and survey', a classic work by Arthur R Hinks (CUP, 1913, 1923, 1933, 1942, 1944, 1947), 'was designed as an introduction to the study of maps and the processes of survey by which they are made'. Beginning with 'A brief history of early maps', accompanied by some reproductions, the modern map in all its complexity is discussed and explained, including British official maps and international maps, maps of the countries of Europe and other foreign maps. The various kinds of survey are explained, with photographs of instruments used and other diagrams in the text, ending with a section of additions and corrections.

913 'Maps for books and theses', by A G Hodgkiss (Newton Abbot: David and Charles, 1970), with illustrations by the author, concerns those maps which are composed to illustrate and to amplify the written or spoken word. A chapter on 'Cartographic illustration' opens the text, followed by 'Map compilation'; 'Drawing instruments and equipment'; 'Lettering'; 'The visual presentation of statistical data'; 'Map design and layout'; 'Specialised maps' and 'Reproducing illustrative maps'. Suggestions for further reading are included and appendices deal with the effects of reduction, scale changing equipment, book and paper sizes and copyright.

914 'Maps of Costa Rica: *an annotated bibliography'*, by Albert E Palmerlee (Lawrence: University of Kansas Libraries, 1965), is one of the University of Kansas Publications, Library series, no 19. The compiler has attempted to be comprehensive, including also maps found in books and other publications. In five major divisions—'General maps of the whole of Costa Rica', 'Subject maps of Costa Rica', such as climate, agriculture, industry and population, 'Provincial, cantonal and district maps', 'Regional maps' and 'City plans', whole sets of topographical maps have been incorporated, such as those of the Instituto Geográfico Nacional 1:25,000 and 1:50,000, and the Aeronautical Charts 1:1M, prepared by the United States Hydrographic Office and the United States Aeronautical Chart and Information Service. References stress the work by Luis Dobles Segreda: *Lista de mapas, parciales o totales de Costa Rica* (San José, 1928) and Jorge A Lines: *Bibliografía aborigen de Costa Rica* (San José, 1944).

915 'Marco Polo: Venetian adventurer', by Henry H Hart (University of Oklahoma Press, 1967), is the successor and, in a sense, a revised edition of *Venetian adventurer* (Stanford University Press, 1942) which went into several editions in English, translations into Spanish, German and Polish and a paperback edition. Excerpts from the narrative itself have been taken from the variorum edition prepared in English and from the version of Giovanni Batista Ramusio, also from the edition in French and Latin published by the Société de Géographie, Paris, 1824. A substantial bibliography represents works used in the course of preparing this volume, there are notes and references throughout the text and 'A note on Ramusio, translator and annotator of the first important collection of accounts of discovery and exploration . . .'. Several reproductions taken from manuscripts and early maps have been included.

916 'Marine cartography in Britain: *a history of the sea chart to 1855',* by A H W Robinson (Leicester University Press, 1962), was sponsored by The Royal Society, The Pilgrim Trust and The Crompton Bequest. A major section of the book is devoted to a group of re-productions, with notes on each. The early manuscript charts of the sixteenth century and the sea atlases are noted, followed by a section on 'The development of an accurate marine survey technique', tracing the improvement of instruments, official hydrography, the private chart publisher and on to the Survey of the British Isles. Appendix A contains useful biographical notes on some of the sixteenth century surveyors and chart-makers; appendix B lists 'Manuscript charts of the Tudor cartographers' and C is a listing of 'The charts of Greville Collins and John Adair'; D, 'Seventeenth century charts'; E, 'Surveys and charts of Murdoch Mackenzie (Senior)'; F, 'Charts and surveys of the "amateur" hydrographers'; G, 'Other published charts and manuscript surveys of the eighteenth century'—ending with detailed lists of the charts and surveys of Admiralty surveyors.

Refer also

C H Andregg: 'The scientific art of mapping and charting', *Surveying and mapping,* June 1969.

G P Britton: *Marine meteorology and oceanography* (University of Reading, 1969).

I D Kember: 'Some distinctive features of marine cartography', *The cartographical journal,* June 1971.

V T Miscoski: 'Marine charting today', *Surveying and mapping,* June 1969.

A Thunberg: 'Hydrographic surveying and data processing', *The cartographic journal,* December 1968.

917 'Marine climatic atlas of the world' *see under Atlas of meteorology.*

918 'Marine geophysical researches', produced quarterly from January 1970 by the Reidal Publishing Company, Dordrecht, an international journal for the study of the earth beneath the sea, mainly in English. Papers in French will also be accepted if accompanied by an abstract and an extensive summary in English; the text figures and captions are bilingual. Included are original research papers, research notes and preliminary papers, papers on instrumentation and methods, letters and concise reports. Work is based largely on the Vening Meinesz Laboratorium, University of Utrecht.

919 'The mariner's mirrour' of Lucas Jansz Waghenaer was reprinted by Theatrum Orbis Terrarum, 1966, with an introduction by R A Skelton; the maps are of particular interest as some of the earliest copper engravings to be done in England.
Refer also
> G R Crone: 'The Mariner's Mirrour, 1588', *The geographical journal*, December 1955.

920 'Maritime history', April 1971–, is published twice a year by David and Charles of Newton Abbot, Devon. Its emphasis is on international merchant shipping and subjects such as ports, naval architecture, maritime law and insurance. Illustrated articles, based on current research, will include many from overseas; and reviews, notes, news on research in progress and a current bibliography complete the text.
Refer also
> Peter H Fricke and E M Fricke, *comp*: *Index of current maritime research* (Cardiff: University of Wales Institute of Science and Technology, 1971).

921 'Marketing and management: *a world register of organisations'*, in English, French and German, is edited by I G Anderson in cooperation with the Institute of Marketing (CBD Research Limited, Beckenham, Kent). Indexed are the publications of organisations, national and international, devoted to the dissemination of information on marketing in all parts of the world.

922 Markham, Sir Clements R is known chiefly for his *General sketch of the history of Persia* (Longmans, 1874) and the *Report on the Geographical Department of the India Office 1867–1877*.

Refer also

A H Markham: *Life of Sir Clements R Markham*, 1917, which includes a list of his publications.

Donovan Williams: 'Clements Robert Markham and the Geographical Department of the India Office 1867–77', *The geographical journal*, September 1968, with a portrait.

923 Marsh, George Perkins (1801–1882) exerted great influence on geographical thought in the United States, notably through his *Man and nature: or physical geography as modified by human action*, 1864 (*qv*).

Refer also

David Lowenthal: 'George Perkins Marsh on the nature and purpose of geography', *The geographical journal*, December 1960.

924 'The material resources of Britain: an economic geography of the United Kingdom', by F J Monkhouse (Longman, 1971), presents in a small book divided into conventional parts—'The physical basis', 'The human basis', 'Agriculture', 'Woodland and afforestation', 'The fishing industry', 'Fuel power and utility', 'Manufacturing industry: general features', 'Some major types of manufacturing industry', 'Transport and communication' and 'Overseas trade'. Endpaper maps pinpoint the main centres, there are several monochrome photographs throughout the text and a few references are given. The work provides a timely summary of the economy at a crucial period of development.

Refer also

Michael Chisholm and Patrick O'Sullivan: *Freight flows and spatial aspects of the British economy* (CUP, 1973).

925 Maury, Matthew Fontaine (1806–1873) inspired the international study of oceanography, notably at the Brussels conference he originated in 1853 to establish a co-ordinated plan for the observation of winds and ocean currents. Maury's *Wind and current charts* and *Whale charts* showed considerable advance on previous work. He produced the first systematic textbook of oceanographic physics, *Physical geography of the sea and its meteorology*, 1855 (reprinted under the editorship of John Leighly, by Belknap Press, 1963). His contributions to geography are revealed also by his voluminous

462

official and semi-official correspondence with scientists throughout the world, which is in the archives of the US Naval Observatory.

Refer also

G E R Deacon: 'Matthew Fontaine Maury' *in USN journal of the Royal Naval Scientific Service*, May 1964.

F L Williams: *Matthew Fontaine Maury, scientist of the sea* (Rutgers UP, 1963).

926 Mawson Institute of Antarctic Research was inaugurated by the University of Adelaide in 1961 to foster polar studies and research. The collections include the library of Sir Douglas Mawson, also his equipment and specimens.

Refer also

Paquita Mawson: *Mawson of the Antarctic: the life of Sir Douglas Mawson* (Longmans, 1964).

927 'Medieval regions and their cities', by Josiah Cox Russell (Newton Abbot: David and Charles, 'Studies in historical geography' series), presents a pioneer study of the structure of medieval regions; the text analyses the relationship of their cities and the size and significance of their populations, setting up a theoretical model for the rank-size series of medieval cities in relation to their regions and economic bases, and, in subsequent chapters, testing it against demographic data for the cities of England, Ireland, the Low Countries, Germany, Italy, Spain and Egypt in the period AD 1000 to 1348, and of India in the seventh century AD. The concluding chapter emphasises the importance of the regions as a basis for late medieval society and their destruction by the plague, leaving conditions favourable for the rise of absolute monarchies and nations.

928 'The Mediterranean lands', by D S Walker (Methuen, 1960, third edition, 1965), deals with all the countries having a coastline on the Sea, with the main emphasis on the European Mediterranean peninsula and islands, in five main sections, each sub-divided: 'General'; 'The Western Basin—Europe'; 'The Western Basin—Africa'; 'The Balkan Peninsula' and 'The Near East'. In the general section, physical and economic features of the whole area are noted and there is a similar introductory approach to each of the individual regions identified. Photographs and sketch-maps illustrate the text, there are a 'Statistical appendix', 'Conversion tables' and

'Suggestions for further reading', including both books and articles. The author pays particular tribute to French geographers, naming especially Professor Pierre Birot and Professor Jean Dresch.

Refer also

    L G Pine: *The Middle Sea: a short history of the Mediterranean* (Newton Abbot: David and Charles, revised edition, 1973).

929 'Mélanges de géographie, physique, humaine, économique, appliquée', was prepared as a festschrift to Professor M Omer Tulippe, edited by José A Sporck (Editions J Ducolot, 1967). In two volumes, it includes a bibliography of the works of Professor Tulippe and a survey of his career. The essays, by scholars of several nationalities, are on many aspects of geography, chiefly in English, French, German and Russian, with some photographs, maps and diagrams in the text.

930 'Mémoires et documents', an invaluable series begun in 1949 by the Centre de Documentation Cartographique et Géographique, Centre Nationale de la Recherche Scientifique, Paris. Each issue is devoted to a particular area: volume I, 1949, Canada; II, 1951, Belgium; III, 1952, British Isles and so on. Section A consists of high level articles; section B and C are invaluable bibliographies, broadly classified as necessary, 'Documentation cartographique' and 'Documentation bibliographique'.

931 'Memoirs of hydrography, *including brief biographies of the principal officers who have served in HM Surveying Service between the years 1750 and 1885'*, compiled by Commander L S Dawson RN, is in two parts; part I, 1750 to 1830; part II, 1830 to 1885 (Eastbourne: Henry W Keay, The 'Imperial Library', 1885). The work was issued in facsimile reprint by the Cornmarket Press, London, 1969. Quoting from the preface to this reprint—'These Memoirs originally published in 1885 have until recently been the only comprehensive work on the activities of the oldest department of the Admiralty, now the Ministry of Defence, and of the naval surveying service acting under its direction. In recent years a continuation of the Memoirs has been increasingly in need and in the early 1950s it was agreed that it should be an official undertaking. Partly owing to the magnitude of the task by reason of the large mass of original material buried in the department's records as well as at the Public Record Office, no author was then found. The next step was the employment of Messrs G B

464

Stigant and L A Luff, both in retirement after a lifetime in the department to index and digest the department's letter and minute books which date back to 1804. Then in 1961 Vice-Admiral Sir Archibald Day was invited to continue the history from 1885 to the present day. It was decided for various reasons to start at 1795 when the department was formed and to end at 1919 . . . With the then available digest of departmental papers and after a search at the Public Records Office, it was sensible to recapitulate Dawson's work up to 1885, particularly as to the activities of the department from its inception; there being at the time no reprint of Dawson in prospect . . . a research worker in the subject must still turn to Dawson for his immensely detailed account of the worldwide surveys undertaken . . .' Details of Commander Dawson's career are given, followed by a list of errata; the books are part of a series of fifty being reprinted in facsimile from originals in the National Maritime Museum Library on naval history, naval strategy, biography, history of the mercantile marine, voyages and hydrography.

Refer also
'The Admiralty Hydrographic Service 1795–1919' (HMSO, 1967).

Admiral G S Ritchie: *The Admiralty chart* (qv).

M Chriss and G R Hayes: *An introduction to charts and their use* (Glasgow: Brown, Son and Ferguson, third edition, 1964).

Per Collinder: *History of marine navigation* (Batsford, translated by Maurice Michael, 1954).

S K Agarwal and A R Boyle: 'A character recognition device for soundings on navigational charts', *Surveying and mapping*, 1972.

A Anthiaume: *Cartes marines: constructions navales voyages de Découverte chez les Normands 1500–1650* (Paris: Dumont, two volumes, 1916).

Carol Bateman: 'Computer controlled drawing of hydrographic charts', *The cartographic journal*, June 1972.

A R Boyle: 'Automatic cartography: special problems of hydrographic charting', *The international hydrographic review*, 1971.

A R Boyle: 'Automation in hydrographic charting', *Canadian surveyor*, December 1970.

Vice-Admiral Sir John Edgell: *Sea surveys* (Longmans, 1948, reprinted 1949; second edition revised by the National Maritime

Museum and Hydrographic Department, Ministry of Defence (Navy), 1965).

L J Harris *et al*: 'British maps and charts: a survey of development', *The geographical journal*, June 1964.

Derek Howse and Michael Sanderson: *The sea chart: an historical survey based on the collections in the National Maritime Museum* (Newton Abbot: David and Charles, 1973).

A D Margrett: *Hydrographic surveying: for development and conservancy* (Kelvin-Hughes (Marine) Limited, 1955).

C H Martin: 'Present and future trends in the maintenance of nautical charts', *Canadian cartography*, 1964.

S R Parsons: 'The Marine Radar Photoplot System', *Journal*, Institute of Navigation, 1962.

F A Pielou: 'Special purpose navigation charts', *The cartographic journal*, June 1971.

A H W Robinson: *Early hydrographic surveys of the British Isles* (Empire Survey Review, 1951).

A H W Robinson: 'The evolution of the English nautical chart', *Journal*, Institute of Navigation, 1952.

A H W Robinson: *Marine cartography in Britain: a history of the sea chart to 1855* (Leicester University Press, 1962).

A H W Robinson: 'Marine surveying in Britain during the seventeenth and eighteenth centuries', *The geographical journal*, December 1957.

O H Shamblin: 'Hydrographic surveys with electronics', *The military engineer*, July–August, 1965.

932 **'Men and meridians:** *the history of surveying and mapping in Canada'*, by Don W Thomson, is in two volumes, 'Prior to 1867' and '1867 to 1917' (Queen's Printer, Ottawa, 1966 and 1967), sponsored by the Department of Mines and Technical Surveys, Ottawa, in English and French editions. It is the first comprehensive, non-technical story of the surveyors of Canadian land and waters and of the maps and charts resulting from their work. A bibliography and reference notes end the work and there are also endpaper maps as well as numerous diagrammatic maps and reproductions throughout the text.

Refer also

Canada in maps: documents drawn from the National Map Collection, Public Archives of Canada.

Lewis J Harris: 'Mapping the land of Canada', *The geo-

933 'Mendelssohn's South African bibliography' is in two volumes, being the 'Catalogue raisonné of the Mendelssohn Library of works relating to South Africa . . .' with a descriptive introduction by I D Colvin (Kegan Paul, Trench, Trubner, 1910). The references, annotated, include periodical articles from periodical literature throughout the world, there is a section on the cartography of South Africa and twenty-six reproduced engravings.

934 'Mercantile marine atlas', first published in 1904 by George Philip and Son and constantly revised since, presents full information on the ocean highways of the world from the point of view of trade and commerce; it is not intended for navigational purposes, and the land areas are of secondary importance. Large-scale charts, on the Mercator projection, tables of distances between ports and much other information, in addition to 135 port plans, make this a unique and invaluable atlas. The index comprises some twenty-five thousand entries.

> *Note Books and the sea: a list of modern books on the sea and shipping*, compiled in collaboration with the National Maritime Museum, Greenwich (School Library Association, 1964).

935 Mercator, Gerard (1512–1594) was a globe and instrument-maker, at first in association with Gemma Frisius, who in the course of his life made great advances in geographical concepts and in all aspects of map design, especially in the construction of atlases. He was a cartographer of great integrity, his maps being compiled and drawn by himself and his family after much careful study. His first world map of 1538 was widely copied or used as a base by Ortelius and others. Another world map on the projection which has since borne his name, was published in 1569. This projection, on which every compass direction is shown as a straight line, was that most used by navigators from the seventeenth century onwards. He produced an edition of Ptolemy's *Geography* and made plans himself for a complete *Geographia*. His concept of geography was threefold: ancient, Ptolemaic and modern, and the *Geographia* was intended to show this progression, but only a few parts of the modern atlas were completed before his death. The parts of the 'Gallia' and 'Germania', however, printed in 1585, and of 'Italia, Slavonia et Graecia', in

1589/90, pointed the way for the modern concept of regional and national atlases. **Rumold Mercator,** who died in 1600, continued his father's work. In 1595, he published a collection of maps embodying his father's genius, the *Atlas sive cosmographicae meditationes de fabrica mundi et fabricati figura*. Mercator's introduction of the italic script for map lettering was not so well known until the publication of *Mercator: a monograph on the lettering of maps, etc., in the sixteenth century in the Netherlands with a facsimile and translation of Ghim's Vita Mercatoris*. Dr A S Osley explains how this work came about (Faber, 1969); the facsimile is of the first edition of Mercator's *Literarum Latinarum . . . scribendi ratio*, 1540, from the only complete copy, with an English translation by Dr Osley, followed by his translation of Walter Ghim's biography of 1595. *Gerhard Mercator und die Geographen unter seinen Nachkommen* (Gotha, 1914) was reproduced in facsimile by N Israel, Meridian and Theatrum Orbis Terrarum, 1969.

Refer also

J van Raemdonch: *Gérard Mercator: sa vie et ses oeuvres*, 1869. F van Ortroy: *Bibliographie sommaire de l'oeuvre mercatorienne*, 1920.

E G R Taylor: 'Gerard Mercator: AD 1512–1594', *The geographical journal*, June 1962.

936 Meridian Publishing Company, Amsterdam, reproduces almost entirely early out of print works of topographical, bibliographical or cartographical interest, frequently in collaboration with Theatrum Orbis Terrarum and N Israel. Notable are *The Cambrian bibliography* (*qv*); W Englemann: *Bibliotheca geographica*, in two volumes, 1857; E Favenc: *The history of Australian exploration . . .*, 1888; L Gallois: *Les Géographes Allemands de la Renaissance*, 1890; and A Neubauer: *La géographie du Talmud*, 1868. General catalogues are issued usually twice a year and frequent advance notices are circulated.

937 'Metallogenic map of Europe', 1969–1971 compiled by the Drafting Committee on the Metallogenic Map of Europe, under the auspices of the Sub-Commission for the Metallogenic Map of the World of the Commission for the Geological Map of the World, has been co-ordinated by Professor Pierre Laffitte of the Ecole Nationale Supérieure des Mines, Paris, and published jointly by Unesco and the Bureau de Recherches Géologiques et Minières, Paris. Nine sheets have been printed in thirty to thirty-six colours, with legends in French; and nine lists of deposits printed separately refer to each of the sheets. An explanatory brochure of about fifty pages is available in English and French (1969) and *The metallogeny of Europe* (1971) is a companion volume. Foremost European specialists in the geology of mineral deposits have combined their efforts to produce this map, which represented a big step forward in metallogenic studies, especially as regards the methodology of prospecting. It offers a variety and a wealth of information such as has never yet been assembled on a map at this scale, *ie* 1:2,500,000.

938 'Meteorite research: *Proceedings of the International Symposium on Meteorite Research, Vienna, Austria, 7–13 August 1968'*, edited by Peter M Millman, was published by the D Reidel Publishing Company, Amsterdam, 1969. The symposium was sponsored by Unesco, the IAU, the International Union of Geological Sciences, the International Association of Geochemistry and Cosmochemistry, the Meteoritical Society and the International Atomic Energy Agency. The subjects presented covered a wide field—early history of meteorites, their composition and structure, isotope studies and chronology and 'orbits'. The discussions are also included.

939 Methuen and Company Limited, London, has a special line of monographs of geographical interest, including T W Freeman: *Ireland . . .*; E G Bowen: *Wales . . .*; Monica Cole: *South Africa*; and revised editions of such thought-provoking works as M I Newbigin: *Southern Europe . . .* in a third edition, 1949. More recently have appeared R J Chorley and Peter Haggett, *editors: Models in geography* (*qv*); and by the same team, *Frontiers in geographical teaching* (*qv*); Paul Wagret: *Polderlands*; B W Hodder: *Economic development in the Tropics*; R G Barry and R J Chorley: *Atmosphere, weather and climate*. Particularly useful is the entire *Methuen's advanced geographies* series, which includes both regional and systematic titles.

940 'Mexico atlas; *atlas géographique et physique de la Nouvelle-Espagne'*, comprises the maps, diagrams and sketches contained in the three works on Mexico written by Alexander von Humboldt between 1811 and 1834, reproduced by Hanna Beck and Wilhelm Bonacker. There are twenty-eight folding and other plates, thirty four pages of editor's introduction in German and ninety-two pages of author's introduction in German and French—issued to mark the bicentenary of Von Humboldt. Particular attention was given in the work to the existing conditions and the potentialities of the Mexican state, using population and production statistics of its constituent administrative divisions to make comparisons between the regions.

Refer also

    M Rippy: *Oil and the Mexican Revolution* (Brill, 1972), originally published in Spanish by Problemas Agricolas e Industriales de Mexico, 1954, under the title *El petróleo y le revolución Mexicana*.

941 'Meyers Neuer Geographischen Handatlas', prepared by the Mannheim Bibliographisches Institut (Harrap, 1967), comprises seventy-one terrestrial maps, with a few pages of astronomical charts and photographs. Scales range from 1:1M to physical and political maps of the world on 1:80M. Contours and layer tinting are used, relief being emphasised by hill shading; the variety of landforms and hydrological features is stressed, including sand fields, lava fields, coral reefs and glaciers. Maps of the oceans incorporate new research completed during the International Geophysical Year. Some maps tend to look rather crowded, especially in areas of dense population, where more complex cultural features are indicated.

942 Michelin: André Michelin wrote his first travel guide book in 1900 and together with the first Michelin road map for car travellers, in 1913, began the tourist service department of the Michelin Tyre Company, Services de Tourisme du Pneu Michelin. About seven million maps are now published each year and are among the most widely used maps in the world. The Michelin road map at 1:200,000 is now completely revised; there is also the road map at 1:1M and maps of various parts of Africa are a new feature. The *Guides rouges* and *Guides verts* contain many maps of topography and roads, together with excellent city plans. For the 1970 edition of the French Guide, composition was mechanised on 'Monotype' machines and the style was rationalised. The text is now divided into six sections under the following headings: general information and places of interest, tourist offices, distances to principal cities, hotels and restaurants (fixed information), hotels and restaurants (variable information) and garages.

Refer also

    'Les services de tourisme du Pneu Michelin: histoire et évolution des publications cartographiques Michelin', *International yearbook of cartography, 1963.*

943 '**The Middle East:** *a physical, social and regional geography'*, by
W B Fisher (Methuen, 1950; sixth edition, revised, 1971), aims 'to
present a factual and reasoned statement on all the principal elements, physical and human, that influence environment, ways of life
and development within the area . . .'. The pattern of the work is
therefore straightforward—'Physical geography of the Middle East',
'Social geography of the Middle East', 'Regional geography of the
Middle East', ending with Appendices, 'Outline of the geological history of the Middle East'; 'Temperature distribution in the atmosphere'; 'The origin of the Mesopotamian plains'; 'The racial and
cultral affinities of the people of Israel'; 'Glossary of geographical
terms, mainly of Arabic origin'; and a bibliography arranged according to the subjects of the chapters. Sketchmaps and diagrams, though
not numerous, are helpfully placed throughout the text and there are
folding maps at the end.

Refer also

Abr-Nahrain, 1959–, (Department of Middle Eastern Studies,
Universities of Melbourne).

M Adams, *ed: The Middle East: a handbook* (Blond, 1971).

Sir Reader Bullard, *ed: The Middle East: a political and economic survey* (Royal Institute of International Affairs, third edition, 1958).

W B Fisher and H Bowen-Jones: 'Development surveys in the
Middle East', *The geographical journal*, October 1974.

S H Longrigg: *The Middle East: a social geography* (Aldine,
second edition, 1970).

S H Longrigg: *Oil in the Middle East, its discovery and development* (OUP, third edition, 1967, for the Royal Institute of International Affairs).

W M Ramsay: *The historical geography of Asia Minor* (Royal
Geographical Society, 1890; photolitho report by Adolf M
Hakkert, Amsterdam, 1962).

J H Stevens and R King: *A bibliography of Saudi Arabia* (University of Durham, Centre for Middle Eastern and Islamic Studies, 1973).

Alice Taylor, *ed: The Middle East* (Newton Abbot: David and
Charles, 1972).

C A O Van Nieuwenhuijze: *Sociology of the Middle East: a
stocktaking and interpretation*, the first volume in the series,

'Social, economic and political studies of the Middle East' (Brill, 1971).

Regional plan of action for the application of science and technology to development in the Middle East (United Nations,

944 'A million years of man', by Richard Carrington (Weidenfeld and Nicolson), presents a non-technical account of the evolution of man from his animal ancestors to present-day intellectual and spiritual achievements, viewed throughout against the background of his environments. In five parts, illustrated in half-tone, the topics stressed include the geological history of the earth and the origin and progress of life forms, man-like creatures, *Homo sapiens*, the contributions of individual civilisations and the human 'adventure' in relation to the whole of nature.

945 Mipofile, used as a protective covering for maps of any kind, is transparent, soft, flexible plastic sheet, which can be bent and creased, without breaking or showing scratches. It is immune against climatic conditions and the passage of time, resistant to acids, alkalis, oil and sea water, giving protection against tearing, corroding and dirt. It is manufactured in the inventor's factory near Cologne and is used all over the world.

946 'Models in geography: *the second Madingley Lectures for 1965'*, edited by R J Chorley and Peter Haggett (Methuen, 1967), comprises seventeen contributions on the theme of geographical generalisation, or model-building.

Refer also

R J Chorley and Peter Hagget, *ed*: *Integrated models in geography* (Part II of *Models in geography* in university paperback; *Physical and information models in geography* (Methuen paperback 1969).

947 'Modern Egypt: *a list of references to material in the New York Public Library'*, compiled by I A Pratt under the direction of Dr Richard Gottheil (The Library, 1929), was reprinted by Kraus in 1969. The work contains references to bibliographies, periodicals and society publications, followed by sections divided under broad subject headings, such as 'Census and vital statistics' and 'Geography'; essential bibliographical information is given on each, with a brief annotation when desirable.

Refer also

K M Barbour: 'The distribution of industry in Egypt: a new source considered', *Transactions*, Institute of British Geographers, July 1970.

K M Barbour: *The growth, location and structure of industry in Egypt* (New York: Praeger; Pall Mall, 1972).

948 '**The modern encyclopaedia of Australia and New Zealand**', in one volume (Sydney: Horwitz-Grahame, 1964), contains brief, unsigned articles ranging from a few lines in length to one or two columns; maps, coloured plates and drawings are included. A concise chronology precedes the main alphabetical section; a 'Quick reference section', tables and statistics and a list of abbreviations follow. There is no index.

949 '**Modern France:** *a social and economic geography'*, by I B Thompson (Butterworth, 1970), presents France as a nation in a state of rapid change. The book incorporates the most recent data available, working on the 1968 census of population, and among its most interesting features is a synthesis of development problems on the basis of the offical planning regions. The text, illustrated by seventy-four maps and diagrams, runs as follows: 'Patterns of social development'; 'Human resources'; 'The geography of population'; 'Rural settlement'; 'Urban development'; 'Patterns of economic activity'; 'State and regional economic planning'; 'The production of energy'; 'Transport'; 'Agriculture'; 'Manufacturing'; 'Regional disparities in economic and social development'.

Refer also

N M Hansen: *France in the modern world* (Van Nostrand Reinhold, 1969).

A Perpillou: 'Geography and geographical studies in France during the war and the occupation', *The geographical journal*, January-February 1946.

950 '**Modern geographers:** *an outline of progress in geography since A D 1800*, by G R Crone (Royal Geographical Society, 1951, reissued 1960, new and enlarged edition, 1970), is a pamphlet reproducing, with revision, seven articles originally contributed to *The geographical magazine* between 1949 and 1951, together with a final chapter on Isaiah Bowman and American geography and some references for further reading.

951 'The Moon', by Zdeněk Kopal (Dordrecht: D Reidel Publishing Company, 1969), attempts to cover almost the entire field of lunar studies, each section being accompanied by bibliographical notes—'Motion of the Moon and dynamics of the Earth-Moon system'; 'Internal constitution of the human globe'; 'Topography of the Moon'; 'Lunar radiation and surface structure'. An outline of the exploration of the Moon is included and there are coloured skeleton maps of near and far sides of the moon at the scale of 1:6M.

Note Reidel publish also *The Moon: an international journal of lunar studies.*

952 'Morskoy atlas' is a major work from the point of view of both oceanography and cartography, compiled in three volumes under the editorship of I S Isakou and produced by the Soviet Naval Cartographic and Hydrographic Staff and the Chief Administration for Geodesy and Cartography in 1950. The Soviet Admiralty and Naval General Staff contributed largely to the work, also the geographers and the administration of the North Sea Route and the Soviet Arctic Institute. General maps of the oceans are on a scale of 1:50M, smaller areas on scales of 1:2M to 1:100,000; port plans are included except for Russian ports. Coast and shore features reveal particularly meticulous cartography.

953 'The mountain geologist', quarterly publication of the Rocky Mountain Association of Geologists, began in 1964. Scope is confined to the Rocky Mountain region and adjoining areas and the emphasis is on the short papers containing original material not normally published in national journals.

954 'The mountain world', published bi-annually by the Swiss Foundation for Alpine Research, Zurich, is translated into English by Michael Barnes and made available in Britain by Allen and Unwin Limited. Descriptions of new discoveries, expeditions and scientific research on mountains throughout the world are magnificently illustrated.

955 'Mountains and rivers of India', edited by Dr B C Law, with a foreword by Professor S P Chatterjee, was published by the National Committee for Geography, Calcutta, 1968, on the occasion of the 21st International Geographical Congress. The text, interesting in itself, brings together much information hitherto unavailable, including also references to the mountains and rivers of early Indian literature.

Refer also

E Ahmad: *Coastal geomorphology of India* (Orient Longman, 1972).

956 **'Multilingual dictionary of technical terms in cartography'** 1973: Commission II of the International Cartographic Association was set up in 1964, under the Chairmanship of Professor E Meynen of the Federal German Republic, to promote the definition, classification and standardisation of technical terms. At the first meeting at Bad Godesberg, September 1965, it was decided that these aims would be best served by the preparation of a multilingual dictionary or glossary. The terms were to be defined in five languages, English, French, German, Spanish and Russian, with equivalent terms, without definitions, in Czech, Dutch, Hungarian, Italian, Japanese, Polish, Portuguese and Spanish. Indexes were prepared in each of the languages. A multilingual list of named map projections, based largely on the work of Dr D H Maling of Swansea, was drawn up, illustrated and including specimen sheet layouts. The work was assisted by the publication of the Royal Society's *Glossary of technical terms in cartography* and the Defense Intelligence Agency *Glossary of mapping, charting and geodetic terms,* 1967. Close contact is being maintained with the revisers of the International Federation of Surveyors dictionary, so as to avoid duplication.

957 **'National atlas of Britain'** had been the subject of discussion and proposals for many years. In 1935, a committee appointed by the Council of the Town Planning Institute recommended a Commission to direct a national survey of the natural and economic resources of the country, and the National Atlas Committee of the British Association also submitted proposals in 1939. In 1941, an advisory committee was established under the chairmanship of the director-general of the Ordnance Survey, as a result of which two map offices were set up, in London and Edinburgh, under the aegis of the Ministry of Local Government and Planning, with the Department of Health for Scotland, to examine the mass of official data to be represented on successive sheets of such a national survey. Large-scale maps, maintained in continuous revision, are available for official use. From these manuscript maps a national series was compiled on a scale of 1:625,000 by the Ministry of Housing and Local Government, with other departments and research organisations, and published by the Ordnance Survey, from whom the current list of published sheets and prices may be obtained. Each map is in two sheets, Scotland and north England, and the rest of England and Wales. Explanatory texts are available for the following sheets: land classification; average annual rainfall; population; limestone; vegetation, the grasslands of England and Wales; local accessibility; vegetation, reconnaissance of the Survey of Scotland.

Refer also

S W E Vince, revised by W A Payne: 'Towards a national atlas', in *Government information and the research worker*, edited by Ronald Staveley and Mary Piggott (Library Association, second revised edition, 1965).

958 **'The national atlas of Canada'**, in its original form, published by the Department of the Interior of the Canadian Government, 1906, was revised and enlarged in 1915. Revised again by J E Chalifour, in 1957 (1958), the work was a superb achievement, in loose-leaf format, covering all aspects of the physical background and economic development of the nation at mid-century. Particularly useful was the series of urban land use maps, linking with the World Land Use Survey of the International Geographical Union. The maps demonstrate a variety of cartographic techniques and are clear and aesthetically pleasing, with notes on the backs of the plates. The gradual opening-up of the country is shown in sections—'Routes of early explorers 1534–1870' and 'Mapping the coasts, 1492–1874'. The first maps from Stephanius to Zaltieri illustrate the emergence of the concept of a new continent of America; Behaim's globe indicates the general belief that Europe and Asia were separated principally by water; Ruysch's map shows the discoveries of Columbus, Cabot, the Corte Reals and Vespucci. The fourth edition of the Atlas constitutes a fresh geographical study of the nation, consisting of three main sections: Physical geography; Human geography and Economic geography. The vast water resources of the country are emphasised, as are the other resources, both natural and man-made. A new map incorporates the census divisions and sub-divisions.

959 **'National atlas of China'**, edited by Chang Chi-Yun, in five volumes (Yang Ming Shan, Taiwan; National War College in co-operation with the Chinese Geographical Institute, 1959–1962) is the latest in a long line of Chinese 'national' atlases, beginning in 1718 with the *Atlas of the empire* commissioned by the Emperor K'ang Hsi. In Chinese and English, the five volumes are arranged as follows: 1, Taiwan, 1959; 2, Tibet, Sinkiang and Mongolia, 1960; 3, North China, 1961; 4, South China, 1962; 5, General maps of China, 1962. The political maps reflect the Nationalist Chinese viewpoint.

960 'National atlas of disease mortality in the United Kingdom', completed in 1962 by G Melvyn Howe on behalf of the Royal Geographical Society in association with the British Medical Association (Nelson, 1963), was the first project of its kind. The first volume covers the period 1954 to 1958; a second edition (Nelson, 1970) was revised and enlarged to include data covering 1959–1963 in Part II, using the 1961 census material. Maps of population density and mortality from all causes are followed by fourteen maps of the chief causes of death. The historical introduction is valuable, and each map is accompanied by descriptive text.

Refer also

G Melvyn Howe: 'A national atlas of disease mortality in the United Kingdom', *The geographical journal*, March 1964.

G Melvyn Howe: 'Environment for disease', *Geographical magazine*, August 1972.

G Melvyn Howe: *Man, environment and disease in Britain: a medical geography of Britain through the ages* (Newton Abbot: David and Charles, 1972).

961 'National atlas of Hungary' (Budapest: Cartographia, 1967) was prepared with the co-operation of the Geographical Committee of the Hungarian Academy of Sciences, edited by Dr Sándor Radó. The work gives a comprehensive survey of natural, social and economic conditions in the country, maps and data being contributed by individual institutes, scientific research organisations and societies; on the basis of the recommendations of the Commission on National Atlases, work began in 1959, with two aims: to promote the work of economic management and planning and to form a historical document for further research. The main divisions of material, all subdivided, are 'Natural conditions', 'Population and settlement', 'Agriculture', 'Industry', 'Transport and communication', 'Retail trade, tourism, foreign trade and international relations', 'Cultural and social standards'. A supplement, inset in the back cover, is 'Administrative map of the Hungarian People's Republic' at 1:500,000, using graded lettering. There are diagrams where necessary, especially in the section on climate, a fine use of symbols, proportional circles, etc, and text introduces each major division.

962 'National atlas of India' was issued in a preliminary Hindi edition, under the direction of S P Chatterjee, in 1957 (Ministry of Education and Scientific Research, Dehra Dun), with text in Hindi and English and translations of map-keys in English on the backs of the sheets. An English edition, also edited by Professor Chatterjee, was published by the Ministry of Education, National Atlas Organization, 1968, comprising fourteen selected maps from the original atlas. Several regional atlases have also been published, which will eventually constitute a national atlas in even greater detail; *An atlas of resources of Mysore State*, in two volumes, 1961 and 1962, is an excellent example.

963 'National atlas of Kenya: *a comprehensive series of new and authentic maps prepared from the National Survey and other governmental sources, with gazetteers and notes on pronunciation and spelling'* was completed in 1959 by the Survey of Kenya; a third edition was published in 1970. The finely produced plates, showing historical aspects, physical features, natural resources, population, social services, industry, communications, power and urban centres, provided an indispensable guide to the country and its resources. Some early maps of the country were reproduced. The third edition was properly bound. Forty-three map plates include some new topics, reflecting particularly the development of Kenya as an independent nation, and each map is accompanied by an informative text on the facing page.
> *Refer also*
> The *Nelson Kenya junior atlas*; *A computer atlas of Kenya*: with a bibliography of computer mapping, edited by D R F Taylor (Ottawa: Carleton University Department of Geography, 1971).

964 'National atlas of Turkey', published by the Faculty of Letters, University of Istanbul, 1961, contains eighty-seven maps and diagrams covering all aspects of the life of the country. This atlas is in

Turkish and English, but the greater part of source material for Turkey is not available in other languages.

Refer also

Bernard Lewis: *The emergence of modern Turkey* (OUP for the Royal Institute of International Affairs, 1961).

Reinhard Stewig: *Byzanz-konstantinople-Istanbul* (Kiel: Schrigt. Geogr. Inst., 1964).

965 'The national atlas of the United States of America', edited by A C Gerlach, a concept of John Wesley Powell some hundred years ago, was begun by the National Research Council, National Academy of Sciences and the first sheets became available in 1957; in 1962, the National Atlas project was transferred to the United States Geological Survey for re-planning and co-ordination. The editors state in the introduction that it is 'designed to be of practical use to decision makers in Government and business, planners, research scholars, and others needing to visualise country-wide distributional patterns and relationships between environmental phenomena and human activities'. It is therefore an eminently practical work, containing 756 maps and a substantial index, bound into a single volume; it is in two main sections, a reference section, containing general maps mainly at 1:2M, also maps of the twenty-seven largest cities at 1:500,000, and, secondly, 281 pages of special subject maps. A twenty-three page section is concerned with exploration, the progress of settlement and territorial growth. The maps dealing with economic features, resources and industries are outstanding and transparent overlays, kept in a back cover pocket, enable positioning of county boundaries and population sites.

Refer also

A C Gerlach: 'The national atlas of the United States of America', *The cartographer*, May 1965.

C O Paullin: *Atlas of the historical geography of the United States* (Carnegie Institution and American Geographical Society of New York, 1932).

Simon Baker and Henry W Still, *comp: The look of our land—an airphoto atlas of the rural United States and the Plains and Praries* (Washington, DC: US Department of Agriculture, Economic Research Service, 1971).

M C Goodman and W W Ristow, *comp: Marketing maps of the USA: an annotated bibliography* (Library of Congress, second edition, 1957).

Norman J W Thrower: 'Cadastral survey and county atlases of the United States', *The cartographic journal*, June 1972.

S S Visher: *Climatic atlas of the United States* (Harvard University Press; OUP, 1954).

966 The National Book League, London, is now associated with Artsmail, a selective information service for arts activities. The main value of the League for geographers lies in the regional bibliographies produced at intervals—on China, for example, the USSR, Greece, Spain—which follow the policy of an introduction to the literature, followed by a bibliography arranged under suitable subdivisions. 'Man and environment' was selected by The Nature Conservancy, the 'Readers' guide to the Commonwealth' by the Commonwealth Institute and the 'Readers' guide to Scotland' (*qv*) as major introductions to the respective source material. In *Books*, the League journal, Summer 1971, was included 'The literature of rivers', concerning some of the great rivers of the world.

967 'National geographic atlas of the world' originated from January, 1958, when a new series of map supplements was introduced for the *National Geographic magazine*, uniform in size and designed to be assembled in a loose-leaf binder (The Society, 1963; second enlarged edition, 1966 third revised edition, 1970). In the new editions each of the double-plate maps were brought up to date. The map of Antarctica was completely redrawn, incorporating the findings of recent surveys; also boundaries were checked and settlement patterns and towns adjusted, especially in those countries which have gained independence since 1963. The three-dimensional quality of many of the maps reflects the style of the Swiss cartographer, Paul Ulmer, who passed on his method to Henri A DeLanghe, the present cartographer of the Society. Changes in place-names were recorded, the most recent population figures possible were consulted and the index contains some 139 thousand entries. There are two editions: the Standard Edition, a flexible, leather-grained plastic cover, and the De Luxe Edition, hard-bound in a cloth cover with matching slipcase. Emphasis is on the USA, but the rest of the world is covered with reasonable balance. Arrangement is by geographical area, each section being preceded by a short description of the country. The aim was to interest laymen as well as scholars, students, travellers and businessmen. A useful list of addresses of information centres is included.

Refer also

Athos D Grazzini: 'Problèmes que présente la préparation de l'Atlas Mondial de la National Geographic Society', *International yearbook of cartography*, 1965.

968 The National Geographic Society was founded in Washington in 1888 as a non-profit making scientific and educational organisation for the diffusion of geographical knowledge and for promoting research and exploration. The Society has sponsored very many major expeditions and scientific projects and has greatly assisted the widespread appreciation and use of maps. The first map supplement of the *National Geographic magazine* was issued in 1899; a new series of supplements formed the basis of the *National Geographic atlas of the world* (see above). The magazine itself is the major periodical of the Society, published monthly since 1888. The articles are of high standard, though not usually technical, and are profusely illustrated, with a lavish use of colour. The cumulative index is complete to 1963, and includes references to both subjects and illustrations. A *Geographic school bulletin* has been issued weekly, October to May, since 1922. The Cartographic Department of the Society has made a considerable contribution to cartographic history. The Society also publishes books from time to time and maintains a News Service Division. Two recently established publications make known the research undertaken by the Society: *Abstracts* includes reviews of research and explorations sponsored by the Society during the previous year, edited by Paul H Oehser under the direction of the Committee for Research and Exploration; and *Research reports*, by the same editor, 1968–, summarise these activities of the Society since 1890.

Refer also

G H Grosvenor: 'The National Geographic Society and its magazine', originally in the index volume 1947–1956, also reprinted separately.

969 The National Maritime Museum catalogue of the Library is being published (HMSO, 1968–); under the heading *Voyages and travels*, chapters are allotted to geographical area or type of voyage and within this section the list is chronological. An important publication of the Museum was *Man is not lost: a record of two hundred years of astronomical navigation with the Nautical Almanac 1767–1967* (1968).

970 National Institute of Oceanography was set up in 1949, incorporating the staff, collections and data of the Discovery Committee (1924–1949) and the National Oceanographic Council was established by Royal Charter in 1950. The headquarters is at Wormley, in Surrey, and the *RRS Discovery* is based on Plymouth. Research has been concerned with long-term investigations into the interchange of energy between the atmosphere and oceans, with the response of the sea surfaces to wind and pressure changes and with the general circulation of the oceans; much research is conducted in the North Sea and English Channel and in far distant waters, such as the Antarctic. During the International Geophysical Year, a series of oceanographic sections was made across the Atlantic Ocean, in collaboration with the Woods Hole Oceanographic Institute, the results being published by the latter Institute in an *Atlantic Ocean atlas*. The *Annual reports* have summarised the work of the Institute, while *Collected reprints* and the *Discovery reports*, published by the Cambridge University Press, have given accounts of research in greater detail. A new Institute of Oceanographic Sciences came into being in June 1973 as a result of the merging of the National Institute of Oceanography, the Institute of Coastal Oceanography and Tides and the Unit of Coastal Sedimentation. The new Institute undertakes applied research and provides services in oceanography to assist government departments, industry and others, including responsibility for scientific instrumentation and equipment services hitherto provided by the research vessel base at Barry, Glamorgan.

971 The National Library of New Zealand Map Room acquires about five hundred maps a year, of which a large number are catalogued for the *New Zealand national bibliography*. Lack of full-time staff has hampered services, but reference enquiries are dealt with, material provided for the preparation of research work and the demand for photocopies has been on the increase.

972 National Library of Scotland Map Room was opened in 1958, but the collection itself dates from the early eighteenth century, comprising a fine set of early maps of Scotland, original work by leading cartographers, official surveys and a representative collection of more modern maps and atlases.

973 National Library of Wales Department of Prints, Drawings and Maps maintains a large collection of early geographies, atlases, maps and charts, especially county maps of Wales. A complete catalogue is not available, but 'Some cartographical works in the National Library', an article by M Gwyneth Lewis in *The National Library of Wales journal,* volume v, 3 1948, has also been issued separately.

974 National Oceanographic Data Center, Washington DC, was set up in 1961 as a division of the US Naval Oceanographic Office, supported by the Bureau of Commercial Fisheries, the National Science Foundation, the Coast and Geodetic Survey, the Department of the Navy, the Atomic Energy Commission, the US Weather Bureau and other government departments. The NODC is equipped to provide all types of data pertaining to oceanography, including the systems devised for geological and geophysical data storage and retrieval; the archives already contain millions of readings from bathy-thermograph observations taken by monitoring stations and research vessels and the Center will eventually provide indexes to quantitative and qualitative data relating to, for example, magnetism, seismicity, radio activity and heat flow.

975 National Parks Commission, now the Countryside Commission, was set up in 1949 to select and label as national parks the most suitable extensive areas in England and Wales 'for the purpose of preserving and enhancing their natural beauty and promoting their enjoyment by the public'. The Commission maintains close liaison with The Forestry Commission and The Nature Conservancy. A descriptive and illustrated booklet, *The National Parks of England and Wales,* was issued in 1967 (HMSO).

> *Refer also*
> 'Our National Parks', *The geographical magazine,* January 1971.
> W M Condry: *The Snowdonia National Park* (Collins, second edition, 1967).

976 National Research Council of the National Academy of Sciences is the national committee representing the United States of America on the International Geographical Union; the council works through special boards and committees, of which the Division of Earth Sciences is the body of greatest interest to geographers. Section E of the American Association for the Advancement of Science is devoted to geology and geography.

977 'Natural disaster research centers and warning systems—a preliminary survey' (Cambridge, Mass: Smithsonian Institution, 1971), prepared at the request of the Office of Science and Technology of the United Nations, this international survey gives details providing background information to the *ad hoc* Working Group of the ECOSOC Advisory Committee for the Application of Science and Technology to Development, in their task of assessing available resources for the development of an international natural disaster warning system.

978 'Nature and resources: *newsletter about scientific research on environment, resources and conservation of nature',* is the *Bulletin* of the International Hydrological Decade, June 1965–, issued by UNESCO four times a year. The programme of the UNESCO Division of Natural Resources Research in the fields of hydrology, geology, soil sciences, ecology and conservation of nature is covered by general and regional articles, reports of symposia, research and meetings and news items. A section devoted to publications received is very useful. Beginning with the March 1971 issue, the editorial policy was enlarged to include activities connected with inter-governmental programmes and, in addition to the original sub-title, 'Bulletin of the Man and Biosphere Programme' was added.

979 The Nature Conservancy was founded by Royal Charter in 1949 as the official government agency responsible for the conservation of wild life and natural features in Great Britain and for the conduct of research work relating to the conservation of nature and natural resources. Since 1965, it has been a component of the Natural Environment Research Council. Nearly 130 nature reserves come within its jurisdiction and there are major research stations at Monks Wood, Huntingdon, Bangor, Edinburgh, Merlewood, Furzebrook and Norwich. A series of 'Habitat teams' are each concerned with one main type of land, such as mountain and moorland, woodland, coasts or wetlands. The experimental stations include many departments, such as 'geographical sciences' branch, 'climatology section', etc. The Biological Records Centre originated as the distribution maps scheme of the Botanical Society of the British Isles, which produced the *Atlas of the British flora* (*qv*) in 1962 and the Critical Supplement to the Atlas in 1968. Publications include the *Nature Conservancy handbook; Nature Conservancy progress* 1964–1968 and for 1968–1970; the *Monks Wood Experimental Station Report*; and

Nature conservancy: the first twenty one years, 1970. Nature conservancy in Northern Ireland is encouraged by the Amenity Lands Act (Northern Ireland) 1965, by which the Ministry of Development is responsible for matters relating to nature, advised by the Nature Reserves Committee, a statutory body of scientists and laymen. *Nature trails in Northern Ireland* (Belfast: Nature Reserves Committee, 1970) consists of eighteen individual leaves in a pocket folder, each giving details of a nature reserve, numbered on a map.

The Nature Conservancy Council, a new independent body financed by the Department of the Environment, was established in 1973 to take over the conservation functions of the Nature Conservancy, a result of the White Paper, 'Framework for Government research and development', 1972. The Conservancy's research activities were to remain with the Natural Environment Research Council, to be undertaken by the newly formed Institute of Terrestrial Ecology.

Refer also

The countryside in 1970: proceedings of the study conference, November 1963, edited by The Nature Conservancy (HMSO, 1964).

The countryside in 1970: second conference, 1965, *Proceedings: reports of study groups* (Royal Society of Arts, 1965).

Man and environment (National Book League in association with The Nature Conservancy, 1970).

Robert Arvill: *Man and environment: crisis and the strategy of choice* (Penguin, revised edition, 1969).

Garth Christian: *Tomorrow's countryside: the road to the 'seventies* (Murray, 1966).

Nan Fairbrother: *New lives, new landscapes* (Architectural Press, 1970).

Robin Feddon: *The continuing purpose: a history of The National Trust, its aims and work* (Longmans, 1968).

C A W Guissisberg: *Man and wildlife* (Evans, 1970).

John Hillaby: *Nature and man* (Phoenix House, 1960, *Progress of science* series).

Joyce Joffe: *Conservation* (Aldus Books, 1969, *Interdependence in nature* series).

J A Lauwerys: *Man's impact on nature* (Aldus, 1969, *Interdependence in nature* series).

Max Nicholson: *The environmental revolution: a guide for the new masters of the world* (Hodder and Stoughton, 1970).

Keith Reid: *Nature's network* (Aldus Books, 1969, *Interdependence in nature* series).

J Rose, *ed: Technological injury: the effect of technological advances on environment, life and society* (Gordon and Breach, 1969).

W M S Russell: *Man, nature and history* (Aldus Books, 1967, *Modern knowledge* series).

Sir L Dudley Stamp: *Nature conservation in Britain* (Collins, 1969).

Mary Anglemeyer, *comp: Natural resources—a selection of bibliographies* (second edition, 1970).

Catalog of the Conservation Library, Denver Public Library (G K Hall, six volumes, 1974).

980 **'Nature in focus',** bulletin of the European Information Centre for Nature Conservation, Council of Europe, is published in English and French; articles, illustrated with photographs, are international in scope and news of projects in all parts of the world is presented non-technically.

981 **'The nature of geography:** *a critical survey of current thought in the light of the past',* by Richard Hartshorne (Association of American Geographers, 1939; reprinted, 1956) is a scholarly assessment, which will surely remain a classic work. In 1959, the author published *Perspective on the nature of geography,* which brought up to date both his and others' thinking on the subject.

982 **'Nederlands Historisch Scheepvaartmuseum catalogus der bibliotheek,** 1960, is distributed by N Israel, Amsterdam, in two volumes, with fifty-four reproductions of title-pages, plates, maps and globes. The library is strong in material relating to the early and later voyages, travels, history and art of navigation, atlases, maritime history and law, ship construction, cartography, including the important collection of early globes. The catalogue was compiled by V Cannenburg, including bibliographical descriptions of nearly thirteen thousand items, together with full indices of personal and geographical names.

983 **'Netherlands India: a study of plural economy',** by J S Furnivall (CUP, 1939, reprinted, 1967), begins with comments on the geography, political geography and the peoples of the area, including a chapter on the East and notes on the East India Company, 1600–1800. There is a 'List of general references' and a glossary.

984 'Netherlands journal of economic and social geography' (*Tijdschrift voor economische en sociale geografie*), is published by the Royal Dutch Geographical Society Editorial Committee in six fascicules a year, illustrated with many figures and sketchmaps.
Refer also
Frank E Huggett: *The modern Netherlands* (Pall Mall, 1971).
A compact geography of the Netherlands (The Hague: NV Cartografisch Instituut, Bootsma, 1970), prepared by Utrecht State University, with a wall map.

985 'Network analysis in geography', by Peter Haggett and Richard Chorley (Arnold, 1969), was designed as supplementary reading to *Locational analysis in human geography* (*qv*), forming the first of a trilogy of volumes dealing with spatial structures of direct concern to geographers. In the first part, three main topics are examined—topological and geometrical characteristics, evaluation of network structures and problems of the growth and transformation of networks. Part II, 'Networks as regional system' discusses the interactions between network structure and regional environments with emphasis on concepts of hierarchy, growth and system interactions. Throughout the text the emphasis is on common research problems rather than the specific features of the empirical networks, as, for example, stream patterns or traffic flows. The text is accompanied by more than a hundred figures, specially drawn, and there is an extensive research bibliography.

986 'The new Cambridge modern history atlas', edited by H C Darby and Harold Fullard, was a new compilation, using the most up-to-date cartographic techniques. With special emphasis on North America, Latin America, the Far East and Australasia, particularly economic and social conditions, double spreads are used to great effect. Maps are arranged on an area basis, as far as possible to the same scale and chronologically within each group. Hill shading is used where especially applicable.

987 'The new contour dictionary' (Harrap, 1971), compiled by J B Goodson and J A Morris, replaces *The contour dictionary*. More than a hundred excerpts from Ordnance Survey maps in full colour are included, six full-page maps in colour and extensive use of small excerpts with reference to contour patterns. Exercises and simple mapping techniques have been introduced, incorporating metric units of length and area.

988 'New geographical literature and maps', begun by the Royal Geographical Society in 1951 and now issued twice a year, in June and December, is a classified list of accessions to the Society's Library and Map Room. From 1958, the scope was increased to include all articles contained in twenty of the most important geographical periodicals in English, French and German, and a selection made from 150 other titles. An annual list of completed geographical theses has been added since 1960. A reading list is included on a topical subject, also notes on books not reviewed in *The geographical journal*. Each number now includes new books, all new atlases and maps received by the Society and a reference list of the most important articles drawn from about 130 periodicals in all the principle languages. A special edition on gummed paper is available.

989 'The new Israel atlas: *Bible to present day'*, compiled by Zev Vilnay (H A Humphrey Limited, 1968), was published to mark the twentieth anniversary of the establishment of the State of Israel. Three thousand years of history are represented in maps, almost all with explanatory texts by Dr Vilnay recording the development of the people, settlement patterns and economic activities. Arranged in four sections, the maps, by Carta of Jerusalem, cover the geography of modern Israel, the struggle for independence, history from Biblical times to 1918 and proposals for a Jewish state. Appended is a gazetteer of settlements, with foundation dates. Photographs and drawings are included and the presentation of the material is remarkably objective.

990 'The new large shining sea-torch' *(De Nieuwe Groot Ligtende Zeefakkel)*, prepared by Johannes and Gerard van Keulen, 1716–1753, was reproduced in three volumes, 1969–1970 by Theatrum Orbis Terrarum Limited, Amsterdam. This atlas is considered by experts as the most attractive, reliable and informative of sea atlases. The original folio volumes contain more than 240 double-page charts showing in detail all the navigable waters, coasts, river estuaries, inlets and harbours known in the first half of the eighteenth century. The charts are decorated with ships, sea-gods and mermaids, as well as with representations of local trades and industries in the ports to which the charts refer. Successive editions of the work show many alterations and improvements. The six original sections were 'The Eastern and Northern navigation', 1728; 'The Western navigation', 1728; 'The Mediterranean', 1716; 'The West-Indies and North America', 1728; 'The Atlantic navigation', 1728; 'The Indian Ocean and South-East Asia', 1753. An introduction to the reproduction was written by Dr C Koeman; the paper for the atlas was manufactured especially to match the tint, texture and thickness of the paper used for the original edition.

991 'New towns of the Middle Ages: *town plantation in England, Wales and Gascony* (Lutterworth Press, 1967), by Maurice Beresford, deals in detail with this topic, illustrated with sketchmaps and diagrams. Chapters 15 to 17 are annotated gazetteers for the three countries. There are frequent references in the text.

992 'The new world': *problems in political geography,* by Isaiah Bowman (*qv*), stemmed from the Versailles Peace Conference in 1919, at which Bowman headed the American delegation (World Book Company, 1921; fourth edition, 1928). The work presents a balanced and broad outlook and, in several editions, made a great impression throughout the world.

993 New York Public Library, Map Division of the Research Libraries has maintained a dictionary catalogue of holdings. Some 175 thousand cards list maps and other cartographical material from early American and European rarities to up to date representations of all parts of the world, including recently explored areas of the universe. The Map Division holds about 280 thousand sheet maps, being a depository for the United States Army Map Service and for extensive series of maps issued by foreign governments. G K Hall reproduced the catalogue in ten volumes in 1970.

994 'New Zealand contemporary dictionary', (Whitcombe and Tombs, 1968) published in association with Collins, contains more than sixty thousand references. A special feature is a supplement giving distinctive New Zealand and Australian terms.

995 'New Zealand geographer', official journal of the New Zealand Geographical Society, has witnessed the expansion of geographical studies in the Dominion, from 1944; edited from the University of Otago, it is intended to meet the requirements of university students and teachers, also with the wider aim of 'satisfying the common curiosity' in the human geography of New Zealand. It has appeared half-yearly since 1945 and each issue has contained articles contributed by specialists on geographical subjects mainly dealing with New Zealand, Australia and the Pacific Islands. A feature, 'Geographic notebook', provides a valuable commentary on themes of current interest, while generous space is usually given to reviews of relevant publications.

Refer also

Muriel F Lloyd Prichard: *An economic history of New Zealand to 1939* (Collins, 1970).

996 New Zealand Geographical Society, as a project, began in 1939 at Christchurch, when a group of enthusiasts formed what in due course became the Canterbury branch. The Society was founded in 1944 at the University of Auckland, with branches at Auckland and Manawatu. In addition to the chief periodical, *New Zealand geographer (qv)*, a *Record of proceedings* is issued as required, *Special publications* series from 1950 and a *Reprint* series, comprising selected articles from the *New Zealand geographer*. A *Research* series is planned to include not only original research, but special lectures and studies.

997 Newbigin, Marion Isabel (1869–1934) came to geographical studies through biology, succeeding J Arthur Thomson as lecturer in biology and zoology in the extra-mural medicine school for women at Edinburgh. Thereafter, as writer and teacher, her influence on geographic thought and methodology was very great, especially in biogeography and in the regional study of Mediterranean lands. From 1902 to her death, she edited *The Scottish geographical magazine (qv)*, and made it a leading national periodical; an annual Newbigin Prize is offered by the Royal Scottish Geographical Society for the best essay in Scotland suitable for publication in the magazine. Among the most outstanding of her published books were: *An introduction to physical geography*, 1912; *Animal geography: the faunas of the natural regions of the globe*, 1913; *Geographical aspects of Balkan problems in their relation to the Great European War*, 1915; *Frequented ways: a general survey of the landforms, climate and vegetation of western Europe . . .* , 1922 and *Plant and animal geography*,

490

reprinted by Methuen, 1961; *Mediterranean lands: an introductory study in human and historical geography*, 1924; and *Southern Europe: a regional and economic geography of the Mediterranean lands*, of which a third edition was prepared by Harrison Church in 1949.

998 **'Newsletters on stratigraphy'**, published by Brill of Leiden, was designed as a forum for the exchange of information on topics of general stratigraphical interest. It includes articles, preferably in English, but also, on occasion, in French, German or Spanish, on such subjects as descriptions of new stratotypes, the subdivision of stratigraphical units and discussions of stratigraphical boundaries; it provides an opportunity also for the publication of comments on and critiques of articles of international interest. The chief editor is Gerd Luttig, assisted by a distinguished team of associate editors.

999 **'Nigeria: a guide to official publications'**, compiled by S B Lock-wood (Library of Congress, General reference and bibliography division, 1966), contains 2,451 entries, mainly references relating to the period 1861–1965 by both the British administration in Nigeria and the Nigerian federal and regional governments; also to selected works on Nigeria issued in the United Kingdom. About a hundred other entries refer to the Cameroons, published by the British administration, the League of Nations and the United Nations.

1000 **Norden, John** (1548–1625 or 1626), topographer and cartographer, contributed greatly to contemporary knowledge of the country. His county maps of England are most informative, especially those for Middlesex, Hertfordshire, Essex, Surrey, Sussex and Hampshire; they were the first to show roads. His estate surveys remain particularly important. The *Speculum Britanniae* was an ambitious project, of which only parts on Middlesex and Hertfordshire were actually published in his lifetime, but his notes, distance tables and 'thumb-nail' maps continued to form the basis for further work for a long time afterwards. His maps were used in the 1607 edition of Camden's *Britannia* (*qv*) and later also by Speed in his *Theatre of Great Britain*.

    Refer also

        William Ravenhill: 'John Norden's Map of Cornwall: a problem in the historical cartography of South-West England', *The cartographic journal*, December 1970.

1001 'Nordic hydrology', published by the Joint Committee for a Nordic Hydrological Journal, was created by the National Committees for the International Hydrological Decade in Denmark, Norway and Sweden and the Geophysical Society of Finland. The scope includes surface-water hydrology, groundwater hydrology, hydrometeorology, snow and ice and hydromechanics, with an emphasis on the study of the hydrological cycle and the process involved. One issue is being published during the year, 1970–.

1002 'Norge', in four volumes, by J W Cappelens, 1963, is an encyclopedic work, magnificently illustrated and containing a superb atlas, the result of co-operation between the Norwegian Geographical Institute, the Army Map Service in Washington and the Esselte AB Kartografiska Institutet, Stockholm. Volume 1 treats of Norway regionally and systematically; volumes 2 and 3 are a geographical encyclopedia of Norway and volume 4 is a historical survey entitled 'Norway in maps', in which are several reproductions of early maps of the country and a sixty-four page atlas. The whole work is well documented, with indexes, a gazetteer, list of sources and a glossary of Lapp terms.

1003 'The North Sea', by George Morey (Muller, 1968) is one of the few texts devoted to this sea, except for specialist hydrographic studies and reports, in spite of its importance through the centuries to the countries bordering on it. The evolution of the Sea is first discussed, followed by an account of the early invaders who crossed it and the development of fishing and trading links. Many details are given concerning individual ports. Photographs and sketch-maps are included, also a bibliography of general works touching on the subject.

1004 'Northern geographical essays in honour of G H J Daysh' (Newcastle-upon-Tyne, Oriel Press, 1966, for the Department of Geography), contains twenty-two essays, a festschrift for Professor Henry Daysh on his retirement. Emphasis is on northern regional geography, but eight of the essays deal with overseas topics.

1005 'Northernmost Labrador mapped from the air' was prepared by Alexander Forbes and others (American Geographical Society, Special publication, no 22, 1938); the work, with six sheet maps of Northernmost Labrador and navigational notes on the Labrador coast, is published in a slip-case. The text includes photographs with explanatory text on narratives and expeditions carried out in the area, the mapping, geology and physiography and phytogeographical observations in Labrador, with an appendix 'An impression of Northernmost Labrador as viewed from the air' and notes on place-names.

1006 'Norway exports', 1957–, the journal of The Export Council of Norway, established by Royal Decree in 1945 to promote Norwegian exports, is a well produced, fully illustrated production containing feature articles and notes about Norwegian products and suppliers. The advertisements are valuable to those interested. Other publications, in English, German and French, circulate information on new products and surveys; and a Directory of Norwegian products and exports, in five languages, gives 2,500 firms and their products.

1007 'Nuevo atlas geográfico de la Argentina', produced by Ediziones Geográficas Peuser, Buenos Aires, 1969, was compiled by José Anesi and is now in an eighth edition. Maps are printed on the recto only, with notes; some are large, folded maps. The layer colour, with contours, shows up particularly well on the coastline, with its islands, and the complex relief of the Andes.

1008 Obruchev, V A (1863–1956) specialised in geology and physical geography, playing a leading part in the development of interest in the earth sciences in Russia. His work on the geomorphology of sand deserts and on the alluvial origin of the Kara Kum sands, also his classification of sand relief into four sub-divisions—barchans, sand mounds, sand ridges and sand steppe—are still accepted. In addition to academic teaching, he carried out a number of surveys and expedition work; his three-volume book, *Frontier Dzungaria, 1912–1940,* embodied the results of research, as did *The geological map of the Lena gold-bearing region*, completed in four volumes. The *Field geology*, in two volumes, ran to four editions, and *Geologie von Sibirien*, later expanded to three volumes, has remained a classic. He wrote also *The history of the geological exploration of Siberia*, in five volumes, completed in 1950. He was an editor of *Izvestiya*, Geological Series. During the later years of his life, he continued to write—*Eastern Mongolia*, for example, accounts of his travels and some novels based on his experiences, such as *Gold seekers in the desert*. It has been estimated that his geological surveys covered some forty-six thousand square miles and his contribution to the exploration of Asia is incalculable. There is a substantial body of literature, in Russian, on his life and work.

1009 'Ocean wave statistics: *a statistical survey of wave characteristics estimated visually from Voluntary Observing Ships sailing along the shipping routes of the world'* was edited by N Hogbem and F E Lumb (HMSO, 1967, for the Ministry of Technology, National Physical Laboratory), to provide systematic information about environmental conditions for use in research on the sea-going qualities of ships. Nearly two million sets of observations on sea conditions were reported over a period of eight years, 1953 to 1961. Several interested organisations helped in the task of preparing and presenting the material. Data Tables are prefaced by introduction and explanation and there is a short list of references.

1010 'Oceanography—*list of terms relating to oceanography and marine resources'* (Office of Conference Services, Terminology Section, United Nations Secretariat, Geneva: *Terminology bulletin* no 265, March 1971) comprises more than four hundred pages of vocabulary in English, French, Spanish, Russian and Chinese, totalling some three thousand items, which, together with synonyms, furnish over four thousand technical terms dealing with such major fields of marine science and technology as geology and geophysics, meteorology, the physics and chemistry of the oceans, marine biology and ecology, the oceans as a source of food, including fisheries technology and the exploitation of the mineral wealth of the sea. Arrangement is alphabetical and a list of acronyms and abbreviations of organisations and programmes concerned with oceanography is given.

1011 O'Dell, Andrew Charles (1907–1966) was a leading academic geographer, especially in Scotland, his particular achievement being the establishment and direction of the Department of Geography in the University of Aberdeen, from 1945. He wrote constantly on the geography of Scotland, notably *The highlands and islands of Scotland*, published with Kenneth Walton, in 1962; he also edited the British Association Aberdeen volume in 1963. Another abiding interest was Scandinavian geography, revealed in his early work on the Land Utilization Survey of Zetland, in his MSc thesis, *The historical*

494

geography of the Shetland Islands, 1933, published in 1939, and in *The Scandinavian world,* 1958. *Railways and geography,* 1956, 1971, made a substantial contribution to the growing literature on transport geography.

1012 Office de la Recherche Scientifique et Technique Outre-Mer (ORSTOM) issues valuable series of publications for geographers, for example, Pierre Vennetier: *Pointe-Noire et la façade maritime du Congo-Brazzaville,* a study in depth, illustrated with photographs, maps and diagrams and having a sound bibliography.

1013 'Official map publications: *a historical sketch, and a bibliographical handbook of current maps and mapping services in the United States, Canada, Latin America, France, Great Britain, Germany and certain other countries',* by Walter Thiele (American Library Association, 1938), is a comprehensive guide to its date.

1014 Ogilby, John (1600–1676), one of the great cartographers who helped to improve topographic mapping in Britain, gained official recognition with the title King's Cosmographer and Geographic Printer. Following on John Norden's work, he established roads as important features of maps. Among his publications were a series of atlases and maps and a road book, which describes the chief roads in England and Wales, from original surveys, published in 1675 as *Britannia, or an illustration of the Kingdom of England and Dominion of Wales . . .*

1015 Ogilvie, Alan Grant (1887–1954) made great contributions to academic geography, particularly at the School of Geography, University of Edinburgh, and exerted a widespread influence on standards of geographic scholarship and map production in the course of his work with the Royal Scottish Geographical Society, the International Club in Edinburgh, the National Committee for Geography, the British Association, the Institute of British Geographers, the Geographical Association, the American Geographical Society and the IGU. He wrote extensively, edited *Great Britain: essays in regional geography,* 1928, and contributed to the foundation work on the Map of Hispanic America 1:1M. *Geographical essays in memory of Alan G Ogilvie,* edited by R Miller and J Wreford Watson (Nelson, 1959), contains 'Essays on Scotland' and 'Essays oversea'.

1016 'On the structure and distribution of coral reefs: *also geological observations on the volcanic islands and parts of South America visited during the voyage of HMS Beagle'*, Charles Darwin's classic account, was published by Ward Lock in 1890 (Minerva Library of Famous Books) and reproduced in paperback in 1963, with a foreword by H W Menard; the text includes illustrations and maps.

Refer also

The Darwin reader, edited Marston Bates and Philip S Humphreys (Macmillan, 1957).

W M Davis: *The coral reef problem* (New York: American Geographical Society, 1928, special publication no 9 in the Shaler Memorial series).

J S Gardiner: *Coral reefs and atolls: being a course of lectures delivered at the Lowell Institute at Boston*, February 1930 (Macmillan, 1931).

D R Stoddart: 'Darwin's impact on geography', *Annals,* Association of American Geographers, 1966.

D R Stoddart: and Sir Maurice Yonge, *ed: Regional variation in Indian Ocean coral reefs*: Symposium of the Zoological Society of London (Academic Press, 1971).

F Wood-Jones: *Corals and atolls: their history, description, theories of their origin both before and since that of Darwin* (1910).

1017 'Orb', the journal of the Geographical Society of the University of Aberdeen, was founded primarily as a platform for undergraduate comment, covering a wide variety of topics within the subject of geography.

1018 'Orbis geographicus', a world directory of geography, was compiled and edited on behalf of the IGU by E Meynen in co-operation with the National Committees and published as a special supplement to the *Geographisches Taschenbuch*, 1960/61 (Franz Steiner Verlag, Wiesbaden). The work, which is in English and French, with the introduction also in German, includes information on the IGU and National Committees, on geographical societies, cartographical societies, geographical chairs and institutes at university level, official agencies, hydrographic offices, cartographic and topographic surveys, important map collections, national authorities and committees on geographical names; also a list of professional geographers, grouped according to their country of residence, with their academic qualifications and appointments. At the International Geographic Congress in Stockholm, it was proposed to publish *Orbis geographicus* every eight years; more frequent revision has proved desirable, however; part I was reissued in 1964 and part II, the 'Who is who of geographers', in 1966. A further revised edition, also in two volumes, covers 1968 to 1970.

1019 Ordnance Survey of Great Britain, the official cartographic agency, was established as the Trigonometrical Survey in 1791, being the outcome of survey operations for the linking of England and France by Cassini and William Roy in 1787. The first task of the Survey was the making of a one-inch map of the country, beginning with the south-eastern counties of England. After the Napoleonic Wars, civil uses of maps became increasingly important and in 1825 the maximum effort was transferred to Ireland to make a six inch to the mile map of the whole of that country for evaluation purposes; this survey was completed about 1840. The subsequent publication history of the various series of topographical maps has been complex, sheetlines and symbols of relief representation being revised to suit changing circumstances and advances in technique.

The Ordnance Survey is responsible for the official surveying and mapping of Great Britain and the Isle of Man, including geodetic surveys and the associated scientific work, topographical surveys and production of maps at appropriate scales from these surveys. Later emphasis has been on restoration, which includes bringing the nineteenth and early twentieth century 1:2,500 surveys up to date and compiling them on a national sheet line system; also making entirely new surveys of the major towns at 1:1,250 scale and of mountain and moorland areas at six inches to one mile. All the new and revised maps produced in this way are kept up to date by a system of continuous revision which ensures that changes on the ground are surveyed soon after they occur. Once National Grid plans at 1:1,250 or 1:2,500 scales have been completed in a locality, the Ordnance Survey appoints surveyors to keep a master copy, called 'field sheets', of each plan up to date. Copies made directly from these sheets may be bought by members of the public who require survey information in advance of the publication of revised editions. The standard of completeness of an Advance Revision Information Sheet is not the same as that of the printed map; but all important changes will have been entered. Shortly to be offered are the principal roads, town and coastline at the 1:625,000 scale.

Discussion has recently been taking place concerning the future of the 1:25,000 series. The Department of the Environment is reviewing the public sector need for this series as part of a review of the entire role of the Ordnance Survey. The new 1:50,000 series (about 1¼ inches to the mile) is replacing the one-inch series. The Sheets covering Wales, with England south of a Morecambe-Bridlington line, were published in 1974 and the northern sheets in 1976. Blue motorways and orange town infilling make urban areas easier to read. Spot heights and contour values are shown to the nearest metre, while distances at sheet edges to nearby towns are shown in both kilometres and miles; major changes have been updated.

In 1968, the Ordnance Survey moved into a new building, functionally designed for it, officially opened in May 1969, on the outskirts of Southampton, thus bringing together the whole of the department except for the regional surveying organisation. An ICL 1902 computer was installed, replacing the smaller punched card system used previously; it carries out calculations from aerial surveys, minor control and levelling and produces management statistics. The Survey is now able also to supply magnetic tape for drawing a map of the United Kingdom coastline digitised at the scale of 1:1,250,000. The Survey continues to study the possible application of automation to cartography. Experimental work has been concentrated on digitising contours directly by encoders attached to the output shafts of stereo-plotting machines with the object of compiling a contour data bank which could be used, with automatic plotting equipment, to produce contours for 1:25,000 and smaller scale maps. The Survey has sought the co-operation of the resources of the Experimental Cartography Unit of the Royal College of Art to investigate some of the difficulties involved in automation and has since 1969 been adjusting to metrication, but it will be many years before the conversion is complete.

The fifty-inches-to-one-mile plans cover most of the large towns and will eventually cover all towns with a population of over 20,000 and other areas of dense population. There are also a number of series at intermediate scales and several special maps such as the Route Planning Map, first issued in 1964. The set of historical and archaeological maps has proved very successful, including 'Britain in the Dark Ages', 'Southern Britain in the Iron Age', 'Ancient Britain', 'Roman Britain', 'Monastic Britain' and 'Hadrian's Wall' second edition, 1972, and, completing the series, in 1974, 'Britain before the Norman Conquest', following in time 'Britain in the Dark Ages',

498

with explanatory text. Three pamphlets issued by the Directorate General of the Ordnance Survey provided guides to understanding the map series, *A description of Ordnance Survey small-scale maps*, 1947, reprinted with an addendum, 1951; *A description of Ordnance Survey medium-scale maps*, 1949, reprinted with corrections, 1951; and *A description of Ordnance Survey large-scale plans*, 1947.

The Survey publishes geological maps on behalf of the Institute for Geological Sciences and soil maps for the Soil Survey of England and Wales and the Macaulay Institute for Soil Research (Scotland). New maps, especially at a large scale, are in constant demand by local authorities, architects and the legal profession. Large-scale maps have been provided from the 1971 Census; the provision of maps and copies of the field plots make it possible for the first time to record a National Grid reference for every dwelling. Outline maps are issued as well at various small scales; they are printed in grey or black and make useful bases for planning or recording purposes. From January 1971 the wholesale distribution of Ordnance Survey maps in England and Wales was undertaken by the Survey direct from Southampton; Thomas Nelson and Sons Limited, of Edinburgh, continues as the distribution centre for Scotland. The standard copyright regulations and licence conditions apply to the reproduction of Ordnance Survey materials.

From 1969, in collaboration with the Ordnance Survey, David and Charles of Newton Abbot have been republishing in exact facsimile the later printings of the first edition of the One Inch Ordnance Survey maps, covering England and Wales in ninety-seven sheets; later the Scottish sheets will be done. The reprint is edited by Dr J B Harley, of the Department of Geography, University of Liverpool, who is providing introductory notes for each sheet, designed to assist in the dating and interpretation of the maps. The sheets will be marketed either flat or folded, within covers; an index map is available, showing the arrangement of the reprint. Also in facsimile reproduction is 'Ancient map of Kent', drawn by Philip Symonson, 1596, as published by Stent about 1650; size and detail of this map was superior to any English county map of its time. A note on the history of the map is printed at the foot of the sheet. The 'Bodleian map of Great Britain' (fourteenth century) has been reproduced in single colour, with the ancient names transcribed in red.

The one hundred and ten sheets of the Old Series Ordnance Survey, together, representing the first overall large scale map of England and Wales, not only provide therefore an important historic document of interest to the layman, but because they portray a landscape now fast disappearing, are also of great value to students, local historians, historical geographers, countryside planners and ecologists; a reproduction is being undertaken and every care is being given to ensure that the sheets selected are of the date of the original publication, or very soon after, including the map sheets of first or early state covering southern Britain and the Mudge map of Kent, now held by the Bodleian Library. Each volume will contain an introductory text by J B Harley and Yolande Jones and will incorporate illustrations of the original surveyor's drawings for the appropriate sheets.

The Council of the Royal Society in 1974 appointed a standing committee to advise it on the requirements of British scientists from the services of Ordnance Survey; the Committee members have been chosen to cover as wide a spectrum of relevant scientific interests as possible consistent with a small committee membership, including the Director General of the Survey. This Committee is one of several recently formed to provide closer contact between the Ordnance Survey and identifiable groups of users of the services of the Survey having common interests. Just as the Royal Society Committee covers the needs of the scientific community, the Standing Committee of Professional Map Users, formed under the aegis of the Royal Institution of Chartered Surveyors, promotes an exchange of information between the Ordnance Survey and professional map users and the Local Authorities' Ordnance Survey Committee provides a forum for consultation and communication between the new Local Authority Associations and the Survey.

The existing services of the Survey may be summed up as follows: control surveys, supply of unpublished survey information, enlargements of large scale plans, reductions, transparencies, microfilms and map mounting. A Map Users Conference meets annually.

From 1885, details of the progress of the Ordnance Survey can be traced through the *Annual reports*. The 1968–69 issue was the first to incorporate the new 'house style' designed by the Central Office of Information. Plates are included showing the programme and progress of publication of map series. Much historical and technical information appears in the *Reports of the departmental committee on the Ordnance Survey*, 1935–38. Early map publications are listed in the *Catalogue of maps*, 1904 and 1920 and a full description of the six-inch and twenty-five-inch maps was given by H St J L Winterbotham in *The national plans*, in the Ordnance Survey *Professional papers*, new series, 16, 1934. A *Publication report* is distributed to those interested, giving exact information on new publications and revisions at all scales, and the 'General information and price list' brochure is frequently revised.

The atlas of Great Britain comprises seventeen quarter-inch maps in a pull-out style; and the *Ordnance Survey gazetteer of Great Britain*, 1969, lists all the names that appear in this atlas, giving National Grid references to all features named.

Field archaeology in Great Britain, partially derived from a professional paper formerly published by HMSO under the title *Field archaeology*, has been completely revised to provide an authoritative work of reference for use in conjunction with Ordnance Survey maps and is now published by the Survey. An *Index to published large scale national grid plans* is produced in loose-leaf form for official use four times a year. It shows by symbols the 1:1,250 and 1:1,250 scale plans that have been published to date but not the date of publication nor the edition of the plans. A series of 'Special leaflets' each concentrates on some interesting feature of the history or development of the Survey.

Refer also

History of the retriangulation of Great Britain, 1935–62 (HMSO for the Ordnance Survey, 1968).

The historian's guide to Ordnance Survey maps, published for The Standing Conference for Local History by The National Council of Social Service, 1964, from a series of articles originally in *The amateur historian*.

Ordnance Survey, its history, organisation and work (OS, 1969).

John Aylward: 'The retail distribution of Ordnance Survey maps and plans in the latter half of the nineteenth century: a map-seller's view', *The cartographic journal*, June 1971.

R V Clarke: 'The use of watermarks in dating old series one-inch Ordnance Survey maps', *The cartographic journal*, December 1969.

Col Sir Charles Close: *The early years of the Ordnance Survey*, 1926; reprinted, with an introduction and index by J B Harley, by David and Charles.

Héloise Collier: 'A short history of Ordnance Survey contouring with particular reference to Scotland', *The cartographic journal*, June 1972.

501

R C A Edge: 'Ordnance Survey at home', *The geographical magazine*, October 1969.

G A Hardy: 'The Ordnance Survey 1:50,000 map series', *The geographical journal*, June 1974.

J B Harley: 'Error and revision in early Ordnance Survey maps', *The cartographic journal*, December 1968.

J B Harley: 'Place-names on the early Ordnance Survey maps of England and Wales', *The cartographic journal*, December 1971.

Capt. M St G Irwin: 'Developments in automated cartography at the Ordnance Survey', *The cartographic journal*, December 1971.

B Lockey: *The interpretation of Ordnance Survey maps and geographical pictures*, sixth edition, 1961.

Ian Mumford and Peter K Clark: 'Engraved Ordnance Survey one-inch maps—the methodology of dating', *The cartographic journal*, December 1968.

F M Sexton: 'The adoption of the Metric System in the Ordnance Survey', *The geographical journal*, September 1968.

Lt Col W R Taylor: 'The Ordnance Survey of Northern Ireland: an outline of its history and present mapping tasks', *The cartographic journal*, December 1969.

E P J Williams: 'Digitized Ordnance Survey maps', *The geographical magazine*, August 1972.

1020 Organisation for Economic Co-operation and Development (OECD) was formed in 1948 between the following countries: Austria, Belgium, Canada, Denmark, Finland, France, Germany, Greece, Iceland, Ireland, Italy, Japan, Luxembourg, Netherlands, Norway, Portugal, Spain, Sweden, Switzerland, Turkey, the United Kingdom and the United States of America; Australia participated in the work of the Development Assistance Committee and Jugoslavia was a full member for confrontation of economic policies, scientific and technical matters, agriculture, fisheries questions, technical assistance and productivity and had observer status in other matters. The later body, with the title The Organisation for European Economic Co-operation (OEEC), came into being to allocate Marshall Plan aid and to work together for post-war recovery; the scope of the organisation was widened to include the dissemination of relevant information in 1961 and to provide a forum for the exchange of ideas and experiences. In the course of its work, a vast number of publications of central importance were produced. The Organisation's Publications Office in Paris and the Center in Washington produced a Catalogue, which is the key to a mine of information. Ten main groups of publications are distinguished: Economics; International trade and payments; Statistics; Development; Agriculture, food, fisheries; Energy; Industry, transport, tourism; Manpower and social affairs; Education and science; General information. Each section is preceded by a short introduction and full annotations to the entries are given as necessary. The *Catalogue* was not published every year, supplements being issued in the intervals. For particulars relating to the entire range of publications between 1948 and 1968, the 1958, 1966 and 1968 catalogues should be consulted.

1021 'Oriental and Asia bibliography: *an introduction with some reference to Africa*', compiled by J D Pearson (Crosby Lockwood, 1966), is concerned with books, whether written in indigenous languages or in European, which relate to this enormous region. Three parts deal with institutions producing literature, the bibliographical apparatus available for control and use of this literature and the libraries and archives where the literature is stored. A vast amount of information is concentrated herein, together with commentary and discussion of problems involved. Appendices set out 'Book-sellers in Asia' and a 'List of works referred to in the text'.

Refer also

J D Pearson: 'Oriental and Asian bibliography', *Progress in library science*, 1967.

1022 'The origin of continents and oceans', by Alfred Wegener, was translated into English by J G A Skerl from the third German edition (Methuen, 1924) and from the fourth German edition by John Biram in 1968 (New York: Dover Publications). The results of *The theory of continental drift* symposium on the origin and movements of land masses both inter-continental and intra-continental, as proposed by Alfred Wegener, were published in 1928 by the American Association of Petroleum Geologists.

Refer also

American Philosophical Society: *Gondwanaland revisited: new evidence for continental drift*, 1968.

A L Du Toit: *Our wandering continents: an hypothesis of continental drift* (*qv*).

A Hallam: *From continental drift to plate tectonics: a revolution in the earth sciences* (OUP, 1973).

S K Runcorn, *ed*: *Continental drift* (New York: Academic Press, 1962).

A symposium on continental drift, held by the Royal Society in 1965 (*Philosophical Transactions*, no 1088).

D H and M P Tarling: *Continental drift: a study of the earth's moving surface* (Bell, 1971).

D H Tarling and S K Runcorn, *ed*: *Implications of continental drift to the earth sciences* (Academic Press, two volumes, 1973).

E G R Taylor: 'The origins of continents and oceans: a seventeenth century controversy', *The geographical journal*, December 1950.

J T Wilson: 'Continental drift', *The scientific American*, April 1963.

J T Wilson: *Continents adrift*: readings from *The scientific American*, introduced by J Tuzo Wilson (Freeman, 1972).

1023 Ortelius, Abraham (1527–1598) became a cartographer and map publisher, probably under the influence of Mercator. His earliest known work dates from about 1564, but his greatest achievement was the *Theatrum orbis terrarum*, which was the first collection of maps known to have been brought together on a scholarly method. The seventy maps were carefully selected, as the long list of 'acknowledgements' shows. Before his death, about thirty editions had been published, increasing in size; an English edition was published in 1606 and his final Latin edition in 1612. The 1606 edition has been reprinted, with a bibliographical note by R A Skelton.

1024 'Our developing world', the well-known work by Sir Dudley Stamp (Faber, 1960), appeared in a Faber paperback edition in 1969, with the statistics brought up to date by Audrey N Clark.

1025 'Our wandering continents: *an hypothesis of continental drift'* by Alex L Du Toit (Oliver and Boyd, 1937, 1957), was dedicated to Alfred Wegener and considers the controversial theory he propounded under the following headings: 'Current theories versus Continental drift', 'Historical and geological principles', 'Gondwana', 'Comparisons between the fragments of Gondwana', 'Laurasia', 'The tertiary history of the lands', 'The oceans', 'The paramorphic zone and its import', 'Application of the paramorphic principle', 'Past climates and the Poles', 'Biological relationships', 'Geodetic evidence', 'The pattern of the earth's orogenies' and 'Causes of continental drift'. There are a number of small sketch-maps and diagrams throughout the text, a glossary of technical terms relating to the subject and a substantial bibliography.

Refer also

G D Garland, *ed: Continental drift* (University of Toronto in co-operation with The Royal Society of Canada, 1966).

See also

'*The origin of continents and oceans*'.

1026 Overseas Geological Surveys, founded in 1947 by the Colonial Office, became in 1961 part of the Department of Technical Co-operation, then of the Ministry of Overseas Development. Work includes the assessment of mineral resources by geological mapping and other scientific techniques, in close co-operation with national governmental geological surveys, in Commonwealth and other countries. Regular publications include the progress bulletins, *Overseas geology and mineral resources* and *A statistical summary of the world mineral industry*, which records world production, imports and exports.

1027 'Overseas railways', a Railway Gazette publication since 1961, is divided into six sections, concerning the Far East, Africa, Europe, the Americas, Australia and New Zealand. Illustrations and sketch-maps in the text usefully support the text.

1028 'The Oxford atlas', 1951, fifth reprint with revision 1963, further printings 1971, 1973, was conceived after the second world war when the need for a new atlas became pressing; a fresh approach and new layout were necessary to illustrate the altered emphases in the strategic, political and economic spheres. There are 112 pages of six-colour maps and a 90-page gazetteer. Uniformity of scale sequence was aimed at in the atlas, to enable comparison between the countries of each continent, and much thought was given also to projections. A valuable feature of each map is a footnote giving full particulars of the projection used and indicating where to look for scale errors and the corrections to be applied to them. In the revised reprint of 1952, edited by Sir Clinton Lewis and J D Campbell, a section of distribution maps was included, by Professor Linton, of Sheffield University. In these, the more detailed maps are confined to areas where the topics chosen are known with sufficient accuracy to warrant representation at large scales. Contour lines have been omitted and the layer tints are limited to those which could be produced by four colours, light blue, yellow, brown and red. The atlas attempts to distinguish between all-weather and fair-weather roads. English forms of placenames have been used when these are in common use, and geographical terms are translated except when the local form is the more familiar. Derived from *The Oxford atlas* are *The concise Oxford atlas, The Oxford economic atlas of the world* (*qv*) and *The Oxford junior atlas* (*qv*). *The Oxford atlas* is also available in a school edition. The *Oxford world atlas* (*qv*), edited by Saul B Cohen, is the latest addition to the Oxford atlases; this work is 'new' in its aim to provide not only maps of the world but to cater for a world readership. The environment maps, particularly useful, collect together in one map series a number of basic elements which are normally mapped separately.

1029 'The Oxford economic atlas of the world', first published in 1953, went into a second edition in 1959, a third in 1965 and a fourth in 1971. The latest editions of this atlas were entirely revised. They present in map form a selection of world physical, political, social and economic topics that is significantly larger than before and in greater detail; the maps illustrate world patterns and a complementary statistical index gives detailed figures for each country. Data have been obtained in such detail as to allow the portrayal of production both by centre of activity and in precise quantitative terms; for many products the maps now show major world trade flows. The demographic section covers population change, birth and death rates, life expectancy, birth control, migration, accidents, disease, medical services, education and employment; there are also maps showing foreign aid, bilateral trade, political structure and economic alliances. Supplementary tables, notes and economic commentary accompany each section. The regional economic atlases are in series with the general atlas, the complete series comprising *The Middle East and North Africa; The* USSR *and Eastern Europe; Africa; The United States and Canada; Western Europe; Latin America; India, China and Japan; South East Asia; Australia and New Zealand.* In these, general reference maps are followed by topical maps, notes and statistics, bibliographies and gazetteers. *The shorter Oxford economic atlas of the world*, in a second edition, with revisions, 1961, contains all the pages of the parent atlas, in paper covers, but omits the statistical index.

1030 'Oxford economic papers' (new series), of which eight issues appeared at intervals between 1938 and 1947, became a periodical in 1949 and is published three times a year by The Clarendon Press. Originally intended as a channel for publication of articles by Oxford authors, contributions from elsewhere are also welcomed. Most of the articles are concerned with economic and allied subjects. Review articles are included and references are added at the ends of articles as necessary.

1031 'The Oxford junior atlas', when published in 1964, was an entirely new atlas; it was reprinted with revision in 1967. The atlas contained forty-eight pages of seven-colour maps and seven pages of gazetteer. Simplicity and clarity were the aims throughout; most of the maps are double-page spreads, without insets. The series of regional maps are useful; Britain is covered by six regional maps at sixteen miles to the inch. Careful instructions are included for using the atlas and both the planning and selection of content and the imaginative three-dimensional relief representation make this an evocative atlas for use by children. Short descriptions of places were added to the gazetteer entries.

1032 'Oxford New Zealand encyclopaedia' is the fourteenth volume of the *Oxford junior encyclopaedia*, reproduced as a self-contained one-volume work, edited by Laura E Salt and John Pascoe (OUP, 1965). The work includes accounts of all aspects of the country and of the great men who have made it, types of farming and the industries arising from farming, the Maori way of life and culture and New Zealand natural features, flora and fauna. There are figures in the text, some four-colour plates and maps of the North and South Islands and of the distribution of the main types of farming.

1033 'Oxford plastic relief maps' are an imaginative series, particularly designed for educational purposes. Of the world series planned, the map of Great Britain and Northern Ireland, 16 miles to one inch, was the first available, 1964–. The maps are in two series, series 1, an outline edition, and series 2, fully coloured.

1034 'The Oxford school atlas', in the third revised and enlarged edition, 1960, reprinted in 1963 and reprinted again, with revision, in

1970, contains 112 pages of six-colour maps and a 32-page gazetteer. In this new edition, the 1:1M maps of Britain show roads as well as railways; new maps include the Mediterranean and Southern Europe, the Middle East and China, and the section of world maps was extended, incorporating a series of economic maps based on the second edition of *The Oxford economic atlas of the world*. *The Oxford home atlas of the world*, in a third edition with revision, 1963, is the general edition of the school atlas. *The shorter Oxford school atlas* is an abridged version of this atlas, giving the broad essentials of world geographical and topographical information; the third edition, revised in 1960, reprinted 1963, contains sixty-four pages of six-colour maps and short index gazetteer. *The little Oxford atlas*, second edition with revision, 1963, is the general edition of *The shorter Oxford school atlas*, giving world coverage, but with a high proportion devoted to Britain. The hill shading technique of the Cartographic Department of the Clarendon Press has produced some striking three-dimensional relief maps. Special regional editions are available for Australia, New Zealand, Canada and Pakistan.

1035 Oxford system of automatic cartography, developed by D P Bickmore, head of the Cartographic Department of the Clarendon Press, and Dr A R Boyle of Dobbie McInnes (Electronics) Ltd, Glasgow, translates map compilations into high quality reproduction material, through the media of magnetic tape and punched cards. This eliminates repetitive plotting and drawing, expensive camera work and checking; it also enables information from different sources to be accurately co-ordinated. Thus maps can be prepared with greater speed, versatility and accuracy, so that the skilled cartographer is able to concentrate on original preparation and experimental work.

Refer also

D P Bickmore: 'Maps for the computer age', *The geographical magazine*, March 1968.

Rolf Böhme: 'Automatic processing of road data for map revision', *International yearbook of cartography*, 1972.

W D Brookes and K G Pinzke: 'A computer program for three-dimensional presentation of geographic data', *Canadian geographer*, 1971.

J Diello *et al*: 'The development of an automated cartographic system', *The cartographic journal*, June 1969.

Torsten Hägerstrand: 'The computer and the geographer',

Transactions, Institute of British Geographers, December 1967.

Peter Haggett: 'On geographical research in a computer environment', *The geographical journal*, December 1969.

D R Hill and R F Jefferson: 'System considerations for a unified cartographic data bank', *Surveying and mapping*, June 1969.

Naftali Kadmon: 'KOMPLOT "Do-it-yourself" computer cartography', *The cartographic journal*, December 1971.

T Lang: 'Rules for robot draughtsmen', *The geographical magazine*, January 1969.

Michael J McCullagh and Robert J Sampson: 'User desires and graphics capability in the academic environment', *The cartographic journal*, December 1972.

Mark S Monmonier: 'The scope of computer mapping', *Bulletin*, Geography and Map Division, Special Libraries Association, September 1970.

Stig Norbeck and Bengt Roystedt: 'Population maps and computerized map production', *La revue de géographie de Montréal*, 1972.

G Petrie: 'The automatic plotter and its consequences', *Proceedings* of the Edinburgh Cartographic Symposium, Glasgow, 1962.

W R Tobler: 'Automation and cartography', *The geographical review*, 1959.

Pinhas Yoeli: 'An experimental electronic system for converting contours into hill-shaded relief', *International yearbook of cartography*, 1971.

Pinhas Yoeli: 'The logic of automated map lettering', *The cartographic journal*, December 1972.

1036 Oxford University Exploration Club published from 1930 to the second world war, a series of *Annual reports*, and, from 1948–, *Bulletins* reporting on Oxford University expeditions, the majority to Africa or the Far East.

1037 Oxford University Press, in addition to cartographic works, produces frequent monographs and series, at various grades, of interest to geographers. *Oxford books, Geography section*, is a newsheet issued from the Educational Department, presenting a selection of books on applied geography for pupils in middle and upper forms of secondary schools. Catalogues, including several sections of direct interest, are issued two or three times a year, in addition to special subject catalogues, such as the *Some Oxford books 1970–71* on Africa. The OUP also publishes books for specialist organisations such as the International African Institute. The 'Oxford social geographies' series is in three sections: *Work and leisure* introduces basic concepts and ideas which, in the subsequent series are built up and expanded by means of sample studies taken from Britain and the rest of the world. *The changing world* selects major environmental themes—urban growth, industry, transport and the changing countryside—which, although applied to Britain, are also of relevance to the rest of the world; while *Regions of Britain* provides detailed local studies which vividly illustrate on a small scale both the geographical method and the problems and concepts illustrated in previous volumes. The Oxford series devoted to fauna and flora are all of interest, particularly *The Oxford book of food plants,* by S G Harrison and others. The series *Oxford in Asia historical reprints* will eventually build up a considerable history on Asia, beginning with Thomas Forrest's *A voyage to New Guinea and the Moluccas 1774–1776* (1779; second edition 1780); the second was the text used for reproduction, introduced by Dr D K Bassett.

    See also   Clarendon Press, Oxford.

1038 Oxford University School of Geography was established in 1899 under the influence of Sir Halford Mackinder, with a Chair of Geography in 1932. The library contains more than twenty-six thousand volumes, some forty thousand maps and atlases, including colonial survey maps and a large collection of Canadian and Australian material, world gazetteers, including a particularly fine set for India, and large collections of pamphlets, reprints and periodicals, making a fine collection for study purposes. For a note on the Oxford special classification for geography, *see* the entry on classification. The map curator, Miss E Buxton, compiled a list of geological, climatic, economic, population and other thematic maps published after 1940 available in the Oxford libraries.

    Refer also

    Juliet Williams: 'The first department', *The geographical magazine*, January 1972.

1039 'Oxford world atlas', edited by Saul B Cohen and produced by the Cartographic Department of the Clarendon Press, 1973, com-

510

prises an attempt to introduce a new approach to the mapping of environment, a more adequate teaching tool and learning aid. The various series of maps are interconnected and each series brings together a number of basic elements which have normally been mapped separately. The individual series begins each with 'The physical and human environmental' aspect, followed by 'The regional topographic series'. 'The urban map series', 'The world thematic series' and 'The regional thematic series'. Contrasts in texture, continuity between symbols, uniformity of scales, stacking and other devices have been used to emphasise data against the physical or other background features. Included are maps of the three main oceans at approximately 1:50M. and a 'General reference map' at the beginning and gazetteers at the end.

1040 'The Pacific Basin: *a history of its geographical exploration*', edited by Herman R Friis (American Geographical Society of New York, 1967), was sponsored by the National Science Foundation as 'an outgrowth of a symposium on "Highlights of the history of scientific geographical exploration in relation to the development of the Pacific map", held as part of the Tenth Pacific Science Congress meeting at the University of Hawaii in Honolulu, August 21–September 6, 1961'. The text is an expanded and revised version of the original papers and there are extensive notes and references for each section. All aspects are considered, including 'The art and science of navigation in relation to geographical exploration before 1900', map compilation, explanation of all parts of the region and, finally, 'The intellectual assumptions and consequences of geographical exploration in the Pacific'. There are a number of reproductions and maps throughout the text.

1041 'A Pacific bibliography: *printed matter relating to the native peoples of Polynesia, Melanesia and Micronesia*', compiled by C R H Taylor (Polynesian Society, Wellington, 1951; revised and enlarged edition, Oxford, Clarendon Press, 1965), has been accepted as the standard bibliography. The scope of the work embraces the most important writings on the peoples of the Pacific islands, including New Zealand, entries being classified by island group and by subject, with appendices and exhaustive index. In general, entries are complete to 1960, references amounting to more than sixteen thousand. The work is well guided and with a comprehensive index.

Refer also

Michael Levison *et al*: *The Settlement of Polynesia: a computer Simulation* (University of Minnesota Press; OUP, 1973).

1042 'Pacific island bibliography', compiled by Floyd M Cammack and Shiro Saito (New York: Scarecrow Press, 1962), covers, with sub-divisions, 'Oceania', 'Melanesia', 'Micronesia' and 'Polynesia'. The work is based on the materials in the Pacific Collection at the University of Hawaii, Gregg M Sinclair Library, alphabetically within the sections.

Refer also

R Gerard Ward, *ed*: *Man in the Pacific Islands: essays on geographical change in the Pacific Islands* (Oxford: Clarendon Press, 1972).

1043 'Palestine exploration quarterly', formerly the *Quarterly statement*, 1869–, has been the journal of the Palestine Exploration Fund, founded in 1865. The issues, many of them now out of print, provide a wealth of information on the archaeology, topography, geology, physical geography and peoples, in addition to excellent maps and photographs. Dawson Reprints, in collaboration with the Palestine Exploration Fund, have reprinted the necessary issues to make the whole series again available; the volume for 1869–70 includes the whole of the Warren Reports on the surveys and explorations of Major-General Sir Charles Warren, 1867–1870.

Refer also

Bibliotheca Geographica Palaestinae: chronologisches verzeichnis der von 333 bis 1878 verfassten literatur über das Heilige Land mit dem Versuch einer kartographie, Reinhold Röhricht (The Universitas Booksellers of Jerusalem, 1963), arranged chronologically, with index.

1044 Pan American Institute of Geography and History was founded in 1929 for the encouragement and co-ordination of cartographic, geographic and related work in the western hemisphere. Separate committees deal with geodesy, geo-magnetism and aeronomy, seismology, topographic maps and air photographs, aeronautical charts, hydrography, tides, special maps and urban redevelopment. The mapping and publications programme is vast; among the most central are the *Revista geografica*, 1941–, *Revista cartografica*, 1952–, and the *Bibliographical bulletin of American oceanography and geophysics*, 1958–, all issued twice a year. A library was established in 1930 at the headquarters in Mexico; the stock includes some seventy thousand books and pamphlets, a valuable collection of periodicals and more than four thousand maps and charts, covering all aspects of the Institute's work, with emphasis on the western hemisphere. Reference and bibliographical services are maintained, and abstracts, reviews and accessions lists are prepared for inclusion in the Institute's publications.

1045 'The passing of tribal man in Africa', edited by Peter C W Gutkind (Leiden: Brill, 1970), brings together nine original papers on changing Africa, in the series 'International Studies in Sociology and Anthropology'. Following an editorial preface, the titles of the papers run thus: 'The passing of tribal man: a Rhodesian view'; 'Reflections on the African revolution: the point of the Biafran case'; 'The illusion of tribe'; 'The passing of tribal man: a West African experience'; 'Rural-urban communications in contemporary Nigeria: the persistence of traditional social institutions'; 'Tribe and social change in south central Africa: a situation approach'; 'Tribal survival in the modern African political system'; 'Political hygiene and cultural transition in Africa'.

1046 Penck, Albrecht (1858–1945) was trained as a geologist and subsequently had a distinguished academic career. As director of the Geographical Institute, Berlin, he exercised considerable influence on geographical thought in Germany. His most lasting achievement was probably the initiation of the 'International map of the world on the millionth scale' (*qv*).

1047 'Penguin historical atlas series', edited by Colin McEvedy, in laminated paper cover format, begins with *The Penguin atlas of ancient history* and *The Penguin atlas of medieval history*, in which, following a general introduction on the area covered and a note on mountains and terrain, each page of text is faced by a map illustrating the events described. The maps are bold and simple; hydrographic features are indicated, but no other physical detail. These attractively produced booklets provide helpful companions to historical studies.
    Refer also

The Penguin world atlas, in paperback, 1974.

1048 'Pergamon general historical atlas', edited by A C Cave and B S Trinder, produced by the Cartographic Department of the Pergamon Press, 1970, under the general editorship of Stanley Knight and A R A Werner, depicts pre-history, ancient Greek and Roman civilizations and British, European and world development to the present day, with special emphasis on political and cultural history and the development of modern economics.

1049 'The Pergamon world atlas', published by the Pergamon Press and printed in Poland by Wojskowe Zaklady Kartografizzne, 1968, was based on the *Atlas Swiata*, 1962, produced by the Polish army and annotated in English for the United States and Canada. The atlas is in loose-leaf form, in a soft leather binding. One feature of special value is the inclusion of maps of Eastern Europe made from sources not readily available in the West. Forty-four pages of thematic maps cover the world and from two to four pages are allotted to thematic maps of each country or group of countries. Some pages unfold to give extra width, but scales are mostly small, especially noticeable in the city plans. Pergamon Press issued a general world atlas in 1966, with S Knight as chief editor, in which were ninety-five maps of areas and topics of international interest. Great Britain is shown on a series of 1:1M maps. The metre system is used throughout, with cross-references to feet; names are in the vernacular form, but there are many English equivalents in the gazetteer.

1050 'The periglacial bulletin', organ of the Periglacial Geomorphology Commission of the International Geographic Union, published by the Polish Scientific Publishers, 1924–, brings together notes on the results of research, both in Poland and abroad. Tables of contents are in English and Russian; articles were first in Polish, French, German and Russian, later in English also, with summaries in other languages.

1051 'The periglacial environment', edited by Troy L Péwé (McGill-Queen's University Press, 1969), is the printed collection of papers read at the Symposium on Cold Climate Environments and Processes held at the University of Alaska, August 1965; some were especially prepared for the volume and all are by acknowledged experts.

514

Refer also

A L Washburn: *Periglacial processes and environment* (Arnold, 1972, 1973).

1052 Periodicals: some specific periodicals have been mentioned in this text; others of interest to geographers may be located in *An annotated world list of selected current geographical serials in English* (*qv*) or, for example, in *Ulrich's periodicals directory*. They stem from the organs of learned and professional societies, from nearly all geographical societies throughout the world, from university geographical departments and societies based on these departments, from industrial concerns and trade organisations; they are international, national or local in scope and may include original source material or report on achievements completed or projected. Some are highly technical, others, generously illustrated, are more popular in appeal.

Refer also

Wilson O Aiyepeku: 'The periodical literature of geography', *Libri*, 1972; includes 'References and notes', 'List of periodical titles in geography arranged in rank order' and 'List of ten most productive geographical periodicals in five selected regions arranged in rank order'.

K M Clayton: *Periodical literature survey in the fields of geography, geomorphology and geology* (School of Environmental Sciences, University of East Anglia, 1969; OSTI Report 5057).

Consult the Index for individual items.

1053 Permanent Committee on Geographical Names for British Official Use was set up in 1919 at the suggestion of the Admiralty, to study and advise on the problems of geographical nomenclature. It is an advisory body composed of representatives of the Admiralty, the Colonial Office, the Foreign Office, the Ministry of Defence, the War Office, the Ordnance Survey, the Ministry of Transport and Civil Aviation, the Post Office, the Royal Geographical Society and the Royal Scottish Geographical Society. The continuing importance of the Committee's work was recognised in 1947, when it became the recipient of a Treasury grant and permanent staff, who are accommodated at the Royal Geographical Society. *Lists* of approved geographical names in countries and regions overseas have been issued, of which a new series began in 1953, and glossaries are prepared covering foreign geographical terms; much work has also been done on conventional alphabets and transliteration systems.

1054 Petermann, August Heinrich (1822–1878) was a pupil at the Geographical Art School in Potsdam, founded by Heinrich Berghaus; he then worked as cartographer for von Humboldt and subsequently at the Johnston cartographic firm in Edinburgh. With this experience he went to London, where he compiled some remarkable population maps, including those in the 1851 census, then to Gotha in 1854, to the firm of Justus Perthes. He was responsible for the great *Stieler atlas* (*qv*) and for the *Mitteilungen* which still bears his name (see below).

1055 'Petermanns Geographische Mitteilungen' from its inception in 1855 to 1938 bore the title *Dr A Petermanns Mitteilungen aus Justus Perthes Geographischer Anstalt*. It combined with *Das Ausland*, with *Aus allen Weltteilen* and with *Globus*. For some forty years it remained unequalled in scientific quality and breadth of interest in geographical studies. It contains not only original articles of great scholarship, but bibliographies and evaluative notices of new publications, and cumulative indexes add to its usefulness as a research tool.

1056 The Petroleum Information Bureau, London, provides information on the oil industry on a world-wide basis. Its work includes the preparation and distribution of a wide variety of printed material, such as factual memoranda about the many aspects of the oil industry and its operation in the various oil-producing areas, *eg* 'The world's oil reserves': a series covering oil development in the USA, the Middle East, the USSR, the Commonwealth countries, Latin America, the Far East, Britain, Western Europe, Africa; 'Oil—a large scale industry'. 'A century of oil: an historical account of the oil industry from 1859 to 1959' and 'Notes about oil', an illustrated outline of the origin and early history of petroleum. Librarians are welcomed on the PIB mailing list of new and revised titles. A monthly newsletter contains comment on topical ·matters connected with oil and statistics such as United Kingdom oil consumption and world oil production. The Bureau maintains a statistics and information department where detailed information is filed and carded and a small library is available for the consultation of journals and other publications. Other services include the provision of charts, diagrams and other visual material; a colour map indicates by symbols the world's oil-producing and oil-refining countries in 1960, with relevant statistics. An associated Films Bureau has about 350 film titles, loaned free of charge to schools and interested organisations.

Refer also

British Petroleum: *Our industry—petroleum* (fourth edition, 1970).

1057 'Petroleum: journal of the European Oil Industry', published monthly from 1939 by Technology Publications Limited, contains illustrated articles and news concerning the world petroleum industry; items are included towards a petroleum industrial directory.

Refer also

The oil and petroleum year book (Walter Skinner, London).

Petroleum in the 1970s (United Nations)

Petroleum times, fortnightly, 1969–.

Peter Hepple, *ed: The exploration for petroleum in Europe and North Africa. Proceedings* of a Joint Meeting between the Institute of Petroleum and the American Association of Petroleum Geologists . . . (Institute of Petroleum, 1969).

Peter R Odell: 'The future of oil: a rejoinder', *The geographical journal*, October 1973.

R D H Simpson: 'Further remarks on the future of oil', *The geographical journal*, October 1973.

E N Tiratsoo: *Oil fields of the world* (Beaconsfield: Scientific Press, 1973).

H R Warman: 'The future of oil', *The geographical journal*, September 1972.

1058 The George Philip Group, now comprising Edward Stanford Limited, Georama Limited, the Maritime Press and Kandy, began as a Liverpool business in 1834, the London House being founded in 1836. With the passing of the 1870 Education Act, the publishing programme expanded to supply the needs of elementary education. In 1902, the London Geographical Institute came into being and, by this time, a number of educational and reference atlases, wall map series and small monographs had become established. The index should be consulted for Philip's publications mentioned in this text. Numerous textbooks on many aspects of the subject are issued, many in series; and the firm has specialised in a great variety of globes, with a wide range of use and price, and in map display fittings. Among published reference works are *A bibliography of British* *geomorphology*, edited by K M Clayton, and *The Geographer's vade-mecum*, compiled by J C Hancock and P F Whiteley. Reference atlases include *The atlas of the earth, The international atlas, The Observer atlas of world affairs, The library atlas, The university atlas* and the *Record atlas*; The *Concorde world atlas* is a political atlas, with graphic hill shading, incorporating recent world changes. The firm is also agent for many publishers overseas and is itself publisher for national organisations, such as the Geographical Association, and plays an important part in international ventures; it is, for example, joint publisher and distributor for the *International year-book of cartography* (*qv*). *Stanford's Whitehall atlas*, 1962, and the *Caxton world atlas*, 1960, edited by W Gordon East, also use Philip maps. The latter atlas was designed to be used in conjunction with a descriptive text, country by country, and it contains many illustrations and sketch-maps.

1059 'Philippine cartography 1320–1899', compiled by Carlos Quirino, is now in a second edition, 1963, with an introduction by R A Skelton. A historical account is given of the various manuscript and printed maps and charts of the area, from the earliest Chinese map, about 1320, to the end of the nineteenth century, when the first detailed atlas of the Philippines was published. Over 1,100 maps are listed and carefully described in chronological order.

Refer also

Among works dealing with the geography of the area.

T M Burley: *The Philippines: an economic social geography* (Bell, 1973).

1060 'Phillip's inland navigation', written by John Phillips in 1792, has been reprinted by David and Charles of Newton Abbot, with an introduction by Charles Hadfield, 1970. The reprint is of the fourth edition, 1805. The work remains a classic, covering every county.

1061 The Photogrammetric Society, London, publishes the *Photogrammetric record*, with which is included the annual report with the President's address. The Society aims to facilitate the exchange of information and ideas and to participate in national and international conferences, to hold meetings and to issue publications, encourage research and maintain a library and collections of photographs, plans and models.

1062 'Photogrammetry and current practice in road design', by K M Keir, is a unique fifteen-page report published by Hunting Surveys and Consultants Limited, summarising the design process and attempting 'to dispel the commoner misconceptions surrounding the technique'.

1063 'Physical and information models in geography: *Parts I, II and V of Models in geography'*, edited by Richard J Chorley and Peter Haggett (Methuen, University paperbacks, 1967; *see also Models in geography*), deals with 'Models, paradigms and the new geography', 'The use of models in science', 'Models in geomorphology', 'Models in meteorology and climatology', 'Hydrological models and geography', 'Maps as models', 'Hardware models in geography' and 'Models in geographical teaching'. The contributors are mainly young geographers working in British universities. There are figures and references in the text.

1064 'Physical atlas of zoogeography', compiled by W E Clark and P H Grimshaw, was issued by Bartholomew in 1911 as part of the proposed *Physical atlas*. More than two hundred maps of the world show the distribution of mammals, birds, reptiles and amphibians, as well as a selection of fishes, molluscs and insects, together with ninety-two pages of explanatory text.

1065 'The physical geography of China', prepared by the Institute of Geography, USSR Academy of Sciences, under the general editorship of V T Zaychikov, was originally published by the 'Thought' Publishing House, Moscow, 1964, and issued in an English translation by the United States Government Joint Publication Research Service, Washington DC, in 1965. A xerox photocopy was distributed by the United States Department of Commerce, Technical Information Service and the work was republished in two volumes by Praeger in 1969. Important as the first major work in a European language on the physical geography of the Chinese People's Republic, the text describes the overall natural conditions and the chief natural regions, based on much field work and the results of research expeditions carried out by Chinese and Russian scholars. The work contains an introduction and six articles by Soviet specialists on topography, climate, inland waters, soils, flora and vegetation, and the animals found in China. The bibliography is comprehensive, including articles, divided into Cyrillic and non-Cyrillic sources; the bibliography in the Praeger edition is arranged alphabetically by author's name.

1066 'Physikalischer atlas of Heinrich Berghaus' was a unique achievement, thought to be the first thematic world atlas (Justus Perthes, 1845; second edition, 1852). It was of particular importance because of its influence on atlas production and the use of techniques. Careful thought was given to the choice of symbols; colour gradations were used to show changing relief, the colours being added by hand, the new lithographical method having been rejected on financial grounds. Maps of ethnographic interest were also included, showing population density, distribution of races, and such aspects as education and government.

Refer also

Gerhard Engelmann: 'Der Physikalische Atlas des Heinrich Berghaus: die kartographische Technik der ältesten thematischen Kartensammlung', *International yearbook of cartography*, 1964.

1067 'Picture atlas of the Arctic', compiled by R Thorén (Elsevier, 1969), follows the plan—'The Arctic Ocean'; 'Drifting Ice Stations', 'The Arctic region of Alaska'; 'The Canadian Arctic'; 'Greenland (Denmark)'; 'Iceland'; 'Norwegian Islands in the Arctic'; 'Arctic Scandinavia' and 'The Soviet Arctic', all sections being divided as necessary. Air and ground photographs are included, also maps in the text, and there are a number of useful references.

1068 'The picturesque atlas of Australasia', edited by Andrew Garran (London, 1886–89), is in three volumes, consisting mainly of text, profusely illustrated with engravings and with map plates at intervals, each volume being complete with its own index. Especially interesting for geographers are sections on the early discoverers, including Captain Cook, early settlement, the topography of individual states, with sections on the chief towns and cities, such as Sydney, Melbourne and the Hunter River district, with maps showing average rainfall, railways and other significant features. It is not systematic or balanced in coverage, but contains a vast amount of information currently to hand.

1069 'The Pioneer histories' series of A and C Black are intended to provide broad surveys of the great migrations of European peoples, for purposes of trade, conquest and settlement, into the non-European continents. They aim to describe a racial expansion which has created the complex world of today, so nationalistic in its instincts and so internationalised in its relationships. Each volume takes for its subject the history of an important movement and, while related to others in the series, is thus complete in itself. Outstanding in the series are Edgar Prestage: *The Portuguese pioneers;* J B Brebner: *The explorers of North America;* Eric A Walker: *The great trek;* J C Beaglehole: *The exploration of the Pacific;* F A Kirkpatrick: *The Spanish conquistadores;* James A Williamson: *The age of Drake;* W P Morrell: *The gold rushes;* Sir William Foster: *England's quest of Eastern trade;* Arthur Percival Newton: *The European nations in the West Indies.*

1070 'Plant science: an introduction to world crops', by Jules Janick and others (Freeman, 1969), constitutes an introductory study of agronomy, horticulture and forestry throughout the world, written by four expert authors. The contents, 'Plants and men', 'Nature of crop plants', 'Plant environment', 'Strategy of crop production', 'Industry of plant agriculture' and 'The market place', present the essential background factors to be considered in any environmental studies: The text is extensively illustrated by small photographs and diagrams.

Refer also

Ronald Good: *The geography of the flowering plant* (Longmans, 1947, 1953, 1964).

Marion I Newbigin: *Plant and animal geography* (Methuen, 1936).

Nicholas Polunin: *Introduction to plant geography and some related sciences* (Longmans, 1960).

1071 'Pleistocene geology, a biology, with special reference to the British Isles', by R G West (Longmans, 1968), concerns mainly the glaciated and periglaciated parts of North-West Europe, with the two final chapters dealing superficially with the Pleistocene of the British Isles. Chapter by chapter, the text presents a general account and synthesis of the Pleistocene—'Ice and glaciers', 'Glacial geology', 'Non-glacial sediments and stratigraphy', 'The periglacial zone', 'Stratigraphical investigations', 'Biological investigations', 'Land/sea-level changes', 'Chronology and dating', 'Climatic change', 'Pleistocene successions and their subdivision', 'Pleistocene history of the flora and fauna of the British Isles'. There are two Appendices: 'Methods of isolating and counting fossils' and 'Lacquer method of treating sections'; plates, figures and diagrams abound throughout the text and references have been appended to each chapter.

Refer also

Eiju Yatsu and Allan Falconer, *ed: Research methods in Pleistocene geomorphology. Proceedings,* second Guelph Symposium on Geomorphology, 1971 (University of Guelph, Ontario, Department of Geography; University of East Anglia, *Geo Abstracts,* 1972).

1072 'The Polar bibliography' is produced by the United States Library of Congress, Science and Technology Division, for the Department of Defense, Washington, 1956–. Covering polar and subpolar regions, abstracts are included for unclassified reports and other documents prepared by relevant organisations since 1939; there are subject and individual author indexes.

Refer also

Polar research: a survey (Washington DC, Committee on Polar Research, National Research Council, National Academy of Sciences, 1970).

1073 'Polar record', a journal of Arctic and Antarctic exploration and research issued three times a year since 1931 by the Scott Polar Research Institute, is one of the most valuable sources for polar studies. Technical articles, review articles and notes are included and a feature is 'Recent polar literature . . .', which includes indicative abstracts. An index is now issued every two years, and a cumulative index is available, 1931–1959, in several volumes.

1074 'The Polar world', by Patrick D Baird (Longmans, 1964), is one of the *Geographies for advanced study* series; among the vast literature on this subject, it is probably one of the most balanced and comprehensive treatises to its date, illustrated with photographs, sketchmaps and diagrams, and including chapter references. Following a general introduction, the history of Arctic exploration is traced, the physical aspects of landforms and seas, flora, fauna and native peoples and transportation. Regional descriptions of special parts include Svalbard and Greenland, after which similar treatment is given to Antarctica and the sub-Antarctic islands.

Refer also

Herman R Friis and S G Bale, *jr., ed: United States polar exploration* (Ohio University Press, 1970).

Richard Perry: *Polar worlds* (Newton Abbot: David and Charles, 1973).

R J Price and D E Sugden, *ed: Polar geomorphology* (Institute of British Geographers, 1972).

G De Q Robin: 'Polar ice sheets: a review', *The polar record*, January 1972.

1075 Polish Scientific Publishers (PWN) include geographical studies as one of their specialities and have published many valuable texts, particularly on the geography, soils and hydrography of Poland. The *Polish geographical bibliography*, compiled by the PAN Institute of Geography, began with the year 1945 (1956–); the first of the retrospective volumes, to be issued as completed, was the volume covering 1936–1944 (1959). PWN has also published for the Institute the *Polish geographical nomenclature of the world. The periglacial bulletin*, organ of the Periglacial Geomorphology Commission of the International Geographical Union, has been published since 1924. *The universal geography of PWN*, to be complete in forty-five volumes, has been issued in parts since 1963, together with the respective sheets of the *PWN atlas of the world* (*qv*).

Refer also

Stanislaw Leszczyck: 'The application of geography in Poland', *The geographical journal*, December 1960.

1076 'Political geography', by N J G Pounds (McGraw-Hill, 1963, 1967), was the outcome of working with students, taking Hartshorne's definition: 'The study of the variation of political phenomena from place to place in intercommunication with variations in other features of the earth as the home of man. Included in these political phenomena are features produced by political forces and the political ideas which generate those forces'. Topics dealt with include 'The state and the nation', 'Area and location of the state', 'Frontiers and boundaries', 'The territorial sea', 'Population', 'Resources and power', 'Core areas and capitals', 'The geography of administrative areas', 'Geographical aspects of relations between states', 'The political geography of foreign trade'. 'The political geography of rivers', 'The political geography of international organisations', 'Colonies and colonisation', 'The undeveloped world', 'The political patterns of the world'.

Refer also

Jean Gottmann: *The Significance of territory* (University Press of Virginia, 1973).

Richard Hartshorne: 'Political geography in the modern world', *Journal of conflict resolution*, 1960.

Albrecht Haushofer: *Allgemeine politische geographie und geopolitik* (Heidelberg: Vowinckel, 1951).

R E Kasperson and J V Minghi, *ed*: *The structure of political geography*, 1970.

Karl Krüger: *Weltpolitische länderkunde: die Länder und Staaten der Erde mit alphabetischen Länderlexikon* (Berlin: Safari-Verlag, 1953).

A E Moodie: *Geography behind politics* (Hutchinson University Library, fourth edition, 1961).

W G East and A E Moodie, *ed*: *The changing world: studies in political geography* (Harrap, 1956).

J R V Prescott: *Political geography* (Methuen, 1972).

J R V Prescott: *The geography of frontiers and boundaries* (Hutchinson University Press, 1965, 1967).

H W Weigert: *Principles of political geography* (New York, 1970).

1077 'Politics and geographic relationships: *readings on the nature of political geography'*, by W A D Jackson (Prentice-Hall, 1964), is in many ways a pioneering work presenting concepts underlying the phenomena and motivation which dictate man's organisation of himself and of the surface of the earth. The problem of boundaries and frontiers is discussed, also core areas and capital cities, the bases of economics and population, politics and transportation, the problem of the sea, international resources and political implications and the political and geographical implications of space research.

Refer also

W A D Jackson: *The geography of state policies*, in the same series, *1968.*

Y M Goblet: *Political geography and the world map* (Philip, 1955, reprinted 1956).

1078 The Polynesian Society, Wellington, New Zealand, exists for the study of the native peoples of the Pacific area; the quarterly *Journal*, 1892–, has provided a major forum for discussion on all aspects of the New Zealand Maori people and other Pacific Island peoples. It includes bibliographies and a substantial book review section. Other publications of the Society include Maori texts, monographs, a reprint series and other miscellaneous publications, distributed by Reed, publishers, of Wellington. Particularly interesting is *Polynesian navigation*, edited by Jack Golson.

Note A W Reed is the acknowledged leading Maori scholar; his *Illustrated encyclopedia of Maori life* is the standard reference work, of which a shortened version, the *Concise Maori encyclopedia*, was published in 1964.

1079 'Population studies': *a journal of demography*, founded by the Population Investigation Committee, has been published since 1947 by the London School of Economics and Political Science. The first four volumes appeared in quarterly parts, thereafter three issues a year were published. The shorter research reports of the committee appear in the journal, together with careful reviews and book lists. In addition, the results of research carried out in other countries are included, with the assistance of advisory editors in France, India, Sweden and the USA.

Compare
    Annales de démographie historique (La Société de Démographie Historique, 1964–).
Refer also
    Population (Paris: L'Institut National d'études démographiques, 1946–).
    International population census bibliography (North American Population Research Center, Department of Sociology, University of Texas; Bureau of Business Research, University of Texas, 1966).
    Paul R Ehrlich and Anne H Ehrlich: *Population, resources, environment* (Freeman, second edition, 1972).
    Pierre George: *Questions de géographie de la population* (Paris: PUF, 1959).
    D V Glass and D E C Eversley, *ed*: *Population in history: essays in historical demography* (Chicago: Aldine Publ.; Arnold, 1965).
    D V Glass and Roger Revelle, *ed*: *Population and social change* (Arnold, 1972).
    William Petersen, *ed*: *Readings in population* (New York: Macmillan, 1972).

G T Trewartha: *A geography of population: world patterns* (Wiley, 1969).

G T Trewartha: *The less developed realm: a geography of its population* (Wiley, 1972).

1080 Portolan charts: Soon after 1200, the seamen of the Mediterranean coasts devised charts to illustrate their *portolani*, or sailing directions. Before the introduction of the compass on board ship, bearings were dependent upon the seamen's readings of the heavens, but from the second half of the century, charts were based increasingly on compass observations. The navigators and cartographers of Northern Italy, notably those of Genoa and Venice, were especially skilful in making these charts, which were drawn on single sheets of parchment, ranging from 36 × 18 inches to 56 × 30 inches. Coastlines were indicated in black, with details of the coastal features marked in black, red or gold, or written in black, as were proper names, perpendicularly to the coastline. A scale of portolano miles, probably 233 metres, was used, and systems of direction lines were drawn, later associated with wind 'roses'. It thus became possible, as knowledge and skill increased, to plot more accurate courses for greater distances away from the coast. The oldest of these maps to have been preserved is the Carte Pisane, which dates from the latter half of the thirteenth century. The *Atlas* of Petrus Vesconte is dated 1318 and the chart of Perrinus Vesconte, 1327. All these cover areas from the Black Sea to Southern England. The best known is probably the great *Catalan Atlas* of 1375, now in the Bibliothèque Nationale.

Refer also

A most useful note (of twenty-seven pages), by A Clos-Arceduc, *L'énigme des portulans: étude sur la projection et le mode de construction des cartes à rumbs du XIVème et du XVème siècle*; communication présentée au Congrès des Sociétés Savantes à Rouen, 4 April 1956, with figures and a short list of references.

Youssouf Kamal: *Hallucinations scientifiques* (les portulans) (Leiden: Brill, 1937).

A E Nordenskiöld: *Periplus: an essay on the early history of charts and sailing directions*, 1897; (New York, 1964).

Edward Luther Stevenson: *Portolan charts: their origin and characteristics with a descriptive list of those belonging to The Hispanic Society of America* (The Society, 1911).

1081 'The Portuguese pioneers', by Edgar Prestage (Adam and Charles Black, 1933, reprinted 1966), has become a classic and probably the best example of *The Pioneer histories* series, edited by V T Harlow and J A Williamson, which was devised to 'provide broad surveys of the great migrations of European peoples . . .' (*qv*). The expeditions here described include the discovery of Madeira, the Azores and the Cape Verde Islands, the coasts of Africa and Brazil and the sea passages to India, Malaya, the Spice Islands, China and Japan, led by such outstanding personalities as Prince Henry the Navigator, Diogo Cão, Cadamosto, Bartholomew Dias and Vasco da Gama. There are four useful maps.

Refer also

C R Beazley: *Prince Henry the Navigator: the hero of Portugal and of modern discovery 1394–1460* (reprinted, 1968).

Gilbert Renault: *The caravels of Christ: an account of the voyages of exploration by the Portuguese in the fifteenth century* (Allen and Unwin, 1959).

Elaine Sanceau: *Henry the Navigator: the story of a great prince and his times* (Archon Books, 1969).

1082 'The Pre-Cambrian along the Gulf of Suez and the Northern part of the Red Sea', by H M E Schürmann (Leiden: Brill, 1966), is a major work, including figures and sketchmaps in the text, fifty-five plates and three folded maps in nine colours and three in black and grey. Special attention has been given to the investigation of the components of conglomerates which are used to clarify the mutual relations among the Pre-Cambrian formations. The work provides a most notable addition to knowledge of the Pre-Cambrian areas of the globe and essential reading for all bedrock geologists, representing the field and the laboratory activity of more than fifty years. Its greatest single value has perhaps been to use all the available methods in establishing the relative and absolute ages of these old formations devoid of fossils.

Refer also

H M E Schürmann: *The Pre-Cambrian in North Africa* (Leiden: Brill, 1974).

1083 'A preliminary bibliography of the natural history of Iran', compiled by Robert L Burgess and others (Pahlavi University College of Arts and Sciences, 1966), is in English and Farsi. More than 1,700 references have so far been entered and more information will be available when the work is more complete.

Refer also

Peter Beaumont: 'Water resource development in Iran', *The geographical journal*, October 1974.

1084 Presses Universitaires Français, Paris, has become noted for the publication of scholarly geographical monographs; these include many regional studies prepared by French academic geographers, sometimes based on doctoral theses. The 'France de demain' series was designed to provide a new and up to date regional geography of France.

1085 'The printed maps in the atlases of Great Britain and Ireland: *a bibliography, 1579–1870, with an introduction by F P Sprent and bibliographical notes on the map-makers, engravers and publishers'*, was compiled by Thomas Chubb, assisted by J W Skells and H Beharrell (Homeland Association, 1927). Sections deal successively with the atlases of England and Wales, Scotland and Ireland, arranged chronologically, with analyses of contents and bibliographical notes.

1086 'The printed maps of Tasmania: *a descriptive bibliography'*, by R V Tooley (Map Collectors' Circle, 1963), begins with the rediscovery of Tasmania towards the end of the eighteenth century and lists, with annotations, the printed maps from that time to 1900.

1087 'Problems and trends in American geography', edited by Saul B Cohen (Basic Books, 1967), sponsored by the Association of American Geographers, provides a summary of contemporary American geographic thought, contributed by nineteen authors. Key problems facing American geographers are analysed, all connected in some way with the understanding of the man-environment confrontation.

1088 'Proceedings of the symposium on the granites of West Africa: Ivory Coast, Nigeria, Cameroon', March 1965, was published by Unesco in English and French, 1968. Specialists in the study of granites in Africa and other continents took part in an itinerant symposium in the field studying the granite formations, comparing and discussing their observations. Conclusions were given in the papers forming this publication.

1089 'Progress in geography: *international reviews of current research'*, the first English work of its kind in the subject, is edited by Christopher Board, Richard J Chorley, Peter Haggett and David R Stoddart, with a further panel of advisory editors from overseas universities, published annually by Arnold from 1969. Within the framework of five or six chapters, a wide range of individual topics is assessed and discussed, illustrated with photographs, sketch-maps and diagrams as necessary. The aim of the editors is to present regular, scholarly reviews of current developments within the field.

1090 'Progress in historical geography', edited by Alan R H Baker (Newton Abbot: David and Charles, 1972), reviews changes in the philosophy and methodology of historical geography; 'Rethinking historical geography', by the editor, is the first section in the book and he wrote also the chapter 'Historical geography in Britain'. Nine other contributors comment on developments in their respective countries: X de Planhol on France, Helmut Jäger on Germany, Austria and Switzerland, S Helmfrid on Scandinavia, R A French on the USSR, A H Clark on North America, R L Heathcote and M McCaskill on Australia and New Zealand, D J Robinson on Latin America and Kwamina B Dickson on Africa. There are extensive notes and references in addition to a bibliography.

1091 'Progress in oceanography, edited by Mary Sears of Woods Hole Oceanographic Institute, began in 1963 (Oxford: Pergamon Press, 1964–) as a medium to make the new developments in oceanography more widely known. It is a combination of original reports, reviews and bibliographies.

1092 'A prologue to population geography', by Wilbur Zelinsky (Prentice-Hall International, 1970, in the *Foundations of economic geography* series), as with all the volumes in this series, concentrates on a major theme of economic geography. The series as a whole is intended to provide a broad cross-section of current research in economic geography, stemming from a concern with a variety of problems. This, the first volume of the series, acts as a bridge between economic and cultural geography, exploring ideas and methods. In three main parts—'What does the population geographer study?'; 'Distribution of the world population'; and 'Towards a typology of population regions'. An Appendix sets out 'Demographic, social and economic indicators of development level for forty-one selected countries' and a selected annotated list of references not already cited in the text is given.

1093 'A prospect of the most famous parts of the world', compiled by John Speed, 1627, may be considered the first printed atlas by an Englishman. The American maps added to the 1676 edition are reproduced in the Theatrum Orbis Terrarum reprint, 1966, with an introduction by R A Skelton.

1094 'Provinces of England: *a study of some geographical aspects of devolution'*, by C B Fawcett, 1919, was re-issued in 1960 by Hutchinson, revised and with a preface by W Gordon East and S W Wooldridge. The book, regarded by its author as 'an essay in the application of geography to a particular political problem, that of the delimitation of Provinces of England', was in three sections: a study and criticism of the existing political divisions of England; secondly, an account of each province—North England, Lancashire, Peakdon, Yorkshire, West Midlands (or Severn), East Midland (or Trent), Devon, Wessex, Bristol, East Anglia, London, Central England—and the remaining topics to be considered, namely the Anglo-Welsh boundary; unity of the Provinces, the Provinces as educational areas, relation of the Provinces to other principle divisions. The thesis of the work was first outlined in a lecture to the Royal Geographical Society entitled 'Natural divisions of England', printed in *The geographical journal* in 1917, pp 124–41. Appendices in the book include 'Population and area of each province' in four categories. There are figures in the text and a folded map, 'Density of population per square mile', 1931. The book proved controversial when published, but must undoubtedly be regarded as a classic of original geographical thought and application.

1095 Ptolemaeus, Claudius, usually known as Ptolemy, worked in Alexandria between 127 and 151 as mathematician, astronomer and geographer. He was the first to deal systematically with latitude and longitude and to attempt the scientific construction of maps; his ideas dominated geographical thinking for centuries, notably his concepts of an encircling 'unknown land' and of a series of climatic zones. His great work, the *Geography*, became a standard, in spite of its numerous errors, because in it Ptolemy aimed at the highest level of precision and completeness and also because, after the second century, no further advance in geographical exploration and knowledge was made for a very long time. The appearance of a Latin translation of the *Geography* in 1410 was particularly important; Renaissance scholars studied the work with greater interest even than Ptolemy's contemporaries had done, and it helped to stimulate a renewed zeal for geography and exploration. The work itself appeared in a great number of editions and a vast literature has grown up around it, both definitive and evaluative, in addition to the attention given to it in histories of cartography and geography. All the maps of the 1490 edition are reproduced in A E Nordenskiöld's *Facsimile atlas . . .* (qv); the Italian editions are analysed in A M Hind: *Early Italian engraving*, 1938. Theatrum Orbis Terrarum of Amsterdam issued in 1969 a facsimile reproduction of the *Geographia*, Venice edition 1511, introduced by R A Skelton outlining the current knowledge of this edition, with a brief biography of Bernardo Silvano of Eboli, who contributed some corrections and improvements to it.

Refer also

L Bagrow: *The origin of Ptolemy's Geographia*, 1946.

G R Crone: 'Epic work of Claudius Ptolemy', *The geographical magazine*, October 1971.

E Lynam: *The first engraved atlas of the world . . .*, 1941.

Douglas W Marshall: 'A list of manuscript editions of Ptolemy's *Geographia'*, *Bulletin*, Special Libraries Association, Geography and Map Division, March 1972.

W H Stahl: *Ptolemy's Geography: a selected bibliography* (New York Public Library, 1953).

H N Stevens: *Ptolemy's Geography*, 1908.

R V Tooley: *Maps and map-makers* (Batsford, second revised edition, 1952).

J Winsor: *Bibliography of Ptolemy's Geography*, 1888.

1096 'The PWN atlas of the world', in four main parts, eight fascicules, comprising altogether five hundred original physical, demographic and economic maps on scales of from 1,250,000 to 1:1.0M, has been supplied with the respective parts of the *PWN universal geography* from 1963. The index includes some 150,000 graphical names. PWN (Państwowe Wydawnictwo Naukowe; Polish Scientific Publishers, Warsaw) are noted also for the publication of scientific journals in several languages and for scholarly monographs in almost every field of knowledge, geography being one of the main interests.

1097 'Quantitative geography: *technique and theories in geography'* by John P Cole and C A M King (Wiley, 1968), is in four parts: 'Introduction, mathematics and statistics'; 'Spatial distributions and relationships'; 'Dimensions of space and time'; 'Models, theories and organization'. This kind of thinking is becoming increasingly important in geography. There are numerous worked examples in this book, a glossary, figures, chapter references and a section 'Mathematical and statistical signs'.

Refer also

H M French and J.–B Racine, *ed*: *Quantitative et qualitative géographie* . . . (University of Ottawa Press, 1971, for the University of Ottawa Department of Geography).

Derek Thompson: 'A selective bibliography on quantitative methods in geography', *Geography*, January 1969.

W V Tidswell and S M Barker: *Quantitative methods*, 1971.

Maurice Yeates, *ed*: *Proceedings* of the 1972 meeting of the IGU Commission on Quantitative Geography (McGill—Queen's University Press, 1974).

1098 **'The quaternary era, with special reference to its glaciation',** in two volumes by J K Charlesworth (Arnold, 1957), is an exhaustive work for reference on all aspects of the Pleistocene epoch. The text is illustrated and includes maps and diagrams.

1099 **'The quaternary of the United States:** *a review volume for the Congress of the International Association for Quaternary Research'*, prepared and edited by H E Wright jr, and D G Frey (Princeton University Press; OUP, 1965), is an essential summary of the field of study, illustrated with maps and diagrams.

Refer also

William D Thornbury: *Regional geomorphology of the United States* (Wiley, 1965).

1100 **'A question of place:** *the development of geographic thought'* (R W Beatty, Limited, 1967, 1969), by Eric Fischer, Robert D Campbell and Eldon S Miller, began as a graduate seminar on the development of geographic thought at the George Washington University; it brings together a vast amount of factual knowledge and comment, in two parts: 'Early geography' and 'Modern geography'. Greek and Roman geographers, Arab geographers, Renaissance and post-Renaissance geographers, 'Fathers of modern geography' are each examined, followed by chapters on the development of geographical studies, particularly in Germany, France, Great Britain, the USSR and the United States.

1101 **'The railway encyclopaedia'**, compiled by Harold Starke, 1963, contains information on the different class locomotives, railways by place-name, eminent persons engaged in railway history in one capacity or another and some interesting out-of-the-ordinary entries, such as 'Amalgamations that failed'. Brief notes are given on each topic.

Refer also

A C O'Dell and P S Richards: *Railways and geography* (Hutchinson University Paperback, Second edition, 1971).

1102 **Raisz, Erwin** (1893–1968), the Hungarian geographer, died in Bangkok, while on his way to the International Geographical Congress in New Delhi. During his professional career in cartography and geography, he had drawn thousands of maps for a variety of publications and had himself written and illustrated some hundred papers and four books and had produced two atlases. His major work, *General cartography*, opened up what was virtually a new field in American geography; he began the first course in cartography at Columbia University and lectured at the Institute of Geological Exploration at Harvard. He was prominent in the first efforts to organise a cartographic section in the Association of American Geographers and was chairman of the Cartography Committee for seven years; he was also the first map editor of the *Annals* and himself designed a number of maps for the National Atlas of the United States.

1103 **Rand McNally Company,** Chicago, has as one of its main interests the publishing of maps, guides, atlases and globes. The atlases include world atlases at various levels, such as *Goode's world atlas (qv)*, the *Collegiate world atlas, the Cosmopolitan world atlas, Current events world atlas, $1.00 world atlas,* the *International world atlas;* historical atlases, including the *Atlas of world history* edited by R R Palmer, the *Historical atlas of the Holy Land*, and the *Rand McNally Bible atlas* by Emil G Kraeling; regional atlases of America and the *Atlas of western Europe,* by Jean Dollus; and a number of atlases showing communications and travel information.

A landmark in the firm's publishing history was the production of the *Rand McNally road atlas*, packed with information especially on the

United States, Canada and Mexico; the atlas has gone into numerous, now annual, editions. Special features include the indication of National Parks, insets of city plans, differentiation of highways and notification of new developments. Relief is not shown, except in the form of spot heights. The *Commercial atlas and marketing guide*, first published in 1876, has world coverage, with emphasis on America; as the new editions have multiplied, the nation's expansion to the west has been traced, the development of railways and the extension of settlements and communications. The firm's series of fifteen pocket sized regional guidebooks of the United States, begun after the second world war, provided another landmark in the expansion of the firm's projects. Geo-Physical Maps Inc, an organisation specialising in producing six-foot geophysical globes for government agencies, commercial firms and educational institutions was absorbed.

1104 'Rare Australiana: *catalogue of facsimiles and other publications of the Libraries Board of South Australia'* (Adelaide: Libraries Board of South Australia, 1965) is, as the Board hopes, 'of historic importance and scholarly work'. Both xerographic/photographic and letterpress methods were used; the facsimile editions are exact reproductions of the original texts and they include all illustrations and charts in colour or black and white. Among the entries are many references to early books on Australia and the Pacific.

1105 'Rare county and other maps' is the title of a collection reproduced by the Royal Geographical Society and John Bartholomew and Son, Limited, of maps in colour from Blaeu's rare atlas of 1648; they include maps of Cheshire, Kent, Lancashire, Middlesex, Norfolk, Warwickshire, Worcestershire, Yorkshire and one of the British Isles.

1106 Ratzel, Friedrich (1844–1904) was a geographer of recognised scholarship, acquired in the course of his studies at a number of universities and during his wide travels; his academic influence, particularly at Berlin and Leipzig, was considerable. Of all his published works, in periodical, treatise and monograph form, the two which have achieved lasting fame were the *Anthropogeographie*, in two volumes, 1882, 1891, revised in 1903; and the *Politische Geographie*, 1897, in a new edition by E Oberhammer, in 1925. Much controversy, both informed and uninformed, has since raged around his ideas, which initiated the theory known as 'geographical

534

determinism' and *Lebensraum*. Ratzel stimulated and wrote the philosophy of the first actual *Weltgeschichte*, carried out by his pupil Hans Helmolt, in nine volumes 1899–1907.

Refer also

Harriet Wanklyn: *Friedrich Ratzel: a biographical memoir and bibliography*, 1961, which contains extensive biographical and bibliographical notes.

E C Semple: *Influences of geographic environment* (*qv*).

1107 'The Reader's Digest great world atlas', 1962, 1965, demonstrates the encyclopedic trend in modern atlases and also the graphic use of relief model techniques. Planned under the direction of Professor Frank Debenham, the atlas is in three sections, 'The face of the world', 'The countries of the world', and 'The world as we know it'; there is a British Isles index and a world index. Many of the maps are pictorial and diagrammatic, accompanied by textual notes and statistics. The conventional maps are by Bartholomew. The new edition was revised and brought up to date; further editions have followed at intervals. There is also *The Reader's Digest atlas of Australia*, which includes Papua and New Guinea, 1968.

1108 'Reader's guide to Scotland: a bibliography', published by The National Book League, 1968, covers all aspects of the country, the subjects being arranged in broad groups, subdivided as necessary. Particularly valuable to geographers are Section I, 'General', for background reading: section II, 'History', especially the subdivisions on the economy, agriculture, industry, commerce, transport and communications; III, 'Tourism', in which are to be found references to maps, as well as books; VII, 'Education', including universities; IX, 'Administration', especially 'Town and country planning'; and X, 'Agriculture, industry and commerce'. The editor of the list is D M Lloyd, Keeper of the Printed Books, National Library of Scotland. In its main outlines, the list follows the plan of that published in 1950, compiled by the late Dr Henry W Meikle and his collaborators.

1109 'Readings in economic geography', edited by H J Roepke and T J Maresh (Wiley, 1967), a collection of papers by American and Australian geographers, consists of a selection of articles, including case studies and examinations of principles and individual topics, grouped within the following framework: 'Population and resources'; 'The exploitation of biotic resources'; 'Intensive subsistence agriculture'; 'Middle-latitude mixed farming'; 'Tropical commercial agriculture'; 'Specialised farming'; 'Metallic minerals'; 'Fuel minerals and energy production'; 'Manufacturing'; 'Transportation and trade'; 'Services and urban activity'. Each main section, prefaced by a summary, contains from four to nine articles. Many maps, sketchmaps, diagrams and some small photographs illustrate the text.

1110 '**Readings in the geography of North America:** *a selection of articles from The geographical review 1916 to 1950*', consists of twenty-two articles re-printed; selection was in commemoration of the American Geographical Society's centennial and as a gesture to foreign geographers attending the Seventeenth Congress of the International Geographical Union (New York: The Society, 1952), illustrated with maps and diagrams and including a bibliography.

1111 '**Recent history atlas:** *1870 to the present day'*, edited by Martin Gilbert (Weidenfeld and Nicolson, 1966; second edition, 1967), includes 121 diagrammatic maps in black and white by John R Flower, presenting the main historical developments of the past hundred years. Each map has been specially designed to help explain some important episode, such as the founding and progress of the League of Nations 1919 to 1939, treaties, alliances or population problems. The work is prefaced by a chronological table of events during the period, mainly in Great Britain, Germany, France, Italy, the United States and the USSR.

1112 **Réclus, Jacques Elisée** (1830–1905) was Professor of Comparative Geography at the Université Nouvelle in Brussels, which he established as a geographical institute. His geographical work, written in the tradition of Ritter and Humboldt, is centred in the comprehensive *La terre*, in two volumes, published between 1867 and 1869, and translated into English by B B Woodward in 1871. His *Nouvelle géographie universelle* in nineteen volumes, 1876–1894, was translated and edited by E Ravenstein and A H Keane, published in London, 1878–94. Again, *L'homme et la terre*, in six volumes, 1905–1908, describes physical milieu and phenomena, the distribution of mankind and the history of human institutions and their interrelations; this work was issued in a new edition by Paul Réclus, G Goujon and others, in three volumes, 1931.

536

1113 Reed of Wellington has published a valuable series, each book giving an outline of its subject within a compass of thirty-two pages, illustrated: Don Wasley: *Airways of New Zealand*; A W Reed: *How the Maoris came, How the Maoris lived* and *How the white men came;* A W Reed: *Pastoral farming in New Zealand;* A N Palmer: *Railways in New Zealand;* J H Millar and A W Reed: *Roads in New Zealand;* A N Palmer: *Shipping of New Zealand.* A second series has proved equally popular and informative: S R West: *A guide to trees;* C S Woods: *Native and introduced freshwater fishes;* D C M Manson: *Native beetles;* Charles Masefield: *Native birds;* D C M Manson: *Native butterflies and moths;* R K Dell: *Native crabs;* Bruce Hamlin: *Native ferns;* David Miller: *Native insects;* J M Moreland: *Native sea fishes;* Sheila Natusch: *Native rock;* H B Fell: *Native sea-stars;* R K Dell: *Native shells;* Bruce Hamlin: *Native trees;* Reed's *Atlas of New Zealand*, compiled by A W Reed, is probably the publishers' most widely known single work (A H and A W Reed, 1952), including large scale maps of regions, followed by distribution maps of farming, vegetation, livestock and the location of air facilities. Some statistical information is included.

1114 'Referativnyi zhurnal geografiya' has been issued bi-monthly from 1951, then monthly from 1956, by the Akademiya Nauk SSSR, Moscow. It is a journal of the greatest scholarship, containing original studies, abstracts, bibliographies and reviews; the contents pages are in English. Some thirty-seven thousand abstracts and quotations are included annually. The *Documentatio geographica* amounts to about 4,500 abstracts yearly.

1115 'Reference guide for travellers' was compiled and edited by J A Neal (New York: Bowker, 1969); arrangement is regional, with an appendix section dealing with individual topics, such as 'Travel periodicals'. Annotations are included as necessary, and there are a place index, a publisher's index and an author-title index.

1116 'A reference guide to the literature of travel', *including voyages, geographical description, adventures, shipwrecks and expeditions,* by E G Cox, is an extensive work of the greatest usefulness in three volumes (University of Washington, 1935–49). Volume 1, covering the old world, 1935, was reprinted by lithography in 1948; volume 2 deals with the new world, 1938, and volume 3 with Great Britain,

1949. Source material is covered to 1800. Volume 3 includes also chapters on maps and charts, general reference books and bibliographies; indexes of personal names are given in volumes 2 and 3. A fourth volume was planned for Ireland.

> *Refer also*
>> John H Beeston, *comp and ed*: *Here, there and everywhere* (Harrap, 1972; a travel anthology).

1117 'Reference pamphlets', published by the Central Office of Information, comprise short factual texts, each concerning some aspect of the Commonwealth; no 25, 'Consultation and co-operation in the Commonwealth'; no 38, 'Nigeria: the making of a nation'; no 45, 'Sierra Leone: the making of a nation'; no 48, 'Tanganyika: the making of a nation'; no 51, 'Jamaica: the making of a nation'; no 52, 'Community development: the British contribution'; no 53, 'Trinidad and Tobago: the making of a nation'; no 54 'Uganda: the making of a nation'; no 55, 'Promotion of the sciences in the Commonwealth'; no 56, 'The Federation of Malaysia'; no 58, 'The Colombo Plan' and no 59, 'Kenya', and so on.

1118 'Regional economic analysis in Britain and the Commonwealth, a bibliographic guide', by F E Ian Hamilton, was prepared for the Commission on Methods of Economic Regionalization, International Geographical Union, established in 1960. The volume is in seven parts: 'The British Isles'; 'The British Commonwealth in general'; 'Africa'; 'Australia and New Zealand'; 'Canada'; 'South and South-east Asia'; 'The smaller territories, British Caribbean and the Atlantic Islands'. Dr Hamilton's introduction, based in part upon a paper presented to the Strasbourg Conference of the IGU Commission on Methods of Economic Regionalization, July 1967, traces the evolution of the regional concept from the works of Camden to the Reports of the Board of Agriculture, the ideas of Halford Mackinder and others through to recent quantitative studies. There is an introduction to each part and the entries in part I include abstracts.

> *Refer also*
>> Michael Chisholm: 'Regional policies for the 1970s' The Eva G R Taylor Memorial Lecture, 1973, published in *The geographical journal*, June 1974.

1119 'Regional geography of the world', by Jesse H Wheeler jr and others, was completely revised for the third edition (Holt, Rinehart and Winston, 1969). Eight regions are distinguished—Europe, the Soviet Union, the Middle East, the Orient, the Pacific world, Africa, Latin America, Anglo-America. The characteristics of each are discussed and their role in the world as a whole, based on the factual physical and cultural features. A new section was entitled 'Processes that shape the geography of areas'. There is a chapter on urban geography, using London as an example; statistics have been revised to 1968 in as many cases as possible, maps and bibliographies have been up-dated and there are many new photographs.

1120 'Regional geography, theory and practice', by Roger Minshull (Hutchinson University Library, 1967, reprinted, 1968), presents a survey of the methods, concepts and objectives of the 'regional' studies undertaken by geographers: 'The regional method of description'; 'Regions as real objects'; 'Formal and functional regions'; 'The nature of regional geography'; 'Alternatives to an inadequate concept'; 'The influence of methods of mapping'; and conclusions. There are figures in the text, notes and references at the ends of chapters and a bibliography.

Refer also

J N H Britton: *Regional analysis and economic geography* (Bell, 1972).

B J L Berry and Allen Pred: *Central place studies: a bibliography of theory and applications* (Philadelphia: Regional Science Research Institute, 1961).

R Campbell: *Personality as an element in regional geography* (Annals of the Association of American Geographers, 1968).

Paul Claval et Etienne Juillard: *Région et régionalisation dans la géographie française et dans d'autres sciences sociales: bibliographie analytique* . . . (Paris: Dalloz, 1967).

J B Cullingworth and S C Orr, *ed*: *Regional and urban studies: a social science approach* (Allen and Unwin, 1969).

George W Hoffman: *Regional development strategy in Southeast Europe: a comparative analysis of Albania, Bulgaria, Greece, Romania and Yugoslavia* (Praeger, 1972).

Gerald Manners *et al*: *Regional development in Britain* (Wiley, 1972).

David Turnock: 'The region in modern geography', *Geography*, November 1967.

1121 'A regional history of the railways of Great Britain', the overall title of a series published by David and Charles of Newton Abbot, includes 'The West Country', 'Southern England', 'Greater London', 'North East England', 'The Eastern Counties', and others in preparation. The texts, which are illustrated, trace the development of the railway systems and relate their progress to economic and social conditions.

1122 'Regional landscapes of Australia: *form, function and change'* (Heinemann Educational, 1972), by Andrew and Mary Learmonth, presents a clear commentary accompanied by 150 black and white photographs, sixteen plates of coloured photographs and sections of coloured maps by Peter Daniell. The work (originally published by Angus and Robertson) is concerned especially with landforms, climate and development.
> *Refer also*
>> Michael Williams: *The making of the South Australian landscape: a study in the historical geography of Australia* (Academic Press, 1974).

1123 'Regional studies: *journal of the Regional Studies Association'*, edited by Dr Peter Hall (Pergamon Press, May 1967–), is published twice a year and is international in scope. Papers are in English, with summaries in English, French, German and Russian. Contributions reflect the application of systematic method to the solution of problems of regional planning. Subjects covered include the machinery of regional economic planning, regional economic development, economic growth in developing countries, metropolitan regional planning and models of regional and urban development. Most articles carry references and the text is illustrated.
> *Refer also*
>> P Birot: *Les régions naturelles du globe* (Paris: Masson, 1970).

1124 'Regional variation in Indian Ocean coral reefs', edited by D R Stoddart and Sir Maurice Yonge, presents the results of a symposium of The Zoological Society of London (Academic Press, 1971). Emphasis is on the geology and morphology of reefs, regional studies and distribution of corals and other reef invertebrate communities and there is a memoir of Thomas F Goreau.

1125 'Régions, nations, grands espaces: *géographie générale des ensembles territoriaux'*, by Paul Claval (Paris: Editions M-Th Génin,

540

1968, in the series *Géographie économique et sociale*), a monumental text, illustrated with a few photographs, sketchmaps and diagrams, is presented in two main parts: 'Théorie des ensembles territoriaux et de leurs rapports' and 'Régions, nations, grands espaces'; the variations of economic geography are examined in all aspects. There is a list of the authors cited in the text, usually in the numerous footnotes.

1126 Reinbek International Forestry Documentation Centre, a unit of the German Federal Research Organization for Forestry and Forest Products, co-operates with the Commonwealth Forestry Bureau, Oxford, the Library of the Department of Agriculture in Washington and with FAO to give a completely international forestry documentation service, dealing with more than ten thousand literature items a year. The Oxford 'decimal system' is used. Work is in progress on a *World forestry atlas* (*qv*); a quarterly 'titles service' is maintained; also quarterly is the *Bibliographie des Forstlichen Schrifttums Deutschlands*, in addition to special bibliographies prepared on request.

1127 'Reinhold one-volume encyclopedias', includes a series of 'Earth sciences' volumes. *The encyclopedia of oceanography* is the first in this series, edited by Rhodes W Fairbridge (1966), a comprehensive work prepared by a large team of specialist scholars. Entries are in alphabetical order, generously illustrated throughout with photographs, sketchmaps, diagrammatic maps, graphs and diagrams, as appropriate; references follow all the main entries.

1128 'Répertoire d'établissements enseignant la cartographie' (Paris: Comité Français de Cartographie, 1968), was compiled by Brigadier D E O Thackwell, with the collaboration of delegates from member countries of the International Cartographic Association, with the aim of collecting information on the different systems in the training of cartographers now in use and of making the information available in as concise and convenient a form as possible. The project arose from discussions on 'Education in cartography' of Commission I, 1964, and was presented at the Fourth Technical Conference on Cartography, New Delhi, 1968. In the catalogue, the distinction is made between essentially cartographic activities, called 'W' and activities complementing others marked 'V'. Entries are listed first alphabetically by country within the categories, then alphabetically by name of institution. Text is in English and French.

Refer also

Brigadier R A Gardiner and H Fullard: 'National qualifications in cartography', *The cartographic journal*, June 1971.

1129 The **'Research digest'** is a semi-annual publication, issued formerly, 1954–, by the Bureau of Community Planning, University of Illinois, now by an informal organisation, Urban Planning Research Group; it is international in scope and is most valuable in its role of bringing together information on all aspects of this growing subject, with an emphasis on methodology and the problems of urban and regional planning. Also published is the *Quarterly digest of urban and regional research*.

1130 **'Research in Japanese sources:** *a guide*', compiled by Herschel Webb and Marleigh Ryan (Columbia University Press for the East Asian Institute, 1965), is presented as continuous explanatory text, divided into sections. The sections on bibliography and general reference works, on geography and place names, will be of most interest to geographers.

Refer also

Yoshida Togo: *Japanese geography: a guide to reference and research materials* (Tokyo: Dai Nihon dokushi chizu, 1939).

Atlas of Japan: physical, economic and social (Tokyo: International Society for Educational Information, 1970).

1131 **'Research index',** 1969–, is in looseleaf form, published by Business Surveys Limited; in each edition are comprehensive references to articles and news items of financial interest appearing in more than a hundred periodicals. Pink pages, I, refer to industrial and commercial news, the most useful from the geographical point of view; blue pages, II, refer to companies in alphabetical order.

1132 **'Resources for geography'** (Geographical Association, 1972–) is a duplicated bulletin issued three times a year, replacing the annual notes, usually in the April issue of *Geography*, on new books at primary and secondary level. Short reviews of new textbooks, wall charts, film strips and other visual aids are included, together with advance notices of field courses and other activities.

1133 **'La revue Canadienne de geographie',** of which three or four issues a year have been published since 1947 jointly by the Geographical Societies of Montreal and Quebec, was the first established Canadian geographical journal of high academic merit. It is mainly in French, with English or French abstracts.

1134 'Revue de géologie et de géographie' has been published twice a year since 1957 by the Académie de la République Populaire Roumaine, Bucharest, in English, French, German and Russian. In addition to scholarly articles, the periodical includes reviews of new work and illustrations, maps and charts.

1135 'Revue forestière français', founded by Léon Schaeffer, is edited by l'Ecole Nationale des Eaux et Forêts, with the collaboration of the Société des Amis et Anciens Elèves de l'Ecole Nationale des Eaux et Forêts, Nancy. Illustrated articles are the main feature, frequently carrying references or bibliographies, followed by a correspondence section and book reviews arranged by country. Five cumulated indexes have so far appeared: covering 1862–1887 (1887); 1888–1902 (1903); 1903–1927 (1930); 1928–1948 (1950); and 1949–1960 (1962).

1136 Ritter, Carl (1779–1859) was one of the great leaders of geographical thought in Germany and holder of the first academic chair in geography at the University of Berlin. Of his numerous publications, two early works made a great impact and remained of lasting importance: the *Europa, Ein Geographisch-Historisch-Statistiches Gemaldes* . . . of which the first volume appeared in 1804 and the second in 1807, with a small atlas volume in 1806; and *Die Erdkunde im Verhältnis zur Natur und zur Geschichte des Menschen oder allgemeine vergleichende Geographie*, of which the first volume, on Africa, was published in 1817, and the second, dealing with Asia, the following year. The second edition was published in nineteen volumes between 1822 and 1859. Ritter was greatly concerned to point the connection between geography and history and to determine the influence of geography upon the human race. He was intimately connected with the direction of the Gesellschaft für Erdkunde, from its foundation in 1828.

1137 'Rivers and river terraces', edited by G H Dury (Macmillan, 1970), in 'The geographical readings series', consists of nine essays: Hugh Miller: 'Methods and results of river terracing'; W M Davis: 'River terraces in New England'; O T Jones: 'Longitudinal profiles of the Upper Towy Drainage System'; G K Gilbert: 'Land sculpture in the Henry Mountain'; R E Horton: 'Erosional development of streams: quantitative physiographic factors'; M Gordon Wolman and Luna B Leopold: 'Flood plains'; Luna B Leopold and M Gordon Wolman: 'River channel patterns'; Walter B Langbein and Luna B Leopold: 'River meanders and the theory of of minimum variance' and G H Dury: 'General theory of meandering valleys and underfit'. Diagrams illustrate the text and references are given at the ends of the majority of essays.

Refer also

Ian Douglas: 'The geographical interpretation of river water quality data', *Progress in geography*, 1972.

George H Lauff, *ed: Estuaries* (American Association for the Advancement of Science, 1967).

M Morisawa: *Streams—their dynamics and morphology* (McGraw-Hill, 1968).

Ray T Oglesby *et al, ed: River ecology and man* (New York: Academic Press, 1972).

Flood studies: an international guide for collection and processing of data (Unesco, 1971).

1138 'The road and tourist map of Norway', published by Cappelen, based on the most recent material from Norges Geografiske Oppmåling and tourist information, is the result of investigations carried out by several hundred contributors throughout the country. Five double map sheets, 1–2, Southern Norway; 3–4, Central Norway; 5–6, North-Central, the Møre and Trøndelag area, all on 1:325,000; 7–8, Nordland; and 9–10, Tromsø and Finmark, both on 1:400,000, present the first modern road and tourist map on this international standard. Road networks are classified according to the latest road regulations. A key, printed on the reverse, indicates sixty symbols referring to useful information, given in English, French and German. Six colours show relative relief features. 'Southern Norway', on 1:1M scale, shows fully-coloured, hillshaded relief, road classifications and distances. All these maps are available in Britain through Bartholomew.

1139 'Road international', quarterly from 1950– (International Road Federation Limited, London), is a truly international periodical, illustrated, presenting new developments, ventures and projects. 'Its controlled circulation takes it to the desks of men involved in the

544

roads and road transport field throughout the world.'

1140 'Roman roads in Britain', by I D Margary (John Baker, 1955, 1957 in two volumes; revised in one volume, 1967), is a well-told narrative, documented and illustrated with fine aerial photographs and with maps and diagrams. 'Only once previously has an attempt been made to give a descriptive account of all the Roman roads in Britain and that was by Thomas Codrington just over sixty years ago, a most valuable work which has remained the standard textbook till our own time . . .' (Preface).

1141 Roxby, Percy Maude (1880–1947) will be chiefly remembered as a geographer for his work on China, but he was also particularly interested in regionalism and aspects of human geography. He made an outstanding contribution to geography teaching both in Britain and abroad, including University Extension lecturing, and added his influence to the historical thinking of geographers.

1142 Royal Canadian Geographical Society, Ottawa, was founded in 1929 for the advancement of geographical knowledge and, in particular, for the general diffusion of information on Canadian geography. The *Canadian geographical journal*, published from 1930, is the chief publication, with text in English or French; book reviews are included, also bibliographies. A cumulative index is available covering volumes 1–59, 1930–1959.

1143 'The Royal English atlas: *eighteenth century county maps of England and Wales',* originally produced by Emmanuel Bowen and Thomas Kitchin in 1762, presented in one elegant folio volume the best contemporary maps of the English counties and of North and South Wales, in a standard format, based on the most accurate sources available to the authors, printed and in manuscript, including the maps in their own *Large English atlas*, published earlier. This work has now been reprinted in exact facsimile, from an uncoloured copy in the British Museum, by David and Charles of Newton Abbot. It contains forty-four finely engraved maps, distinguished by much geographical detail and beauty of craftsmanship, each map being embellished with an elaborate cartouche, portraying scenes within the county, views of cathedrals and so on. The introduction, by J B Harley and Donald Hodson, outlines the publication history of the atlas within the framework of the eighteenth century London map trade, analysing the sources used in the compilation of the maps.

1144 Royal Geographical Society, London, had its origin in the amalgamation of the Association for Promoting the Discovery of the Interior Parts of Africa, founded in 1788, and the Palestine Association, which dated from 1805, together with the Raleigh Dining Club. By 1830, the need for a more completely organised institution for the advancement of geography became apparent and the Geographical Society of London was created, which gained a Royal Charter in 1859. The development of the work of the Society through the years may be traced through the issues of *The journal*, 1830–1880, and of *The geographical journal* (*qv*). Sir C R Markham recorded the early work of the Society in *50 years work of the RGS*, 1881; the centenary volume, *The record of the Royal Geographical Society 1830–1930*, by H R Mill (RGS, 1930), was continued by G R Crone in *The Royal Geographical Society: a record, 1931–1955* (RGS, 1955). Membership includes academic geographers, explorers and interested amateurs. The Map Room is open to the general public, the library to members only. The Society's contribution to world geography has been considerable. Discovery and exploration have been actively encouraged by grants, advice, loan of instruments and the preparation of maps. Publications have been of a high standard, notably *The geographical journal* (*qv*) and *New geographical literature and maps* (*qv*) which in 1951 succeeded *Recent geographical literature, maps and photographs added to the Society's collections*, 1918–1941; the original maps reproduced in *The geographical journal*, usually drawn by the Society's cartographic staff, are particularly valuable. The *Research series* and the *Library series* include many useful works, such as *Current periodicals in the library of the RGS*, 1961, *A classification for geography*, 1962 and *Publications of the Royal Geographical Society 1830–1964*, 1964. The Society has reproduced facsimiles of *The map of the world*, by J Hondius, English county maps, the Catalan world map, the Hereford world map, the Gough map and *Early maps of the British Isles, AD 1000–1579*. The library holds more than 100,000 volumes and fine collections of lantern slides and photographs, and the map room has a unique collection of maps and atlases, both historical and modern.

Refer also

L M Cantor: 'The Royal Geographical Society and the projected London Institute of Geography 1892–1899', *The geo-*

graphical journal, March 1962.

James A Casada: 'James A Grant and The Royal Geographical Society', *The geographical journal*, June 1974.

G R Crone: 'The library of the Royal Geographical Society', *The geographical journal*, March 1955.

E W Gilbert: 'The Royal Geographical Society and geographical education in 1871', *The geographical journal*, June 1971.

L P Kirwan: 'The RGS and British exploration: a review of recent trends', *The geographical journal*, June 1964.

1145 Royal Geographical Society of Australasia, South Australia branch, was founded at Adelaide in 1885, and a Queensland branch at Brisbane in the same year. Publications include Annual *Proceedings* and occasional *Reports*. The library holds more than thirty thousand volumes.

1146 Royal Meteorological Society of London was founded in 1850 as The British Meteorological Society for the promotion of the science of meteorology in all aspects; a Royal Charter was granted in 1866 and the name was changed to The Meteorological Society, the present full name being acquired in 1883. In 1921, the Society amalgamated with the Scottish Meteorological Society. A Scottish centre is based on Edinburgh University, a Manchester centre at Manchester University and a Canadian branch has centres at Montreal, Toronto and Winnipeg. The Society possesses one of the greatest meteorological libraries in the world, comprising more than forty thousand books and pamphlets and some 1,500 manuscripts, besides periodicals and lantern slides. Periodical publications include the *Quarterly journal*, 1871– and *Weather: a monthly magazine for all interested in meteorology*, 1946–, which includes a 'Weather log', with map. *The Meteorological glossary*, begun in 1916, was issued in a fifth edition, 1972; and *The marine observer*, a quarterly journal concerned with marine meteorology, is prepared by the Marine Division of the Meteorological Office.

Note The publications and services of the Office are listed in *Government publications*, Sectional list no 37 (HMSO) revised at intervals.

Refer also

T J Chandler: *Modern meteorology and climatology* (Nelson, 1972).

Michael Chisholm *et al, ed: Regional forecasting: Proceedings* of the Twenty-Second Symposium of the Colston Research Society, 1970).

F W Cole: *Introduction to meteorology* (Wiley, 1970).

R W Longley: *Elements of meteorology* (Wiley for the University of Alberta, 1970).

B J Mason: 'The role of meteorology in the national economy', *Weather*, November 1966.

1147 Royal Scottish Geographical Society was founded in 1884 with the aim of extending geographical education in Scotland, of maintaining contact with Scotsmen abroad and with others interested in the subject. A cartographic section was formed in 1960. The main publication is the *Scottish geographical magazine* (*qv*); the Society has also published *The early maps of Scotland*, in a second revised edition, 1936. The library holds a valuable collection of more than forty thousand books and some sixty thousand maps, including a set of early maps of Scotland, and about two hundred periodicals. Overseas visitors holding any geographical society membership may use the Society's library and rooms.

1148 The Royal Society has always taken a scientific interest in geographical matters and acts as the National Committee for Geography. A cartography sub-committee was set up in 1960 to advise on cartographical topics affecting the United Kingdom. The Council of the Royal Society in 1974 appointed a standing committee to advise it on the requirements of British scientists from the services of the Ordnance Survey; the Committee members have been chosen to cover as wide a spectrum of relevant scientific interests as possible consistent with a small membership, including the Director General of the Survey.

1149 The Royal Tropical Institute, Amsterdam, had its origins in the mid-nineteenth century and was incorporated as an Association in 1910. The aim of the Institute is to collect and disseminate knowledge concerning tropical countries; the Central Library is one of the most extensive in the world in books, periodicals, maps and charts within the subject field.

1150 'Rubber developments', a central source in its subject, is issued quarterly by The Natural Rubber Producers' Research Association (Malayan Rubber Fund Board), London. Articles are of technical, historical or regional application and are illustrated; the main articles are preceded by brief abstracts. Shorter notes on items of current interest are also included.

Refer also

Natural rubber news (Natural Rubber Bureau, Washington, D C, 1950–).

Rubber age (Palmerton Publishing Company, New York, 1917–).

1151 'Rumanian studies: *an international annual of the humanities and social sciences'*, edited by K Hitchens, began publication by Brill of Leiden in 1970. It had its origin in the feeling among Rumanian scholars that an opportunity was needed to inform a wider audience about the new directions in research and the changes in interpretation that are taking place in their country. Bibliographical items are to be a feature.

1152 'Russia and the Soviet Union: *a bibliographic guide to Western-language publications'* was edited by Paul L Horecky (University of Chicago Press, 1965), with particular emphasis on English publications. Materials are arranged under broad subject headings, divided into more specific categories. Main divisions include 'General reference aids and bibliographies'; 'General and descriptive works'; 'The land'; 'The people, ethnic and demographic features'; 'The nation: civilizations and politics'; 'History'; 'The state'; 'The economic and social structure'; 'The intellectual and cultural life'. Brief annotations are appended and there is an index.

1153 'Russian land, Soviet people: *a geographical approach to the USSR'*, by James S Gregory (Harrap, 1968), is a study of man within his environment. The work begins with a comprehensive account of Russian geography, showing how the environment of the Great Russian Plain influenced the development of cultures, followed by studies of the regions according to climate, soil and natural vegetation, with a particular study of the progress of agriculture. The second part deals in depth with 'The regions of the USSR'. There are maps in the text and a bibliography.

Refer also

Russian history atlas, the sixth in Martin Gilbert's series of historical atlases (Weidenfeld and Nicolson, 1972), which traces Russian historical progress in all its variety from the earliest times to the present day, including also a bibliography of works consulted.

Alexander Baykov: *The development of the Soviet economic system: an essay on the experience of planning in the USSR* (CUP, 1970).

I P Gerasimov *et al, ed*: *Natural resources of the Soviet Union: their use and renewal* (Translated by J I Romanowski; English edition by W A Douglas Jackson, Freeman, 1971).

R Hutchings: *Seasonal influences in Soviet industry* (OUP, 1971).

Erich Strauss: *Soviet agriculture in perspective* (Allen and Unwin, 1969).

S P Suslov: *Physical geography of Asiatic Russia* (Translated by N D Gershevsky; San Francisco: Freeman, for the University of Leningrad, 1961).

L J Symons: *Russian agriculture* (Bell, 1972).

1154 Sahab Geographic and Drafting Institute, Tehran, founded under the direction of Professor A Sahab, has for thirty years specialised in the printing of maps of Iran and the Middle Eastern countries for scientific and educational purposes, also atlases and globes. The current programme includes a national atlas of Iran, a geographical encyclopedia in Persian, the preparation of a complete set of maps on the Middle East at 1:1M and the completion of a regional map series of Iran, of which some sheets are already available.

1155 Saxton, Christopher (*c* 1542–1610 or 1611) attempted the first national survey of England and Wales. Under the royal patronage, he surveyed and drew maps of all the counties. The British Museum possesses one of the earliest copies of the atlas, finished in 1579, and has arranged for the reproduction of the maps in colour. They are of remarkable accuracy, considering the instruments available, showing a systematic approach to the delineation of ground features in map form; varying sizes of lettering are used to show relative importance of settlements, for example, and the maps are finished with a wealth of artistic detail. They should not be confused with the maps drawn in 1607 to accompany Camden's *Britannia* (*qv*).

1156 'Scandinavian lands', by Roy Millward (Macmillan, 1964) covers Norway, Sweden, Denmark and Finland, treating first the regional geography of each country, then 'Some facets of Scandinavian geography'. Brief notes are appended and a bibliography. Aerial photographs, sketchmaps and diagrams have been carefully selected; the balance between the individuality of the four countries and their essential unity is skilfully presented vis à vis the rest of the world.

1057 'The Scandinavian world', by Andrew C O'Dell (Longmans, 1957) broke new ground in considering the countries of Finland, Sweden, Denmark, Norway, the Arctic islands, Faeroes, Iceland and Greenland as an entity. The approach is direct—'Physical and historical introduction', 'Regional geography', 'Economic geography'. Throughout the text are numerous photographs, sketch-maps, diagrammatic maps and figures; an appendix sets out Conversion Tables, metric to British units and a selected bibliography, arranged regionally.

Refer also

Brian Fullerton and Alan F Williams: *Scandinavia: an introductory geography* (New York: Praeger; Chatto and Windus, 1972).

W R Mead: *An economic geography of the Scandinavian states and Finland* (University of London Press, second edition, 1964).

1158 'The scenery, antiquities and biography of South Wales', by Benjamin Heath Malkin, published by T N Longman in 1804, is probably the most important work dealing with South Wales at the beginning of the nineteenth century, based on material collected by Malkin in 1803 and embellished with many views drawn on the spot and engraved by Laporte. The work has been reproduced by SR Publications Limited, East Ardsley.

1159 'School book guide', in a revised edition, 1973 (Education Book Distributors, Limited), sets out to list every book which could be used in a secondary school geography course. Titles are subdivided initially by subject, arranged alphabetically, followed by a title index, including series titles, an author index, index of publishers with addresses and a list enabling readers to identify publishers from their standard book numbers. For each title are given details such as the price of the book, the age range for which it is intended, the inclusion of maps, photographs, exercises, the use of colour and, in some cases, brief annotations.

1160 School of Oriental and African Studies Library was built up on the collection of Oriental books owned by the London Institution; the University Library and the libraries of King's College transferred their Oriental books in exchange for the Western books from the London Institution Library. Acquisition policy attempts completion in all significant publications relating to Asia, Africa and Oceania in all languages, in humanities and social sciences; there is also a rapidly growing collection of lantern slides, transparencies and photographs. The catalogues were reproduced by G K Hall and Company in 1964 (dated 1963) and are available as a complete set or in sections. Analytical entries are included for periodicals, festschriften and bibliographies. Several bibliographies and special catalogues have been compiled by the staff, also the *Monthly list of periodical articles*, 1954– and *Theses on African studies*, 1964.

1161 'Schweizerischer Mittelschulatlas' (Zurich, 1898–), though not readily available in Britain, has been influential in the development of educational atlases. The chief source of the foreign topographical maps until 1910 was the *Stieler atlas;* for the revisions, 1927–32, under the direction of Professor Imhof, the principal source was the *Grande atlante del Touring Club Italiano* and, since then, the 1954 *Atlas mira, The Times mid-century edition* and the national mapping services. The atlas was redesigned in 1955 and again in a thirteenth edition, in 1962, for the Konferenz der Kantonalen Erziehungsdirektooren, an outstanding feature being the new method of relief representation evolved by Professor Imhof. The atlas begins with maps of the home country, working from it to other parts of the world.
Refer also
Eduard Imhof: 'The Swiss Mittelschulatlas in a new form', *International yearbook of cartography*, 1964.

1162 'Science in New Zealand', edited by F R Callaghan (Wellington: Reed, 1957), was prepared for the meeting of the Australian and New Zealand Association for the Advancement of Science at Dunedin in 1957. Individual subjects are treated by experts, such as 'Geography' by G Jobberns. Other relevant topics include climate, meteorological progress, geophysics, sea fisheries, native and introduced birds, changed and changing vegetation, science and agriculture, history of soil science, science in the fruit industry, science in the dairy industry and post-war developments in oceanography.

1163 'The science of geography: *report of the ad hoc Committee for Geography'*, Earth Sciences Division, National Academy of Sciences, National Research Council, Washington, 1965, surveys the problems facing contemporary geographers and makes some suggestions for future development.

1164 Scientific Committee on Antarctic Research was set up by the International Council of Scientific Unions in 1958 to continue the co-operative scientific exploration of Antarctica after the completion of the IGY research, 1957–1958.

1165 Scott Polar Research Institute, Cambridge, was established in 1920 to encourage and facilitate polar research and to disseminate information on polar regions. The library holds some ten thousand books and reprints, in addition to collections of maps, manuscripts, photographs, prints, films, log-books and records; all the collections are available for use by any genuine research worker. More than three hundred periodicals are indexed by the library staff and the feature 'Recent polar literature', a select list of books, pamphlets and articles, with indicative abstracts, is prepared for inclusion in the Institute's *Polar record* (*qv*). Practical experience in the library through eighteen years enabled Brian Roberts to adapt the Universal Decimal Classification schedules for use in polar libraries; this was published jointly by the Institute, the Fédération Internationale de Documentation and the British Standards Institution (second revised edition, 1963). A series of special publications began in 1952; one of these of particular interest is the *Illustrated ice glossary*, by Terence Armstrong and Brian Roberts, 1956, 1973.

1166 'Scottish geographical magazine', the organ of the Royal Scottish Geographical Society (*qv*), published three times a year since 1885, has always contained articles of world interest, with an emphasis on Scottish affairs. A new editorial policy began in 1966, whereby a large part of most issues consists of articles on regions of Scotland and geographical studies of various aspects of Scottish life, work and natural background, on a systematic plan. References on Scottish geography are included. An index is prepared every second year. The two sections of reviews, for books and for atlases and maps, are not extensive, but sound and instructive.

1167 'The sea: *ideas and observations on progress in the study of the seas'* (Wiley International, 1962–1963, 1970), an advanced and technical work, yet readily understandable, was conceived and the first three volumes edited by M N Hill and others, illustrated by maps and diagrams. The three volumes run as follows: 'Physical oceanography', 1962, which deals with fundamentals, the interchange of properties between sea and air, the dynamics of ocean currents, the transmission of energy within the sea, waves, turbulence and the physics of sea ice; 'The composition of sea water: comparative and descriptive oceanography', 1963, concerned with the fertility of the oceans, currents, biological oceanography and oceanographical miscellanea; and 'The earth beneath the sea', including the history of geophysical exploration, topography and structure and sedimentation. After Dr Hill's death, the fourth volume, dedicated to his memory, was edited by Dr A E Maxwell; contributions were made by seventy-seven scholars. The volume shows how the study of the sea-floor has progressed through the techniques described, including seismic, magnetic, geothermal, topographic, earthquake epicentre, palaeontological, plus other geophysical and geological information on a world-wide basis.

Refer also

Bibliography of oceanographic publications (Washington, DC: Inter-agency Committee on Oceanography of the Federal Council for Science and Technology, USA, 1963).

Manual on international oceanographic data exchange (Unesco, third revised edition, prepared by the Inter-governmental Oceanographic Commission, 1973.

Netherlands journal of sea research (Netherlands Institute for Sea Research, four parts to a volume, published as available).

Oceanographic index, organismal cumulation 1946–1973, compiled by Mary Sears (Reprint, G K Hall, two volumes, 1974).

'Sea-ice symposium', Reykjavík, 1969, sponsored jointly by the Geo-Science Society of Iceland, the Icelandic Glaciological Society, the Marine Research Institute and the Icelandic Meteorological Office.

The technology of the sea and the sea-bed: Proceedings of the Conference held at the Atomic Energy Research Establishment, Harwell . . ., sponsored by the Ministry of Technology . . . (HMSO, three volumes, 1967).

554

B B Baker *et al*: *Glossary of oceanographic terms* (Washington, DC: US Naval Oceanographic Office, 1960; second edition, 1966).

Harold Barnes, *ed*: *Oceanography and marine biology: an annual review* (Allen and Unwin, 1963–).

Daniel Behrman: *Exploring the ocean* (Unesco, 1969–70–).

R H Belderson *et al*: *Sonographs of the sea floor: a picture atlas* (Elsevier, 1972).

C H Cotter: *The physical geography of the oceans* (Hollis and Carter, 1965).

R C Cowen: *Frontiers of the sea: the story of oceanographic exploration* (New York: Doubleday; Gollancz, 1960).

W M Cromie: *Exploring the secrets of the sea* (Allen and Unwin, 1964).

R A Davis: *Principles of oceanography* (Reading, Mass.: Addison-Wasley, 1972).

G E R Deacon, *ed*: *Seas, maps and men . . .* (Garden City: Doubleday, 1962).

Margaret Deacon: *Scientists and the sea 1650–1900: a study of marine science* (Academic Press, 1971).

R Dietz and J Piccard: *Seven miles down* (New York: Putnam, 1961).

David B Ericson and Goesta Wollin: *The ever-changing sea* (MacGibbon and Kee, 1968).

T F Gaskell: *The Gulf Stream* (Cassell, 1972).

T F Gaskell: *World beneath the oceans* (Aldus Books in association with W H Allen, 1964).

P Groen: *The waters of the sea* (Van Nostrand, 1967).

Bruce C Heezen and Charles H Hollister: *The face of the deep* (OUP, 1971).

P J Herring and M R Clarke, *ed*: *Deep oceans* (New York: Praeger, 1971).

Donald W Hood, *ed*: *Impingement of man on the oceans* (Wiley Interscience, 1971).

L M Hunt and D G Groves: *A glossary of ocean science and undersea technology terms* (Arlington: Compass Publ., 1965).

C P Idyll, *ed*: *The science of the sea* (Nelson, 1970).

C A M King: *Oceanography for geographers* (Arnold, 1962).

Otto Kinne: *Marine ecology* (Wiley, 1970–).

Blair Kinsman: *Wind waves: their generation and propagation on the ocean surface* (Prentice-Hall, 1965).

E B Kraus: *Atmosphere-ocean interaction* (Oxford: Clarendon Press, 1972).

Alexander McKee: *Farming the sea: first steps into inner space* (Souvenir Press, 1967).

D H Macmillan: *Tides* (CR Books, 1966).

Gerhard Newmann and W J Pierson, *jr*: *Principles of physical oceanography* (Prentice-Hall, 1966).

Mary Sears and Mary Swallow, *ed*: *Deep-sea research and oceanographic abstracts* (Woods Hole Oceanographic Institution and National Institute of Oceanography).

Mary Sears, *ed*: *Oceanography* (American Association for the Advancement of Science, 1961).

W E Yasso: *Oceanography: a study of inner space* (New York: Holt, Rinehart and Winston, 1965).

1168 '**Sea surveys:** *Britain's contribution to hydrography*', by Vice-Admiral Sir John Edgell (HMSO, 1965), is in five sections—'The early hydrographers', 'The hydrographers of the British Navy', 'Then and now', 'The work of the surveyor in war', 'Sea surveys, 1948–1965', the last named by Lt Commander P B Beazley. Included is the list of names of the Hydrographers of the British Navy and there is a selection of photographs and reproductions.

1169 '**Sedimentation:** *annotated bibliography of foreign literature*', was first edited by E Goldberg in 1965 and published for the United States Department of Agriculture and the National Science Foundation by the Israel Program for Scientific Translations, covering 1959–1964. Literature published in English from non-English countries was also included. Further volumes have covered the literature of one or two years and the index is cumulative.

Refer also

Henri et Geneviève Termier: *Erosion and sedimentation* (Translated and edited by D W and E E Humphries, Van Nostrand, 1963).

1170 '**The seismicity of the earth, 1953–1965**' was prepared by Professor J P Rothé, in English and French (Unesco, 1969), listing all earthquakes equal to or greater than 6, recorded during the period under review. Maps of each region give the epicentres, classified according to their magnitude and depth of focus. 286 pages of tables cover fifty-one regions, accompanied by notes.

1171 '**Seismicity of the earth and associated phenomena**', by B Gutenberg and C F Richter (Princeton University Press, 1949, 1954) was reproduced in facsimile by Hafner Publishing Company, 1965. The 1954 edition was used; following an introduction to the materials and methods employed, a classification is given of shocks, their mapping and the frequency and energy of earthquakes. Regional discussions are concerned with the Circum-Pacific belt, the Alpine belt, non-Alpine Asia, Oceanic Arctic belts, rift zones and the seismicity of marginal to stable masses. Each section is divided into more specific chapters. Tables and references take up about a third of the book.

Refer also

G A Eiby: *Earthquakes* (Muller, second revised edition, 1967).

Haroun Tazieff: *Volcanoes* (Prentice-Hall, 1962, translated by Arthur Tannenbaum from *Les volcans*, Paris: Dalpire, 1961).

S Thorarinsson: *Surtsey* (Reykjavik: Almena Bkafélagid, 1965, translated by Solvi Eysteinsson).

1172 '**Seismicity of the European area**', by Vít Kárník (Amsterdam: Reidel, in collaboration with Academia of Prague, 1969–), was carried out in accordance with the resolutions of the European Seismological Commission and its Subcommittee for Seismicity of the European Area, of which the author is Chairman. The history of the project is summarised in the introduction: section 2, 'Seismological information', includes definitions, national catalogues of earthquakes, earthquake parameters entering into the catalogue, their determination and accuracy; 3, 'Uniform classification of earthquakes'; 4, 'Statistical data'. A catalogue of earthquakes 1901–1955 forms the bulk of the book. Sources of information are given. A second volume followed.

1173 '**Seismology**: *a brief historical survey and a catalogue of exhibits in the Seismological Section of the Science Museum'*, a useful and practical booklet, was edited by J Wartnaby for the Ministry of Education: Science Museum (HMSO, 1957), *Geophysics handbook*, no 1. The text provides a compact summary of aspects of the topics concerned, both historical and current: 'The causes of earthquakes' deals with theories from myths to contemporary scientific explanations; 'The detection of earthquakes' and 'Interpreting the records' include descriptions and figures of the instruments used.

'The distribution of earthquakes' is followed by sections on 'Micro-seism' and 'Seismic prospecting'. The catalogue contains forty-five items, mainly instruments, pieces of equipment, and specific items such as the 'Chang Heng seismoscope' to 'Oil exploration in Britain' and the Geophone. A bibliography of monographs and articles is appended.

Refer also

Earthquake information bulletin (ESSA's National Earthquake Information Center, Rockville, Maryland).

K E Bullen: *An introduction to the theory of seismology* (CUP, third edition, 1963).

1174 'Selected bibliography of coastal geomorphology of the world', compiled by John T McGill (University of California, 1960), consists principally of references from books and periodicals used in the preparation of the 'Map of coastal landforms of the world', with a separate map, and was based mainly on materials in the libraries and map collections of the University of California.

1175 'Selected bibliography on Kuwait and the Arabian Gulf', compiled by Soraya M Kabeel (Kuwait University, 1969), includes some 1,300 entries of articles and books on the subject, both primary and secondary material; the first part is classified by subject order, the second is an alphabetical listing of authors, titles and subjects.

1176 'A selected list of books and articles on Japan in English, French and German', compiled by Hugh Borton and others (Harvard University Press for the Harvard-Yenching Institute, Cambridge, Mass, revised and enlarged edition, 1954), contains bibliographies, reference works, periodicals and, among other subject entries, 'Geography' and 'Economics', with sub-divisions. The index is comprehensive.

1177 'Selection of international railway documentation', monthly from January 1964, is edited jointly by the International Union of Railways, Paris, and the International Railway Congress Association, Brussels, prepared under the direction of the International Railway Documentation Bureau, with the co-operation of the documentation services of a great number of railway administrations. Three separate editions are in English, French and German. Each entry bears a running number, the UDC number, the classification number utilised by the International Railway Documentation Bureau and, if applicable, the numerical reference of a microfilm. Five broad subject headings are distinguished: 'General—economic and historic matters'; 'Railway operation'; 'Rolling stock and railway traction'; 'Fixed railway installations' and 'Technique of the other transport methods, general technique and miscellaneous'. The abstracts are initialled. Each issue includes an order form for microfilms or photocopies.

Refer also

Railway age, 1856–, semi-monthly by the Simmons-Boardman Publishing Corporation, Bristol, Conn.

1178 Semple, Ellen Churchill (1863–1932) is remembered especially for her *Influences of geographic environment . . . (qv)* in which she attempted to elucidate and interpret to English-speaking readers the theories of Ratzel, to whom she refers in the preface as 'the great master who was my teacher and friend during his life, and after his death my inspiration'. Her contribution as an academic geographer in her own right was, however, considerable. She taught intermittently in several American universities and played an important part in establishing the Graduate School of Geography in Clark University, being herself trained in economics and sociology as well as in geography. Of her other publications, the best known is *American history in its geographic conditions*, 1903, which was revised by C F Jones in collaboration with the author, 1933.

1179 'Serial atlas of the marine environment' has been in process of publication by the American Geographical Society since 1962. When completed, the work will constitute a unique source of co-ordinated data; high speed electronic computers assist in sorting and the results are being plotted on loose-leaf double sheets of transparent material to facilitate comparison, in a series of separate folios.

1180 'Settlement and encounter: *geographical studies presented to Sir Grenfell Price'*, edited by F Gale and G H Lawton (OUP, 1969), comprises a series of studies linked by the central theme of the practical and political implications of recent settlement and colonisation, with special reference to Australia, a theme of particular interest to Sir Grenfell Price. Included is an appreciation of Sir Grenfell, by A Marshall, and there is a bibliography of his works.

1181 'Shell nature lovers' atlas of England, Scotland, Wales' was compiled by James Fisher (Ebury Press and Michael Joseph, 1966), with maps by John R Flower, 'inspired by the revolution in conservation since 1945'. Included in the atlas are the natural 'treasures' to which public access is possible. Full use has been made of the published documents of such conservation bodies as the Nature Conservancy, the Forestry Commission, the Council for Nature, the Society for the Promotion of Nature Reserves, the National Trust for Scotland, the network of County Naturalists' Trusts, the Royal Society for the Protection of Birds, the Scottish Wildlife Trust, the Wildfowl Trust and the Wildfowlers' Association for Great Britain and Ireland. Each category of site has been represented in text and on maps by a symbol or letter; also useful is a list of addresses of relevant national organisations. Ordnance Survey maps have been used as a base for the maps; the scale throughout is 1:760,320, except for the map of the Greater London area, which is at 1:411,840, and the work ends with a summary of the Ordnance Survey maps particularly useful in naturalist work, either in walking or motoring, with notes on the application of the National Grid system. Handy to use with the Atlas is *The Shell book of exploring Britain*, compiled by Garry Hogg (John Baker, 1970), a new kind of touring guide, presenting carefully planned itineraries and introductions to the history, geography, agriculture and way of life of each area; also the *Shell County Guides*, edited by John Betjeman and John Piper.

1182 'Sierra Leone in maps', edited by John Clarke, was published in 1966 by the University of London Press for Fourah Bay College, Freetown, in a second edition, 1969. The work comprises fifty-one maps, with commentaries by thirteen past and present members of the college staff, who present comprehensively the nature and resources of the country. A bibliography, divided into five categories, is arranged by author.

Available also are *Tanzania in maps* and *Zambia in maps*.

1183 'Sino-Portuguese trade from 1514 to 1644: *a synthesis of Portuguese and Chinese sources'*, by T'ien-Tsê Chang (Leiden: Brill, second edition, 1969), is a photomechanical reprint, with some corrections of the first edition of 1933, which brings together important source material hitherto separated or unknown. The seven sections cover 'An historical sketch of China's maritime trade down to 1513'; 'The

560

early Sino-Portuguese trade relations'; 'The expulsion of foreigners from China and the prohibition of foreign trade'; 'Trade or no trade'; 'The rise of Macao'; 'The arrival of other Europeans in the Far East and the position of the Portuguese'; 'Macao in days of tribulation and the decline of Sino-Portuguese trade'. A bibliography is included.

1184 'Sir Francis Drake's voyage around the world: *its aims and achievements',* by Henry R Wagner, has been reprinted from the 1926 edition by N Israel, Amsterdam, 1969. The same firm also published *Sir Francis Drake: a pictorial biography*, by Hans P Kraus, in 1970, with an historical introduction by Lt Commander David W Waters and Richard Boulind and a detailed catalogue of the author's collection of manuscripts, printed books, maps and views, portraits and medals, mostly dating from Drake's own lifetime; included are 133 reproductions.

Refer also

K R Andrews: *Drake's voyages: a re-assessment of their place in Elizabethan maritime expansion* (Weidenfeld and Nicolson, 1967).

1185 Skelton, Dr R A (1906–1970) devoted his professional life to the study of historical cartography, passing on his scholarship by means of numerous books and articles. He was Superintendent of the Map Room of the British Museum and held office on national and international bodies, such as the editorial committee of *Imago mundi*, the Hakluyt Society, the Commission of Ancient Maps. Outstanding among his published works were his English edition of the *Geschichte der Kartographie, Explorers' maps, County atlases of the British Isles 1579–1850, Decorative printed maps* . . . and his contribution to the study and evaluation of *The Vinland map and the Tartar Relation;* among scores of articles, he contributed to special numbers of *The geographical magazine* devoted to maps and map-making and wrote innumerable reviews, prefaces and introductions.

1186 Smith: *J Russell Smith: geographer, educator, and conservationist,* by Virginia M Rowley (University of Pennsylvania Press, 1964) is a detailed study, including illustrations and a bibliography.

1187 Smithsonian Institution, Washington, is unique among the learned organisations of the world. *The Smithsonian Institution,* by

Walter Karp, 1965, produced by the editors of *American Heritage*, tells of the bequest under which the Institution was founded, its early years and its vast reputation among scholars everywhere. The *Smithsonian meteorological tables*, in a sixth revised edition, by Robert J List, is a reference work consisting of 174 tables—conversion, wind and dynamic, barometric and hypsometric, geopotential and aerological, standard atmosphere, etc. Other publications include *The large Magellanic cloud*, by Paul W Hodge and Frances W Wright, 1968; a boxed set containing a book and an identification atlas, consists of 168 separate photographic charts, with text giving a historical survey of discoveries about the nature and properties of the cloud, including a summary of current knowledge. *Opportunities in oceanography*, third edition in 1968, was prepared by the Interagency Committee on Oceanography; *Museums directory of the United States and Canada*, second edition, 1965, is a joint publication of the American Association of Museums and the Institution. Another fine production is *Seabirds of the tropical Atlantic Ocean*, a Smithsonian identification manual, by George E Watson. *Flora of Japan*, a much revised and extended translation, by Jisaburu Ohwi, edited by F G Meyer and E H Walker, 1965, contains some 4,500 species. In addition, there are many more works on climate and meteorology, anthropology, biology, botany and forestry, exploration, regional geography and the Harriman Alaska series of reports, setting out the findings of the Harriman Alaska Expedition of 1899. *Lighthouse of the skies: the Smithsonian Astrophysical Observatory; background and history, 1846–1955* was completed by B Z Jones in 1965.

1188 'Snow structure and ski fields', by Gerald Seligman, was a key work in the subject, prepared for the International Geophysical Assembly at Edinburgh, in 1936, when the Association for the Study of Snow and Ice was formed. Soon after, the association became the British Glaciological Society and has finally progressed to become the International Glaciological Society.

Refer also

Terence Armstrong *et al: Illustrated glossary of snow and ice* (Scott Polar Research Institute, second edition, 1973).

D E Pedgley: 'The shapes of snowdrifts', *Weather*, February 1967.

Snow hydrology, Proceedings of workshop seminar held at the University of New Brunswick, February 1968 (Canadian National Committee, International Hydrological Decade).

1189 The Snowy Mountains Scheme, Australia, is probably the largest single venture undertaken in that continent. First envisaged as an irrigation project and later a hydro-electric operation, it is complex and far-reaching in effects which will continue to have social and technical advantages, as the following monographs point out: Lionel Wigmore: *Struggle for the Snowy: the background of the Snowy Mountains Scheme* (Melbourne: OUP, 1968); C Meeking: *Snowy Mountains conquest: harnessing the waters of Australia's highest mountains* (Hutchinson, 1968); R S Coggins: *The Snowy Mountain Scheme* (Longmans, 1959).

1190 Social statistics: The growing interest in social conditions and the rapid expansion of the social services in recent decades have brought in their wake a wealth of statistical documents about all aspects of our constantly changing society, all of interest to geographers. Notable are the wide range of social surveys by Government departments, Royal Commissions and other special committees. In 1970, the General Register Office for England and Wales was merged with the Government Social Survey to form the new Office of Population Censuses and Surveys.

1191 Société de Géographie de Paris, the first specialist geographical society, has, since its foundation in 1821, exerted the greatest influence on geographical opinion and research. The *Bulletin*, with its successors, 1822–, has provided a forum for discussion of the highest scholarship and has reflected the development of geographical studies through this formative period. In 1941, the periodical joined with the *Annales de géographie* (*qv*) under the new title of *Annales de géographie et bulletin de la Société de Géographie*. The Society has published also the *Acta geographica* since 1947 and issues a monthly bibliography. The library holds a valuable collection of more than four hundred thousand volumes.

1192 Society for the Bibliography of Natural History, founded in 1936, promotes the study of natural history in the widest sense, including geology, botany and zoology. The *Journal* has included a number of facsimiles of rare natural history works and, in 1959, the first of a series known as the Sherborn Fund Facsimiles was published. The first reproduction in this series was that of Alexander von Humboldt's *Essai sur la géographie des plantes*, 1807. The Society has no central headquarters, the Secretariat being located at the British Museum (Natural History), London.

1193 Society for Environmental Education, founded in 1968, to provide opportunities for the discussion of ideas on the role of the environment in education, seeks to further the development of Environmental Studies in schools as an inter-disciplinary contribution to the curriculum, based on fieldwork. A *Bulletin* is published twice a year.

1194 The Society for the History of Discoveries was founded in 1960 for the purpose of stimulating publications in research in the history of geographical exploration. Membership, on an international basis, is interested mainly in geography, history, the relevant literature and science. The *Annals* of the Society, *Terrae incognitae*, are both catholic and eclectic in publication of articles. In 1964, a book review section was added to the Society's semi-annual *Newsletter*. *Terrae incognitae*, an annual, was authorised at the 1966 Annual Meeting and the Society also sponsors a monograph series jointly with the Newberry Library of Chicago and the University of Chicago Press.

1195 The Society for Nautical Research was founded in 1910 to encourage research into nautical antiquities, matters relating to seafaring and shipbuilding in all ages and among all nations, the language and customs of the sea and other subjects of nautical interest. Among other early activities of the Society was its influence in the establishment of the National Maritime Museum at Greenwich and the *Victory* Museum at Portsmouth. *The mariner's mirror*, the quarterly journal, contains illustrated articles, shorter notes, careful and informative signed reviews and short notices (monthly from January 1911 to September 1914 and from July 1919 to December 1923); an index of volumes 1 to 35 has been compiled by R C Anderson. Also published are 'Occasional publications' and *A treatise on shipbuilding . . .,* edited by W Salisbury and R C Anderson.

1196 Society of University Cartographers, established in Glasgow in 1964, has now a Canadian branch, based on York University, Toronto. An annual summer school and annual meeting are held; symposia deals with such topics as the needs and interests of practising cartographers, thematic mapping of all kinds and the history of cartography. A sub-committee has been formed to investigate the training of cartographers. The *SUC bulletin*, published twice a year, contains articles and notes concerning new publications.

1197 'Socio-economic models in geography', edited by Richard J Chorley and Peter Haggett (Methuen, university paperback, 1967, 1968), deals with 'Models, paradigms and the new geography', 'Demographic models and geography', 'Sociological models in geography', 'Models of economic developments', 'Models of urban geography and settlement location', 'Models of industrial location', 'Models of agricultural activity', well illustrated with diagrams and figures. There are end-of-chapter references.

1198 'Soil biology and biochemistry', an international journal dealing with soil organisms, their biochemical activities and influence on the soil environment and plant growth, is prepared by an editorial committee and regional editors under Professor E W Russell (Oxford: Pergamon Press). Original work is included on quantitative, analytical and experimental aspects of these studies, providing a record of the progress of such studies throughout the world. The periodical also contains short communications and notes concerning current experiments, techniques, equipment and significant observations.

1199 'Soil biology, reviews of research' (Unesco, 1969) is one of the Natural Resources Research series. Chapters are included on methodological problems in soil biology in various parts of the world, the biological fixation of atmospheric nitrogen by free-living bacteria, ecological associations among soil micro-organisms, biology and soil fertility, microbial degradation and the biological effects of pesticides in soil, with emphasis on the humid tropical and semi-arid soils and on the related problems of conservation or reclamation.
Refer also

Brian T Bunting: *The geography of soil* (Hutchinson University Library, second edition, 1967).

N M Comber: *An introduction to the scientific study of the soil* (Arnold, fourth edition revised by W N Townsend, 1961).

James Cruikshank: *Soil geography* (Newton Abbot: David and Charles, 1972).

I P Gerasimov and M A Glazovskaya: *Fundamentals of soil science and soil geography* (Jerusalem: Israel Program for Scientific Translation, 1965).

1200 Soil Survey of Great Britain: Soil Survey maps are published by the Ordnance Survey on behalf of the Soil Survey of England and Wales and the Macaulay Institute for Soil Research in Scotland. Individual *Memoirs—Bulletins of the Soil Survey of Great Britain; Memoirs of the Soil Survey of England and Wales; Memoirs of the Soil Survey of Scotland*—contribute to the full use and understanding of the soil maps. In many cases, folded copies of the maps are included in the *Memoirs*.

Refer also

Soil Survey Bulletin of the National Soil Survey of Ireland, 1964–.

Anthony Young: 'Soil Survey procedures in land development planning', *The geographical journal*, February 1973.

1201 Somerville, Mary, (1780–1872) during her long life had a great influence on academic education in several branches of the natural sciences. Her work *On the connexion of the physical sciences*, 1836, included a discussion of tides, currents, climate, plant geography and other natural phenomena. One of the best known of her works and of lasting value for its methodology was *Physical geography*, 1848, which was revised in a sixth edition by H W Bates in 1870 (last edition, 1877). In this work, a general review of the continents is followed by more detailed regional treatment; topics, such as the ocean, rivers, vegetation and the distribution of life forms from insects to humans, are discussed, incorporating regional examples throughout.

Refer also

J N L Baker: 'Mary Somerville and geography in England', *Geographical journal*, 111, 1948, reprinted in *The history of geography: papers by J N L Baker*, 1963.

1202 Sorre, Maximilien (1880–1962), a pupil of Paul Vidal de la

Blache and Emmanuel de Martonne, continued the inspiration of the French school of geography and was a leading figure in academic geography, especially at Lille, Clermont-Ferrand, Aix-Marseille and at the Sorbonne, where he succeeded Albert Demangeon. He wrote prolifically, especially on his main interests, the relationships of geography with biology, medicine and sociology, and the influence of environment on human development. He contributed some volumes to the *Géographie universelle* and many papers to the *Annales de géographie;* among his major works are the three-volume *Fondements de la géographie humaine*, completed in 1952, and *L'homme sur la terre: traité de géographie humaine*, 1961.

1203 'Source book for geography teaching', prepared by the Commission on the Teaching of Geography of the International Geographical Union (Longmans/UNESCO, 1965), superseded the earlier UNESCO publication, *A handbook of suggestions on the teaching of geography*, 1951. It was published 'in the belief that geography can make a meaningful contribution to the advancement of mutual understanding between peoples'. Sections include 'Importance and educational value of geography'; 'The nature and spirit of geography teaching'; 'Teaching techniques: direct observation'; 'Teaching techniques: indirect observation'; 'Teaching material'; 'The geography room'; 'The organisation of geography teaching'. 'Sources of documentation' by B Brouillette, is a particularly useful section, arranged by such broad subject groupings as periodicals, bibliographies, a succinct international bibliography, teaching material and international statistics. In 1973 discussion began concerning a new edition.

1204 'Sources of the Nile: Explorers' Maps, 1856–1891' contains reproductions of maps from the archives of the Royal Geographical Society, maps made in the field in East Africa by such men as Livingstone, Speke, Grant and Gordon, who discovered and explored the Nile, with introduction and notes by G R Crone.

1205 'South African bibliography', compiled by Reuben Musiker (Crosby Lockwood, 1970) is a companion volume to the *Guide to South African reference books (qv)*.

1206 'South and Southeast Asia: *a bibliography of bibliographies'*, compiled by G Raymond Nunn (University of Hawaii, East-West

Center Library, 1966), is arranged principally by countries, subdivided by date.

1207 'South Asian government bibliographies', in three volumes, published by Mansell, London, provide the most comprehensive history of central government publications of Ceylon, India and Pakistan, prepared under the aegis of the Centre of South Asian Studies, Cambridge. Much of the material has not been systematically recorded elsewhere. The three volumes comprise *Union catalogue of the Government of Ceylon*, edited by Teresa Macdonald; *Union catalogue of the Central Government of India publications;* and *Union catalogue of the Government of Pakistan publications*, both edited by Rajeshwari Datta.

1208 'South East Asian archives', July 1968– (Kuala Lumpur: SARBICA), reflects all the major archival activities in the South East Asian region. The journal is published annually; the first issue being devoted mainly to the proceedings of the inaugural conference of the new organisation and the second mainly containing the papers on archives presented to the International Conference on Asian History held in Kuala Lumpur in August 1968.

1209 The South Sea Commission is an advisory and consultative body concerned with the economic and social development of the non-self-governing territories administered by the six Member Governments in the South Pacific region: Australia, France, Great Britain, New Zealand, the Netherlands and the United States of America. Work programmes have included research on the improvement of air and sea transport, fishing and other basic industries and agriculture. Publications include the *Proceedings*, issued twice a year; the *Quarterly bulletin*, 1951–1959, re-named the *South Pacific bulletin*, 1960–. A library was set up in 1948, with headquarters at Noumea, which collects basic reference books, official publications, relevant maps and essential standard works, as well as files of the monographs, information bulletins, technical reports and pamphlets published by the Commission.

1210 'South-east Asia: *a critical bibliography'*, compiled by Kennedy G Tregonning (University of Arizona Press; University of Malaya Press, 1969), covers the countries of Burma, Thailand, Cambodia, Vietnam, North Vietnam, Malaysia, Indonesia and the

Philippines. Each section is introduced by short comments and annotations are appended to the entries as necessary.

Refer also

C A Fisher: *South-east Asia: a social, economic and political geography* (Methuen; New York: Dutton, 1964).

Donald W Fryer: *Emerging south-east Asia: a study in growth and stagnation* (Philip, 1972).

1211 'South-west Pacific: *a geography of Australia, New Zealand and their Pacific Island neighbourhoods',* by K B Cumberland (Whitcombe and Tombs; Methuen, fourth edition, 1968), remains a basic introduction to the area, well illustrated and including maps in the text and a bibliography. The area covered includes New Guinea, New Hebrides, New Caledonia, Fiji, Samoa, Tonga and the Cook Islands. For the latest edition, all the maps have been re-drawn in a bold, clear style.

Refer also

Gordon Swaine: *Agricultural zoology in Fiji* (Foreign and Commonwealth Office, Overseas Development Administration, Overseas Research Publication, no 18, HMSO, 1971).

1212 'Soviet and East European abstracts' series has been edited and published quarterly at the Institute for Soviet and East European Studies, University of Glasgow, replacing the former *Information supplement to Soviet studies.* It covers Albania, Bulgaria, Czechoslovakia, the Democratic Republic of Germany, Hungary, Poland, the USSR and Yugoslavia. Each issue contains about a thousand abstracts of books, newspapers and journals published in these countries.

1213 'Soviet geography: *accomplishments and tasks: a symposium of fifty chapters, contributed by fifty-six leading Soviet geographers',* was edited by a committee of the Geographic Society of the USSR, Academy of Sciences of the USSR, of which the Chairman was I P Gerasimov, and was translated from the Russian by Lawrence Ecker. The English edition was edited by C D Harris and published by the American Geographical Society in 1962, as Occasional paper no 1. The work begins with 'Geography in the Soviet Union: an introduction' by I P Gerasimov and 'Russian geography', by A A Grigoryev. Part I then continues with 'The history and present state of Soviet geography'; II, 'The specialised geographic sciences'; III,

'Integrated scientific problems and trends'; IV, 'The role of geographers in the transformation of nature'; V, 'Methods of geographic research'; VI 'Geographic education and popularization of scientific geographic knowledge'; VII, 'The Geographic Society of the USSR'. Chapters within these parts are by individual authors. The text is illustrated and references are included.

Refer also

G Melvyn Howe: 'Geography in the Soviet universities', *The geographical journal*, March 1968.

1214 'Soviet geography: *review and translation',* published by the American Geographical Society, supported by the National Science Foundation, ten times a year (September to June) from 1960, aims to make available in English reports of current Soviet research in geography. The chief editor and translator is Theodore Shabad. Most of the reports are translations from *Izvestiya Akademii Nauk SSR, seriya geograficheskaya; Izvestiya vsesoyuznogo geograficheskogo obshchestva; Vestnik Moskovskogo Universiteta, seriya geografiya; Khozyaystvo;* and *Voprosy geografii.* Brief abstracts precede the articles. Most issues also contain news notes on Soviet political and economic developments of interest to geographers. Lists of references usually follow the articles and frequent surveys of Soviet geographical literature are included. A transliteration table is given for the general information of readers and for the identification of the geographical names on the maps reproduced in *Soviet geography.*

Refer also

L S Berg: *Natural regions of the USSR* (Macmillan, 1950).

J P Cole and F C German: *A geography of the USSR: the background to a planned economy* (Butterworth, 1961, reprinted, 1962).

Paul L Horecky, *ed: Russia and the Soviet Union: a bibliographic guide to Western language publications* (University of Chicago Press, 1965).

Georges Jorré: *The Soviet Union: the land and its people* (Longmans, second edition, 1961, translated and revised by E D Laborde).

P E Lydolph: *Geography of the USSR* (Wiley, 1964).

Theodore Shabad: *Geography of the USSR: a regional survey* (Columbia UP; OUP, 1951).

1215 'Soviet trade directory', edited by Alec Flegon (Flegon Press,

1964), provided the first such guide to the industry of the Soviet Union to be published outside Russia; it was comprehensive, reflecting changing circumstances in trading with the non-Communist world and a changed attitude to the publication of information. The directory was based entirely on official Russian sources. A list of Soviet factories, in Russian and English, is classified by industry and included is a map of the principal centres of ferrous and non-ferrous metallurgy.

1216 'Soviet Union', a colourful monthly pictorial, covering every aspect of life in the USSR, is available in matching English and Russian editions, from Central Books, London.

1217 'Spacial analysis: *a reader in statistical geography'*, edited by B J L Berry and D F Marble (Prentice-Hall International, 1968), consists of thirty-six individual contributions on aspects of the subject.

1218 Special Committee on Oceanic Research was set up in 1957 by the International Council of Scientific Unions to frame a programme of research, especially on climate, fertility of the sea and on the disposal of radio-active waste. A special research programme was organised in the Indian Ocean during 1962–63.

1219 Special Libraries Association of New York has devoted much thought to geographical collections and maps. The Geography and Map Division was organised as a unit of the Washington Chapter in 1941. The first number of the *Bulletin* appeared in November, 1947, thereafter twice a year until 1953, when it became quarterly; it has gradually expanded to include research articles, lists of new maps and books, bibliographies, book reviews and news valuable to geographers, librarians and earth scientists. Findings of surveys and recommendations are frequently incorporated in the *Bulletin*, such as the final report on the cataloguing and classification practices of the larger American libraries in no 24, April 1956. Other papers of geographical interest appear from time to time in *Special libraries*. An important research tool published by the Association was *Map collections in the United States and Canada: a directory (qv). The cartographic research guide*, includes bibliographies and selected references relating to the various aspects of maps, map-making, map research and study; Part IV treats of *The catalogue library and the map librarian*.

1220 'Speculum orbis terrarum', the work of Gerard de Jode (Antwerp, 1578), was reproduced by TOT in 1965, with an introduction by R A Skelton. From a cartographic point of view it is just as important as Ortelius' great achievement.

1221 Speed, John (1552–1629) was not himself a cartographer, but he collected together a wealth of detailed information and views and so continued the work of Saxton and Norden (*qv*) in systematically making known the topographical features of the country. His most notable work was the *Theatre of the Empire of Great Britaine*, 1611. Speed's maps were the first on which were shown the territorial divisions of each county. *A prospect of the most famous parts of the world*, 1627, has been reprinted in facsimile by TOT, with a bibliographical note by R A Skelton.

1222 'The spirit and purpose of geography', by S W Wooldridge (*qv*) and W G East (Hutchinson University Library, 1957, third edition 1966), is a classic introduction to geographical studies, dealing with the development of geography as a subject discipline and examining some of the main aspects of the contemporary subject and the concepts involved in physical geography, biogeography, mapping, historical, political, economic and regional geography.

1223 Stamp, Sir Laurence Dudley (1898–1966) was a practical as well as a theoretical geographer and the outstanding personality among academic English geographers during recent years. He worked and held appointments in many parts of the world; he was in the Chair of Geography at the London School of Economics between 1945 and 1948 and was appointed to the Chair of Social Geography when that was created in 1948. His major achievement is usually considered to have been his organisation of the Land Utilisation Survey of Great Britain (*qv*); he became the leading authority on land use and a pioneer in urging the planned use of land resources in every country. In 1942 the Minister of Agriculture appointed him to be his adviser on rural land utilisation and he thus became one of the first geographers to be used by the government in Britain. At the time of his death, he was appointed to head a committee to advise the government on the use of natural resources and land. He was director of the World Land-Use Survey of the International Geographical Union (*qv*). By his ability, academic integrity and personality, in the course of innumerable commitments, both international and national, he advanced the prestige of British geography throughout the world and through his published works he brought a fresh impetus to the understanding of geographical matters to students, to his professional colleagues and to laymen alike. In addition to contributions to periodicals, prefaces and forewords, inaugural and presidential addresses, he wrote or edited many textbooks, edited the UNESCO *History of land use in arid lands*, 1961, *A glossary of geographical terms* (*qv*) and *Longman's dictionary of geography* (*qv*). His *A commercial geography* is in a ninth revised edition (Longman) and *The British Isles* . . . written with S H Beaver, was revised in a sixth edition (Longman, 1971). The Dudley Stamp Memorial Fund was established in 1967 for the encouragement of geographical study and research, especially for young geographers; and a Dudley Stamp Memorial cumulative index for *Geography* has been prepared, 1972.

1224 'Standard encyclopedia of the world's mountains' and *Standard encyclopedia of the world's oceans and islands*, both edited by Anthony Huxley, and *Standard encyclopedia of the world's rivers and lakes*, edited by R Kay Gresswell and Anthony Huxley, are all published by Weidenfeld and Nicolson, 1962, 1965, and are all constructed on approximately the same pattern. Each comprises an introductory general article, followed by alphabetical entries of varying length. Many coloured and monochrome plates and text illustrations are included, also locational maps.

Refer also
W S Bristowe: *A book of islands* (Bell, 1969).

1225 Stanford, Edward, Limited, was founded in 1852. In 1884, the Stationery Office transferred the entire government stock to it. The firm's policy changed in 1947 when the map printing and publishing became absorbed into George Philip & Son Ltd, and Stanford became a clearing house for sheet maps and atlases, maintaining an excellent bibliographical service. Revised catalogues are issued at frequent intervals. The Stanford 'Planfile', designed specially to accommodate Ordnance Survey maps and plans, can accommodate up to two hundred sheets by a method of suspension filing, and an index to the contents can be mounted on the inside of the lid. *The Stanford reference catalogue of maps and atlases*, in loose-leaf format, is a unique reference guide and sales catalogue of modern cartography, compiled from information supplied by map and atlas publishers throughout the world. Individual sections include maps of each continent, region and country of the world, also the sky and planets; national official surveys, thematic maps, wall maps and atlases of the world, regions and countries, road maps and atlases, town plans, tourist maps and guidebooks are listed, by title, publisher, scale, characteristics, date, size and price in sterling. For maps consisting of a number of sheets, there is an index showing which sheets have been published and, where appropriate, the various editions of each sheet. Amendments and additions, together with revised pages, are issued in twice yearly bulletins. Details are given also of equipment stocked or which can be supplied, with information of other services offered; new publications are noted, price changes, corrections and deletions. There is a thumb index. At intervals, a 'catalogue' sheet presents information of catalogues and lists available, under the headings 'General', 'Tourist', 'Nautical' (including Stanford's coloured charts, Maritime Press publications and Kandy books), 'Business', 'Academic' and a 'box' left free for 'Special requirements'.

1226 'Stanford's geological atlas of Great Britain and Ireland' was first published in 1904. A revised edition, in 1964, re-written and redrawn by T Eastwood, includes comprehensive information. Excellent geological maps of the counties are accompanied by geological descriptions of the scenery on all main railway routes and accounts of the topography, county by county.

1227 'States and trends of geography in the United States, 1957–1960', published by the Association of American Geographers in 1961, was a report prepared by the Association, in collaboration with the National Academy of Sciences, National Research Council, for the Commission on Geography of the Pan American Institute of Geography and History.

1228 'Statistical analysis in geography', by Leslie J King (Prentice-Hall International, 1969), attempts a review of the applications of statistical analysis in geography to date, examining some of the achievements along these lines and the relative strengths and weaknesses of different analyses, with emphasis on the unique spatial problems of point pattern analysis, areal association and regionalisation. 'Emerging trends and future prospects' are touched upon; a glossary of terms and symbols is included, as well as a bibliography.
Refer also

574

Joyce Ball, *ed: Foreign statistical documents: a bibliography of general, international trade, and agricultural statistics, including holdings of the Stanford University Libraries* (Stanford, Hoover Institution on War, Revolution and Peace, Stanford University, 1967).

1229 'Statistical mapping and the presentation of statistics', by G C Dickinson (Arnold, 1963, reprinted 1964; Second edition, 1973), names four special categories of reasons for compiling statistical maps, namely: to arouse greater interest in the subject matter concerned; to clarify it, simplify it or explain its more important aspects; to prove a point referred to; or to act as a statistical 'quarry' for other users. Statistical techniques are examined, as affecting the compilation of maps and diagrams, followed by sections dealing with 'Sense from statistics: the search for the significant'; 'Choosing the right method and making the most of it'; 'General aspects of map design'; 'Some worked examples' and 'Sources of statistics'. An appendix gives a 'List of Census Reports for Great Britain, 1801–1931'. Sketchmaps and diagrams illustrate the text.

1230 'Statistical methods and the geographer', by S Gregory (Longmans, 1963; 'Geographies for advanced study' series), provides an introduction to the assessment of quantitative data in geographical studies, dealing with such topics as 'The nature of the raw material'; 'The calculation and use of the mean'; 'Deviation and variability'; 'The normal frequency distribution curve and its uses'; 'Other frequency distribution curves'; 'Characteristics of samples'; 'Methods of sampling'; 'The comparison of sample values'; 'The problem of correlation'; 'Regression lines and confidence limits'; 'Fluctuating and trends' and 'Scope for the future'. There is a short bibliography.

1231 'Statistics: *African sources for market research',* by Joan M Harvey (CBD Research Limited, Beckenham, Kent, 1970), is arranged by 'Country sections'; there is an index of titles and one of organisations. For each entry, the address of the central office is given, any bibliographical material available, a statistical summary, production, external trade, a quarterly trade survey and relevant libraries.

1232 Stefansson, Vilhjalmur (1879–1962) was a vigorous personality, an original thinker and a practical pioneer. His greatest achievements lay in his exploration of the Arctic, in his development of techniques for living in Arctic conditions and in making the polar environment more widely understood. His published works on the Arctic include *The friendly Arctic* . . ., 1921; *Unsolved mysteries of the Arctic*, 1939; and *Ultima Thule* . . ., 1942. He collected an invaluable polar library, which he gave to the University of Dartmouth; the Stefansson Collection, moved to new quarters in 1959, now comprises more than seventy thousand items and tape recordings. *Dictionary catalog of the Stefansson Collection on the Polar regions* was reproduced by G K Hall in eight volumes, 1966. Stefansson's second abiding interest was in exploration generally, particularly in the theory he put forward in *The northward course of empire*, 1922, a work of compelling interest. Among his other notable contributions to the literature of exploration were *Great adventures and explorations: from the earliest times to the present, as told by the explorers themselves*, 1947, and *Northwest to fortune: the search of western man for a commercially practical route to the Far East*, 1960.

1233 Stembridge, J H (1889–1969) was a pioneer in geography teaching, committed early in his career to the improvement and status of geography as a major subject in the academic curriculum; he was influential in the development of the geographical equipment available and himself wrote a wide range of textbooks. His appointment as Geographical Editor of the Oxford University Press was of great significance and he supervised the production of a number of educational atlases. He is perhaps most widely known for his 'World-wide geographies', 1930–; his *Germany* went into a fourth edition, 1950; *A portrait of Canada* was published in 1943 and *Africa* in 1963.

1234 Steward, J H, Limited, London, is one of the most notable firms specialising in surveying, drawing, optical and meteorological instruments—compasses and clinometers, altimeters, telescopes, thermometers, hygrometers, stereoscopes, plane tables, planimeters, hypsometers, soil samplers, etc. Catalogues and price lists are issued at intervals, in addition to special leaflets and interim news sheets.

1235 'Stieler's atlas of modern geography' has been notable for scholarship balance and technical excellence since the first definitive edition of 1831. Particularly interesting new editions have been the

576

centenary edition of 1925 and the international edition of 1934, completely revised by Herman Haack and others. The chief use of the atlas is locational; the excellent index contains some three hundred thousand entries.

Refer also

Dr Werner Horn, in *Petermanns Geographische Mitteilungen*, 1967, part 4: an appreciation of Adolf Stieler and a list of the 144 maps produced by Stieler between 1798 and 1837. His early maps were drawn for a periodical, the *Allgemeine Geographischen Ephemeriden;* later he co-operated with Justus Perthes.

1236 **'The storage and conservation of maps',** a report prepared by a Committee of the Royal Geographical Society in 1954, was printed separately and also included in *The geographical journal*, June 1955.

Refer also

British Standard Specification for the Storage of Documents: Topographical maps and drawings.

1237 **'The story of maps',** by Lloyd A Brown (Little, Brown and Company, Boston, 1949; McClelland and Stewart Limited, Canada), is now a rare classic. The text follows a chronological trend: 'The earth takes shape; the habitable world'; 'The world of Claudius Ptolemy'; 'The Middle Ages'; 'Charts and the haven-finding art'; 'The map and chart trade'; 'The latitude'; 'The longitude'. 'Survey of a country'; 'Survey of a world'. There are extensive notes and a bibliography and line drawings and map extracts in the text. Lloyd A Brown was former curator of the fine collection of maps at the William L Clements Library, University of Michigan, then Librarian, Peabody Institute of Baltimore.

1238 **Strabo,** Greek historian and geographer, born about 63 BC, travelled widely and with lively intelligence, setting down his observations, together with references from his equally wide reading, in a seventeen-volume *Geography*, thus providing one of the chief sources for contemporary topographic knowledge, beliefs and geographic thought. Following the introductory books, two deal with Spain and Gaul, two with Italy, one with northern and eastern Europe, three with Greece, one with Asia and the Far East, three with Asia Minor, one with Persia and India, one with the Tigris-Euphrates area, Syria and Arabia, and one with Africa. He advanced the concept that physical geography could not be separated from human geography and, in fact, confined geographical science to the inhabited world. The Loeb edition, 1917–32, by H L Jones, includes a bibliography.

1239 'The stratigraphy of the British Isles', by Dorothy H Rayner (CUP, 1967), is concerned mainly with surface and near surface processes and the rocks resulting from them, in a straightforward, not too technical style. A particular feature is the integration of Irish stratigraphy with that of the rest of the British Isles. The impact of other branches of earth sciences, such as sedimentology and geochronology, is taken into account. An appendix sets out 'Stratigraphical divisions and zonal tables'. There are a few excellent photographs, a number of diagrammatic maps and figures, and references at the ends of chapters.

Refer also

    E A Middlemiss: *British stratigraphy* (Allen and Unwin, 1969).

1240 'Studies in cartobibliography, *British and French and in the bibliography of itineraries and road-books',* a unique work by Sir H G Fordham, 1914, has been reprinted by Dawsons of Pall Mall, London, 1969. Revised papers include 'An introduction to the study of the cartography of the English and Welsh countries, with an index list of the maps of Hertfordshire, 1579–1900'; 'British and Irish itineraries and road-books'; 'Descriptive list of the maps of the Great Level of the Fens, 1604–1900'; 'John Cary, mapseller and globe-maker'; 'Descriptive catalogues of maps and methods of arrangement, with specimens of full and abridged descriptions of maps of various dates'; 'An itinerary of the sixteenth century: *La guide des chemins d'Angleterre';* 'The cartography of the Provinces of France, 1570–1757', concluding with 'A bibliography of works of reference relating to British and French topography and cartography'. Notes and references are cited throughout.

1241 'Studies in the climatology of South Asia', compiled by V Schweinfurth and others, in 1970, consists of 'A rainfall atlas' of the Indo-Pakistan sub-continent based on rainy days. In thirty-two pages are fifteen, mostly coloured, maps at 1:7,500,000, with three text contributions and a bibliography of rainfall conditions in India and Pakistan between 1945 and 1969.

1242 'Studies in urban history', an Arnold series designed to fill gaps in existing publications on cities and the development of urban areas and to demonstrate particular techniques of research or approach. Their fore-runner was *The study of urban history*, edited by H J Dyos, Professor of Urban History, University of Leicester, also general editor of the new series. The volumes have a standard format but in all other respects remain completely unstereotyped.

Note The Commission on the Processes and Patterns of Urbanisation was established at the New Delhi International Geographical Union Congress, 1968.

1243 'Studies of a small democracy: *essays in honour of Willis Airey'* (Paul's Book Arcade for the University of Auckland), edited by Robert Chapman and Keith Sinclair, contains a portrait, diagrams, reference notes and commentary on the work of Willis Thomas Goodwin Airey.

1244 'Subject catalog of the Special Panama Collection of the Canal Zone Library-Museum: *the history of the Isthmus of Panama as it applies to interoceanic transportation'* was printed in one volume by G K Hall, 1964. Nearly half of this collection is related to the planning and construction of the existing Panama Canal; these items include some five thousand books, reports, engineering drawings, maps, diaries and photographs. Other holdings of the Canal Zone Library-Museum pertain to pioneer exploration and voyages in the region; early surveys for a canal and a railroad and post-1914 projects for improvement of the canal and for a sea-level waterway. Twenty-six pages of maps and photographs are included.

Refer also
Ian Cameron: *The impossible dream: the building of the Panama Canal* (Hodder and Stoughton, 1971).

1245 Suess, Eduard (1831–1914) was one of the major influences in physical geography during his academic career, particularly in Vienna, where he was professor of geology. His great work, *Das Antlitz der Erde*, published in four volumes between 1883 and 1909, was translated into French by de Margerie and into English as *The face of the earth*.

1246 Suggate, Leonard S (1889–1970) was one of the leaders of the 'new' geography, which developed so rapidly after the second world war. In addition to the influence of his imaginative teaching, which helped to establish geography in schools, he produced the classic *Africa*, which went into many editions, also *Australia and New Zealand*, besides numerous notes and contributions to journals. He was one of the earliest teachers to recognise the value of field studies, illustrations and visual aids in teaching.

1247 'The surface water year book of Great Britain' (Water Resources Board and Scottish Development Department, HMSO, 1968), in its latest edition, includes hydrometric statistics for British rivers, together with related rainfalls and river water temperature for the year ended 30 September 1965. This volume was the first in a new series, designed to be in conformity with new annual publications presenting statistics of rainfall and groundwater. A supplement, published soon after the parent volume, is to be issued every five years, containing descriptions, information and explanation. Five yearbooks and one supplement will constitute one complete volume.
  Refer also
    Water in Britain: a study in applied hydrology and resource geography (Macmillan, 1972).

1248 'A survey of the mineral industry of Southern Africa', by R B Toombs, was published by the Department of Mines and Technical Surveys, Mineral Resources Division, Canada, in 1962, as a record of the Seventh Commonwealth Mining and Metallurgical Congress, 1961. A section considers the minerals of the country, followed by regional mineral production, relevant comments on the geography and geology, also on the minerals as part of the economy. Statistics are included, also illustrations and maps, in addition to maps in a pocket.

1249 Sverdrup, Harald Ulrik (1888–1957) contributed largely to research work in oceanography and polar science, especially as professor of meteorology at the Geophysical Institute in Bergen, as director of the Norwegian Polar Institute and director of the Scripps Institute of Oceanography of the University of California. One of his major published works, in association with other scientists, was *The oceans: their physics, chemistry and general biology*, 1942 (Allen and Unwin, 1944); his *Oceanography for meteorologists* was published by Allen and Unwin in 1945.

1250 'Sweden books', a small catalogue compiled by Dillons's University Bookshop in co-operation with the Swedish Institute, London, 1970, contains a section on 'Geography' and another on 'Tourism'.

1251 SYMAP, the Synagraphic Mapping System, is capable of composing spatially distributed data of wide diversity into a map, a graph or other visual display, its main advantages being its adaptability and utilisation of widely available computer hardware, notably the line-printer, to produce the displays. The system has been developed at the Northwestern University's Technological Institute by Professor H T Fisher, Professor of City Planning at the Harvard Graduate School of Design; he was the founder and is the Director of the Laboratory for Computer Graphics and Spatial Analysis, where, with financial aid from the Ford Foundation, techniques for graphic display are being developed, using the accuracy, thoroughness, speed and low cost of computers.

1252 'A system of world soil maps', worked out by Soviet soil scientists, serves as a basis for new soil maps of the world and of separate continents; it was included in the Physico-Geographical atlas of the world. The five groups are: Polar soil formation: arctic and tundra soils; Boreal soil formation; Sub-boreal soil formation; Sub-tropical soil formation; and Tropical soil formation.

Refer also

M S Simakova: *Soil mapping by color aerial photography* (Israel Program for Scientific Translations for Oldbourne Russian Translations programme).

D G Vilenskii: *The Russian school of soil cartography and its influence on the soil cartography of the world, 1945* (Jerusalem: Israel Program for Scientific Translations, 1968, translated by N Kaner).

1253 'Tabula Imperii Romani' was initiated by O G S Crawford at the International Geographical Congress of 1928—a series of maps covering the whole of the Roman Empire at 1:1M scale. Sheets were produced for the Aberdeen and Edinburgh areas, but, in fact, the British sheets were superseded by the Ordnance Survey *Map of Roman Britain*. Elsewhere, in Italy, Egypt, France and Germany, the project was carried further, according to plan; Alexandria, Cairo, Aswan and Wadi Halfa, with Lugdunum (Lyons) sheets appeared during the 1930s and Mogontiacum (Mainz) in 1940. After the war, other European sheets were completed. Each sheet is accompanied by an alphabetical catalogue of the sites shown thereon, listing under each entry the evidence for identification and other notes concerning the wealth of detail brought together. A progress report was issued by the Ordnance Survey in 1933; a further Congress concerning the project was held at the Royal Geographical Society headquarters in 1935 and the resolutions were published by the Ordnance Survey under the title 'International map of the Roman Empire, London Congress, 1935'.

Refer also
R A Gardiner: 'The international map of the Roman Empire', *The geographical journal*, February 1973.

1254 'Tanzania today: *a portrait of the United Republic'* (University Press of Africa for the Ministry of Information and Tourism, 1968), is illustrated and contains a folding map. In conjunction with this publication it would be useful to use *Tanzania in maps*, edited by L Berry (University of London Press, 1971), which consists of black and white maps, each with a facing page of text, a geographical survey including contributions by many authoritative writers. There are numerous illustrations and statistics covering every aspect of the geography of the country.

1255 'Taxonomy and geography: *a symposium'*, edited for the Association (The Systematics Association, 1962) by David Nichols, presents papers read at the Symposium, 1959. Professor C H Lindroth, of Lund, Sweden, and Professor (later Sir) Dudley Stamp contributed a foreword and postscript respectively. There are diagrams and sketchmaps in the text and references at the ends of sections. Topics discussed included 'The taxonomic problems of local geographical variation in plant species'; 'Towards a zoogeography of the mosquitoes'; 'Pest pressure an underestimated factor in evolution'; 'Geographic variation and speciation in Africa with particular reference to *Diospyros*'; 'Some aspects of the geography, genetics and taxonomy of a butterfly.'

1256 Taylor, Eva Germaine Rimington (1879–1966) worked with A J Herbertson at Oxford, and, subsequently, as professor of geography at Birkbeck College, became a leader of geographical thought in Gt. Britain, specialising in the historical geography of the Tudor and

Stuart periods, in mathematical and navigational geography, and in the history of cartography, regarding these special topics as elements in the gradual development of the relationship between man and his environment. Among her prolific writings, besides innumerable articles and reviews, were a number of works on human and economic geography: *Tudor geography, 1485–1583; Late Tudor and early Stuart geography, 1583–1650; The Haven-finding art; The mathematical practitioners of Hanoverian England 1714–1840* (CUP for the Institute of Navigation, 1966); *The mathematical practitioners of Tudor and Stuart England; Early Hanoverian mathematical practitioners;* for the Hakluyt Society, an edition of Roger Barlow's *Briefe summe of geographie; The writings and correspondence of the two Richard Hakluyts; Sketchmap geography* and *The geometrical seaman.* The annual Eva G R Taylor lecture began in 1960, at the Royal Geographical Society headquarters.

See A bibliography of her works, 1905–1966, *in Transactions of the Institute of British Geographers*, volume no 45.

1257 Taylor, Thomas Griffith (1880–1963) led a varied and adventurous life and was a pioneer in geographical thought and in the practical application of geographical concepts. His influence on academic geography was very great, especially in Australia, where he gave the first lectures in geography at Sydney in 1907, being appointed to a Chair as associate professor of geography in Sydney in 1910; between 1928 and 1935 he was at Chicago University, after which he established the Department of Geography in the University of Toronto, before returning to Australia in 1951. He made particular studies of the geography of Australia and Canada; among his chief published works are: *Australia: a study of warm environments and their effect on British settlement*, 1940; and *Canada: a study of cool continental environments and their effect on British and French settlement*, 1947. The influence of environment on human development and settlement was an abiding interest, reflected in his *Environment and nation*, and *Environment and race*, followed by *Environment, race and migration: fundamentals of human distribution, with special sections on racial classification and settlement in Canada and Australia*, and *Urban geography: a study of site, evolution pattern and classification in villages, towns and cities. Journeyman Taylor*, 1958, is an entertaining, but informative, piece of autobiography. He also edited *Geography in the twentieth century* (*qv*). A festschrift in his honour was entitled *Frontiers and men: a volume in memory of Griffith*

Taylor . . ., edited by J Andrews (Melbourne: Cheshire, 1968).

1258 'Teaching geography' series, published by The Geographical Association in a sensible and clear format and style, includes: A D Walton: *A topical list of vertical photographs in the national air-photo libraries;* P G Hookey: *Do-it-yourself weather instruments;* J A Bond: *The uses of a revolving blackboard in geography teaching,* with R A Beddis: *A technique using screen and blackboard to extract information from a photograph* and E F Trotman: *Producing a slide set with commentary for elementary fieldwork;* L J Jay: *Geography books for sixth forms;* D G Mills: *Teaching aids on Australia and New Zealand;* R J P Newman: *Fieldwork using questionnaires and population data;* E W Anderson: *Hardware models in geography teaching;* a series of map exercises using Ordnance Survey map extracts; D P Chapallez *et al: Hypothesis testing in field studies;* M M Baraniecki and D M Ellis: *A market survey—technique and potentialities.*

1259 'Techniques in geomorphology', by C A M King (Arnold, 1966), treated a wide range of techniques in a rapidly-developing field in a manner which no other work had yet done. Observations of form and process in the field are described, also laboratory experiments with scale models, morphometric analysis of maps and photographs, the analysis of sediments and the statistical analysis of geomorphic data.

Refer also to Dr King's *Beaches and coasts.*

C H Hapgood and J H Campbell: *The earth's shifting crust* (New York: Pantheon, 1958; Museum Press, 1959; revised edition 'a key to some basic problems of earth sciences', 1968).

1260 'Terra' has been an influential quarterly since 1888, with text in Finnish and Swedish and summaries in English and German, published by Geografiska Sällskapets i Finland Tidskrift, Helsinki. The book reviews are authoritative and bibliographies are frequently included.

1261 'Terra Australia Cognita: *or voyages to the Terra Australis or Southern hemisphere, during the sixteenth, seventeenth and eighteenth centuries',* written by John Callander and published in three volumes 1766–1768, is a work of importance and value on the early history of Australasia, including Tierra del Fuego, Southern Patagonia, and the Falkland Islands, which was reproduced in 1967 by N Israel,

584

Meridian and TOT.

1262 'Terrae incognitae: *the annals of the Society for the History of Discoveries'* (Amsterdam: N Israel, 1969–) covers the development of aspects of geography, history, literature and science relevant to the main theme, with neither geographic nor chronological limits. The project was authorised, on an annual basis, at the 1966 Annual Meeting of the Society, to support a monograph series published jointly with the Newberry Library of Chicago, by the University of Chicago Press, and a semi-annual *Newsletter. Terrae incognitae* . . . is an attractively produced journal; articles are welcomed from 'all who do research in the general area of the history of discoveries' and there is a useful review section.

1263 The Textile Council, Education and Information Department, Manchester, issues a number of teaching aids, wall charts, films and illustrated booklets. Wall charts include 'The production of rayon'; 'Textile processing'; 'Cotton flow chart'; 'Cotton growing countries'. Samples of cotton fabrics are available and a film, 'Britain's cotton'. Booklets include 'Growing cotton plants' and 'Introducing cotton'. The films, such as 'Spinning your future', 'Cotton—nature's wonder fibre' and 'Needle and cotton', are available on loan free of charge and there is a filmstrip on cotton growing, with an accompanying booklet. A variety of similar aids on silk are to be had on application to The Silk Education Service.

1264 'Textile history', published from 1968 by David and Charles of Newton Abbot, is aimed to bring together the work of scholars engaged in original research into all aspects of the history of textiles. The processes of spinning, bleaching and knitting, the social and economic aspects of the industry and trade, studies of Courtaulds and of James Longsdon, the fustian manufacturers, are some of the topics so far included in the journal. References to new publications in the field are included in each issue.

Refer also

Annales textiles, 1948—(Association des Anciens Élèves de l'École Superieure des Industries Textiles de Mulhouse).

Textile industries, 1898—(Atlanta: Smith Publishing Company).

1265 The Textile Institute issues three periodicals of interest to geographers: the monthly *Journal of the Textile Institute*, the chief medium for the publication of original research work in textile science and technology, accounts of practical investigations, literature reviews and other surveys; *The Textile Institute and industry*, also monthly, in which are shorter papers of more practical bias, conference papers, etc; and, quarterly, *Textile progress*, each issue of which contains a critical review of recent developments in the technology of a particular sector in the industry, prepared by international authorities.

1266 'Le Théatre françois', by Maurice Bouguereau (Tours, 1594), constitutes the first national atlas of France, the sixteen maps having been prepared by Gabriel Tavernier and others, with an introduction by F de Dainville. This rare work was reproduced in facsimile by TOT in 1966.

1267 'Theatrum orbis terrarum' was the title of the famous collection of maps by Abraham Ortelius (*qv*) and is the title given to the series of facsimile atlases and other rare works, a magnificent venture by the Theatrum Orbis Terrarum Publishing Company, Amsterdam. The late R A Skelton and Alexander O Vietor were the first advisory editors; now acting with Alexander Vietor are Dr Helen Wallis and Dr Ir C Koeman. The atlases chosen for inclusion have been those of importance in the early history of cartography and rare in the original editions. Reproduction is in original size and in black and white as being considered the best way to show the delicacy and the splendour of the engraving and the work of the cartographer in its true form. They include important editions of Ptolemy's *Geography*, terrestrial atlases by Ortelius, De Jode, Mercator, Hondius, Jansson and Blaeu; nautical chartbooks by Waghenaer, Blaeu, Colom Dudley, Goos and Roggeveen; topographical works such as the *Civitates orbis terrarum* (*qv*) and special regional atlases, including *Speed's atlas of Great Britain*, and *Le théatre françois* (*qv*). One of the greatest achievements in the publication programme so far has been the reproduction of the third centenary edition of Blaeu's *Le grand atlas*, in twelve volumes, and another is *De Nieuwe Groote Ligtende Zee-fakkel*. These series make available a corpus of early atlases and other works illustrating the progress of geographical and cartographical knowledge from the time of Ptolemy to the seventeenth century. Each volume is accompanied by an English introduction, a bibliographical note, collation, references and list of literature, prepared by an acknowledged specialist in the field of the history of cartography. Sebastian Münster's *Cosmographei* ... , 1544, has also been reproduced, from the 1550 Basle edition, with an introduction in German and English by Professor Dr Ruthardt Oehme; more recent productions have included *A list of geographical atlases in the Library of Congress, with bibliographical notes*, by Philip Lee Phillips (*qv*), from the reprint of the Washington edition 1909–1920; the *Coelum Stellatum: a history of extraterrestrial cartography*, comprising facsimiles of the most important early star atlases, chosen by an international board of advisory editors and *Links with the past*, edited by Dr Ir C Koeman, a facsimile atlas with descriptive text illustrating the historical cartography of Suriname from 1500 to the near present, available in a wooden box. Other series are 'The English experience, its record in early printed books'; 'Mundus novus', a series of facsimiles of basic works from the fifteenth to the eighteenth centuries in the fields of geography, astronomy and cosmography, discovery and travels. Each facsimile is reproduced in its original size and by the use of full scale photography. Some books are being written especially for this series, including Dr K H Meine: *A history of lunar cartography*, and Dr A J M Wanders: *A history of Martian cartography*. Another new series, 1970–1971, is 'Neudrucke Ausdem Geographischen jahrbuch', edited, with introduction and indexes, in twelve volumes, by Dr Werner Horn, which will provide a compact source of invaluable information. Dr Horn, who has been associated with the *Geographisches Jahrbuch* and with historical geography and cartography in particular, has selected contributions from some hundred volumes of the yearbook and the 'Geographen-Kalender'. TOT issues general catalogues usually twice a year, a monthly *Newsletter* and frequent handouts announcing individual projects. Illustrated catalogues, brochures and advance notices are issued frequently.

Refer also

'Facsimile atlases', *The cartographic journal*, June 1965.

W W Ristow: 'New maps for old: trends in cartographic facsimile publication', *The Canadian cartographer*, June 1968.

1268 'Theoretical geography', by William Bunge (Gleerup for The Royal University of Lund, Sweden, Department of Geography, second revised edition, 1966, *Lund studies in geography* series), is 'centred on the character of geographic theory'—'A geographic methodology', 'Metacartography', 'A measure of shape', 'Descriptive mathematics', 'Towards a general theory of movement', 'Experimental and theoretical central places', 'Distance, nearness and geometry', 'The meaning of spatial relations' and 'Patterns of location' being the main topics, subdivided as required. There are a number of sketchmaps and diagrams in the text and appended is a list of *Lund studies in geography*.

1269 Theses *See* under Theses in Index, also
Clyde E Browning: *Bibliography of dissertations in geography, 1901–1969: American and Canadian universities* (University of North Carolina, Department of Geography, 1970).

1270 'Theses on Asia', compiled by B C Bloomfield, contains those accepted by the universities of the United Kingdom and Ireland, 1877–1964 (Cass, 1967). The offshore islands and Oceania are included; arrangement is by region, by country and then by a stereotyped list of subject headings.

1271 'The three voyages of Martin Frobisher in search of a passage to Cathay and India by the North-West, AD 1576–1578', was edited by Vilhjalmur Stefansson in two volumes (Argonaut Press, 1938); this fine production reproduces the original text of George Best and includes illustrations, maps, notes and a bibliography.

1272 '3-D junior atlas', edited by Frank Debenham (Harrap, revised edition, 1963), was an exciting experiment in atlas design. General maps of world communications and vegetation are followed by maps of the British Isles and of the countries and regions of Europe, Asia, Africa, the Americas, Australia, New Zealand and the world oceans. The new techniques of relief presentation are emphasised by layer colouring and oblique hill shading.
Refer also
'Three-D geography: a steroscopic aid for the study of terrain' developed by The Geographical Association in conjunction with C F Casella and Company Limited.

1273 'Tibet: international studies', the quarterly journal of The Jawaharlal Nehru University School of International Studies, New Delhi, has an emphasis on current affairs and economy; bibliographies are included from time to time.

1274 'Tijdschrift voor Economische en Sociale Geografie' (Brill of Leiden for Nederlandsche vereeniging voor economische en sociale geografie 1910–1966; Koninklijk Nederlands aardrijkskundig genootschap, Amsterdam, 1967–), contains articles in English or Dutch, with abstracts, and a few reviews; notes and selected readings are usually included, also maps.

1275 Timber Research and Development Association, London, holds a comprehensive library on timber and allied subjects, also a film library administered from the Head Office. Publications include a current list, booklets on the timbers of individual countries and on the uses of timbers; standard design sheets; timber information leaflets; data sheets; technical brochures and leaflets; reprints of special articles and research reports; advisory service leaflets; test records and test memoranda and a series of three volumes, *World timbers*, covering botanical and common names, seasoning strengths, durability, working qualities, uses and supplies. Teaching aids include wall charts, timber specimens, films and film strips. TRADA is an independent research organisation, jointly financed by the Department of Scientific and Industrial Research and a number of firms or individuals in all branches of the industry.

1276 'The Times atlas of the moon', edited by H A G Lewis, contains material from the Ranger, Surveyor and Orbiter photographic surveys, cartography being executed by Fairey Surveys Limited and Hunting Surveys Limited from the original United States AF charts, for John Bartholomew, Edinburgh. The work comprises 110 pages of detailed maps in full colour, numerous colour pictures and diagrams and the astronauts' maps specially prepared from lunar landing missions; there are three pages of maps of the far side of the moon. Lunar flight techniques are explained, precise physical data and a history of moon mapping and theories on the origin of moon features all make the atlas more intelligible and interesting. A key picture of the moon, with a super-imposed graticule and map page divisions enables an area to be pinpointed and there is a complete index of all lunar features, with latitude and longitude references.

1277 'The Times atlas of the world', compiled and published in sheets under the direction of Dr John George Bartholomew in

1922, was issued in a revised 'mid-century edition' by Dr John Bartholomew and his cartographic department for The Times Publishing Company between 1955 and 1960. The contents of the five volumes are arranged as follows: 1, The world, Australia, East Asia, 1958; 2, South West Asia and Russia, 1960; 3, Northern Europe, 1955; 4, Southern Europe and Africa, 1956; 5, The Americas, 1957. Geographical authorities throughout the world contributed to the accuracy of the maps, many of which are double-page spreads. The most significant areas are on the scale of 1:1M. Each map area is portrayed on the projection and by the cartographic techniques most suited to it; and a unique feature at this date was the nine-plate coverage of the USSR on the scale of 1:5M, based on the *Atlas mira*. The final maps were printed by deep-etch photo-offset, giving sharp outlines and excellent registration. The style is typical of the House of Bartholomew; the paper used is of fine texture, the entire layout is spacious, the range of colour tints judicious and aesthetically pleasing, and the lettering is legible, especially the small names in Times roman. Some historical and reference data are included and each volume carries a full gazetteer. The successor to this work was the *Comprehensive edition*, 1967, second edition, 1969, in one volume; nevertheless, this work contains greater detail, as well as considerable additional material, with no loss of scale, this being achieved by printing on both sides of the paper, using narrower margins and including a single index. Some revisions and improvements were made; endpaper keys show which parts of the world are covered by which plates; an international glossary gives the English equivalents of common namewords. Some discoveries by satellite surveys were included. A 'family' version, *The Times concise atlas*, is directed to 'students of all kinds'. The forty-page introduction covers most relevant topics, from the origin and geology of the earth to considerations of social and population geography, trade, tourism and travel. 144 pages of maps are reproduced in six colours. Under the new imprint, Times Books, was issued in 1974 *The Times atlas of China*, edited by Professor D C Twitchett and P J M Geelan.

1278 'The Times index gazetteer of the world', 1966, a locational guide containing about 345,000 geographical locations, is more extensive than the index to the mid-century edition of *The Times atlas of the world* and is intended primarily as an independent work of reference, although map references to the atlas are given when applicable. Latitude and longitude co-ordinates are included.

1279 Topicards, introduced by Macmillan, were announced as 'a new approach to secondary geography, a classroom-tested card scheme, designed for group, project or individual work for CSE or revision at 'o' level.' Fitting in with the increasing realisation of the utility of audio-visual aids in teaching, the cards quickly became widely used, providing a framework around which an imaginative teacher could build, and, having built up a stock, could be used in different combinations, as required. The introductory series dealt with basic concepts in geography—'Latitude and longitude'; 'Climate and weather'; 'Map interpretation'; 'Rivers'; 'Coastlines'; 'Vegetation'; 'Agriculture'; 'Manufacturing industries'; 'Communications' and 'Settlement'. Each set combined four copies of three different cards with teacher's notes. 'Map interpretation', for example, comprised 'Scale and measurement', 'Map symbols' and 'Relief', with subdivisions of each text, illustrated by photographs, sketchmaps and graphs, and including a number of exercises. Later series included sample studies of field work and more detailed topics which could be linked with the original basic ones.

See also under Education

1280 Touring Club Italiano is one of the great cartographic agencies, founded in Milan in 1894. The mapping department is modern and very efficient, having for many years exerted considerable influence on the standard of publication of travellers' guides, monographs, maps, atlases, yearbooks, manuals and periodicals, and has compiled and edited cartographic works of high scientific merit, notably the *Atlante internazionale della Consociazione Turistica* (*qv*) and the *Atlante fisico-economico d'Italia*, a land use map of Italy and the *Carta automobilistica d'Italia*, 1:200,000; the *Road map of Europe* 1:500,000 is also very widely used.

1281 'Town and townscape', by Thomas Sharp (Murray, 1968), presents an analysis of the elements of character and individuality in a town and the factors necessary in good building. The author then attempts to show how to examine present day towns and to appreciate the changing relationships between the buildings and their adjacent streets and open spaces. Finally, the effects of motor traffic and the trend for building high blocks are examined. There are numerous photographs, town plans and drawings.

Refer also

591

Publications of the Town and Country Planning Association, available from The Planning Bookshop, London, including *Town and country planning*, the journal of the Association; *Planning bulletin;* and *Bulletin of environmental education*, a monthly guide to sources and resources for teaching and learning about the environment.

The Planning Forum, a discussion group established under the auspices of the Town and Country Planning Association, provides the opportunity for students, experts and other interested people to debate the wide range of physical, social and economic planning subjects.

Gerald Burke: *Towns in the making* (Arnold, 1971).

1282 'Trade and commerce', a monthly report on Western industry, published by Sanford Evans Publishing Company, contains notes on all aspects, including photographs and statistics in the text.

1283 'Trade and industry', incorporating the *Board of Trade journal* and *New Technology*, issued weekly, contains practical news items, statistics, graphs of imports, exports, etc, and, as a main feature, 'Programme of trade promotions'.

1284 'Traité de géographie physique', completed by Emmanuel de Martonne in 1909, became a standard reference work; the seventh edition, 1948, was expanded to three volumes. E D Laborde made an English translation of the work, with the cooperation of the author, published in 1927 under the title *A shorter physical geography;* in his foreword to the work, Laborde refers to de Martonne as 'the leading exponent of Physical Geography. Perhaps the first writer to realise clearly the exact amount of scientific basis required for the subject, his work is strikingly different from English texts in the absence of over much geology and physics. His method is strictly synthetic, and consists of building up geographical principles through the examination of typical regions. In this way the reader feels that he is dealing with Geography, and not with abstract science.'

Refer also

F A V Meinesz: *The earth's crust and mantle* (Amsterdam: Elsevier, 1964).

A Miller: *The skin of the earth* (Methuen, second edition,

1965).

F M Miller and E G R Taylor: *The physical basis of geography* (Philip, twelfth edition, 1965).

1285 'Transactions of the Asiatic Society of Japan', has been prepared by the Asiatic Society of Japan, Tokyo, in a first series 1872 to 1922; second series 1924 to 1940; and a third series from 1948. It is one of the largest and most important collections of studies on all aspects of Japanese civilisation. An index to volumes 1–50 was given in the second series, 1928.

1286 'The transformation of the Chinese earth: *aspects of the evaluation of the Chinese earth from earliest times to Mao-Tse-tung',* by Keith Buchanan (Bell, 1970), compares 'the Chinese earth to a palimpsest: today there is new writing on this ancient manuscript, writing whose characters are bold and clear and confident'. This quotation, plus the sub-title of the introduction, 'with their own strength they made the landscape . . .', shows the approach to this study. 'The occupation of the Chinese land'; 'The unity and diversity of the Peoples of China'; 'The density of the Chinese earth'; 'Underdevelopment and development in China'; 'The rise of the people's communes'; 'Contrasts in the microgeography of selected communes'; 'The agricultural regions of China'; 'Agricultural production in China'; 'The industrial sector'; 'Transport and the integration of the Chinese living space'; 'Population: spatial patterns'; 'China: over-populated or under-populated?'; 'Towards a reappraisal of China's intellectual resources'; and 'A summing up: after the dust has settled . . .'. An appendix explores 'The basic units in the environment of China' and there is a useful bibliography. A group of excellent photographs in the centre of the text and a number of sketchmaps and cartograms demonstrates particular topics.

Refer also

Keith Buchanan: *The Chinese people and the Chinese earth* (Bell, 1966).

1287 'Transport history', published by David and Charles from 1968, three times a year, in conjunction with the University of Strathclyde, contains original articles on the history of all forms of transport, including shipping, road transport, railways and canals, particularly in the British Isles. The social and economic aspects of the subject are examined, together with relevant developments in engineering. In each issue are book reviews, notes and news items, illustrated and with figures in the text.

1288 'Transport research', which has been published quarterly by the Pergamon Press for the Institute of Transportation, Los Angeles, is prepared with the assistance of an international editorial board, for the rapid dissemination of the most significant scientific results in the field. In addition to articles, there are notes, queries and answers, a section announcing forthcoming events and abstracts in English, French, German and Russian.

Refer also

J H Appleton: *A morphological approach to the geography of transport* (University of Hull, Occasional Papers in Geography, 1965).

Catalog of the Transportation Center Library, Northwestern University (G K Hall, twelve volumes, 1973).

R E G Davies: *A history of the world's airlines* (OUP, 1964).

B S Hoyle, *ed: Transport and development* (Macmillan, 1973).

W R Siddall: *Transportation geography: a bibliography* (Kansas State University Library, revised edition, 1967).

1289 'Trends in geography: *an introductory survey'*, edited by Ronald U Cooke and James H Johnson (Pergamon Press, 1969), a collection of twenty-six short essays, had its origin in a conference for geography teachers organised by the University of London Institute of Education, 1968, each contribution presenting a personal view of a particular field of study. Each chapter in the four parts—physical, human, applied geography and area studies—attempts to guide the reader through the literature of the 'fifties and 'sixties, evaluating new concepts and methods, followed by a select bibliography.

Refer also

K C Edwards: 'The broadening vista', *Geography*, July 1967.

Thomas R Glennon: 'Some recent works on geographic thought: a review article', *Bulletin*, Special Libraries Association, Geography and Map Division, March 1971.

Peter R Gould: 'Methodological developments since the fifties', *Progress in geography*, 1969.

Sydney W Gould: *Geo-Code* (New Haven: The Gould Fund, 1968).

T Hägerstrand: 'The computer and the geographer', *Trans-actions*, Institute of British Geographers, 1967.

Peter Haggett: 'On geographical research in a computer environment', *The geographical journal*, December 1969.

1290 'Tropical agriculture: the development of production', by G Wrigley (Faber, 1961, revised 1969), explains the increase in agricultural production and soil fertility and how this may be maintained. Factors affecting tropical agriculture in particular are dealt with as a whole, not as they affect individual crops. Crop ecology is considered, also crop culture, crop improvement and production, with some reference to cattle-raising.

Refer also

Hans Ruthenberg: *Farming systems in the Tropics* (Oxford: Clarendon Press, 1971).

C C Webster and P N Wilson: *Agriculture in the Tropics* (Longmans, 1966).

1291 'Tropical man', continuation of the *International archives of ethnography*, yearbook of the Department of the Royal Tropical Institute, Amsterdam (Leiden: Brill, 1968–), now known as The Department of Social Research, is a series of bulletins appearing at irregular intervals—'the voice of the Department'. Its primary purpose is for publications of the Fellows of the Department, but contributions from others may be accepted in English and French. The journal also contains book reviews; each issue includes the annual report and is illustrated.

1292 'Tropical science', the quarterly journal of The Tropical Products Institute (formerly The Colonial Products Laboratory), is distributed by HMSO. The 'News round-up' feature is most useful; each issue contains an average of two main articles in addition to reports of investigations at the Institute. Careful reviews, a list of recently issued reports and an extensive bibliography of items recently added to the Library, arranged alphabetically within subject headings, serve as an excellent 'current awareness' service.

Refer also

Pierre Gourou: *The tropical world: its social and economic conditions and its future status* (Paris: PUF, 1948; Longmans, fourth edition, 1966, translated by E D Laborde).

W Arthur Lewis, *ed*: *Tropical development 1880–1913: studies in economic progress* (Allen and Unwin, 1970–).

Publications of the Unesco Humid Tropics Research Programme.

J Tricart: *The landforms of the humid tropics, forests and savannas* (Longman, 1972).

1293 'Tudor geography 1485–1583', by E G R Taylor (Methuen, 1930; Octagon Books, 1968), must surely remain a classic of scholarship amid the vast literature dealing with the history of exploration and geographical thought. Quoting from the author's preface: '. . . Elizabeth's day saw the map and the globe as the necessary furniture of the closet of scholar, merchant, noble and adventurer alike, and dreams of Empire were formulated which found expression in Drake's achievement and Humfrey Gilbert's splendid failure. The date of the latter has been chosen for the term of this study, for it was marked also by the withdrawal of John Dee, the man behind the scenes of overseas enterprise: it saw, too, the firm establishment of the younger Richard Hakluyt as the propagandist for expansion. His work as a geographer, and that of his emulator, Samuel Purchas, will form the thesis of a later volume.' Valuable appendices follow: 'Catalogue of English geographical or kindred works (printed books and *mss*) to 1583, with notes'; List of John Dee's geographical and related works'; 'Catalogue and bibliography of contemporary libraries' and 'Illustrative and evidential documents'. A few plates depict contemporary instruments and maps.

1294 'Turkey: the challenge of growth', by Z Y Hershlag (Leiden: Brill, 1968; second revised edition of *Turkey: an economy in transition*), investigates the implications of the challenge of growth in Turkey, the background of past experience, of theoretical and empirical issues of central planning in a developing economy and of the interrelation of economic quantitative variables and social and institutional qualitative values. A projection of future trends and of methods of planning is suggested on the scrutinisation of the currently executed five-year plan, its shortcomings and achievements, as reflected in such major issues as manpower and labour, productivity, utilisation of available resources, international economic relations and the economic and social results of the process of growth. The study is supplemented by nineteen charts, thirty-five tables, sixty-six supporting tables and an economic map of Turkey.

Refer also

Peter Benedict *et al, ed: Turkey, geographic and social perspectives* (Leiden: Brill, 1974).

1295 'Tuttitalia: *enciclopedia dell'Italia antica e moderna',* issued by the Istituto Geografico de Agostini, Novara, in 1963, covers all aspects of the life of the country and is superbly illustrated, often in colour. Twenty-four volumes have a regional arrangement, in Italian, with a summary and index in each volume and textmaps throughout, where suitable. Beginning with Piemonte—Valle d'Aosta, the regions set out continue with Liguria, Lombardia, Le Venezie, Emilia—Romagna, Toscana, Marche, Umbria, Lazio, Abruzzo—Molise, Campania, Puglie—Basilicata, Calabria, Sicilia and Sardegna, some in two volumes, and the Venice region in three.
Refer also
Pierre George: *Géographie de l'Italie* (Paris: PUF, 1964).
G Kish: *Italy* (Van Nostrand Reinhold, 1969).
D S Walker: *A geography of Italy* (Methuen, second edition, 1967).

1296 The Uganda Geographical Association, founded in 1961, arranges lectures, meetings and excursions; the annual journal is the *East African geographical review.* Close association is maintained with the centre of academic geography in the Department of Geography at Makerere University College, and with the various government departments, also with the East African Institute of Social Research, at Makerere. A series of glaciological expeditions to the Ruwenzori Mountains made a significant contribution to the observations of the International Geophysical Year.

1297 'Ulster and other Irish maps c1600', edited by G A Hayes-McCoy (Irish Manuscripts Commission, 1964), contains facsimiles of twenty-three manuscript maps, fifteen of areas within Ulster, six of places in Munster, one of part of the Outer Hebrides and one a plan of Dublin Castle. The first twelve maps were the work of Richard Bartlett.
Refer also
Manuscript sources for the history of Irish civilisation (G K Hall, 1965, in eleven volumes, for the National Library of Ireland, Dublin).
John Andrews: *Ireland in maps: an introduction: with a catalogue of an exhibition mounted in the Library of Trinity College,*

Dublin, 1961, by the Geographical Society of Ireland and the Ordnance Survey of Ireland (Dublin: The Dolmen Press, 1961).

S Maxwell Hajducki: *A railway atlas of Ireland* (Newton Abbot: David and Charles, 1972).

Sir William Petty: *Hiberniae Delineatio, a topographical survey based on work in the field between 1654 and 1660* . . .

1298 'The USSR and Eastern Europe: periodicals in Western languages', compiled by Paul L Horecky and Rogert G Carlton (Library of Congress, Slavic and Central European Division, 1958; second edition, 1964), is a selective listing, by country, and including publications outside Europe, if relevant to the study of the area. Brief annotations are usually appended.

1299 'United Kingdom glossary of cartographic terms' had its origin in 1964, when the International Cartographic Association appointed a Commission with the object of establishing some degree of standardisation in the use of terms by map makers and users throughout the world. It was decided to publish a multi-lingual dictionary of technical terms in cartography. The Royal Society British National Committee for Geography worked on the United Kingdom contribution and the final text was completed in the autumn of 1966. This was published by the Royal Society in advance of the international work, with an introduction by W D C Wiggins. The International Cartographic Association Special Commission II agreed on a standard form and format for the dictionary; each term to be defined in full, with explanatory notes in English, French, German and Russian, possibly also in some cases, in Spanish. In addition, single-word equivalents were to be listed, but not defined, in up to eight other languages, Dutch, Hungarian, Italian, Japanese, Polish, Portuguese and Swedish.

Refer also

Glossaire français de cartographie, Bulletin du Comité français de cartographie, special issue no 46.

1300 'United Kingdom publications and theses on Africa', 1963, was published by Heffer of Cambridge in 1966 for the Standing Conference on Library Materials on Africa. The work lists 1,260 books and periodical articles on Africa. Published in the United Kingdom, during 1963, including also an index of references to Africa made during the sessions of both Houses of Parliament and a list of theses on Africa accepted by universities in the United Kingdom and Ireland during the academic year 1962–63. A second volume, *United Kingdom publications and theses on Africa, 1964,* was also published in 1966.

Note The *Newsletter* of the Standing Conference on Library Materials on Africa, published in three issues a year.

1301 United Nations Organization: Much of the work of the UN and its specialised agencies, especially of Unesco, WMO (*qv*) and FAO (*qv*), is of direct or indirect interest to geographers. Publications of particular importance include *World cartography* (*qv*) and *The demographic yearbook* (*qv*).

In the 1970 issue of the latter, a special study was added—'What we know about the state and evolution of world population'. Reports and surveys of economic conditions are numerous, notably *The world economic survey* (*qv*), *The yearbook of international trade statistics, The statistical yearbook, The commodity survey, Economic survey of Europe, Economic survey of Asia and the Far East* and such specific reports as the *Quarterly bulletin of coal statistics for Europe, Timber bulletin for Europe, Industrial research news, 1966*—and the *Economic survey of Europe* in 1971, which was issued in two parts: *The European economy from the 1950s to the 1970s* and *The European economy in 1971. The growth of world industry* comes in two volumes. In 1972, *The work of the Economic Commission for Europe* was published, also a special statistical handbook, *The ECE region in figures*.

The most complete record of the work of the United Nations is to be found in the *Yearbook of the United Nations,* published since 1947; there is also *Everyman's United Nations . . .* and *Your United Nations: the official guide book.* The *UN monthly chronicle* is a central source of information and, in addition to frequent brochures and advance notices, the general catalogue is divided into sections, according to subject matter; supplements for each section are issued as soon as new publication becomes available. *Information letter* of the UN Conference on the Environment began with the issue for June 1971, a series which the Secretariat of the UN Conference on the Environment published over the whole period to the opening of the Conference at Stockholm, June 1972; a report circulated to help appreciation of the effort still remaining to be accomplished in this field was entitled *ECE Symposium on problems relating to environment.* It has been decided that two United Nations publications, *Current issues: a selected bibliography on subjects of concern to the United*

Nations and *New publications in the Dag Hammerskjold Library* be merged into one publication, *Current bibliographical information*, twenty-two issues to be published each year; in addition, a special feature of the new serial is the inclusion of publications of selected agencies. Among UNESCO publications, the series of reports, *Bibliographical services throughout the world,* the first two prepared by Miss L N Malclès, 1955, and the summary 1950–1959 cumulated by R L Collison, 1961, followed by another summary, 1960–1964, by Paul Avicenne, is an invaluable series; *Bibliography, documentation, terminology*, continues the coordination of such information from all member countries. Relevant individual bibliographies include the UNESCO *international bibliography of economics*. Invaluable also are the publications which derive from specialist research, such as the 'Arid zone programme' and the 'Humid tropics research programme', or from such co-operative projects as the International Hydrological Decade (*see* 'Nature and resources'). Frequently the results of co-operative research, seminars or conferences are summarised in monograph form, such as *Arid lands: a geographical appraisal,* edited by E S Hills, 1966, and the *Source book for geography teaching* (*qv*). The 'Natural resources research' series began in 1963; *La protection de la grande faune et des habitats naturels en Afrique centrale et orientale*, by Sir Julian Huxley, was published in 1961 (now *op* in English; French edition still available); and the 'Science policy studies and documents' series sets out factual information concerning the science policies of various Member States. *Guide to the world inventory of sea, lake and river ice* was completed in 1972. Other series include the 'Ecology and conservation' series, the 'Earth sciences' series, 'Studies and reports in hydrology' series and the 'Intergovernmental Oceanographic Commission technical series'. The *Unesco statistical yearbook*, as with most of these publications, is issued in two forms, in paper and in cloth. Periodicals include *Impact of science on society, International marine science* (irregular) and *Nature and resources* (*qv*).

Scientific maps sponsored by Unesco, with the collaboration of the relevant bodies, include various maps of Africa, the International geological map of Europe, the International quaternary map of Europe, the Metallogenic map of Europe, the International hydrogeological map of Europe, the Bioclimatic map of the Mediterranean region, the Soil map of the world, the Vegetation map of the Mediterranean region and the *Atlas of the international co-operative investigations of the Tropical Atlantic*. The sub-section of Geography and

600

Map Libraries of the Special Libraries section of IFLA is, with Unesco, working on a world directory of geography and map libraries.

1302 The United States Department of Agriculture, National Agricultural Library: *See* below, no 1307.

1303 United States Antarctic Research Program of the National Science Foundation issues an 'Acquisitions list of Antarctic cartographical materials', through the Office of Coordinator for Maps, Department of State; this document continued as part of the *Antarctic report*, retaining its consecutive numbering system begun in 1961. The Office of Coordinator for Maps continues to prepare the list from contributions made to the Office by participating organisations or agencies of the United States. New lists appear as the volume of material warrants. Four categories of documents are distinguished—gazetteers, geodetic data, maps and charts, and photography.

1304 US Board on Geographic Names was first set up in 1890, the present Board being established in 1947, to consider the standardisation of geographical names throughout the world and the terms and abbreviations used on maps and charts. Since 1953, the Board has issued several parts each year of the *Gazetteers* (Washington, Government Printing Office, 1955–) each issue being devoted to a separate country.

1305 United States Coast and Geodetic Survey, established as the Coast Survey in 1807, was by an Act of 1871 expanded to include responsibility for geodetic work throughout the country. Hydrographic, oceanographic and topographic surveys are undertaken and coastal surveys co-ordinated. Nautical and aeronautical charts are published and distributed. Other publications include geodetic control data, planimetric maps, coast pilots and annual tables of tide and current predictions.

1306 United States Geological Survey was created by Act of Congress in 1879, taking over at that time the functions and records of earlier surveys. Work is carried on through five branches: administrative, geological, topographic, conservation and water resources. Numerous publications, valuable not only to United

States geologists, but to those interested in the subject throughout the world, includes the *Bulletin,* 1883–: *Professional papers,* 1902–: the *Monographs series,* 1890–: *Water supply papers,* 1896–: *Annual reports,* 1880–. *Mineral resources of the United States* was published by the survey between 1882–1923, thereafter by the Bureau of Mines, to which the Mineral Resources Division was transferred in 1925. The Survey discontinued publication of its monthly journals, *Abstracts of North American geology* and *Geophysical abstracts* as from January 1972, and also the annual bibliography of North American geology after the completion of the 1970 volume, in view of the similar services covered by the American Geological Institute and the Geological Society of America. The library is considered to be the largest geological library in the world; acquisitions are as complete as possible in geology, palaeontology, mineralogy, ground and surface water, cartography and mineral resources, and are strong also in the related fields of mathematics, engineering, physics, chemistry, soil science, botany, zoology, oceanography and natural resources. The catalogue of the library was published by G K Hall in twenty-five volumes in 1964.

The Survey has enlarged its Map Information Office into the National Cartographic Information Center (NCIC), relocated in Reston, Va., at the new national headquarters of the Geological Survey, by the end of 1973. This organisation is to act as the national clearing house for cartographic information, classifying and cataloguing data and encouraging the use of standard descriptors for such data, operating a communication network between user information centres and data repositories and publishing acquisition lists and catalogues.

1307 The United States National Agricultural Library, US Department of Agriculture, one of the focal points in the world for agricultural documentation, has introduced a new cataloguing and indexing system (CAIN) on magnetic tape. These tapes contain a store of bibliographic data encompassing the broad field of agriculture, including agricultural economics and rural sociology, agricultural products, animal industry, engineering, entomology, food and human nutrition, forestry, plant science, soils and fertilisers and other related topics previously included in the *Bibliography of agriculture,* the *National agricultural library monthly catalog* and the *Pesticides documentation bulletin.* All references cited in the *American bibliography of agricultural economics,* a new publication issued by the American

Agricultural Economics Association, 1970–, are also included. Subject, author, biographical and organisational indexes can be compiled from the tapes, as well as comprehensive bibliographies. All tapes are nine track, 800 bpi, designed for use in the IBM 360 series computer.

Refer also

James R Anderson: *Geography of agriculture in the United States' Southeast* (Budapest: Publishing House of the Hungarian Academy of Sciences, 1973, 'Geography of world agriculture', no 2).

John T Schlebecker: *Bibliography of books and pamphlets on the history of agriculture in the United States, 1607–1967* (Santa Barbara, California: American Bibliographical Center, Clio Press, 1969).

1308 Universities: Information about universities is to be found in *Orbis geographicus*, in geographical journals, such as *The geographical journal*, *'University news'*, and in academic journals themselves. Most geography departments now issue at least one journal, prepared usually by staff and/or students, sometimes including contributions by former students; many maintain their own presses. Some sponsor research and collaborate, if the opportunity occurs, with other relevant bodies. Most geography departments specialise in a few specific aspects of geography; nearly all are building up fine research collections and offer a range of services, bibliographical, cartographic, photographic, etc. Many have important special collections, such as the collection of aerial photographs at the University of Keele, or have specialised in periodical files, reports of symposia, area studies or have some individual acquisition policies, such as maintaining collections of early travel literature or national atlases.

See also under Education; individual names of universities.

Refer also

E A Ackerman: *Geography as a fundamental research discipline* (University of Chicago, Department of Geography, Research Paper, no 53, 1958).

'Geography as a professional field', compiled by the Association of American Geographers and the National Council for Geographic Education, US Department of Health, Education and Welfare, *Bulletin* no 10, 1966.

'A matter of degree' (particulars of geography courses

available in Britain), *The geographical magazine*, November 1972.

William Warntz: *Geography now and then: some notes on the history of academic geography in the United States* (American Geographical Society, Research series, no 25, 1964).

1309 'The university atlas', in a new, thirteenth edition prepared by a team of international cartographers, edited for George Philip and Son by H Fullard and Professor H C Darby, is of major significance. 176 pages of maps in full colour, 24 pages of graphs concerning selected stations throughout the world and an index of more than fifty thousand place-names are a few of the features which make a first-class reference atlas.

1310 The University Tutorial Press has published three series of relevance to geographers—the *Secondary school geographies*, the *Advanced Level geographies* and, of particular interest, the *Modern geography* series, in which there are the following texts, all suitably illustrated: D M Preece: *Foundations of geography;* D M Preece and H R B Wood: *The British Isles;* D M Preece and H R B Wood: *Europe;* A W Coysh and M E Tomlinson: *North America;* W B Cornish: *Asia;* A W Coysh and M E Tomlinson: *The southern continents;* D C Money: *Australia and New Zealand.*

1311 Unstead, J F (1876–1965) was among the leaders of geographical thought in Britain in the early years of this century, revealing the influence of Halford Mackinder, who supervised his early work. He helped to establish academic geography in Britain, especially through his position at Birkbeck College, where he built up the Department of Geography and was in 1922 appointed first professor of geography. His innumerable articles and texts made notable advances in the teaching of geographical method, especially in regional geography; he advocated the study of small 'unit-areas', combining these to form regions, then world divisions.

1312 'Urban affairs', quarterly journal sponsored by the City University of New York, 1970– is world-wide in scope, with a certain bias towards America; in addition to articles, reviews are included and there is an annual index.

Refer also

K J Driscoll: *Town study—a sample urban geography* (Philip,

1971).

J Haddon: *Local geography in towns* (Philip, 1971).

1313 'Urban analysis: *a study of city structure with special reference to Sunderland'*, by B T Robson (CUP, 1969), attempts a 'geographical method of analysing the social structure of a single town and the use of the results of this analysis in a spatial examination of one facet of the towns sociology . . .'. The work has been published as one of the early series of books and monographs issued by The Syndics of the Cambridge University Press, *Cambridge geographical studies,* which either describe and illustrate new ideas and techniques now re-shaping geographical studies, or books which embody the results of new research. They are not to be regarded as textbooks. In this study are four sections—Methodology, Analysis, Application and Conclusion—with a number of appendices, sketchmaps, diagrams and a bibliography.

Refer also

Harold Carter: *The study of urban geography* (Arnold, 1972).

W K Davies: 'Data analysis in urban geography', *Geography,* July 1972.

W K, Davies: *Urban essays: studies in the geography of Wales* (Longmans, 1970).

J N Jackson: *The urban future*, 1972,

1314 'Urban core and inner city, *Proceedings of the International Study week in Amsterdam, 1966'*, was published by Brill of Leiden under the auspices of the Sociographical Department, 1967. The idea of making scientific researches into the problems of the inner city of Amsterdam was first conceived in the Sociographical Department of Amsterdam University in the summer of 1962. The term 'inner core' was adopted as a functional concept for that section of a city which is the centre of its life, where is a concentration of offices, stores, services, production and traffic. The study-week was planned as a means of exchanging views with workers in the same field in other European countries. The main themes under discussion included the basic concepts, definitions and theoretical approaches; the delimitation, inner tensions and shifting of the urban core; static form versus dynamic function; the application of research finding to the planning of urban cores and research methodology and technics.

Refer also

Centres of art and civilisation series (Paul Elek): for example,

Stewart Perowne: *Rome*, 1971.

1315 'Urban land: news and trends in land development', official publication of The Urban Land Institute, is issued monthly, with the July and August issues combined; in addition to articles and information notices, the feature 'Notes of relevant publications' is of obvious practical value.

1316 'Urbanism and urbanization', edited by Nels Anderson (Leiden: Brill, 1964), consists of a valuable selection of articles, published in two volumes for the International Studies in Sociology and Social Anthropology.

1317 'Urbanization in newly developing countries', by Gerald Breese (Prentice-Hall International, 1966), one of the 'Modernization of traditional societies' series, provides a broad-based introduction to the characteristics of urbanisation, the various types and the implications for emerging nations compared with the urbanised western countries. Field studies of large urban areas in Europe, Africa, the Middle East, the Indian subcontinent and South-East Asia are analysed.

Refer also

J Beaujeu-Garnier and G Chabot: *Urban geography* (Longmans, 1967, translated by G M Yglesias and S H Beaver).

B J Berry and F E Horton: *Geographical perspectives on urban systems: with integrated readings* (Prentice-Hall, 1970).

K Briggs: *Field work in urban geography* (Oliver and Boyd, 1970).

G Burke: *Towns in the making* (Arnold, 1971).

Jean Chardonnet: *Métropoles économiques* (Paris: Colin for the Cahiers de la Fondations Nationale des Sciences Politiques, 1968).

Peter Cowan, *ed*: *Developing patterns of urbanisation* (Oliver and Boyd, 1970).

Peter Hall: *Introduction to urban and regional planning* (Newton Abbot: David and Charles, 1974).

F S Hudson: *A geography of settlements* (Macdonald and Evans, 1970).

R J Johnston: 'Towards a general model of intra-urban residential patterns . . . ', *Progress in geography*, 1972.

R J Johnston: *Urban residential patterns: an introductory*

review (Bell, 1971).

Emrys Jones: *Towns and cities* (OUP, 1966).

T G McGee: *The Southeast Asian city* (Bell, 1971).

Peter Schöller, *ed: Trends in urban geography: reports on research in major language areas* (Paderborn: Ferdinand Schöningh, 1973).

R L Singh, *ed: Urban geography in developing countries* (National Geographical Society of India, 1973).

1318 Van Nostrand Company Limited publishes a series of monographs of interest to geographers, the *Searchlight books* series, each of which considers some aspect of political geography or effect of geography on world affairs. General editors are George W Hoffman and G Etzel Pearcy. Several titles have been issued each year since 1962; most of them have been written by geographers or by specialists in allied sciences, for example: R J Harrison Church: *Environment and policies in West Africa*, 1963; W Gordon East: *The Soviet Union*, 1964; Harris B Steward: *The global sea*, 1964; V H Malmström: *Norden: crossroads of destiny*, 1965; David J M Hooson: *A new Soviet heartland*, 1964; Donald J Patton: *The United States and world resources*, 1968; Robert D Hodgson: *The changing map of Africa*, second edition, 1968 and many others.

1319 Varenius, Bernard (1622–1650) produced two works of great geographical interest: *Descriptio regni Japoniae et Siam*, Amsterdam, 1649, Cambridge, 1673; and *Geographia generalis*, Amsterdam, in four editions, 1650, 1664, 1671 and 1672, and two Cambridge editions, 1672 and 1681. A number of English translations are of varying merit. In 'The geography of Bernard Varenius', J N L Baker (Institute of British Geographers, *Transactions and papers*, 1955) gives a re-assessment of his work and a summary of other writers' comments.

Refer also

S Gunther: *Varenius*, 1905, reproduced by TOT, 1970.

1320 'Vegetation and soils: *a world picture'*, by S R Eyre (Arnold, 1963, second edition, 1968), provides an introduction to this complex subject, keeping the emphasis on salient features; systematic treatment of climate, for example, is limited to an appendix in which some mean monthly precipitation and temperature figures are tabulated for two or three stations within the area occupied by each vegetation type. The four main divisions are: 'Vegetation and soil development', 'Vegetation and soils outside the tropics', 'The British Isles', and 'Tropical regions', concluding with a note on 'The outlook for wild nature'. Appendices contain 'Vegetation maps of the continents', 'Climatic correlations with vegetation' and a 'Glossary of technical terms'. Maps and diagrams are clear and evocative; there were references and short bibliographies in the first edition, extended for the second.

Refer also

Edited by the same author, *World vegetation types.*

P Buringh: *Introduction to the study of soils in tropical and subtropical regions* (Wageningen: Centre for Agricultural Publication and Documentation, 1968).

J Gentilli: *The geography of vegetation* (Hutchinson University Library, 1968).

K D Glinka: *The great soil groups of the world and their development* (Ann Arbor: Edwards, 1927; Allen and Unwin, 1928, second edition, 1937, translated by C F Marbut).

1321 'Vegetation map of the Mediterranean region, 1:5M' (Unesco, 1970) is one of the *Unesco scientific maps* series. The map was prepared by a panel of plant ecologists set up jointly by Unesco and FAO, led by Professor Gaussen and others; the cartography was assisted by the staff of the Institut Géographique National. Two sheets, east and west, are printed in eleven basic colours, covering an area stretching from the temperate region of Europe and Central Asia to the tropical rain forests below latitude 12 degrees north in Africa, and from western Africa to the Indus Valley. 105 main vegetation types are shown, divided into fifty-two climatic formations, forty-six edaphic formations and seven of introduced or transformed vegetation; these main types are also subdivided, bringing the total number of differentiated vegetation types to 246. The general principle followed has been to show the 'potential' vegetation as it would be unchanged by man or animals. Cultivated areas are not indicated, but vegetation produced by irrigation and afforestation is marked. Desert areas are especially carefully indicated; also the mountain areas where vegetation belts change over very short distances. An explanatory booklet, in English and French, accompanies the map. Also to be noted is the companion map, *Bioclimatic map of the Mediterranean zone* on the same scale (Unesco and FAO, 1963).

Refer also

A W Küchler: *Vegetation mapping* (New York: Ronald, 1967).

1322 Vidal de la Blache, Paul (1845–1918) studied history and geography, and throughout his life was preoccupied with the concept of the integration of historical and geographical factors, together with the influence of man on his environment; he substituted the theory of 'possibilisme' for Ratzel's environmentalism or determinism. He became the supreme influence in French geography, dominating academic geography from his position at the Sorbonne. He was one of the founders of the *Annales de géographie* and the annual *Bibliographie;* his *Etats et nations de l'Europe*, 1889, his *Atlas*, 1894, the *Tableau de la géographie de la France*, 1903 and the *France de l'Est*, 1917 are all classic works, well illustrating his methods. The *Principes de géographie humaine* was constructed after his death by de Martonne from articles and an unfinished manuscript: the work ran into five editions, the fifth being published by Colin in 1955, and a translation from the first French edition was made by M T Bingham (Constable, 1926), edited by Emmanuel de Martonne, in which the editor's preface and the translator's note analyse the plan and scope of the work. The great *Géographie universelle* (*qv*) was conceived by him before the first world war and renewed by Lucien Gallois after his death. Regional and local geographical studies owe much to his insistence on a firm understanding of the geological background, and the mutual relations of soil, climate and living organisms.

1323 'The Vinland map and the Tartar Relation', as a separate publication, was prepared by R A Skelton, Thomas E Marston and George D Painter (Yale University Press, 1965), with a foreword by Alexander O Vietor. The reproduction of this map and the manuscript caused excitement, scepticism, much discussion and published comment; in Alexander Vietor's words—'The present publication of these remarkable documents is designed to be a preliminary work; completeness or finality is not claimed for the commentaries, which are to be considered a springboard for further investigation'. One of the most balanced commentaries was that by G R Crone, 'The Vinland map cartographically considered', in *The geographical journal*, March 1966. An interesting comparison is 'The finding of Wineland the Good: the history of the Icelandic discovery of America' by A D Reeves, 1895.
    Refer also

609

J R L Anderson: *Vinland voyage* (Eyre and Spottiswoode, 1967).

Einar Haugen: 'Sources of the Vinland map', *Arctic*, December 1966.

H M Ingsted: *Westward to Vinland: the discovery of pre-Columbian Norse house-sites in North America* (St Martin's Press, 1969, translated by E J Friis).

F J Pohl: *The Viking explorers* (New York: Crowell, 1966).

R A Skelton: 'The Vinland map', *Journal* of the Society of Archivists, April 1967.

J R Swanton: *The Wineland voyages* (Smithsonian Miscellaneous Collections, 107, 12, 1947).

W E Washburn, *ed*: *Proceedings* of the Vinland Map Conference (University of Chicago Press for the Newberry Library, 1971).

'The strange case of the Vinland Map: a symposium'; a series of papers presented to the Royal Geographical Society on 4 February 1974, published in *The geographical journal*, June 1974.

1324 'Vocabularium geographicum', compiled by G Quencez, in co-operation with scholars representing each country, in French, German, Italian, Dutch, English and Spanish (Council for Cultural Co-operation of the Council of Europe, 1968), was based on an analysis of a number of secondary school text books of the countries involved.

Refer also

H Baulig: *Vocabulaire franco-anglo-allemand de géomorphologie* (Faculté des lettres de Strasbourg, Editions Ophrys, 1970).

1325 Vogt, William (1902–1968) was a scholar devoted to the study of world population and the effects of human cultures on the natural environments. Field naturalist and lecturer for the National Association of Audubon Societies 1935–39, he then turned to studies of the climate, population and resources of Chile; his publication, *Road to survival*, 1948, made him known to a wider audience. He published a work on Scandinavia, 1950–51 and *People* in 1960, while working for the Conservation Foundation.

1326 'Volcanoes: an introduction to systematic geomorphology', by

Cliff Ollier (Cambridge, Mass: MIT Press, 1969), gives an account of volcanoes, their activity and landforms, especially for high school and university students. In twelve main sections 'Volcanic rocks', 'Volcanic eruptions', 'Types of volcano', 'Craters and calderas', 'Lava flows', 'Pyroclastic fall deposits', 'Pyroclastic flow deposits', 'Intrusive igneous rocks', 'Hydrology and drainage of volcanic areas', 'Weathering and erosion', 'Patterns of volcanic distribution' and 'Aspects of vulcanology' are treated, with many photographs, diagrams and sketch-maps accompanying a lucid text. A bibliography includes glossaries of definitions and relevant geological terms and a comprehensive list of articles and books referred to in the text.

    Refer also

    Bulletin volcanologique

    Catalogue of the active volcanoes of the world (International Association of Volcanology).

    F M Bullard: *Volcanoes in history, in theory, in eruption* (Edinburgh, 1962).

    Gordon A Macdonald: *Volcanoes* (Prentice-Hall, 1972).

1327 'A voyage towards the South Pole performed in the years 1822–24 *containing an examination of the Antarctic Sea'* was the classic work of James Weddell, 1825 and 1827. David and Charles of Newton Abbot made a reprint from the second edition in 1970, with an introduction by Sir Vivian Fuchs. To the second edition, Weddell added *Observations on the probability of reaching the South Pole* and *An account of a second voyage performed by the Beaufroy to the same seas*.

1328 Waghenaer, Lucas Jansz (*d* 1593) is particularly remembered for *De spieghel der zeevaerdt*, the first atlas of sea charts of the coasts of Northern Europe, 1584. There are numerous inaccuracies on the coasts, but the indications of safe anchorages and the representations of parts of the coasts as seen from the sea provided an important aid to navigation. Admiral Lord Howard of Effingham sponsored an English version, which was published as *The mariner's mirrour* in 1588. *Bibliographie de l'oeuvre de Lucas Jansz Waghenaer*, describing all the editions of the atlas, page by page, and noting all known variants of the issues of the charts as well as of the text, appears in *Bibliotheca Belgica*, first series, also reprinted by N Israel of Amsterdam in the 1880–1890 volume, 1961.

Refer also

C Koeman: 'Lucas Janszoon Waghenaer: a sixteenth century marine cartographer', *The geographical journal*, June 1965.

1329 'Walkabout', 'Australia's way of life magazine', has been published monthly since 1934 by the Australian National Travel Association, Melbourne. Of interest to the layman as well as to the geographer, it is illustrated and includes informative book reviews.

1330 War Office, Geographical Section, General Staff, issued a *Catalogue of maps* in 1947, plus supplements; the edition of 1952 omitted the sheets at 1:250,000 and larger scales, which had been withdrawn from public sale. A detailed classification scheme is used by which each map sheet bears a unique location number.

1331 'Warne's natural history atlas of Great Britain', edited by Arnold Darlington, with illustrations by Charles King, shows the approximate location throughout Britain of the six most widely occurring land types and, in an identification section, illustrates some of the vertebrates, invertebrates and plant species associated with them.

1332 'Water, earth and man: *a synthesis of hydrology, geomorphology and socio-economic geography',* edited by Richard J Chorley, including contributions by twenty-five authors (Methuen, 1969), is illustrated with figures and maps in the text, also with charts and references. The following is the train of thought: 'The world', 'The Basin', 'Precipitation', 'Evapotranspiration', 'Surface run-off', 'Ground water', 'Channel flow', 'Snow and ice', 'Short-term run-off patterns', 'Annual run-off characteristics', 'Long-term trends' and 'Choice in water use'. Each of the chapters develops the theme by proceeding from the many aspects of water occurrence to a deeper understanding of natural environments and their fusion with the activities of man in society and the hydrological cycle as a conceptual link between the various aspects of geography.

Refer also

A K Biswas: *History of hydrology* (Amsterdam: North Holland Publ., 1970).

R J M de Wiest: *Geohydrology* (Wiley, 1965).

R Furon: *The problem of water: a world study* (Faber, 1967, translated from *Le problème de l'eau dans le monde*).

André Guilcher: *Précis d'hydrologie: marine et continentale*

(Paris: Masson, 1965).

J Linton Gardner and Lloyd E Myers, *ed*: *Water supplies for arid regions* (University of Arizona, 1967).

David K Todd, *ed*: *The water encyclopedia* (New York: Water Information Center, 1971).

R C Ward: *Principles of hydrology* (McGraw-Hill, 1967).

Water Resources Centre: *Archives*, 1890–((University of Boston, Mass; *Dictionary catalogue* . . . (G K Hall reprint in five volumes); *Annual reports*.

H Wellish: *Water resources development, 1950–1965: an international bibliography* (Jerusalem: Israel Program for Scientific Translations, 1967).

Association française pour l'étude des eaux (AFEE): *Thesaurus national de l'eau.*

—*Information eaux* (formerly *Eaux et industries*). American Water Resources Association: *Water resources abstracts*, 1968–; *Water resources bulletin*. United Nations: *Water resources journal*, 1967–.

Water resources research (American Geophysical Union, Washington, DC, 1965–).

1333 **'Weather economics'**, based on the papers and discussions presented at the eleventh agricultural meteorology symposium held at the Welsh Plant Breeding Station near Aberystwyth on March 13, 1968, was edited by James A Taylor and published for the University College of Wales, Aberystwyth (Pergamon Press, 1970), as *Memorandum* no 11. The discussions following each paper are appended at the end of each section. The papers illustrate and measure the import of weather hazards on the budgets of weather-sensitive industries, such as farming, agriculture and forestry; the effect of snowstorms on communications in built-up areas, types of physical weatherproofing and the adjustment of day to day programmes to particular weather probabilities. The keynote of the symposium might be said to be the encouragement of more serious, long-term economic assessments of weather hazards. 'The cost of British weather', for example, 'The effect of the weather on farm organization and farm management', 'Weather and risk in forestry'. James Taylor includes an edited report of the discussions . . . and an 'Economic postscript' was contributed by G N Rubra.

Refer also

W J Maunder: *The value of the weather* (Methuen, 1970).

Alan Watts: *Weather forecasting ashore and afloat* (Adlard Coles, 1967).

1334 'Webster's geographical dictionary', first published in 1949 (second revised edition, 1960, Merriam of Springfield, Mass), is a dictionary containing names, places and geographical terms, together with geographical and historical information, pronunciations and 151 maps. The latest census figures were given for Great Britain, Canada and the USA. The maps are useful and a thumb index helps quick reference. *Webster's new geographical dictionary,* 1972, has been again completely revised, having 47,000 entries and 217 maps, updated to the end of 1971.

1335 'Welsh landforms and scenery', by G Melvyn Howe and Peter Thomas (Macmillan, 1963), portrays the variety of Welsh landforms, tectonic, igneous and gradational. Cross-referencing is employed frequently throughout the text, which is illustrated by well-chosen photographs, block diagrams, maps and sketchmaps. There is a short bibliography.

Refer also

John Challinor *et al*: *Geology explained in North Wales* (Newton Abbot: David and Charles, 1973).

Margaret Davies: *Wales in maps* (University of Wales Press, second edition, 1958).

G M Howe: *Wales from the air: a survey of the physical and cultural landscape* (University of Wales Press, 1957).

Colin A Lewis, *ed*: *The glaciations of Wales and adjoining regions* (Longman, 1970).

R Millward and Adrian Robinson: *The Welsh Marches* (Macmillan, 1971). (*qv*)

T R Owen: *Geology explained in South Wales* (Newton Abbot: David and Charles, 1973).

William Rees, *comp*: *An historical atlas of Wales from early to modern times* (Faber, second edition 1959).

Alan Wood, *ed*: *The Pre-Cambrian and Lower Palaeozoic rocks of Wales*. Report of a symposium held at the University College of Wales, Aberystwyth (University of Wales Press, 1969).

1336 'The Welsh Marches', by R Millward and Adrian Robinson (Macmillan, 1971), is the fourth work in the 'Landscapes of Britain' series, dealing with 'the country that lies between the valley of the lower Severn and the hills across which King Offa fixed the western frontier of Mercia and Wales in the eighth century. From north to south the area covered by the book reaches from the Vale of Llangollen to the north of the Wye'. Part One covers 'The physical and human setting of the Welsh Marches' and its historical geography, while the Second Part considers twelve areas in detail, appending a few references. A 'Glossary for the General Reader' is included and there are text photographs and sketch-maps throughout; a work useful to the non-geographical reader, as well as a companion to field studies.

1337 'Die Welt des Islams' is an international journal concerned with the development of contemporary Islam, edited by Otto Spies under the direction of E G Gómez, K Jahn and G Jäschke (Leiden: Brill, founded in 1913 under the title *Die Welt des Islams: Zeitschrift der Deutschen Gesellschaft für Islamkunde*, then edited by Georg Kampffmeyer). The journal ceased publication during the second world war and resumed in 1951 as an independent periodical with a new, more international character. Sections are devoted to documents, communications and reports, in addition to factual contributions by leading authorities; much space has always been given to reviews of new scholarly publications on the world of Islam.

1338 'Weltatlas: *die Staaten der Erde und ihre Wirtschaft'*, edited by Professor Edgar Lehmann with the assistance of Professor Heinz Sanke (Leipzig: VEB *Bibliographisches Institut*, 1952), is an entirely new atlas, useful for students of economic geography. Each map faces a corresponding location map on the same scale. The relevant economic information is shown by a uniform system of colouring and conventional signs. The basis of the economic maps is land utilisation, shown by solid colour, and twelve categories are distinguished, from first class arable to steppe and desert, with superimposed symbols in colour to indicate the predominant crops. Mineral resources are shown by signs and letters mostly in black, and industries similarly in red or blue. Germany is treated in great detail; in addition to general maps, the country is covered in five plates at a scale of 1:1.4m. For other European countries and Asia, where the information is of necessity often generalised, the scales are much smaller.

1339 'De Weltmeere: *Taschenatlas mit den wichtigsten tatsachen aus Meteororologie und Nautik'* (Gotha: Haack, 1956) is in the fifteenth edition. Twenty-three maps of oceans and seas and excellent port plans are accompanied by text covering information on weather, oceanography, navigation and navigational equipment, and shipping. A subject index increases the reference value of the work.

1340 'Welt-Seuchen-Atlas', world atlas of epidemic diseases, first edited by H Zeiss (Gotha, 1941–45), was revised in an enlarged edition by E Rosenwaldt (Hamburg, 1952, 1956). Sponsored by the Bureau of Medicine and Surgery, Navy Department, Washington, the work is an outstanding contribution to the study of the relationship of diseases, physical environment and man.

1341 'West African studies of Mary H Kingsley', with a new introduction by John E Flint, was reproduced in a third edition by Cass, 1964, including Mary Kingsley's Preface to the first edition of 1899, and the introduction to the second edition by George A Macmillan. Mr Flint, in the introduction, considers Mary Kingsley's life and achievement. The original appendices are not included.

1342 Westermann, Georg, Publishing House, Brunswick, founded in 1838, has become world-famous for the production of maps, atlases, wall maps and charts, and a variety of monographs and bibliographical works. *Westermanns Geographische Bibliographie*, inaugurated in 1954 (1955–), covers all geographical periodicals in German and the important ones published in other countries; in addition, all publications of German university institutes of geography and academies are included. Ten numbers are issued each year and the entries are produced on perforated slips ready for mounting on index cards. *Westermann Lexikon der Geographie*, edited by Dr Wolf Tietze in four volumes and a fifth volume, 'Register' 1968–1970, also contains biographies of contributors to geography, articles on the terminology, the concepts of geographers and much material from allied sciences, such as cartography, geodesy and ethnography. In 200,000 entries and numerous maps and other illustrations, the editor aims to provide details not easily available to the general reader. Earlier theories, which have by now been amply digested, such as Ratzel's 'Anthropogeographie', are treated exhaustively. A world oil atlas (*Erdol Weltatlas*) was published in 1966, containing admirable maps and diagrams. The *Diercke Weltatlas*, also a fine production, includes introductory pages about Germany, settlement patterns and landscape types within the country, and town plans.

1343 Whitcombe and Tombs Limited, publishers and printers, as well as book-sellers, Christchurch, have a special interest in all aspects of Australasian affairs. Catalogues are issued frequently, including special educational catalogues. The *New Zealand topical geographies* series comprises seventeen booklets on various aspects of New Zealand life and landscape, based on a systematic, rather than regional, approach. The firm is publisher for the New Zealand Council for Educational Research—the *Educational research* series and *Studies in education*. Periodicals published include *Historical news* in association with the History Department, University of Canterbury; *New Zealand geographer* (*qv*) and the *New Zealand journal of educational studies*. Many of the firm's monographs are available in Britain.

1344 'The white road: *a survey of polar exploration'*, by L P Kirwan (Hollis and Carter, 1959), was the first English language detailed and scholarly survey of Arctic and Antarctic exploration, beginning with the earliest known voyages and continuing to the transpolar voyage of the nuclear powered submarine, *Nautilus*, with an emphasis on the trends and influences at work throughout polar history. The Commonwealth Trans-Antarctic Expedition is included, also the results of research achieved during the International Geophysical Year, ending with a bibliography. There are some photographs and reproductions and a few maps, including a folding map of the North-west Passage, indicating some of the voyages undertaken in the hope of finding it.

1345 'Whyte's atlas guide', compiled by Fredrica Harriman Whyte (New York: Scarecrow Press; Bailey Brothers and Swinfen, 1962), is a helpful list, classified by region and subject, of the maps in twenty atlases most likely to be found in American libraries. Sections are devoted to groups of countries, individual countries, island groups, oceans, city plans and areas of unique interest, such as the Great Lakes and the Polar Regions. Most of the maps carry a brief annotation and there is a place-name index.

1346 'The wildscape atlas of England and Wales', planned in two volumes for publication 1971–1972, is based on selected data

617

from the Second Land Utilization Survey of Britain. There will be approximately sixty different combinations of basic colour and overprinted habitat symbols on the maps. Text gives details of field and cartographic techniques and also quantitative, ecological and planning analyses of findings from research undertaken during European Conservation Year. A map showing the colour key, a map index to the sheets, photographs and an annotation to the first, experimental, sheet, that of Wensleydale, is given in an article by Alice Coleman, 'A wildscape atlas for England and Wales' in *The geographical magazine* for October 1970.

1347 Wiley, John, and Sons Limited: In addition to the texts of more general background interest, many of the *Interscience* series are relevant to geographical studies. Those of central interest include P J Darlington: *Zoogeography: the geographical distribution of animals;* O W Freeman: *Geography of the Pacific;* Edward Higbee: *American agriculture: geography, resources, conservation;* G H T Kimble and Dorothy Good: *Geography of the northlands;* P E Lydolph: *Geography of the USSR;* A H Robinson and R D Sale: *Elements of cartography;* Guy-Harold Smith, *ed: Conservation of natural resources;* L D Stamp: *Africa: a study in tropical development.*

1348 Woods Hole Oceanographic Institution, at Woods Hole, Mass, sponsors research in all aspects of the oceans, including the physics, chemistry, biology, geology, geophysics and meteorology of the water masses; the bottom and margins of the seas and the interaction with the atmosphere. Of the many publications, the *Woods Hole Oceanographic Institution atlas* series, 1960–, is one of the most outstanding. The *Catalog* of the Library of the Marine Biological Laboratory and the Woods Hole Oceanographic Institution was published by G K Hall in twelve volumes and a separate volume, *Journals catalog,* 1972.

1349 Wooldridge, S W (1900–1963), a leading geomorphologist, especially on the London Basin and South East England, exerted also great influence in almost all aspects of geography, both practical and philosophical, particularly in his position as professor of geography at King's College, London, and through the offices he held in the British Association, section E, and the Geographical Association. He was also a founder of the Institute of British Geographers and an inspiration to the Field Studies Council. He was a stylist and his writings made a considerable impact on the profession at large, especially *The spirit and purpose of geography* (*qv*), which he wrote in collaboration with W G East. *The geographer as scientist: essays on the scope and nature of geography*, 1956, is a collection of some of his most interesting work.

1350 The Wordie Collection of Polar Exploration, National Library of Scotland, was founded by Sir James Wordie, geologist and explorer (1889–1962); it covers Arctic and Antarctic exploration and research, including works in many languages, altogether some five thousand items, mainly from the eighteenth and nineteenth centuries, also Sir James' files as a member of the Discovery Committee of the British Colonial Office. The catalogue has been published in one volume, 1964.

1351 'The World Aeronautical Chart', at 1:1M scale, was devised by the Aeronautical Chart Service of the United States Air Force; when the International Civil Aviation Organisation was set up, the chart was put at its disposal. Features on the ground must be shown in such a way that they can be easily identified from the air; international boundaries are important, but not internal ones. The size and shape of settlements are essential features, and roads and railways are important as landmarks. Placenames are of low priority, but additional information such as radar aids and technical air traffic control data are vital, in addition to the location of airfields.

1352 'World agricultural economics and rural sociology abstracts', published quarterly from 1959, in English, French, German and Spanish, by the Commonwealth Agricultural Bureaux, Farnham Royal, in co-operation with the International Association of Agricultural Libraries and Documentalists and the International Association of Agricultural Economists, is the only abstracting journal to include world literature on agricultural economics and rural sociology (North Holland Publishing Company, Amsterdam, 1959–). Entries, covering books, reports, bulletins and articles, are classified, including a section for 'Reference material'; annual author and subject indexes are issued.

1353 'World atlas of agriculture', published by the Istituto Geografico de Agostini, Novara, under the aegis of the International Association of Agricultural Economists and prepared for the Committee for the World Atlas of Agriculture, is in four volumes, 1969–1972. The complete work will comprise sixty-two maps of land utilisation and four volumes of monographs illustrating the agricultural economy of the various states and territories. The basic scale of the maps is 1:5M; Europe, except for Russia, part of Asia Minor, the Middle East, Japan, New Zealand, parts of North and South Africa, are represented at 1:1,250,000. For a few islands of limited area the scales used are 1:1,250,000, 1:1,500,000 and 1:2,500,000. Central America is depicted at 1:3M and the less populated areas of Canada and Alaska at 1:12,500,000. The monographs, carried out on a uniform plan and edited by Professor K C Edwards and Dr John Giggs, deal with 'Europe, USSR, Asia Minor'; 'South and East Asia, Oceania'; 'Americas' and 'Africa'. They are illustrated by line-drawings and statistics, showing development and present-day conditions. The germ of the project was created at the ninth International Conference of Agricultural Economists and plans were discussed during the period 1956 to 1959. The General Secretariat was established at the University of Padua, the Cartographic Department at the University of Bologna and the Monograph Department at the University of Nottingham, with the initial co-operation of the Department of Geography of the London School of Economics and Political Science. Local collaborators were nominated in every country and the final phase of organisation was the adoption of the project by the International Association of Agricultural Economics on the occasion of the Eleventh International Conference of Agricultural Economists held at Cuernavaca in 1961. On the back of each map, in addition to the sheet-lines of adjoining areas, the contour lines are drawn, for they could not be shown on the maps themselves without impairing legibility; in some cases, small additional maps are given, showing selected crops of special significance to the country concerned, which could not be shown on the maps themselves, the main consideration being comparability of content. The project is the first presentation of agricultural resources on medium-scale maps on a uniform basis and a superb example of international co-operation.

Refer also

René Dumont: *Types of rural economy: studies in world agriculture* (Methuen, 1970).

1354 'World atlas of mountaineering', edited by Wilfrid Noyce and Ian McMorrin (Nelson, 1969), is more than an atlas; it is a finely produced review of mountaineering activity, containing an invaluable range of information on the great mountaineering areas of the world. A series of articles covers every area—the Alps and Himalaya, Japan, New Zealand, the American continent, central Africa and polar regions—each article by a writer who knows the area from his own climbing experience. There are 260 black and white illustrations, some in colour, maps and sketchmaps.

Compare

Standard encyclopaedia of the world's mountains (qv).

Refer also

R Frison-Roche: *Les montagnes de la terre*, in two volumes, 1964.

Yoshimi Yakushi: *Catalogue of the Himalayan Literature* (Kyoto, 1972).

1355 'World cartography', issued approximately annually since 1951 by the Cartographic Office, Department of Social Affairs of the United Nations, New York, is the best single source of information on activities, progress and plans in the field of cartography throughout the world. In English and French, the fascicules include longer or shorter articles, reports, notes and valuable bibliographies. The second major source of information of world-wide scope stems from the regional cartographic conferences of the United Nations for Asia and the Far East, of which the first was held in Mussoorie, in 1955; the *Proceedings* and *Technical papers* are invaluable for informed discussion on general topics and for reviews of achievements in individual areas, not entirely confined to the Far East.

1356 'The world cities', by Peter Hall (Weidenfeld and Nicolson, *World university library*, 1966), begins with a chapter on 'The metropolitan explosion', followed by chapters devoted to the centres of population based on London, Paris, Randstad Holland, Rhine-Ruhr, Moscow, New York and Tokyo. A forecast of 'The future metropolis' completes the text, which is generously illustrated by photographs, sketchmaps and town plans; bibliographical notes are included.

Refer also

William A Robson and D E Regan: *Great cities of the world: their government, politics and planning* (Allen and Unwin, two volumes, 1954, 1957, 1972).

1357 'World directory of geographers', prepared in 1952 by the

American Geographical Society for the International Geographical Union, on the occasion of the Washington Congress, 1952, was the first attempt at such a world list, in which the special interests of leading geographers were featured. The work has been continued as *Orbis geographicus* (*qv*).

1358 'The world economic survey', issued since 1948 by the United Nations Department of Economic and Social Affairs, New York, presents in English, French and Spanish an annual analysis of world trade, payments, production, industrialisation and development. Each issue since 1956 has included a special study of a major economic subject. With the 1964 edition (1965), a new publishing policy began; in a cloth edition for the first time, in two parts, part I focuses attention on development plans and provides an appraisal of targets and progress in the developing countries and part II is a review of recent developments in the world economy and a discussion of a number of topical problems.

Refer also

E W Zimmermann: *World resources and industries: a functional appraisal of the availability of agricultural and industrial materials,* third edition, 1972.

1359 'World fisheries abstracts', prepared by FAO in English, French and Spanish since 1950, was published quarterly to 1961, subsequently bi-monthly. Abstracts of important publications and articles, prepared on cards for ready reference filing, review the world's technical literature on fisheries and related subjects. The *Handbook for world fisheries abstracts,* 1950–, available free with the subscription, contains detailed descriptions of alternative systems for filing the *Abstracts.*

1360 'World fishing' (incorporating Fish industry) is a monthly magazine covering every aspect of the commercial fishing industry in all parts of the world (Grampian Press, London). Sections include notes entitled 'Comment'; Correspondence; Short informative articles on new developments; 'Top boats of the month', grouped under port headings; 'European fishing vessel completions during . . . (the previous year). There are many monochrome photographs and the advertisements are naturally of significance to those specialising in the industry.

Refer also

James R Coull: *The fisheries of Europe* (Bell, 1972).

G L Kesteven: *Fisheries glossary* (Elsevier).

Anthony Netboy: *The Atlantic salmon: a vanishing species?* (Faber, 1968).

Eric W Young: *Farming, fishing and forestry throughout the world* (Arnold, 1971).

1361 'World forestry atlas' has been in process of compilation for some thirty years at the Federal Research Centre for. Forestry in Reinbeck, near Hamburg. Over sixty maps showing the distribution of forests throughout the world were published by the early nineteen seventies.

1362 'A world geography of irrigation', by Leonard M Cantor (Oliver and Boyd, 1968; Praeger, 1970), sets out 'to gather information from a variety of sources' and 'to provide for the student of geography a synoptic picture of world irrigated agriculture'. In the first two sections, 'Irrigation in perspective' and 'The regional geography of irrigation', the work achieves probably the most systematic and comprehensive survey to date. Forty photographs illustrate the variety of landscape and methods of agriculture referred to and sixty maps and diagrams help to show regional distributions, major developments, water resources and methods of application.

Refer also

C J Wiesner: *Climate, irrigation and agriculture: a guide to the practice of irrigation* (Angus and Robertson, 1970).

1363 'World highways', the monthly duplicated news sheet of the International Road Federation (Highway Transportation Consultant to United Nations and Co-operating Agency of the Organization of American States and Organisation for European Economic Cooperation, is an invaluable document in its field. Items, arranged under the names of countries or areas concerned, give details of road projects in progress or completed, in all parts of the world.

Refer also

Herman Schreiber: *The history of roads: from amber route to motorway* (Barrie and Rockliff, 1961, translated by Stewart Thomson).

1364 World Land Use Survey was inaugurated to show by examples what could be done on a co-ordinated plan, adapting methods where necessary, and to stimulate countries to carry out for themselves a land use survey similar to the Land Utilisation Survey of Great Britain (*qv*), using the scheme agreed by the Commission on a World Inventory of Land Use, brought into being for the purpose at the International Geographical Union Congress, Lisbon, 1949. Important *Reports* were presented to the Washington Congress of 1952 and to the Rio Congress of 1956. *Occasional papers* have been produced irregularly since 1956, published by Geographical Publications Limited; regional monographs have appeared, as completed, since 1958.

1365 'World map, 1:2,500,000', based on the International Map of the World, 1:1M, was achieved by co-operation between the cartographic organisations of Bulgaria, Czechoslovakia, the German Democratic Republic, Hungary, Poland, Romania and the Soviet Union. It covered the world, including seas and oceans, at a uniform metric scale and, using sixty-four internationally accepted map symbols, a comprehensive survey of the physical, political and economic-geographical conditions. Three variant base maps were available for use for thematic maps, with the written agreement of the general editor. The naming of the sheets, explanation of conventional signs, etc, are in Russian and English; within the maps, only Latin lettering has been used, all names being in their official forms. Physical relief is shown by contours and a layering system at convenient intervals; twelve colours were used.

1366 'World map of climatology' *see Atlas of meteorology*. . . .

1367 World Meteorological Organization had its origin in the International Meteorological Organisation, founded at a meeting in Utrecht in 1878, following which a system of Regional Commissions, Technical Commissions and special working groups was built up. This organisation dissolved at the meeting of directors in Washington in 1947 and the WMO gradually took shape as an intergovernment body, holding the first Congress in Paris in 1951, when the new organisation became a specialised agency of the United Nations, with a full secretariat led by professional meteorologists. The World Meteorological Congress meets at least once every four years. Regional associations, one for each continent, meet once in four years and, in the interim, working groups research into subjects of regional interest. The eight technical commissions also meet every four years. Additional working groups are convened for specific purposes, as, for example, to organise the research during the International Geophysical Year. Observations have been internationally standardised. The most important of all the WMO documents are the series known as 'Publication no 9, weather reports—stations, codes, transmissions', a complete guide on the availability of basic meteorological data to the world's meteorological services, in several volumes, kept constantly up to date, complete and accurate. In addition, a vast publications programme is maintained, including the *Technical regulations, The technical publication and technical notes series,* the *International cloud atlas* and special publications, such as those connected with the International Geophysical Year. *The WMO bulletin* keeps all members informed. Methods have been revolutionised by the use of meteorological satellites, radio or landline teleprinter circuits and facsimile transmissions. The *Catalogue of meteorological data for research,* issued looseleaf since 1965, contains published synoptic or climatological data and information from the eighty-eight member states of WMO, grouped under subject headings—current periodical publications, former periodical publications, occasional publications, data included in other publications, future plans, address to which requests for publications should be sent. Details include a brief history of the publications and an abstract of contents; it is planned to increase the information given on unpublished data. In its first report to the United Nations, WMO recommended the creation of a 'World weather program' (*qv*).

1368 'World mining', an excellent monthly world report, has the editorial centred in Brussels, the printing department in the Netherlands and the circulation department in San Francisco. A yearbook is also issued, in June, *Catalog, survey and directory number,* including a 'Catalog index of equipment and manufacturers'.

1369 'The world of the soil', by Sir E John Russell (Collins, 1957, second edition, 1959; in the *New naturalist* series), with its fine photographs and diagrams, figures and select bibliography, has become a classic work. The text analyses the structure of soil, how it has developed, the circulation of water and gases which give the soil an atmosphere and a succession of climates quite different from the air above, and dealing with the varied forms of life made possible or impossible by the individual conditions. Sir John Russell's other major work, *Soil conditions and plant growth,* has gone through many editions during his years as Director of the Rothamsted Experimental

Station; he created a world famous institution which became the centre of the Commonwealth Soil Bureau.

Refer also

E M Bridges: *World soils* (CUP, 1970).

G R Clarke: *The study of the soil in the field* (OUP, third edition, 1941).

E A FitzPatrick: *Pedology: a systematic approach to soil science* (Oliver and Boyd, 1971).

A D Hall and E J Russell: A report on the agriculture and soils *of Kent, Surrey and Sussex* (HMSO, 1911: a pioneer work).

W L Kubiena: *The soils of Europe* (Murby, 1953).

Soil Survey of Great Britain, *Reports* (*qv*).

United States Department of Agriculture: *Soil survey manual*.

1370 'The world on paper: *a descriptive catalogue of cartographical material published in Amsterdam during the 17th century'*, with introduction by H de la Fontaine Verwey and commentaries by Marijke de Vrij, has been reprinted by TOT, Amsterdam; originally compiled for the exhibition arranged to commemorate the International Conference on Cartography in Amsterdam, the Catalogue has grown into a valuable study on the role played by map publishers and cartographers in Amsterdam at this time. Included are twenty-four photographs of maps, title-pages and seamen's instruments. Text is in English and Dutch.

1371 'World political geography', by G Etzel Pearcy and others (New York: Crowell, 1948, 1957, fifth printing, 1963), shows the world at mid-century. Thirty-eight chapters are grouped under six regional headings: 'Primary concepts', 'The western hemisphere', 'Europe', 'Africa and the Middle East', 'Eastern Asia and Australasia' and 'World political geography at mid-twentieth century'. The text is illustrated by a number of sketchmaps; there are end of chapter references and a bibliography, which is placed after the contents of each chapter. A glossary defines many of the technical terms used in the text.

1372 'World political patterns', by Lewis M Alexander (Rand McNally; Murray, 1957, 1963), is one of the *Rand McNally geography* series. The text examines the nature and development of political geography, the structure of the state as a politico-geographic unit, the changing nature of international boundaries and the states as a viable political unit before continuing with individual studies of the United States, Canada, Latin America, the European countries, the Arab world, Africa and parts of Asia and the Pacific. More than a hundred small sketchmaps illustrate the points being made and there are end of chapter references.

Refer also

S B Cohen: *Geography and politics in a divided world* (Methuen, 1963).

H J de Blij: *Systematic political geography* (Wiley, 1967).

1373 'World population and food supply', by J H Lowry (Arnold, 1970), at first-year university level, provides a useful introduction to this subject and its implications. The increase in world population is analysed and potential food requirements estimated; the possibilities of extending and intensifying world agriculture and of producing unconventional and synthetic foods are then examined, including 'Unconventional and synthetic foods' in detail. Numerous illustrations are included throughout the text, also sketchmaps and diagrams.

Refer also

Georg Borgstrom: *The hungry planet: the modern world at the edge of famine* (New York: Macmillan; Collier-Macmillan, second printing, 1966).

Josué de Castro: *Geography of hunger* (Gollancz, 1952).

Q H Stanford, *ed: The world's population: problems of growth* (Toronto: OUP, 1972).

1374 World Population Congress, established in Rome in 1955, is concerned with population problems and with the analysis of statistical data from all parts of the world. Great stress is laid on the need for uniformity in population mapping; the official Commission of the International Geographical Union on Population Mapping, set up at the Rio Congress in 1956, has done much to achieve this, particularly on the scale of 1:1M.

Note that the Commission on the Geography and Cartography of World Population was set up at the London IGU Congress, 1964; in 1968, at New Delhi, the Commission was voted to continue, with the title Commission on Population Geography.

Refer also

A G Ogilvie: 'The mapping of population, especially on a

scale 1/м', IGU Commission for the Study of Population Problems, *Report*, 1952.

1375 'World railways', edited by Henry Sampson (Sampson Low in many editions at intervals), presents 'A world-wide survey of equipment and operation of the railways of the world'. Included are illustrated reports of progress and proposed developments of major railways throughout the world—some 1,500 altogether—new features in economic development and physical characteristics affecting individual railway systems, with detailed analyses of the systems in each country, illustrated with photographs, maps, statistics and gauge diagrams. Separate sections cover underground railways, manufacturers of diesel engines for rail traction and other specialist topics.

1376 'World shipping: *an economic geography of ports and seaborne trade',* by Gunnar Alexandersson and Göran Narström (Wiley, 1967), filled a gap in the English language reference material concerning ports, the economics of transportation and cargoes. First a general survey is made of international shipping, trade, cargo and shipbuilding and repair; the rest of the study is arranged regionally, covering the ports in Atlantic Europe, the Mediterranean, Anglo-America, Latin America, Africa south of the Sahara, Asia and Oceania. Photographs, sketchmaps and diagrams abound throughout the text; there is a short glossary and a section listing statistical sources, followed by an author index, an index of persons, vessels and corporations, one of ports and places and a subject index.

Refer also

Chamber of Shipping of the United Kingdom: *British shipping statistics*

Ports of the world, annual, 1946–.

Shipping world year book . . .

James Bird: *Seaports and seaport terminals* (Hutchinson University Library).

J T Williams: 'The changing design of ports', *The journal of the Royal Society of Arts . . .* , July 1972.

World ports (formerly *World ports and marine news*), eight issues a year, 1914–, Paul A Amundsen, Washington, DC).

1377 'World survey of climatology' is the title of a series of fifteen volumes prepared under the editorship of Professor H E Landsberg

(Amsterdam: Elsevier, 1969–1973). Three introductory volumes, by H Flohn, discuss general climatology, followed by volume 4, 'Climate of the free atmosphere', by D F Rex; 5, 'Climates of northern and western Europe' and 6, 'Climates of central and southern Europe', both by C C Wallén; 7, 'Climates of the Soviet Union', by P E Lydolph; 8, 'Climates of northern and eastern Asia' and 9, 'Climates of southern and western Asia', both by H Arakawa; 10, 'Climates of Africa', by J F Griffiths; 11, 'Climates of North America', by R A Bryson; 12, 'Climates of Central and South America', by W Schwerdtfeger; 13, 'Climates of Australia and New Zealand', by J Gentilli; 14, 'Climates of the polar regions', by S Orvig; and 15, 'Climates of the oceans', by H Thomsen. Graphs and tables are included in the texts and bibliographies concerning individual areas.

1378 'World timbers', compiled and edited in three volumes by B J Rendle (Benn; University of Toronto Press, 1969), show representations of timbers in colour at every opening, with descriptions on the opposite pages. The current series of *World timbers* was preceded by the journal *Wood*, which began publication in 1936, in which a feature was the series of colour plates of timbers, accompanied by technical information on their properties and values; the first series, under the name 'Wood specimens', covered the years 1936–1960; these were followed by the work under review. A selection of one hundred wood specimens was reproduced in the first two editions, now out of print. The timbers are now selected mainly for their economic importance or interest for the world markets.

1379 'World trade annual', in four volumes (New York: Walker 1963–), is planned for publication every year, with further expansions. Imports and exports of individual countries are included, relating to over a thousand items of the United Nations Standard International Trade Classification, totals are followed by a number of sub-divisions and commodity figures are analysed, giving origin, destination and values.

1380 'World vegetation', by Denis Riley and Anthony Young (CUP, 1968), is a slim volume of fine photographs, some in colour, with explanatory text on the following themes: 'Plant communities and environment'; 'Deciduous woodlands'; 'Coniferous forests'; 'Rain forests'; 'Grass lands'; 'Savannas'; 'Vegetation of dry environments'; 'Tundra and mountain vegetation'; 'Freshwater and coastal vegetation'. Appended are an essay on soils, a map showing 'Distribution of the main world vegetation types' and an index of terms.

Refer also

S R Eyre, *ed: World vegetation types* (Macmillan, 1971).

A H de Lemps: *La végétation de la terre* (Paris: Masson, 1970).

1381 World Weather Program, formerly the World Weather Watch, recommended by the World Meteorological Organisation (*qv*), is a unique system for observing, collecting, processing and distributing weather information, using the latest developments in communication, data processing and space technology. It is designed to support the weather services of individual nations by providing them with the basic weather information that can best be handled through international co-operation. The main elements of the research plan were worked out with the US National Academy of Sciences. The Tiros Operational Satellite system, begun in 1966, marked a major advance in global weather observation; automatic picture transmission equipment permits direct readout of cloud photographs at local stations throughout the world as the satellites pass over. Three World Weather Program centres have been designated, in Washington, Moscow and Melbourne.

An invaluable report, 'World weather watch: collection, storage and retrieval of meteorological data', was published in 1969 by WMO (Planning report, no 28). The first two chapters review the problems still to be solved in this sphere; chapter 3 deals with the types of data which should be stored permanently and the main part of chapter 4 lists the data to be stored at the world, regional and national meteorological centres. The following chapters consider the methods to be used in the collection of data, emphasising the advantages of using the global telecommunication system for this purpose; the problem of quality control, with special reference to real time checking by computer; guiding principles for the storage of meteorological data; the retrieval of archive data and the necessity for a definite classification system and standard cataloguing.

1382 'World weather records' is the continuing title of a series of publications. The first three publications were prepared by H H Clayton and Miss F L Clayton and published by the Smithsonian Institution in 1927, 1934 and 1947. The fourth, prepared at the Blue Hill Meteorological Observatory, was published by the United States Weather Bureau, covering 1941–1950, 1959. These earlier issues, which included climatological information through 1950, had global distribution and were widely used in research. At its fourth Congress in Geneva, April, 1963, the WMO sponsored the publication of the 1951–60 *World weather records* by the United States Weather Bureau; six volumes covered North America, Canada and Mexico; Europe; South America, Central America, West Indies, Caribbean and Bermuda; Asia; Africa; Antarctica, Australia and Oceania and Ocean weather stations. Requests for data were sent to more than 150 meteorological services throughout the world and the data were transferred to punched cards for machine sorting.

1383 'The world's landscapes', under the editorship of J M Houston, is the title of a new series by Longmans, 1970–, beginning with *China*, by Yi-Fu Tuan; *Wales*, by F V Emery; *The Soviet Union*, by W H Parker; *Ireland*, by A R Orme; and *New Zealand*, by K B Cumberland and J S Whitelaw, all published in 1970. The purpose of the series is stated to be the explanation of man's effect on the different landscape types. Freedom of treatment has been given to the authors, as regards length of text, number of illustrations, etc, but physical format is uniform and the approach is not too technical.

1384 'World-wide directory of mineral industries education and research', edited by Herbert Wohlbier and others, was published by the Gulf Publishing Company, of Houston, Texas, in 1968; 512 citations have been brought together, from sixty-eight countries.

1385 Wright, John Kirtland (1891–1969), one of the outstanding scholar-geographers of modern times, Librarian and Director of the American Geographical Society, has passed on his inspiration by means of his lectures, meetings with other geographical societies throughout the world and, most important, by means of his writings. He inaugurated *Current geographical literature . . . (qv)*; compiled, with Elizabeth T Platt, *Aids to geographical research*, second edition, *1947;* wrote the classic historico-geographical work, *Geographical lore at the time of the Crusades*, compiled the history of the American Geographical Society, entitled *Geography in the making: the AGS 1851–1951*. His vintage work was *Human nature in geography (qv)*.

1386 Wye School of Rural Economics and Related Studies, at Ashford in Kent, had its origin in 1922, with the appointment of Mr James Wyllie to the staff of the South Eastern Agricultural College;

the College absorbed the former horticultural Swanley College in 1945 and the systematic study of commercial horticulture dates from 1951, when Dr R Folley joined the staff. Professor G P Wibberley, appointed in 1954, introduced the study of land economics. Research is now conducted in local studies, land economics, agrarian development, horticultural production economics, farm economics and farm management. The *Press notices* issued at intervals draw attention to the publications resulting from these surveys and research: 'The British Isles tomato survey', for example, 'Farm business statistics for South-East England', 'Optimum harvesting systems for cereals'. Monographs are published from time to time: I D Carruthers: *Irrigation development planning aspects of Pakistan experience*, 1969, among others. The *Farm management pocket book*, by John Nix, has been extensively revised in a fourth edition.

1387 'The Yorkshire and Humberside Planning Region: *an atlas of population change 1951–1966'*, prepared by D G Symes and E G Thomas, with R R Dean, was published by the University of Hull, Department of Geography, 1968. Sixteen maps began as an experimental exercise in mapping characteristics of population change; based on the 1961 figures, they deal with absolute change, total percentage change, natural increase, birth and death rates and fertility. Conventional mapping employs proportional spheres or 'standard score' methods, using chloropleth shading in black and red, on a fold-out sheet, giving a shading key and standard deviation graphs. All maps are on the same scale, 1:565,000. No placenames are marked, but a transparent overlay shows the administrative boundaries. Tables at the end add statistics for individual places. An introductory text explains the cartographic method used.

1388 The Young Explorers' Trust (YET), inaugurated in London in January 1972, was recognised before the end of the year as an educational charity. Improved contacts between societies and the interchange of knowledge and experience are aimed at; the Trust will become the national negotiating body for pre-university expeditions, members of the Council being representative of relevant organisations. Bulletins and leaflets have been published; an Iceland Unit formed later in 1972 has also published a bulletin.

1389 'Yukon bibliography' was published in a preliminary edition, compiled by J R Lotz (*Yukon Research Project* series, Northern Co-ordination and Research Centre, Department of Northern Affairs and Natural Resources, Ottawa, 1964). The Yukon Research Project is a long term research programme in the social, economic and historical fields in the Yukon territory. Following a general section, items are grouped within broad subject headings, such as 'Bibliographies', 'Forests and forestry', 'Glaciology and permafrost' and so on; the *Arctic bibliography* number is given when relevant.

1390 'Zambia in maps', edited by D Hywel Davies (ULP, 1971), consists of fifty-five black and white maps with facing pages of text, on the major aspects of the geography of the country. It is a corporate work, prepared by the University of Zambia, with contributions from government departments and cartography by G H Adika, Department of Geography, University College of Cape Coast, Ghana. Selected references are included.

1391 Zeiss, Carl, VEB, Jena are acknowledged experts in the field of precision instrument making; their precision co-ordinatograph, for example, with accessories for special work, such as the fitting microscope, circle tracing device, line interrupter, dual tracing device, mirror attachment setting projector and lead sharpener. A *Precision co-ordinatograph instruction manual* is available, with illustrations in a back folder. Similar comprehensive instruction booklets describe the firm's Aerial-Photograph Converter and the Stereopantometer.
    See also the *Jena review.*

1392 'Zeitschrift für Geopolitik', first issued in 1924, heralded the acceptance of the new trends of thought as an independent subject in Germany. R Kjellén, one of the promoters, called it 'a science which treats of the State as a geographical organism or a spatial phenomenon', but such an association with geography was by no means universally accepted at that time.

1393 Zinc Development Association is typical of the organisations concerned with specific resources, whose libraries and publications provide source material for the geographer. The library was formally organised in 1943 and holds a stock of nearly twenty thousand pamphlets and more than a thousand books, in addition to patents, reports and directories on the world literature of zinc and its uses. *Zinc abstracts* and its companion, *Lead abstracts*, are prepared by the Zinc Development Association and Lead Development

Association Abstracting Service. Between them, the two publications review all current world literature on the uses of the metals and their products.

INDEX

References are to the entry numbers

635

African Studies Centre, University of Chicago 21
African Studies in Canada Committee, University of Alberta 21
'The African Studies Library of North-western University', H E Panofsky 737
African Studies Unit, University of Leeds 21
An African survey, revised 1956 . . . 22
The African world . . . , *ed*: R A Lystad 22
Africana 21
Africana catalogues 23
Africana notes and queries 25
Afrika Kartenwerk 23
Afrikaforum 25
L'Afrique, Pierre Gourou 22
L'Afrique Australe et Madagascar, R Battistini 22
Afsher, Iradj: *Bibliography of Iranian bibliographies* 219
Index Iranicus 219
Afzelins, Nils: *Books in English on Sweden* 1
Agarwal, S K and A R Boyle: 'A character recognition device for soundings . . .' 931
The age of Drake, J A Williamson 1069
The age of reconnaissance, J H Parry 437
Agenda for survival . . . , H W Helfrich 483
Agostini, Giovanni de 26
Agrarmeteorologische bibliographie 223
An agricultural atlas of Scotland, J T Coppock 27
An agricultural atlas of Scotland, H J Wood 27
An agricultural atlas of Scotland, 1966 27
Agricultural development and economic integration in Latin America 453
Agricultural development in Asia, R T Shand 80
Agricultural development in Nigeria . . . 28
Agricultural Economics Research Institute, University of Oxford 29
The agricultural economy of Nigeria, S W Skinner 812
Agricultural geography, W B Morgan and R J C Munton 31
Agricultural geography, L J Symons 200
An agricultural geography of Great Britain 30
Agricultural geography symposium: a report . . . , 1964 31

Agricultural index 251
Agricultural meteorology 32, 466
Agricultural planning and village community in Israel . . . 571
Agricultural research in tropical Africa 33
Agricultural typology and land use mapping 34
Agricultural Typology Commission, IGU 34
Agricultural zoology in Fiji 1211
Agriculture 31, 73, 174, 188, 200, 255, 331, 332, 361, 377, 380, 511, 524, 534, 585, 599, 726, 791, 844, 1153, 1290, 1302, 1307, 1333, 1347, 1352, 1369, 1373
  bibliography 186, 223, 1302
  maps 105, 1353
Agriculture and trade of the Caribbean region . . . 304
Agriculture in the Australian economy 188
Agriculture in the Tropics 1290
Agroclimatological methods symposium 35
Agronomy 243, 1070
Aguilar nuevo atlas de España 36
Ahmad, E: *Coastal geomorphology of India* 955
Ahmad, K S: *A geography of Pakistan* 459
Ahmad, Q: *Indian cities* . . . 713
Aids to geographical research . . . 37, 579, 1385
Air photo atlas of rural land use 312
Air photo packs 315, 552
'Air photographs for small expeditions' 12
Air photographs—man and the land (Geographical Association) 552
Air survey, C A Hart 312
Air survey in economic development 312
Airborne Profile Recorder 312
'Airborne radio echo sounding by the British Antarctic Survey' 628
'Airborne radio echo sounding of the Greenland ice sheet' 628
Airey, W T G, festschrift 1243
Airways 576, 638, 1288
Airways of New Zealand 1113
Aiyepeku, W O: 'The periodical literature of geography' 768
Akademiya Nauk SSSR 38
Aki, K *et al, ed: Nippon Keizai Chizu* 152
Akram, Mohammed: *Bibliographie analytique de l'Afghanistan* 219

637

639

Antarctic 50, 60, 61, 72, 183, 269, 359, 396, 410, 423, 426, 466, 628, 670, 720, 762, 879, 926, 1072, 1073, 1074, 1164, 1165, 1303, 1327, 1344, 1350
maps 65, 94, 123, 519, 967
Antarctic 59
The Antarctic, H G R King 65
Antarctic bibliography 60
Antarctic ecology 61
Antarctic journal of the United States 62
'Antarctic links with the Andes' 65
Antarctic map folio series 47, 63, 312
Antarctic record 59
Antarctic report 1303
Antarctic research . . . 64, 287
Antarctic Research, Biological Working Group of the Scientific Committee 61
Antarctic research series (American Geophysical Union) 65
The Antarctic Treaty 65
Antarctica, ed. Trevor Hatherton 65
Antarctica: the story of a continent 65
L'Antarctique, A Cailleux 65
Anthiaume, A: *Cartes marines* . . . 931
Anthropogeographie 1106, 1342
Anthropology 749, 1045, 1187
maps 110
Antilles 304
Antique maps, P J Radford 411
Antique maps and their cartographers 66
Antique maps for the collector 66
Antique maps of Europe, the Americas . . . 66
Das Antlitz der Erde 1245
Apenchénko, V S: *Atlas narodov mira* 119
Appalachian Trail 523
Appleton, J H: *A morphological approach to the geography of transport* 1288
'The application of geography in Poland' 1075
'Application of information theory in generalisation of map contents' 909
'Application of information theory to maps' 909
Applications de la photographie aérienne . . . 312
Applied climatology . . . 358
Applied coastal geomorphology 367
Applied geography and the human environment 483
Applied geography in Hungary 700
Approaches to environmental studies . . . 462, 464

Arabia 212, 248
Arabian Gulf, bibliography 1175
Arakawa, H: on climates of Asia 1377
Arasteh, A R: *Man and society in Iran* 897
Arcano del mare 67
Arceduc *See* Clos-Arceduc
Archaeology, industrial 715, 716
Archambault, M *et al*: *Documents et méthode pour le commentaire de cartes* . . . 312
Archer, J E and T H Dolton: *Fieldwork in geography* 560
Arctic 50, 61, 294, 295, 346, 426, 762, 1072, 1073, 1074, 1157, 1165, 1171, 1252
bibliography 71, 72, 227, 1389
exploration 688, 1232, 1344, 1350
maps 130, 466, 519, 1067
Arctic 68, 72
Arctic and Alpine research 69
The Arctic basin 70
The Arctic bibliography 71, 72, 1389
Arctic environment and resources 70
Arctic Institute of North America 39, 68, 70, 71, 72, 357
Arctic journeys . . . 670
Arctic Ocean 70
Area 73, 728
Areas of economic stress in Canada . . . 294
Argentina 219, 1007
Argentina, George Pendle 666
La Argentina: suma de geografia 74
Arid land research institutions . . . 77
Arid lands 75, 418, 419, 690, 1223
bibliography 224
See also Deserts
Arid lands: a geographical appraisal 75
Arid lands in perspective . . . 76
Arid lands in transition 75
Arid Zone newsletter (CSIRO) 380
Arid Zone research (Unesco) 77, 690
Arizona University, arid zone studies 75, 77, 419
Armen, Garbis: 'A classification of cities and city regions in England and Wales . . .' 354
Armstrong, Terence and Brian Roberts, ed: *Illustrated ice glossary* 1165
Armstrong, Terence *et al*: *Illustrated glossary of snow and ice* 1188
Arnberger, E: *Lehrbuch der kartographie*

312
Arnold, Edward (Publishers) Limited, London 78
Arnold, T J I, *comp: Bibliographie de l'oeuvre de Lucas Jansz Waghenaer* 211
Art. Institut Orell Füssli A G 783
The art of navigation in England . . ., D W Waters 79, 669
Artsmail 966
Arvill, Robert: *Man and environment . . .* 979
Ash, M: *Regions of tomorrow . . .* 608
Asher, A and Co, publishers 84
Asher, G M: *A bibliographical and historical essay on the Dutch books and pamphlets relating to New-Netherland . . .* 207
Asia 21, 32, 80, 81, 150, 263, 329, 441, 467, 508, 536, 585, 610, 690, 702, 797, 804, 807, 815, 1008, 1037, 1136, 1153, 1171, 1208, 1241, 1317, 1371, 1372, 1377
  bibliography 80, 81, 83, 219, 329, 341, 1021, 1206, 1207, 1210, 1270
  exploration 83, 502
  maps 66, 80, 159, 164, 318, 371, 687, 747, 908, 1029
Asia, W B Cornish 1310
Asia . . ., *ed*: Guy Wint 668
The Asia bulletin . . . 80
Asia, East by South . . . 81
Asia: a guide to basic books 80
Asia Publishing House 80
Asian sample studies (Geographical Association) 552
Asian survey . . . 82, 510
Asia's lands and peoples . . . 83, 836, 886
Asiatic Society of Japan, Tokyo 1285
L'Asia méridionale 83
Aslib 182, 219, 272
'Aspects of change in the landscape of East-Central and South-east Europe' 451
Assault on the unknown . . . 762
Associated Publishers, Amsterdam 84
Association de Géographie Français 217
Association for the Advancement of Science 359
Association for Promoting the Discovery of the Interior Parts of Africa 1144
Association for the Study of Snow and Ice 1188
Association Française pour l'Etude des

Eaux 85, 1332
Association of American Geographers 86, 312, 350, 357, 905, 1087, 1102, 1227, 1308
Association of Canadian Map Libraries 298
Association of Geography Teachers of Ireland 87, 569
Association of German University Teachers of Geography 440
The Association of Planning and Regional Reconstruction 348
Astrafoil 312
The astronomical and mathematical foundations of geography 88, 312
Athens Center of Ekistics 89
Atlante Farnesiano 629
Atlante fisico-economico d'Italia 1280
Atlante internazionale della Consociazione Turistica 90, 1280
Atlante mondiale (Agostini) 793
Atlante Veneto 629
Atlantes Neerlandici . . . 91, 308
Atlantic 408, 438, 439, 752, 970, 1187
Atlantic Education Trust 182
Atlantic Information Centre for Teachers, London 182
Atlantic Ocean atlas 970
The Atlantic salmon . . . 1360
Atlas, figure 831
Atlas 92
Atlas aérien 93
Atlas aerofotográfico 74
Atlas and gazetteer of Canada 296
Atlas and glossary of primary sedimentary structures 742
Atlas Antarktiki 94
Atlas botanic 95
Atlas Československé Socialistiché Republiky 96
Atlas de Belgique 97
Atlas de Colombia 98
Atlas de Economia Colombiana 98
Atlas de France 99, 781
Atlas de la France de l'est 100
Atlas de la France rurale 100
Atlas de Moçambique 101
Atlas de Paris et de la région Parisienne 102
Atlas de Schweiz 103
Atlas de Venezuela 104
Atlas der Deutschen Agrarlandschaft 105
Atlas der Deutschen Volkskunde 286
Atlas der Donauländer 106

641

647

Group 70, 274, 865
British Glaciological Society 1188
British Guiana 746
British Guiana, Michael Swan 391
British history atlas 275
British Honduras 304
British interests in the Persian Gulf 276
The British Islands and their vegetation 265
British Isles 197, 230, 259, 363, 405, 517, 585, 597, 835, 930, 931, 1071, 1239, 1320
See also United Kingdom; Great Britain
maps 314, 318, 363, 395, 614, 843, 903, 1105, 1144
The British Isles, Albert Demangeon 413
The British Isles, D M Preece and H R B Wood 1310
British landscapes through maps series 552
The British Library *See* British Museum
'British maps and charts . . .' 931
British Medical Association 960
British Museum (British Library, Reference Division) 259, 277, 308, 324, 325, 357, 903, 905
British Museum Quarterly 277
The British Museum Society bulletin 277
British national bibliography 219, 905
British National Committee for Geography 278
British Parliamentary Papers 791
British Petroleum: *Our industry—petroleum* 1056
British pioneers in geography 279
British Schools Exploring Society 464
British shipping statistics 1376
British Speleological Association 326
British Standard Specification Storage of Documents 1236
British stratigraphy 1239
British topography 634
British Trust for Ornithology 127
British Universities Film Council 182
British Waterways Board 394
British weather in maps 280
Britton, G P: *Marine meteorology and oceanography* 916
Britton, J N H: *Regional analysis and economic geography* . . . 534, 1120
'The broadening vista' 1289
Brock, G C: *Physical aspects of air photography* 312

Brockhaus *See Der Grosse Brockhaus*
Der Neue Brockhaus
Broek, J O M and J W Webb: *A geography of mankind* 570
Brooke, M Z: *Le Play, engineer and social scientist* . . . 852
Brookes, W D and K G Pinzke: 'A computer program for three dimensional presentation of geographic data' 1035
Brookfield H C: 'On the environment as perceived' 483
ed: The Pacific in transition . . . 184
and G H Dury: 'Cartographical appreciation' 904
and Doreen Hart: *Melanesia* . . . 417
Brouillette, B: 'Sources of documentation' 1203
Brouwer, G J: bibliography of America 321
Brown, D A *et al*: *The geological evolution of Australia and New Zealand* 188
Brown, E H: 'Data processing and the study of landforms' 617
Brown, L A: *Mapmaking* . . . 312
The story of maps 1237
Brown, Norman, *ed*: *India, Pakistan, Ceylon* 713
Brown, R J E: *Permafrost in Canada* . . . 294
Browne, Sir Thomas 904
Browning, C E: *Bibliography of dissertations in geography* . . . 1269
Browning, D G: *El Salvador* . . . 848
Bruk, S I and V S Apenchénko, *ed*: *Atlas narodov mira* 119
Brun, C F: *Maps and charts published in America* . . . 908
Brunei, bibliography 341
Brunet, Roger: *Le croquis de géographie* 312
Brunhes, Jean 281
La géographie humaine 281, 573
Géographie humaine de la France 281
and C Vallaux: *La géographie de l'histoire* 281
Brunnschweiler, R O, *ed*: *Ancient Australia* . . . 188
Brunsden, D, *ed*: *Slopes* . . . 617
and John Doornkamp, *ed*: *The unquiet landscape* 617
Brunswick, International School Book Institute 282
Brussels University, Institut de Sociologie 815

653

history of the Orient 807
Cahiers de géographie de Québec 288
Cahiers d'outre mer . . . 289
Cahiers Népalais 212
Cahir, J: *Principles of climatology* . . . 359
Cailleux, A: *L'Antarctique* 65
Introduction to climatic geomorphology 358, 785
Le modèle des régions sèches 76, 419
Cairngorm Mountains 10
CALCOMP 290
Calder, Ritchie: *Men against the frozen north* 346
California, bibliography 665
California University 21, 82, 320, 1174, 1249
Callaghan, F R, *ed*: *Science in New Zealand* 1162
Callander, John: *Terra Australia Cognita* . . . 1261
Calmann, John, *ed*: *Western Europe* . . . 668
Camap 27
Cambodia 81, 467
bibliography 341, 1210
maps 159
Cambrian bibliography . . . 291, 936
Cambridge Block Order Scheme 292
Cambridge expeditions journal 292
Cambridge geographical studies series 1313
Cambridge University 21, 29, 292, 293
Camden, William: *Britannia* 266, 395, 405, 1000, 1118, 1155
Cameron, Ian: *The impossible dream* . . . (Panama Canal) 1244
Cameroon, granites 1088
Cammack, F M and Shiro Saito, *comp*: *Pacific Island bibliography* 1042
Camp Fortune Skiing Area, photomap 500
Campbell, E M J, *ed*: *Imago mundi* 709
Campbell, J D: *The Oxford atlas* 1028
Campbell, J H: *The earth's shifting crust* . . . 1259
Campbell, R: *Personality as an element in regional geography* 1120
Campbell, R D *et al*: *A question of place* . . . 1100
Canada 50, 184, 231, 239, 294, 295, 300, 557, 695, 782, 824, 930, 1067, 1187, 1233, 1334, 1372
bibliography 3, 214, 218, 219, 231, 294,

340, 1118
Department of Mines and Technical Surveys (Department of Energy, Mines and Resources) 3, 130, 295, 312, 901, 905, 932, 1248
exploration 231
Geological Survey 612
Humanities Research Council 215
maps 121, 130, 158, 161, 253, 296, 466, 692, 871, 899, 902, 932, 958, 1029, 1013, 1034, 1038
National Air Photo Library 182
National Map Collection 296, 298
See also Anglo-America
Canada . . . , J B Brebner 294
Le Canada, L-E Hamelin 294
Canada . . . , D Q Innis 294
Canada . . . , R R Krueger and R G Gorder 294
Canada . . . , T G Taylor 1257
Canada: a geographical interpretation 294
Canada in maps 296, 932
'The Canada Land Use Inventory . . .' 294
Canada's changing geography . . . 294
Canada's changing north 294
Canadian Association of Geographers 294, 297
Canadian cartography 298, 905
Canadian cartography, ed: L J O'Brien 130
Canadian geographer 297
Canadian geographical journal 1142
Canadian Historical Association 680
Canadian Institute of Surveying 298, 312, 500
'Canadian maps', Betty May 296
Canadian Permanent Committee on Geographical Names 312
Canadian reference sources . . . 294
Canadiana 299
Canadiana before 1867 300
Canal Zone Library-Museum 1244
Canals 262, 405, 1287
Cannenburg, V 982
Cantor, L M: 'The Royal Geographical Society and the projected London Institute of Geography . . .' 1144
Cape Town University 312
Cape Verde Islands 219, 1081
Capello, C F and M L Chionetti: *Elementi di cartografia* 312
Cappelen road maps 197, 301, 1138

657

658

659

661

The conceptual revolution in geography 501, 596

Concise encyclopedia of explorations 382

Concise encyclopaedia of world timbers 527

A concise glossary of geographical terms 383

Concise Maori encyclopedia 1078

The concise Oxford atlas 1028

Concise practical surveying 312

The Concorde world atlas 1058

Condliffe, J B: The development of Australia . . . 422

'Conference on the History of Cartography' 384

Conflict and harmony . . . 483

Congo-Brazzaville 1012

Congress See Library of Congress

Conkling, E C: Geography of international trade 601

Connaissance du monde 385

Conover, H F: Nigerian official publications . . . 219

The conquest of the material world 534

La conquête de la terre . . . 437

Cons, G J, ed: Handbook for geography teachers 663

Conservation 188, 372, 376, 394, 483, 484, 493, 528, 545, 765, 779, 839, 896, 900, 978, 979, 1181, 1199

Conservation, Joyce Joffe 979

Conservation in the Soviet Union 609

'The conservation of maps', R A Skelton 905

Conservation of natural resources 1347

Conserving life on earth 484

'Considerations on the state of development with regard to topographical maps . . .' 308

Consociazione Turistica 90, 1280

'Les constantes de la cartographie' 909

The construction and drawing of block diagrams 312

'The construction of globes' 629

'Construction of a map of the world on a scale of 1:1 million' 769

'Containing China?' 455

The containment of urban England 608

Contemporary China . . . , Peter Berton and Eugene Wu 386

Contemporary China . . . ed: E S Kirby 344

'A contemporary handbook to the Molyneux globes' 629

A continent takes shape 188

Continental drift 102, 408, 1025

Continental drift, ed: S K Runcorn 1022

Continental drift . . . , D H and M P Tarling 1022

'Continental drift', J T Wilson 1022

Continental shelf 146

Continents adrift . . . 1022

'A continuing need: education for map librarianship' 905

The continuing purpose . . . 979

Contour dictionary 312, 987

'Contribution of geographical congresses and the IGU to the development of cartography' 308

Contributions to Asian studies 815

Contributions to bibliography of Australia . . . 387

Cook, Captain James 9, 475, 479, 795, 1068

Cook Islands 1211

Cooke, H L, jr, cartographer 150

Cooke, R U: 'The landscape revealed by aerial sensors' 589

and J H Johnson: Trends in geography . . . 1289

and Andrew Warren: Geomorphology in deserts 419

Cooper, St G C: Agricultural research in tropical Africa 33

Coordinate systems and map projections 788

Copper 624

Copper 388

Copper abstracts 3, 388

Copper Development Association 3, 388

Coppock, J T: An agricultural atlas of Scotland 27

An agricultural geography of Great Britain 30

The changing use of land in Britain 839

and Alice M Coleman: 'Land use and conservation' 839

and H C Prince, ed: Greater London 153

Copyright 905, 913

Coradi, G, Limited, Zurich 389

Coradograph 389

The coral reef problem 1016

Coral reefs and atolls . . . 1016

Corals 1124

Corals and atolls . . . 1016

Corbellini, Pietro 90

Cornell, James and John Surowiecki: State-of-the-earth report . . . 446

669

Dudley, Sir Robert: *Arcano del mare* 67

The Dudley Stamp Memorial Fund 278, 1223

Dufresnov, L: *Catalogue des meilleures cartes géographiques* . . . 905

Duignan, Peter, *ed*: *A guide to research and reference works on sub-Saharan Africa* 21

Handbook of American resources for African studies 664

Dumont, M E and L De Smet: *Bibliographie géographique de la Belgique* 219

Dumont, René: *Types of rural economy* . . . 1353

Dunbar, C O: *The earth* 617

Dunkle, J R: *Atlas of Florida* 143

Duplex, Jean *ed*: *Atlas de la France rurale* 100

Dupois, Jacques: *L'Asie méridionale* 83

Dupong, J 108

Durand-Dastès, T: *Géographie de l'Inde* 713

Durham, England, maps 153

Durham County and City with Teesside, ed: J C Dewdney 270

Durham University, Department of Geography 153, 544

Durrenberger, R W: *Environment and man* . . . 484

Dury, G H: 'Cartographical appreciation' 904

'Climatic change as a geographical backdrop' 359

'General theory of meandering valleys and underfit' 1137

Map interpretation 312, 904

ed: *Rivers and river terraces* 1137

and M I Logan, *ed*: *Studies in Australian geography* 188

and J A Morris: *The land from the air* . . . 312, 835

Dutch West India Company 207

Dutilly, A A: *Bibliography of bibliographies on the Arctic* 227

Dutt, A K, *ed*: *India* . . . 713

Dwyer, D J, *ed*: *The city as a centre of change in Asia* 83

ed: *The city in the third world* 608

Dyer, K R: *Estuaries* . . . 367

The dynamic earth . . . 617

'The dynamics of large cities' 608

Eager, A R: *A guide to Irish bibliographical material* . . . 648

Eames, Wilberforce: American bibliography 245

Early charts of New Zealand . . . 443

'Early experience in the photomapping technique' 901

Early Hanoverian mathematical practitioners 1256

Early hydrographic surveys of the British Isles 931

Early Italian engraving 1095

Early maps of the British Isles . . . 1144

The early maps of Scotland 1147

The early years of the Ordnance Survey 1019

The earth, C O Dunbar 617

The earth and its resources 886

Earth resources 174

Earth Science Editors 444

Earth science reviews 445

Earth Science Symposium on Hudson Bay 446

Earth sciences 331, 620, 621, 780, 894, 1008, 1022

bibliography 620

See also Geomorphology

The earth sciences . . . , *ed*: T W Donelly 446

Earth Sciences Laboratory, U S Army Natick Laboratories 77

Earth sculpture and the origin of landforms 538

Earthquake information bulletin 447, 1173

Earthquakes 1170, 1171, 1172, 1173

Earthquakes, G A Eiby 1171

Earthquakes . . . , *ed*: C Lomnitz 447

Earthquakes, J P Rothé 58

The earth's crust and mantle 1284

The earth's drifting crust . . . 1259

The earth's mantle . . . 617

The earth's problem climates 359

East, W G 1094

ed: *Caxton world atlas* 1058

ed: *Europe* . . . (Shackleton) 393

The geography behind history 589

The Soviet Union 1318

The spirit and purpose of geography 703, 1222, 1349

and O H K Spate, *ed*: *The changing map of Asia* . . . 83

and S W Wooldridge, *ed*: *Provinces of England* (Fawcett) 512

East Africa . . . , *ed* W T W Morgan 165
The East African economic review 448
The East African geographical review 448, 1296
East African Institute of Social Research, Makerere 1296
East Anglian bibliography . . . 219
East Asia . . . , Albert Kolb 81, 449
East India Company 276, 712, 983
East Midland geographer 450, 556
Easterbrook, D J: *Principles of geomorphology* 617
Eastern Europe . . . , *ed*: S W Hoffman 451, 599
Eastern Europe, Norman Pounds 599
Eastern Mongolia 1008
Eastman Kodak Research Library 312
Eastwood, T, *ed*: *Stanford's geological atlas of Great Britain and Ireland* 1226
Eaux et industries 85
Echavarria, J M: *Social aspects of economic development in Latin America* 453
Echo sounding 339, 628
Eckert, Max: *Die Kartenwissenschaft* . . . 312
Eckert Projection 312
Ecological animal geography 784
Ecology 61, 483, 484, 515, 587, 895, 978, 979
Ecology of Health and Disease, IGU Commission 133
Economic abstracts 3
Economic and social atlas of Greece 147
Economic and Social Council 312
Economic and social history of the Orient 807
Economic aspects of agricultural developments in Africa 726
Economic aspects of pigmeat marketing 726
Economic atlas of Ontario 452
Economic atlas of the Soviet Union 116
Economic bulletin for Latin America 453
Economic changes in British agriculture 726
Economic Commission for Latin America 453
Economic co-operation in Africa . . . 22
Economic development in East Asia 83
Economic development in Latin America . . . 453
Economic development in the Tropics 939
The economic development of China and Japan . . . 343

Economic development of Latin America . . . 811, 848
Economic development of modern Malaya 164
Economic geography 454
Economic geography, C F Jones and G G Darkenwald 534
An economic geography of China, T R Tregear 287, 455
An economic geography of oil 200
An economic geography of the Scandinavian States and Finland 1157
Economic geography of the USSR . . . 609
An economic geography of West Africa 200
An economic history of New Zealand to 1939 995
Economic implications of the size of nations . . . 456
Economic policy and industrial growth in Pakistan 459
Economic, social and political studies of the Middle East 457
Economic survey of Latin America 458
Economics 200, 398, 734, 806, 1028, 1029, 1352, 1358, 1386
The economics of Africa 22
The economics of African development 22
The economics of Australian industry . . . 188
The economics of irrigation in dry climates 29
The economics of subsistence agriculture 31
The economics of urban areas 608
The economy of cities 348
The economy of Pakistan . . . 459
Ecosystems 35
Ecuador, bibliography 219
Edge, R C A: 'Ordnance Survey at home' 1019
Edgell, Vice-Admiral Sir John: *Sea surveys* 931, 1168
Edinburgh, atlas 135
  Cartographic Symposia, 1962 272
  Geographical Institute 197
Edinburgh British Honduras-Yucatan Expedition 73
Edinburgh University 21, 27, 272, 312, 1015, 1146
The Edinburgh world atlas 197, 460
Edlin, H L: 'The Forestry Commission in Scotland . . .' 528

671

936
English, P W and R C Mayfield, *ed*: *Man, space and environment* . . . 484
The English atlas 477
English Channel 970
The English climate 363
English colonization of North America 439
English county maps . . . 325, 357, 905
The English gazetteer 478
The English Pilot 479
English-Russian dictionary on cartography . . . 312
'Engraved maps from the English topographers . . .' 395
'Engraved Ordnance Survey one-inch maps . . .' 1019
'Entwicklung und Methodik der Freytag-Berndt Schulwandkarten' 531
Environment 11, 69, 70, 133, 183, 188, 224, 274, 330, 332, 348, 354, 405, 480, 483, 493, 518, 534, 542, 553, 563, 585, 598, 719, 797, 852, 853, 895, 898, 944, 960, 979, 985, 1051, 1079, 1153, 1178, 1193, 1202, 1232, 1256, 1257, 1281, 1317, 1322, 1325, 1332, 1340
bibliography 483, 484
Environment 480
Environment and economic life . . . 481
Environment and land use in Africa 482
Environment and man . . . , R W Durrenberger 484
Environment and man, R H Wagner 483
Environment and nation . . . 491, 1257
Environment and policies in West Africa 1318
Environment and race 1257
'Environment for disease' 960
'Environment management' 483
'Environment on record' 483
Environment psychology . . . 484
Environment, race and migration . . . 1257
Environmental conservation 483
The environmental future . . . 483
Environmental geoscience . . . 484
The environmental handbook . . . 483
The environmental revolution . . . 483, 979
Environmental Science Series Administration 312
'Environmental studies in schools' 462
'Epic work of Claudius Ptolemy' 1095
L'epiderme de la terre . . .' 617
Epstein, T S: *South India* . . . 713
Eratosthenes 485, 578

Erde 3, 626
Die Erde . . . 408, 486
Erdei, Ferenc *et al*, *ed*: *Information Hungary* 722
Erdkunde 487
Die Erdkunde . . , Carl Ritter 1136
Erdol Weltatlas 1342
Ericson, D B and Goesta Wollin: *The ever-changing sea* 1167
Erosion 173, 741
Erosion and sedimentation 1169
'Error and revision in early Ordnance Survey maps' 1019
Escribano, A C: *Atlas Porrua de la Republica Mexicana* 177
Espenshade, E B, *jr*, *ed*: *Goode's world atlas* 633
Essai sur l'évolution de la géographie humaine 573
Essai sur la géographie des plantes 1192
'Essay on the life and work of Hakluyt' 660
Essays in Australian geomorphology 188
Essays in geography and economic development 534
Essays in geography for Austin Miller 514
Essays in political geography, *ed*: C A Fisher 488
Essays on agricultural geography . . . 514
Esselte Corporation, Stockholm 308, 312, 489, 744, 748, 882, 905, 1002
Map Service 403, 783
Essentials of geography 886
Essentials of map-reading 312
Essex, England, maps 1000
Estall, R C: *New England* . . . 200
and R O Buchanan: *Industrial activity and economic geography* . . . 714
Estienne, P and A Godard: *Climatologie* 359
Estuaries . . . , K R Dyer 367
Estuaries, *ed*: G H Lauff 1137
Etats et nations de l'Europe 1322
Ethiopia, atlas 136
bibliography 219
The ethnographic survey of Africa 738
Europa . . . , Carl Ritter 1136
Europe 34, 184, 195, 309, 393, 399, 435, 438, 451, 491, 520, 566, 585, 599, 610, 668, 683, 876, 928, 937, 997, 1027, 1056, 1057, 1069, 1071, 1119, 1172, 1212, 1317, 1322, 1360, 1371, 1372, 1369, 1377
bibliography 219, 490, 1298

673

Faccioli, Ezio: 'Soil dynamics research in Mexico' 155
The face of the deep 1167
The face of the earth 1245
The face of the earth as seen from the air 312
Facsimile atlas to the early history of cartography . . . 506
Facsimile atlas . . . , A E Nordenskiöld 1095
'Facsimile atlases' 1267
Fact sheets on the Commonwealth 379
'A factual key for the recognition of Australian soils' 126
Faeroes 1157
Fairbridge, R W: *The encyclopedia of oceanography* 1127
Fairbrother, Nan: *New lives, new landscapes* 979
Fairchild Camera and Instrument Corporation, New York 312
Fairey Plotterscope 312, 507
Fairey Surveys Limited 312, 507, 1168, 1276
Falconer, Allan: *Research methods in Pleistocene geomorphology* . . . 1071
Falke, Horst: *Die Geologische Karte* . . . 408
Falkland Islands 1261
Falkland Islands Dependencies Survey 269
Far East 343, 556, 797, 815, 1027, 1056, 1119, 1127, 1183, 1232
  exploration 1036
  maps 159, 986
The Far East and Australasia (Europa) 508, 510
Far East trade and development 509
Far Eastern survey 510
The farm economist 29, 726
Farm management pocket book 1386
Farming 30, 34, 1333, 1386
Farming, fishing and forestry . . . 1360
Farming the sea . . . 1167
Farming systems in the Tropics 1290
Farming systems of the world 511
Farrington, J H: *Morphological studies of English canals* 262
Favenc, E: *The history of Australian exploration* . . . 936
Fawcett, C B 512, 853
  The bases of a world commonwealth 512
  Frontiers . . . 512
  Provinces of England . . . 512, 1094

bibliography 512
Fawcett, S: 'Problems on the maintenance of Admiralty charts' 9
Febvre, Lucien: *A geographical introduction to history* 563
Fedder, R G: *Global atlas of relative cloud cover* . . . 366
Feddon, Robin: *The continuing purpose* . . . 979
Federal Research Centre for Forestry, Reinbeck 1361
FID 357
  Abstracting services in science . . . 3
Feeken, Erwin and Gerda: *The discovery and exploration of Australia* 183, 422
Feldman, Herbert: *Pakistan* . . . 459
Fell, H B: *Native sea-stars* (New Zealand) 1113
Fellman, J D: *A comprehensive checklist of serials of geographic value* 768
  International list of geographical serials 768
Fenland, England 30, 1240
The Fenland in Roman times . . . 513
Fennia 142
Ferguson, Sir John: *Bibliography of Australia* 219, 225
Ferrar, A M 905
  'The management of map collections and libraries in university geography departments' 905
Fertilizers, bibliography 243
Festschriften 461, 514, 556, 557, 689, 790, 803, 837, 872, 910, 929, 1004, 1015, 1180, 1243, 1257
Fetros, J G: 'Developing the map collection in smaller libraries' 905
Fiala, F: *Mathematische Kartographie* 312
Fiches, faune et flore de la Méditerranée 753
Field geology 1008
Field Group studies (Nottingham University) 516
Field natural history . . . 515
'The field of geography' (Methuen) 501
Field studies 38, 464, 516, 517, 545, 559, 560, 592, 852, 853, 856
Field studies 516
Field Studies Council 516
'Field studies for schools' series 516, 560
Field studies in the British Isles 517
Fielden Jones, Clarence and G G Darkenwald: *Economic geography* 534

and Sir Edmund Hillary: *The crossing of Antarctica* . . . 65, 396

Fullard, Harold: 'Atlas production for the 1970's' 380

ed: Cassell's new atlas of the world 316

'The construction of globes' 629

ed: Geographical digest 554, 905

'National qualifications in cartography' 1128

The new Cambridge modern history atlas 986

and H C Darby: *The library atlas* 859

and H C Darby: *The university atlas* 1309

Fullerton, Brian and A F Williams: *Scandinavia* . . . 1157

Fundamentals of economic geography . . . 534

Fundamentals of soil science and soil geography 1199

Fung, K I, cartographer 162

Furde, C D: *Habitat, economy and society* . . . 484

Furnivall, J S: *Netherlands India* . . . 983

Furon, R: *The problem of water* . . . 1332

Furtado, C: *Economic development of Latin America* . . . 811, 849

'Further light on the Molyneux globes' 629

'Further remarks on the future of oil' 1057

'The future of the International Million Map of the World' 769

'The future of oil . . .', P R Odell 1057

'The future of oil', H R Warman 1057

Gabler, R E, *ed: A handbook for geography teachers* 663

Gadgil, P D: 'Plant ecology of the Lower Swansea Valley' 881

'Soil biology of the Lower Swansea Valley' 881

Gaits, G M: 'Thematic mapping by computer' 499

Gakkai, J C: *Bibliography on geography* 219

Gale, D W: 'Register control in map reproduction' 312

Gale, F and G H Lawton, *ed: Settlement and encounter* . . . 1180

Gallois, Lucien 535

Les géographes allemands de la Renaissance 535, 936

Géographie universelle 535, 575, 1322

Régions naturelles et noms de pays 535

Galloway, R L: *Annals of coal mining* . . . 405

Galperin, G L, *comp: English-Russian dictionary on cartography, geodesy and aerial phototopography* 312

Galton, Francis 546

The Gambia 327

bibliography 219

Gandjei, M: *Geographical bibliography* 219

Gardiner, J S: *Coral reefs and atolls* . . . 1016

Gardiner, Brigadier R A: 'The international map of the Roman Empire' 1253

'A re-appraisal of the International Map of the World (IMW) on the millionth scale' 769

and H Fullard: 'National qualifications in cartography' 1128

Gardiner-Hill, R C: *The development of digital maps* 1019

Gardner, J L and L E Myers, *ed: Water supplies for arid regions* 76

Garland, G D, *ed: Continental drift* 1025

Garms, Harry: *The natural history of Europe* 599

Garnett, Alice, on H J Fleure 520

The geographical interpretation of topographical maps 312

'Teaching geography . . .' 462

Garnier *See* Beaujeu-Garnier

Barran, Andrews, *ed: The picturesque atlas of Australasia* 1068

Garvey, Gerald: *Energy, ecology, economy* 598

Gascony, towns 991

Gaskell, T F, *ed: The earth's mantle* 617

The Gulf Stream 1167

Physics of the earth 617

World beneath the oceans 1167

Gaskin, D E: 'The origin of the New Zealand fauna and flora . . .' 473

Gatineau Park, photomap 500

Gaussen, Henri 781, 1321

Gay, J: *Bibliographie des oeuvres relatifs à l'Afrique et à l'Arabie* 215

Gay, J D: *The geography of religion in England* 605

Gay, Peter: *Bibliography of reference materials for Russian area studies* . . . 241

Gazetteer of the British Isles 197

Gazetteer of the Persian Gulf, Oman and

683

912, 957, 1013, 1085, 1111, 1226, 1253, 1331
See also Britain; British Isles, United Kingdom and under specific places
Great Britain . . . , ed A G Ogilvie 1015
The great capitals . . . 390
Great cities of the world . . . 1356
The great soil groups of the world . . . 1320
The great trek 1069
Greater London, ed: J T Coppock and H C Prince 153
Greater London, W S Dancer and A V Hardy 597
Greater London . . . , Christopher Trent 875
Greater London Development Plan 875
Greater London: an industrial geography 200
Greece 451, 1120
  bibliography 216, 219, 966
  maps 147
Greek geography 686
Green, G H: *The British bulletin of publications on Latin America . . .* 271
Greenaway, John: *Bibliography of the Australian aborigines . . .* 226
Greenhill, Basil: *James Cook . . .* 795
Greenland 628, 1074, 1157
  maps 466, 1067
Greenland past and present 522
Greenwood, David: *Mapping* 312
Greer-Wootten, Bryn: 'Metropolitan regional analysis' 354
Gregg M Sinclair Library, Pacific collection 1042
Gregor, H F: *Environment and economic life . . .* 481
  Geography of agriculture . . . 31, 511
Gregory, J S: *Russian land Soviet people . . .* 1153
Gregory, K J and E H Brown: 'Data processing and the study of landforms' 617
  and W L Ravenhill, *ed: Exeter essays in geography . . .* 514
Gregory, S: *Statistical methods and the geographer* 1230
Grenyer, N: 'An introduction to recent developments in geography teaching . . .' 462
Gresswell, R K 639
  Geology for geographers 639
  Physical geography 639

The physical geography of glaciers . . . 639
The physical geography of rivers and valleys 639
  and Anthony Huxley, *ed: Standard encyclopedia of the world's rivers and lakes* 1224
The Griffin 640
Griffiths, J F: *Applied climatology . . .* 358
  'Climates of Africa' 1377
Grigg, David: *The harsh lands . . .* 31
Grigoryev, A A, on Russian geography 1213
Grimshaw, P H: *Physical atlas of zoogeography* 1064
Groen, P: *The waters of the sea* 1167
Grondona, L St Clare: *Australia in the 1960's* 188
Der Grosser Bertelsmann Weltatlas 203, 641, 885
Der Grosse Brockhaus and *Atlas* 642
Das Grosse Duden-Lexikon, world atlas 643
Grosse Elsevier atlas 466
Grosse Shell-atlas of Germany and Europe 890
Grosvenor, G H: 'The National Geographic Society and its magazine' 968
Ground level climatology 359
Ground water 1247, 1332
Ground water . . . , (van der Leedon) 644
Ground water in the permafrost regions of Alaska 627
Ground water year book (HMSO) 644
Groundwater studies . . . (Unesco) 644
Grove, A T: *Africa south of the Sahara* 17
Groves, D G: *A glossary of ocean science . . .* 1167
The growth and control of world population 570
The growth, location and structure of industry in Egypt 947
The growth of world industry (UN) 645
Guatemala, bibliography 219
Gudmandsen, P: 'Airborne radio echo sounding of the Greenland ice sheet' 628
Guernsey, H J Fleure 520
Guest, Arthur: *Advanced practical geography* 10
Guggisberg, C A W: *Man and wildlife* 898, 979
Guiana *See* British Guiana; Guyana

690

The heart of the Antarctic . . . 670
Heathcote, R L, on historical geography 1090
Heawood, Edward: *A history of geographical discovery* . . . 688
Hebrew University, Jerusalem 151, 219, 799
Heezen, B C and C H Hollister: *The face of the deep* 1167
Heffer, W and Sons Limited, Cambridge 671
Hefford, R K: *Practical geographer* 312
Heimpel, Professor Hermann 210
Heissler, Viktor: *Kartographie* 312, 408 and G Hake: *Kartographie* . . . 820
Helfrich, H W: *Agenda for survival* . . . 483
Helleneiner, F M: *International geography* 337
Hellenic Geographical Society, Athens 219
Helmfrid, S, on historical geography in Scandinavia 1090
Helmolt, Hans: *Weltgeschichte* 1106
Helsinki University 142, 219
Henderson, Elizabeth, *comp*: *Food aid* . . . 524
Henderson, G P, *comp*: *Current European directories* 399
ed: *European companies* . . . 492
Henry the Navigator, Prince 107, 277, 1081
Henry the Navigator . . . , Elaine Sanceau 1081
Henry, J M *et al*: *Thésaurus des symboles* . . . 429
Hepple, Peter, *ed*: *The exploration for petroleum in Europe and North Africa* . . . 1057
Herak, M and V T Stringfield, *ed*: *Karst* . . . 617
Herbage abstracts 377
Herbert, David: *Urban geography* . . . 608
Herbert, M J, *ed*: *Glossaria interpretum* 630
Herbert, Wally: 'The first surface crossing of the Arctic Ocean' 70
Herbertson, Andrew John 512, 672, 852, 888, 1256
and F D Herbertson: *Man and his work* 672
Memorial lecture 672
and J G Bartholomew: *Atlas of meteorology* 154, 827

Here, there and everywhere 1116
Hereford mappa mundi 15, 673, 1144
Herodotus 674
Herodotus . . . , J L Myres 674
Herring, P J and M R Clarke, *ed*: *Deep oceans* 1167
Herring atlas 754
Hershlag, Z Y: *Turkey* . . . 1294
Hertfordshire, maps 1000, 1240
Hertling, Knud *et al, ed*: *Greenland past and present* 522
Hespéris 219
Hesse, R *et al*: *Ecological animal geography* 784
Hettner, Alfred 581, 675, 892
Die Geographie . . . 675
on the surface features of the earth 617, 675
Hewson, J B: *A history of the practice of navigation* 669
The Heyden new world atlas 676
Hiberniae Delineatio . . . 1297
Hiersemann, Anton: re-issue of *A bibliographical guide* . . . *to the principal collections of town plans and views published* . . . *in Die Alten Städtebilder* . . . 208
Higbee, Edward: *American agriculture* . . . 1347
Higgins, A L: *Elementary surveying* 312
The highlands and islands of Scotland 1011
Hill, C A and Associates 312
Hill, D R and R F Jefferson: 'System considerations for a unified cartographic data bank' 1035
Hill, M N *et al, ed*: *The sea* . . . 1167
Hill *See* Gardiner-Hill
Hillaby, John: *Nature and man* 979
Hillary, Sir E: *The crossing of Antarctica* . . . 65, 396
Hilling, D: *Seaports and developments in tropical Africa* 22
Hills, E S, *ed*: *Arid lands* . . . 75
Hillslope form and process 617
Hilton, K J, *ed*: *The Lower Swansea Valley project* 881
Hilton, Ronald, *ed*: *Handbook of Hispanic source materials* . . . 665
Hind, A M: *Early Italian engraving* 1095
Hinks, A R 677
Map projections 312, 788
Maps and survey 312, 788, 912

691

Hogg, Garry, *comp: The Shell book of exploring Britain* 1181

Hogg, H S 894

Holdgate, M W, *ed: Antarctic ecology* 61

Holdridge, L R: *Forest environments in tropical life zones* . . . 526

Hole, William, map engraver 266

Holland, G S, on the RGS cartographic productions 905

Hollister, C H: *The face of the deep* 1167

Holmback, Bure *et al: About Sweden 1700–1963* . . . 1

Holt, G: 'Tips and tip working in the Lower Swansea Valley' 881

The Holt world atlas 692

Holy Land 151, 682, 1103

Holzen, E, atlases 505

L'homme et la terre, J E Réclus 1112

L'homme sur la terre . . . , Maximilien Sorre 1202

Hondius, Jodocus 629
atlases 1267
The map of the world 1144

Honduras, bibliography 219

Honegger, D, cartographer 500

Honeybone, R C, *ed: Handbook for geography teachers* 663

Hong Kong 467

Honour, V G *et al, ed: The Jacaranda atlas* 794

Hood, D W, *ed: Impingement of man on the oceans* 710, 1167

Hood, P J *et al, ed: Earth science symposium on Hudson Bay* 446

Hookey, P G: *Do-it-yourself weather instruments* 1258

Hooson, D J M: *A new Soviet heartland* 1318

Hooton, D J, *ed: New Zealand* . . . 401

Hoover Institution, Stanford University 21, 386, 654, 664

Hopkins, M F S: *Learning through the environment* 464

Horecky, P L, *ed: Russia and the Soviet Union* . . . 1152, 1214
and R G Carlton, *comp: The USSR and Eastern Europe: periodicals* . . . 1298

'The horizon of geography' 583

Horn, Werner 5, 1267
on Adolf Steiler 1235

Horrabin, J F: *An atlas of European history from the second to the twentieth century* 140

Horticulture 377, 1070

Horton, F E: *Geographical perspectives on urban systems* . . . 1317

Horton, R E: 'Erosional development of streams . . .' 1137

Hoselitz, B F and W E Moore, *ed: Industrialization and society* 714

Hoskins, W G: *The common lands of England and Wales* 372

Hotine, M: 'Rapid topographic surveys of new countries' 312

Hough: *Encyclopaedia of American woods* 527

Houston, J M, *ed: The world's landscapes* 1383

'How far automation?' 312

How the Maoris came 1113

How the Maoris lived 1113

How to find out in geography . . . 693

How to identify old maps and globes . . . 629, 694

How the white men came (New Zealand) 1113

Howard, Admiral Lord, of Effingham 1328

Howard, F: *Agricultural development and economic integration in Latin America* 453

Howarth, O J R: 'The centenary of section E (Geography)' (British Association for the Advancement of Science) 270

Howe, G M: 'Environment for disease' 960
'Geography in the Soviet universities' 1213
Man, environment and disease in Britain . . . 960
National atlas of disease mortality in the United Kingdom 960
Wales from the air . . . 1335
and Peter Thomas: *Welsh landforms and scenery* 1335

Howse, Derek and Michael Sanderson: *The sea chart* . . . 931

Hoyle, B S, *ed: Transport and development* 1288
and D Hilling, *ed: Seaports and developments in tropical Africa* 22

Hoyt, J B: *Man and the earth* 895

Hsieh, Chiao-Min: *Taiwan-Ilha Formosa* . . . 287

Hudson, F S: *A geography of settlements* 608, 1317

Hudson, Norman: *Soil conservation* 243

Hutchings, R: *Seasonal influences in Soviet industry* 1153
Hutchinson university library series 703
Hutton, John, ed: *Urban challenge in East Africa* 165
Huxley, Anthony, ed: *Standard encyclopedia of the world's mountains* 1224
ed: *Standard encyclopedia of the world's oceans and islands* 1224
ed: *Standard encyclopedia of the world's rivers and lakes* 1224
Hyde, F E: *Liverpool and the Mersey* . . . 872
Hydro-biologische Anstalt der Max-Planck Gesellschaft zur Fönderung der Wissenschaften 45
Hydrogeology, bibliography 646
Hydrographic Department, Admiralty 704
Hydrographic Department, British Cartographic Society 272
Hydrographic surveying . . . 931
'Hydrographic surveying and data processing' 916
'Hydrographic surveys with electronics' 931
Hydrography 9, 312, 339, 764, 855, 916, 931, 1168, 1305
Hydrological mapping 765
Hydrology 419, 667, 741, 780, 810, 978, 1001, 1188, 1247, 1332
bibliography 741
Hynes, M C: *Lists of theses and dissertations on Canadian geography* 214
Hypothesis testing in field studies 1258

Ibadan University 20, 23
Ibn Battuta 705
Ice 627, 763, 1001, 1067, 1071, 1074, 1165, 1167, 1332
Ice 706, 763
The ice age in Britain 627
Ice ages, their nature and effects 627, 707
Ice and snow, properties, processes and applications 707
Ice atlas of Arctic Canada 130
The Icefields Ranges Research Project 707
Iceland 603, 1157
maps 466
Icelandic Glaciological Society 1167
Icelandic Meteorological Office 1167
The idea of China . . . 344, 836
Idrisi *See* Al-Idrisi

Idyll, C P, ed: *The science of the sea* 1167
Ifo Institute for Economic Research, Munich 25
Illies, Joachim: *Biogéographie* 784
Illinois University, Bureau of Community Planning 1129
Illustrated encyclopedia of Maori life 1078
Illustrated glossary of snow and ice 1188
Illustrated ice glossary 1165
Image and environment . . . 909
Imago mundi . . . 196, 308, 709
Imhof, Eduard 103, 312, 461, 783, 1161
festschrift 514
Gelände und Karte 312
Kartographische Geländedarstellung 821
'The Swiss Mittelschulatlas in a new form' 1161
'Tasks and methods of theoretical cartography' 312
Thematische Kartographie 312
et al: *Karte und Luftbild* . . . 855
'The impact of photography from space on . . . cartography' 909
Imperial Academy of Sciences 4
Impingement of man on the oceans 710, 1167
Implications of continental drift to the earth sciences 1022
'The importance of biogeography' 784
'The importance of cartographic information for the comprehending of messages . . .' 909
'The importance of cartography to modern states' 909
The impossible dream . . . (Panama Canal) 1244
Inco-Mond nickel 771
Index bibliographicus 3
Index India 711
Index Iranicus 219
Index of current maritime research 920
Index to Australian resources maps of 1940–1959 192
Index to maps in books and periodicals (AGS) 47
India 34, 81, 83, 133, 150, 276, 537, 610, 690, 711, 782, 815, 927, 955, 1081, 1241, 1317
bibliography 219, 234, 713, 1207
maps 312, 712, 962
India . . . , ed: A K Dutt 713
India . . . , ed: R L Singh 713
India and Ceylon . . . , ed: Philip Mason

695

698

219
Kennedy, B A: *Physical geography . . .* 617
Kennedy, T F, *ed: A descriptive atlas of the Pacific Islands . . .* 417
Kennedy Round 435
Kenrick, J: *The Egypt of Herodotus* 674
Kent, William, *ed: An encyclopaedia of London* 472
Kent, England 1105, 1369
Kenya 327, 482, 1117
  maps 372, 963
Kenya junior atlas 963
Kerala State, India, bibliography 234
Kern, R and G Rushton: 'Mapit . . .' 864
Kerr, D G G, *ed: A historical atlas of Canada* 680
Kesteven, G L: *Fisheries glossary* 1360
Ketchum, B H, *ed: The water's edge . . .* 367
'Key to the Photographs of the Ancient Map of the World preserved in Hereford Cathedral' 673
Khalaf, N G: *Economic implications of the size of nations . . .* 456
Khozyaystvo 1214
Kienauer, Rudolf: *Bibliographie kirchengeschichtlicher karten Österreichs* 210
Kilford, W K: *Elementary air survey* 312
Kimble, G H T: *Tropical Africa* 22
  and Dorothy Good: *Geography of the Northlands* 1347
King, C A M: *Beaches and coasts* 198, 367, 1259
  Glacial and periglacial geomorphology 627
  Numerical analysis in geomorphology . . . 617
  Oceanography for geographers 1167
  Quantitative geography . . . 1097
  Techniques in geomorphology 1259
King, G E, *ed: Conflict and harmony . . .* 483
King, H G R: *The Antarctic* 65, 423
King, L C: *The morphology of the earth . . .* 1259
King, L J, *ed: Geographical analysis . . .* 551
  Statistical analysis in geography 1228
King, R: *A bibliography of Saudi Arabia* 943
King, Timothy: *Mexico . . .* 155
  Regional economic development . . . (Mexico) 155

Kingery, W D, *ed: Ice and snow, properties, processes and applications* 707
Kingmatic Automatic drafting machine model 312
Kingsbury, R C: *An atlas of European affairs* 137
  An atlas of Middle Eastern affairs 124
Kingsley, Mary H 1341
Kinne, Otto: *Marine ecology* 1167
Kinship and geographical mobility 825
Kinsman, Blair: *Wind waves . . .* 1167
Kinvig, R H 826
  History of the Isle of Man 826
Kinvig Geographical Society 826
Kinzl, Hans, festschrift 514
Kip, William, map engraver 266
Kirby, E S, *ed: Contemporary China . . .* 344
  Economic development in East Asia 83
Kirby, M J: *Hillslope form and process* 617
Kirkaldy, J F: *Outline of historical geology* 614
Kirkham, N: *Derbyshire lead mining glossary* 326
Kirkland, W: 'Experimental studies of map typography' 909
Kirkpatrick, F A: *The Spanish conquistadores* 1069
Kirwan, John: *An empty land . . .* (Australia) 188
Kirwan, L P: 'The RGS and British exploration . . .' 1144
  The white road . . . 1344
Kish, George: *Economic atlas of the Soviet Union* 116
  Italy 1295
Kitchin, Thomas: *Large English atlas* 1143
  The Royal English atlas . . . 1143
Kjellén, R 1392
Klawe, J J: 'Photography in the service of cartography' 312
Kleiner Bertelsmann Weltatlas 203
Klemp, Egon, *ed: Africa on maps dating from the 12th to the 18th century* 15
Das Klima der bodennahen Luftschicht 358
Die Klimat der Geologischen Vorzeit 827
Klimatologie, H R Scultetus 359
Knight, Stanley, *ed: Pergamon general historical atlas* 1048
  The Pergamon world atlas 1049
Knöpeli, Rudolf: 'Map revision' 909

703

706

Leopold, L B: 'Flood plains' 1137
'River meanders . . .' 1137
and M G Wolman: 'River channel patterns' 1137
Leppan *See* Angus-Leppan
Leprosy, distribution maps 133
The less developed realm . . . 1079
Leszczyck, Stanislaw: 'The application of geography in Poland' 1075
Let me enjoy . . . 858
Letts, Malcolm: 'The pictures in the Hereford mappa mundi' 673
Leutscher, Alfred: *Field natural history* . . . 515
Leverhulme Trust 27
Levison, Michael *et al*: *The settlement of Polynesia* . . . 1041
Lewis, Bernard: *The emergence of modern Turkey* 964
Lewis, C A, *ed*: *The glaciations of Wales and adjoining regions* 1335
Lewis, Sir Clinton: *The making of a map* 312
and J D Campbell, *ed*: *The Oxford atlas* 1028
Lewis, D C: *The classification and cataloging of maps and atlases* 325, 357, 905
'Maps . . .' 905
Lewis, David: *We, the navigators* . . . 669
Lewis, E W: 'The development of geography in the Polytechnics of England and Wales' 462
Lewis, H A G, *ed*: *The Times atlas of the Moon* 1276
Lewis, M G: 'Some cartographical works in the National Library' (Wales) 973
Lewis, Roy: *Sierra Leone* 391
Lewis, S R, *jr*: *Economic policy and industrial growth in Pakistan* 459
Lewis, W A, *ed*: *Tropical development 1880–1913* . . . 1292
Lewis, W V, *ed*: *Investigations on Norwegian cirque glaciers* 145
Lexicon geographicum 248
Lexique anglais-français des termes appartenent aux techniques en usage à l'Institut Géographique National 312, 725
Líbal, Dobroslau: *The towns and cities of Czechoslovakia* 96
Libault, André 905
La cartographie 312
Histoire de la cartographie 625
Les mesures sur les cartes et leurs incertitude 312
Liberia in maps 602
Librarianship, map 905
The library atlas 40, 859, 1058
The library catalogue of the School of Oriental and African Studies 860
Library classification and cataloging of geographical materials 357, 905
'The library classification of geography' 357, 905
Library guide for Brazilian studies 861
Library of Congress 17, 23, 60, 219, 251, 283, 299, 308, 312, 323, 325, 357, 647, 768, 861, 862, 868, 869, 905
publications 17, 18, 60, 158, 206, 219, 402, 848, 866, 999, 1072, 1298
'The Library of Congress computerised map cataloging project' 325
'The Library of the Royal Geographical Society' 1144
Libro dei Globi 629
Licate, J A, on geographical periodicals 768
Lieth, H: *Climatological atlas of the world* 154
Life of Sir Clements R Markham 922
Lighthouse of the skies : . . 863, 1187
Lim, Beda: *Malaya, a background bibliography* 219
Limits of land settlement . . . 261
Lindberg, J B: *A preface to economic geography* 534
Lindzen, R S: *Atmospheric tides, thermal and gravitational* 181
Linen industry 832
Lines, J A: *Bibliografia aborigen de Costa Rica* 914
ines, J D: 'Spot photography for map revision' 312
Linge, G J R and R M Frazer, *comp*: *Atlas of New Zealand geography* 157
Linklater, Eric: *The voyage of the Challenger* 333
The Linmap system of line-printer mapping 864
Linton, David Leslie 865
maps 1028
ed: *Sheffield and its region* . . . 270
Structure and surface drainage in South-East England 728, 865
List, R J: *Smithsonian meteorological tables* 1187
A list of American doctoral dissertations on Africa 866

707

McKee, Alexander: *Farming the sea . . .* 1167

Mackenzie, Murdoch, charts 916

Mackenzie Delta bibliography 887

Mackinder, Sir Halford John 512, 672, 803, 823, 888, 1038, 1118, 1311
  Britain and the British seas 264, 888
  The Rhine . . . 888
  'H J Mackinder and the new geography', J F Unstead 888
  'Mackinder's democratic ideals . . .' 888

McKnight, T L: *Australia's corner of the world . . .* 188

McLintock, A H, ed: *A descriptive atlas of New Zealand* 416
  An encyclopaedia of New Zealand 473

Macmillan, D H: *Tides* 1167

Macmillan, G A 1341

Macmillan and Company Limited, London 889
  Atlas of the Arab world and the Middle East 124
  audio-visual material 182
  Topicards 1279

McMorrin, Ian: *World atlas of mountaineering* 1354

Madagascar 22, 602
  bibliography 219
  See also Malagasey Republic

Madeira, discovery 1081

Madingley Lectures 533

Magee, G A: 'The Admiralty chart . . .' 9

Magellan of the Pacific, Edouard Roditi 26

Maggs, K R A: *Land Use Survey handbook* 839

Mahar, J M: *India . . .* 713

Mainsprings of civilisation 702

Mair, Volkmar: 'Strassenkarten aus Mairs Geographischen Verlag' 890

Mair Geographical Publishing House, Stuttgart 197, 420, 890

Major, R H: bibliography of Christopher Columbus 375

Major documents in American economic history 1307

Major documents in American history 158

Major foreign language geographical periodicals with English summaries of articles 768

The major seaports of the United Kingdom 891

Makerere University College, Department of Geography 1296

The makers of modern geography 892

The making of the Dutch landscape . . . 893

The making of a map 312

The making of a nation (COI booklets) 327

The making of the South Australian landscape . . . 1122

Malagasey Republic 17, 602
  See also Madagascar

Malaria, distribution maps 133

Malawi 327, 482
  bibliography 219
  maps 372

Malaya 558, 1081
  bibliography 236
  maps 164

Malaya, Indonesia, Borneo and the Phillippines 467

Malaya University, Kuala Lumpur 817

Malaysia 81, 467, 558, 1081, 1117
  bibliography 219, 236, 323, 341, 1210
  maps 372

Malclès, L N: *Bibliographical services throughout the world* 1301

Maling, D H, on photogrammetry 312
  Coordinate systems and map projections 788
  'Recent trends in map use and presentation' 312
  'Some thoughts about miniaturization of map library contents' 905

Malins, P B: *Early charts of New Zealand . . .* 443

Malkin, B H: *The scenery, antiquities and biography of South Wales* 1158

Malmström, V H: *Norden . . .* 1318

Malta 327
  bibliography 219

Mammals, maps 1064

Man, evolution 944
  racial distribution 110

Man and Africa . . . 22

Man and the earth 895

Man and environment . . . , Robert Arvill 979

Man and the environment . . . , A S Boughey 895

'Man and environment' (bibliography) 966

Man and his work . . . 672

Man and his world 894

Man and the land . . . , G F Carter 895

Man and the land, Sir Dudley Stamp 372

Man and nature . . . 896, 923

713

May, J M 690
  ed: Atlas of diseases 133
  Studies in medical geography 133
May, W E: *From lodestone to gyro-compass* 312
  A history of marine navigation 669
Mayfield, R C: *Man, space and environment* 484
Mayhew, Alan: *Rural settlement and farming in Germany* 105
Mayhill, R D and H G Bawden: *New Zealand geography* 473
Mead, W R: *An economic geography of the Scandinavian States and Finland* 1157
Meak, Lidia *et al, comp: Glossary of geographical names in six languages* . . . 630
Meally, Victor *et al, ed: Encyclopaedia of Ireland* 469
'The mechanisation of analytical hill shading' 312
The Medeba map 151
Mediaeval geography . . . 673
Medical geography . . . 133
'Medical geography in India and Pakistan' 713
Medical geography of India, R P Misra 133
The medieval Fenland 30
Medieval regions and their cities 397, 927
Mediterranea 753
Mediterranean 2, 370, 753, 895, 997
  maps 1034, 1321
Mediterranean . . . , Ernle Bradford 753
The Mediterranean, Richard Carrington 753
Mediterranean lands . . . , M I Newbigin 997
The Mediterranean lands, D S Walker 928
Meeking, C: *Snowy Mountains conquest* . . . 1189
Megalopolis 158, 349, 484
Mehra, P L: *The Younghusband Expedition* 80
Meigs, Peveril: *Geography of coastal deserts* 419
Meikle, H W: bibliography of Scotland 1108
Meine, Karl-Heinz: 'Aviation cartography' 312
'Considerations on the state of development with regard to topographical

maps of the different countries of the earth 308
A history of lunar cartography 1267
Die Kartographie, 1943–1954 . . . 312, 905
Meinesz, F A V: *The earth's crust and mantle* 1284
Meinig, D W, *ed: On geography* . . . 858
Mekong Basin, atlas 159
Melanesia, bibliography 1041, 1042
  maps 417
Mélanges de géographie . . . 929
Melbourne, maps 1068
Melbourne University: *Abr-Nahrain* . . . 2
Mellor, R E H: 'Transport statistics and notes' (USSR) 284
  and J P Cole: 'The Soviet iron and steel industry' 284
Mémoires et documents . . . 331, 905, 930
Memoirs of hydrography . . . 931
Men and meridians . . . 932
Mendelssohn Library 933
Mendelssohn's South African bibliography 933
Mercantile marine atlas 934
Mercator, Gerard 629, 935, 1023, 1267
  bibliography 935
Mercator, Rumold 831, 935
Mercator Projection 67, 312, 934, 935
The merchant's world . . . 598
Meridian Publishing Company, Amsterdam 84, 207, 211, 252, 259, 291, 375, 578, 636, 870, 935, 936, 1261
Merrien, Jean: *Christopher Columbus* . . . 375
Merseyside, England, marketing map 548
Mesopotamia 800, 943
Les mesures sur les cartes et leurs incertitude 312
Metallogenic map of Europe 937
The metallogeny of Europe 937
Metcalf, R L: *Advances in environmental sciences and technology* 11
Meteorite research . . . 938
Meteorites 436
Meteorites and their origins 359
Meteoritical Society 938
Meteorological abstracts and bibliography 3
The meteorological glossary 1146
Meteorological Institute, Bucharest: *Climatological atlas of Rumania* 364

Muris, Oswald and Gert Saarmann: *Der globus im Wandel der Zeiten* . . . 629

Murphy, R E: *The American city* . . . 46

Murray, Jacqueline: *The first European agriculture* . . . 599

Murray, Sir John 333

Murray's handbook for Devon and Cornwall 405

Murray's handbook for Scotland 405

Museum directory of the United States and Canada 1187

Musiker, Reuben: 'The bibliographical scene in South Africa' 737

comp: *Guide to South African reference books* 655

South African bibliography 655, 1204

Les mutations recentes de l'économie française . . . 529

Mutton, F A: *Central Europe* 599

Myers, L E: *Water supplies for arid regions* 76

Myers, R H: *Chinese peasant economy* . . . 455

Myres, J L: *Herodotus* . . . 674

Mysore, maps 962

Nairn, A E M, ed: *Problems in palaeoclimatology* 358

Naish, M C: *Some aspects of the study and teaching of geography in Britain* . . . 462

Naples University Oriental Institute 41

Narström, Göran: *World shipping* . . . 1376

Natal University, Department of Land Surveying 312

National Aeronautics and Space Administration 312

National Agricultural Library monthly catalog 1307

National atlas of Britain 957

The national atlas of Canada 958

National atlas of China 959

'The national atlas of Cuba', C G Clarke 258

National atlas of disease mortality in the United Kingdom 960

National atlas of Ghana 233

National atlas of Hungary 961

National atlas of India 962

National atlas of Kenya 963

National atlas of Turkey 964

National atlas of the United States 965,

1102

'The national atlas of the United States of America', A C Gerlach 965

The National Book League, London 966, 1108

National Centre for Scientific Research 12

National Council for Geographic Education 808

National Environmental Teach-in, 1970 483

National Geographic atlas of the world 967, 968

National Geographic magazine 39, 967, 968

National Geographic Society 39, 228, 968

'The National Geographic Society and its magazine' 968

National Grid system 1181

National Institute of Oceanography, Wormley 334, 412, 970

The National Library of New Zealand, Map Room 971

National Library of Scotland, Map Room 972

National Library of Wales, map collection 973

'The national map collection of Canada' 902

National Maritime Museum, Greenwich 931, 935, 969, 1195

National Nature Week 493

National Oceanographic Council 970

National Oceanographic Data Center, Washington, DC 974

National Organisation for Audio-Visual Aids 182

National parks 898

National parks, Vaughan Cornish 390

National Parks Commission 394, 975

The national parks of England and Wales 975

The national plans, H St J L Winterbotham 1019

'National qualifications in cartography' 1128

National Record of Industrial Monuments 715

National Research Council, National Academy of Sciences 976

Photogrammetric Research Section 500

The National Trust 979

National Trust of Scotland 1181

National Urban Coalition, Washington,

DC 352

Native and introduced freshwater fishes (New Zealand) 1113
Native beetles (New Zealand) 1113
Native birds (New Zealand) 1113
Native butterflies and moths (New Zealand) 1113
Native crabs (New Zealand) 1113
Native ferns (New Zealand) 1113
Native insects (New Zealand) 1113
Native rock (New Zealand) 1113
Native sea fishes (New Zealand) 1113
Native sea-stars (New Zealand) 1113
Native shells (New Zealand) 1113
Native trees (New Zealand) 1113
NATO 137, 169
Natural disaster research centers and warning systems 977
A natural ecology, Michael Graham 587
Natural Environment Research Council 312, 979
The natural geography of plants 254
Natural history, atlas 1331
bibliography 1192
The natural history of Europe 599
A natural history of man in Britain 372, 520
The natural landscapes of Canada . . . 294
Natural regions of the USSR 1214
Natural resources (bibliography) 979
Natural resources for US growth . . . 438, 1307
Natural resources of the Soviet Union . . . 1153
Natural rubber news 1150
The Natural Rubber Producers' Research Association 1150
Nature and man 979
Nature and resources . . . (Unesco) 765, 978
Nature Conservancy 265, 394, 484, 966, 975, 979, 1181
Nature conservancy: the first twenty-one years 979
Nature conservancy handbook 979
Nature Conservancy progress 979
Nature conservation in Britain 372, 979
Nature in focus 980
The nature of geography . . . 981
Nature trails in Northern Ireland 979
'Nature versus ideology in Hungarian agriculture . . .' 451
Nature's network 979
Natusch, Sheila: Native rock (New Zealand) 1113

Nautical Almanac 969
Navalani, K: Indian periodicals . . . 219
'The navigating manual of Columbus' 375
Navigation 79, 88, 479, 669, 704, 847, 931, 969, 982, 1060, 1078, 1256, 1339
'Navigation and cartography of the Discovery' 438
Neal, J A, ed: Reference guide for travellers 1115
Near East 150, 928
maps 318
'The need for efficient base maps . . .' 909
'The need for state cartographers' 462
Needham, Joseph, on Chinese medieval navigation 669
Nef, J U: The conquest of the material world 534
Negretti, Henri, balloon photographs 312
Nepal, bibliography 214, 219
Netboy, Anthony: The Atlantic salmon . . . 1360
Netherlands 7, 207, 413, 893, 927, 984, 1209
bibliography 216, 219, 308
cartography and maps 66, 91, 131, 178, 252, 308, 312, 411, 525
Netherlands India . . . 983
Netherlands journal of economic and social geography 984
Netherlands journal of sea research 1167
Network analysis in geography 78, 985
Neubauer, A: La géographie du Talmud 936
Neuberger, H and J Cahir: Principles of climatology . . . 359
Der Neue Brockhaus 642
Neumann, Gerhard and W J Pierson, jr: Principles of physical oceanography 1167
Neundörfer, Ludwig, ed: Atlas of social and economic regions of Europe 163
Neville-Rolfe, E: Economic aspects of agricultural developments in Africa 726
New and current English atlas (Cary) 314
New British atlas 314
New Brunswick University 312, 627
New Caledonia 213, 1211
The new Cambridge modern history atlas 986
'The new Commonwealth Institute after

719

Nigerian geographical journal 3
Nile, exploration 1205
 maps 504
Nippon 796
Nippon Keizai Chizu (economic) 152
Nippon Rekishi Chizu (historical) 152
Nishioka, T and S Hattori, *ed*: *Nippon Rekishi Chizu* 152
Nix, John: *Farm management pocket book* 1386
Noble, W A: *Bibliography of Kerala State, India* 234
Noh, Toshio: *Japanese geography: a guide* . . . 219, 796
Noranda Lectures, Expo 67 894
Norbeck, Stig and Bengt Roystedt: 'Population maps and computerised map production' 1035
Norden, John 1000, 1014, 1221
Norden . . . 1318
Nordenskiöld, A E: *Facsimile atlas* . . . 506, 1095
 Periplus . . . 1080
Nordic Council 435
Nordic hydrology 1001
Nordisk Världs atlas 312
Norfolk, England, maps 347, 1105
Norge 1002
'Normalisation of symbols in thematic cartography' 909
Norman, Charles: *Discoverers of North America* 439
Norström, Göran: *World shipping* . . . 601
North, F J: *Sir Charles Lyell* . . . 883
North America 527, 668, 803, 1090, 1110, 1377
 exploration 438, 439, 502, 1069
 maps 158, 161, 687, 747, 986
 See also America
'North America' 610
North America, A W Coysh and M E Tomlinson 1310
North America, N J G Pounds 158
North America: its countries and regions 158
North Borneo 391
North London geographer 153
The North Pole, Robert E Peary 70
North Sea 970
The North Sea, George Morey 1003
North West Passage 346
Northcote, K H: 'A factual key for the recognition of Australian soils' 126

Northern Australia Regional Survey 380
Northern geographical essays . . . 514, 1004
The northern myth . . . (Australia) 183
Northern Science Research Group, Department of Indian Affairs 887
Northernmost Labrador mapped from the air 1005
The northward course of empire 1232
North-west England 597
The north-west frontier of West Pakistan . . . 459
North-west Passage 1344
Northwest to fortune . . . 1232
North Western Polytechnic, London, Department of Geography 640
 (Polytechnic of North London)
Northwestern University 21, 737, 871, 1251, 1288
Norway 491, 603, 1002, 1156, 1157
 bibliography 216, 219
 maps 145, 197, 301, 525, 1002, 1138
Norway exports 1006
Norwegian Antarctic Expedition ('Fram') 65
Norwegian Geographical Institute 1002
Norwegian Polar Institute 1249
Notes africaines 724
'Notes on Africana in the Yale University Library' 737
Notes on the cataloging, care and classification of maps and atlases . . . 905
'Notes on the classification, arrangement and cataloguing of a large map collection' 905
Notice d'un atlas en langue Catalane 318
Nottingham and its region . . . 270
Nottingham University, Department of Geography 108, 284, 285, 450, 556, 559
 Field Group studies 516
Nouveau précis de géographie humaine 570
Nouvel atlas général (Bordas) 505
Nouvelle carte de France 307
Nouvelle géographie universelle 1112
Noyce, Wilfrid and Ian McMorrin, *ed*: *World atlas of mountaineering* 1354
Nuevo atlas geográfico de la Argentina 1007
Nuffield Foundation 376, 881
Numerical analysis in geomorphology . . . 617
'Numerical methods for map analysis'

909

Nunn, G E: *The geographical conceptions of Columbus* 375

Nunn, G R, *comp: South and Southeast Asia . . .* (bibliography) 1206

Nuovo atlante geografico moderno 793

Nyasaland, bibliography 219

Nyasaland, Frank Debenham 391

Nystrom, A J, *ed: The journal of geography* 808

Oboli, H O N and R J Harrison Church: *An outline geography of West Africa* 22

O'Brien, C I M: 'The place of large scale mapping in . . . developing countries' 909

O'Brien, L J, *ed: Canadian cartography* 130

Obruchev, V A 1008
Eastern Mongolia 1008
Field geology 1008
Frontier Dzungaria 1008
The geological map of the Lena gold-bearing region 1008
Geologie von Sibirien 1008
Gold seekers in the desert 1008
The history of the geological exploration of Siberia 1008

The observer atlas of world affairs 1058

Obst, Erich: *Allgemeine Wirtschafts-und Verkehrsgeographie* 855

Ocean wave statistics . . . 1009

Oceania 688, 1160, 1270
bibliography 1042

Oceanographic index . . . 1167

Oceanography 312, 320, 333, 334, 412, 710, 736, 739, 770, 780, 916, 918, 925, 952, 970, 974, 1009, 1044, 1091, 1127, 1162, 1167, 1179, 1187, 1218, 1249, 1306, 1348
bibliography 1167
charts and surveys 1305, 1339

Oceanography . . . (Dietrich) 1167

Oceanography, ed: Mary Sears 1167

Oceanography . . . (Yasso) 1167

Oceanography and marine biology . . . 1167

Oceanography for geographers 1167

Oceanography for meteorologists 1249

Oceanography: list of terms . . . 1010

Oceanography Research Institute, Cronulla 380

Oceans 1022, 1025, 1224

The oceans . . . , H U Sverdrup *et al* 1249

O'Connor, Maeve: *Man and Africa* . . . 22

O'Dell, Andrew Charles 1011
'Geography and planning' 585
The highlands and islands of Scotland 1011
The historical geography of the Shetland Islands 1011
The Scandinavian world 876, 1011, 1157
and P S Richards: *Railways and geography* 1011, 1101

Odell, P R: *An economic geography of oil* 200
'The future of oil . . .' 1057

Oehme, Ruthardt 392, 1267

'Of central places, cities and seaports' 891

Office de la Recherche Scientifique et Technique Outre-Mer 1012

Official map publications . . . 308, 1013

Offshore geography of northwestern Europe . . . 599

Ogendo, R B: *Industrial geography of Kenya* . . . 602

Ogilby, John 1014
Britannia . . . 267, 1014

Ogilvie, A G 546, 1015
festschrift 557
ed: Great Britain . . . 1015
'The mapping of population . . .' 1374

Oglesby, R T *et al, ed: River ecology and man* 1137

Ogunsheye, F A, *comp: Nigerian library resources in science and technology* 219

Ohio State University 308, 312, 551

Oil 124, 200, 1056, 1057
maps 1342
See also Petroleum

Oil and the Mexican Revolution 940

The oil and petroleum year book 1057

Oil fields of the world 1057

Oil in the Middle East . . . 943

Old decorative maps and charts 411

Ollier, Cliff: *Volcanoes* . . . 1326
Weathering 617

Olsen, Örjan: *La conquête de la terre* . . . 437

Olsen, T D: *Bibliography of Old Norse-Icelandic studies* 219

O'Malley, Patrick: *Irish industry* . . . 790

Oman 536

Ommaney, F D: *Lost leviathan* 879

On the connexion of the physical sciences 1201

728

Pollock, N C: *Studies in emerging Africa* 287

Polo, Marco 318

Polunin, N, *ed: The environmental future* . . . 483

Introduction to plant geography . . . 254, 1070

Polynesia, bibliography 213, 1041, 1042
maps 417

Polynesian navigation . . . 1078

The Polynesian Society, Wellington 1078

Pompidou, President 114

Popovici, Lucia and Constanta Moruzi: *Atlas botanic* 95

Population 10, 119, 570, 598, 755, 1092, 1190, 1229, 1325, 1373, 1374
bibliography 206
maps 160, 570, 1387
See also Demography

Population 1079

Population and social change 1079

Population Association of America 206

Population Estimates . . . Seminar, 1967–68 156

Population growth and land use 837

Population in history . . . 1079

'Population maps and computerised map production' 1035

The population of Czechoslovakia 402

The population of Europe . . . 599

Population, resources, environment 1079

Population studies . . . 1079

Port Arthur 405

Porter, H D: *Research in the Antarctic* 65

Porter, R T: 'The library classification of geography' 357, 905

Portolan charts . . . 1080

Portolani 318, 339, 1080

A portrait of Canada 1233

Ports 405, 601, 872, 891, 920, 934, 1376
plans 952, 1339

Ports and harbours 703

Ports of the world 1376

Portugal 561
bibliography 216, 219, 271, 308, 665
national atlas 107

Portuguese Africa . . . (bibliography) 18

The Portuguese pioneers 1069, 1081

Possibilism 1322

'Possibilities for computer animated films in cartography' 312

Posthumous, N W 807

'The potential contribution of cartography in liberal education' 462

'Potentialities and problems of adapting a systems approach to the study of change in human geography' 786

Potter, P E: *Atlas and glossary of primary sedimentary structures* 742

Poulsen, T M: 'Administration and regional structure in East-Central and Southern Europe' 451

Poultry and eggs . . . 726

Poultry and eggs in Britain . . . 29, 726

Pounds, N J G: *Eastern Europe* 599

The geography of iron and steel 703

An historical geography of Europe . . . 393

An introduction to economic geography 534

North America 158

Poland 550

Political geography 1076

ed: USA . . . 438, 1307

'The urbanization of East-Central and Southeast Europe . . .' 451

and R C Kingsbury: *An atlas of European affairs* 137

and R C Kingsbury: *An atlas of Middle Eastern affairs* 124

Powell, J W: and the national atlas of USA 965

Powers, W E and C F Kohn: *Aerial photo-interpretation of land-forms* . . . 312

Practical field surveying and computations 312

Practical geography, R S Coggins and R K Hefford 312

Practical microclimatology 359

Practical work in geography, J Beaujeu-Garnier 312

Prairie Provinces, North America, maps 161

Pratt, I A, *comp: Modern Egypt* . . . 947

The Pre-Cambrian along the Gulf of Suez . . . 1082

The Pre-Cambrian and Lower Palaeozoic rocks of Wales 1335

Précis de biogéographie 784

Précis de climatologie 358

Précis de géographie économique 534

Précis de géographie rurale 31

Précis de géomorphologie, M Derruau 617

Précis de géomorphologie, Jean Tricart 617

Précis d'Hydrologie . . . 1332

732

Rodger, E M: *The large scale county maps of the British Isles* . . . 843
Rodgers, H B: *An atlas of North American affairs* 158
Rodier, J, comp: *Bibliography of African hydrology* 222
Roditi, Edouard: *Magellan of the Pacific* 246
Rodopi N V, publishers 84
Rodwell Jones Memorial Volume 803
Roepke, H J and T J Maresh, ed: *Readings in economic geography* 1109
Rogers, G W: *Alaska in transition* . . . 39
ed: *Change in Alaska* . . . 228
Rognon, P: *Les zones tropicales arides et sub-tropicales* 75
Rolands, W: *Cambrian bibliography* . . . 291
'The role and relations of physical geography' 617
'The role of meteorology in the national economy' 1146
'The role of a national map library' 905
Rolfe *See* Neville-Rolfe
Rollins, R R: 'Printing management for maps and charts' 312
Roman Empire, maps 1253
Roman roads in Britain 1140
Romania 364, 451, 606, 1120, 1151
bibliography 216, 219
maps 106, 113, 364
Romanian scientific abstracts 219
Romanowski, J I, translator 1153
'Geographic research and methodology on East-Central and Southeast European agriculture' 451
Romans, geography 686
Rome, Stewart Perowne 1314
Roneo Flushline Vertical Planfile 905
Rorenwaldt, E, ed: *Welt-Seuchen Atlas* 1340
Rose, J, ed: *Technological injury* . . . (environment) 979
Rosenfeld, A: 'Automatic imagery interpretation' 312
Rosenthal, Eric, ed: *Encyclopaedia of Southern Africa* 474
Rosing, K E and P A Wood, comp: *Character of a conurbation* . . . 338
Ross, J O'C: *This stern coast* . . . (New Zealand) 443
Rothé, J P: *Earthquakes* 58
The seismicity of the earth . . . 1170
Rotorua, bibliography 232

Route-mapping and position locating in unexplored regions 312
Row, E F, ed: *La géographie humaine* (Brunhes) 573
Rowe: *Perambulation of Dartmoor* 404
Rowley, H H, ed: *Atlas of Mesopotamia* . . . 800
Rowley, V M: *J Russell Smith* . . . 1186
Roxby, P M 546, 1141
Roy, General William 317, 1019
Royal Afghan Embassy, London Information Bureau 13
Royal Asiatic Society, Malaya Branch 219
Royal atlas, A K Johnston 802
Royal Canadian Geographical Society, Ottawa 1142
Royal College of Art, Experimental Cartography Unit 312, 1019
Royal Dutch Geographical Society 984
Royal Dutch Shell Group 312
The Royal English atlas . . . 405, 1143
Royal Geographical Society, London 197, 252, 357, 384, 584, 673, 677, 728, 768, 769, 823, 888, 905, 960, 1053, 1094, 1144, 1253, 1256, 1323
publications 145, 154, 312, 383, 504, 513, 564, 591, 628, 988, 1105, 1205, 1236
The Royal Geographical Society . . . , G R Crone 1144
'The RGS and British exploration . . .' 1144
'The Royal Geographical Society and geographical education in 1871' 1144
'The Royal Geographical Society and the projected London Institute of geography . . .' 1144
Royal Geographical Society of Australasia 1145
Royal Greenwich Observatory 651
Royal Institute of Chartered Surveyors 312
Royal Institute of International Affairs 22, 732
Royal Meteorological Society of London 1146
Royal Netherlands Geographical Society 178
Royal Scottish Geographical Society 905, 997, 1015, 1053, 1147, 1166
Royal Society 278, 916, 1148
British National Committee for Geo-

graphy 312, 1299
Cartographic Sub-Committee 312, 905
A symposium on continental drift 1022
Royal Society for the Protection of Birds
1181
Royal Swedish Academy of Sciences 480
Royal Tropical Institute, Amsterdam
775, 1149, 1291
Roystedt, Bengt: 'Population maps and
computerized map production' 1035
Roze, R and M Lelarge, *ed: Biblio-
mer* . . . 244
Rubber and the rubber industry 433, 526,
735
Rubber abstracts 3
Rubber age 1150
Rubber and Plastics Research Associ-
ation, Library 735
Rubber developments 433, 1150
Rubin, V, *ed: Caribbean studies* . . . 304
Rubra, G N, on weather economics
1333
Ruellan, F: *Photogrammétrie* . . . 312
Rugg, D S: 'Aspects of change in the
landscape of East-Central and South-
east Europe' 451
'Developing the university map library'
905
Ruggles, Richard: *Manitoba historical
atlas* . . . 899
'Rules for robot draughtsmen' 1035
Rumanian studies . . . 1151
Runcorn, S K, *ed: Continental drift* 1022
*Implications of continental drift to the
earth sciences* 1022
*The rural landscape of the Welsh Border-
land* 842
Rural settlement and farming in Germany
105
Rural settlement and land use 837
Rushton, G: 'Mapit . . .' 864
Russell, Sir E J: *A report on the agricul-
ture and soils of Kent, Surrey and
Sussex* 1369
Soil conditions and plant growth 243,
1369
The world of the soil 1369
Russell, E W 1198
ed: Soil conditions and plant growth (Sir
E J Russell) 243
Russell, J C: *Medieval regions and their
cities* 397, 927
Russell, Ronald: *Lost canals of England
and Wales* 262

Russell, W M S: *Man, nature and history*
979
Russia and the Soviet Union . . . 1152,
1214
*Russia: nineteenth-century source ma-
terial* 241
Russian agriculture 1153
Russian history atlas 1153
Russian land Soviet people . . . 1153
*The Russian school of soil car-
tography* . . . 1252
Ruthenberg, Hans: *Farming systems in
the Tropics* 1290
Ruwenzori Mountains 1296
R V-Katalog 611, 905
Ryan, Marleigh: *Research in Japanese
sources* . . . 1130
Ryder, D E, *ed: Canadian reference
sources* . . . 294
Rydings, H A: *The bibliography of West
Africa* 219
Ryle, George: *Forest service* . . . 528

Saarmann, Gert: *Der globus im Wandel
der Zeiten* . . . 629
Sabin, Joseph *et al, comp: Bibliotheca
Americana* . . . 245
Sahab, A 1154
Sahab Geographic and Drafting Insti-
tute, Tehran 1154
Sahara 690
Die Sahara und ihre Randgebiete 419
St Joseph, J K S: *The uses of air photo-
graphy* . . . 312
St Lawrence waterway 300
St Leger-Gordon, D: *Dartmoor* 372
St Petersburg Academy of Sciences 4
Saito, Shiro: *Pacific island bibliography*
1042
Sakhalin Island Scientific Research In-
stitute 4
Sale, R D: *Elements of cartography* 465,
1347
Salichtchev, K A 148
Atlas nationaux 308
Cartography 312
'Contribution of geographical con-
gresses and the International Geo-
graphical Union to the development of
cartography' 308
'Present-day thematic cartography . . .'
909
'The subject and method of car-
tography . . .' 909

737

740

743

1223
and W G Hoskins: *The common lands of England and Wales* 372
See also 'Sir Dudley Stamp and his life and times', M J Wise 837
Standard encyclopedia of the world's mountains 1224
Standard encyclopedia of the world's oceans and islands 1224
Standard encyclopedia of the world's rivers and lakes 1224
Standing Commission on Library Materials on Africa 16
Standing Conference on Library Materials on Africa 21, 1300
Stanford, A H and W Moran: *Geography* . . . 583
Stanford, Edward, Limited 905, 1058, 1225
Stanford, Q H, *ed*: *The world's population* . . . 1373
Stanford Planfile 905, 1225
The Stanford reference catalogue of maps and atlases 308, 1225
Stanford Research Institute, California 312
Stanford University 21, 386, 627, 1228
Stanford's geological atlas of Great Britain and Ireland 1226
Stanford's Whitehall atlas 1058
Starke, Harold, *comp*: *The railway encyclopaedia* 1101
Stars, maps 168
The state of British agriculture . . . 726
The state of food and agriculture (FAO) 524
States and trends of geography in the United States . . . 86, 1227
Statistical analysis in geography 1228
Statistical bulletin for Latin America 453
Statistical mapping and the presentation of statistics 1229
Statistical methods and the geographer 1230
A statistical summary of the world mineral industry 1026
Statistics 10, 14, 29, 51, 81, 186, 188, 256, 284, 524, 553, 554, 565, 622, 913, 1009, 1190, 1229
 bibliography 1228
 maps 160, 162, 312
Statistics: *African sources* . . . 1231
Staton, F M and Marie Tremaine, *ed*: *A bibliography of Canadiana* . . . 231

The status of world topographic mapping 308
Staveley, Ronald and Mary Piggott: *Government information and the research worker* 957
Stea, David: *Image and environment* . . . 909
'Studies of geographic learning' 583
Stedenboek 687
Steel, R W and C A Fisher, *ed*: *Geographical essays on British tropical lands* 558
 and Richard Lawton, *ed*: *Liverpool essays in geography* . . . 872
 and J W Watson: *Geography in the United Kingdom 1968–1972* 595
Steers, J A, *ed*: *Applied coastal geomorphology* 367
 The coast of England and Wales in pictures 367
 The coastline of Scotland 497
 ed: *Field studies in the British Isles* 517
 ed: *Introduction to coastline development* 367
 An introduction to map projections 312, 788
 The sea coast 372
 The unstable earth . . . 617
Stefansson, Vilhjalmur 426, 1232
 The friendly Arctic . . . 1232
 Great adventures and explorations . . . 1232
 The northward course of empire 1232
 Northwest to fortune . . . 1232
 ed: *The three voyages of Martin Frobisher* . . . 1271
 Ultima Thule . . . 1232
 Unsolved mysteries of the Arctic 1232
Stefansson Collection 1232
Stegena, Lajos, *ed*: 'Industrial signs in atlas cartography' 312
Stellenbosch University, Department of Geography 6
Stembridge, J H 1233
 Africa 1233
 Germany 1233
 A portrait of Canada 1233
Stephen, C G: *The soil landscapes of Australia* 126
Stephens, N and R E Glasscock, *ed*: *Irish geographical studies* 790
Stephenson, R W: 'Atlases of the western hemisphere . . .' 308
Stereopantometer (Zeiss) 1391

Stereoplotting 312

Stern, P M: *The golden encyclopaedia of geography* 632

Steven, L W: *Food, clothing and shelter* 889

Stevens, H N: *Ptolemy's Geography* 1095

Stevens, J H and R King: *A bibliography of Saudi Arabia* 943

Stevens, S D: 'Planning a map library' 905

Stevenson, E L: *Portolan charts* . . . 1080
Terrestrial and celestial globes . . . 629
Willem Janszoon Blaeu . . . 252

Steward, H B: *The global sea* 1318

Steward, Harry, *comp*: *Education and training in the mapping sciences* . . . 463

Steward, J H, Limited, London 1234

Stewart, C L: *Land use information* . . . 838

Stewart, G A 834

Stewart, John: 'An account of Prince Edward Island . . .' 300

Stewig, Reinhard: *Byzanz-Konstantinople-Istanbul* 964

Steiler, Adolf 1235
atlas 1054, 1161, 1235

Stigant, G B 931

Still, H W: *The look of our land* . . . (USA) 965

Stobart and Son, Limited, London 527

Stockdale, John, cartographer 314

Stockwell, Robert, on R V Tooley 910

Stoddart, D R: 'Climatic geomorphology . . .' 617
'Darwin's impact on geography' 1016
Growth and structure of geography' 689
ed: *Regional variation in Indian Ocean coral reefs* 1124
et al, ed: *Progress in geography* 1089

Stode, H J, cartography 610

Stone, J C: 'Foundations of a Malaysian nation' 467

The storage and conservation of maps . . . (RGS) 905, 1236

Storm surges 58

Storry, Richard: *Japan* 797

The story of maps, L A Brown 1237

The story of Utopias . . . 397

Strabo 892, 1238

Strahler, A N: on geomorphology 173
Introduction to physical geography 617
Planet earth . . . 617
and A H Strahler: *Environmental geo-*

science . . . 484

Strandberg, C H: *Aerial discovery manual* 312

'The strange case of the Vinland Map: a symposium' 1323

'Strassenkarten aus Mairs Geographischen Verlag' 890

Stratigraphy 263, 756, 998

The stratigraphy of the British Isles 1239

Strauss, Erich: *Soviet agriculture* . . . 1153

Streams—their dynamics and morphology 1137

Streyffert, T: *World timber* . . . 527

Strickland, J D H and T R Parsons: *A manual of sea-water analysis* 736

Strietelmeier, J H: *Geography in world society* . . . 596

Stringer, E T: *Foundations of climatology* . . . 359
Techniques of climatology 359

Stringfield, V T: *Karst* . . . 617

Strong, Maurice *et al*: 'Human environment . . .' 483

Structural landforms . . . 617

Structure and field geology . . . 538

Structure and growth of the Scottish economy 497

The structure of human populations 570

The structure of political geography 1076

Structure and surface drainage in Southeast England 728, 865

Struggle for the Snowy . . . 1189

Struik, C (Pty) Limited, Cape Town 21

The student's elements of geology 883

Studia geographica 337

Studies in Antarctic meteorology 359

Studies in Canadian geography 215

Studies in cartobibliography . . . 1240

Studies in the climatology of South Asia 1241

Studies in emerging Africa 287

'Studies in historical geography' series 405

Studies in the history of science and medicine 883

Studies in Hungarian geographical sciences 700

Studies in medical geography, J M May 133

Studies in medical geography, L D Stamp 133

Studies in speleology 326

Studies in urban history 1242

747

Thomson, Sir Wyville 333
Thorarinsson, S: *Surtsey* 1171
Thorén, R, comp: *Picture atlas of the Arctic* 466, 1067
Thornbury, W D: *Principles of geomorphology* 617
Regional geomorphology of the United States 1099
Thorne, J O: *Chambers's world gazetteer* . . . 336
Thornhill, Patrick: *Land and water* 833
Thornton, John: *The English Pilot* 479
Thorp, Rosemary: *Latin America in the international economy* 250
Thorpe, David: *The geographer and urban studies* 544
'Three types of reconnaissance mapping' 312
The three voyages of Martin Frobisher . . . 1271
'Three-D geography . . .' 1272
3-D junior atlas 410, 1272
Three-dimensional maps . . . 312
Thrower, N J W: 'Cadastral survey and county atlases of the United States' 965
Maps and man . . . 911
Original survey and land subdivision 312
Thum, E et al, ed: *Vermessungskunde für kartographen* 312
Thunberg, A: 'Hydrographic surveying and data processing' 916
Tibet 1273
Tides 181, 970
Tides, D H Macmillan 1167
Tidswell, W V and S M Barker: *Quantitative methods* 1097
Tietze, Wolf, ed: *Westermann Lexikon der Geographie* 1342
Tijdschrift voor economische en sociale geographie 263, 1274
Timber 527, 1378
Timber Research and Development Association, London 1275
The Times atlas of the moon 1276
The Times atlas of the world 197, 1277, 1278
The Times concise atlas 1277
The Times index gazetteer of the world 1278
The Times mid-century edition 1161
Timms, D W G: *The urban mosaic* . . . 608
Timor, bibliography 341

Tin and its uses 778
Tin international 778
'Tips and tip working in the Lower Swansea Valley' 881
Tiratsoo, E N: *Oil fields of the world* 1057
Tiros operational satellite system 1381
Titmuss, F H: *Concise encyclopaedia of world timbers* 527
Tivy, J: *Biogeography* . . . 784
The Glasgow region . . . 497
Toase, Mary: *A guide to British periodicals* 219
Tobago 327, 1117
Tobler, W R: 'Automation and cartography' 1035
'Automation in the preparation of thematic maps' 312
'The geographic ordering of information . . .' 312
Todd, D K, ed: *The water encyclopedia* 1332
Togo, Yoshida: *Japanese geography* . . . 1130
Tolansky, S: *The history and use of diamond* 685
Tolley, H and K Orrell: *Yorkshire* 597
Tomlinson, M E: *North America* 1310
The southern continents 1310
Tomlinson, R F, ed: *Geographical data handling* 553
Tomorrow's countryside . . . 979
Tonga 1211
bibliography 232
Toniolo, Sandro: 'The new edition of the 'Atlante Internazionale' 90
Tooley, R V 355
A dictionary of mapmakers 430, 903
A history of cartography . . . 687
ed: *Map collectors' series* 903
Maps and map-makers 910, 1095
One hundred foreign maps of Australia . . . 192
The printed maps of Tasmania . . . 1086
Toombs, R B: *A survey of the mineral industry of Southern Africa* 1248
Topfer, F and W Pillewizer: 'The principles of selection' 312
A topical list of vertical photographs . . . 1258
Topicards 1279
Topics in geography 889
'Topocart' 312
'The topographic map in a world of computers' 312

751

Valck, Gerhard, globemaker 629
Vallaux, C: *La géographie de l'histoire*
281
'Value of maps as reference tools' 905
The value of the weather 359, 1333
Van Baak, B C P H: *Drainage of agricultural land: a bibliography* 31
Van Baren, F A 776
van de Gohm, Richard: *Antique maps for the collector* 66
van der Leedon, F: *Ground water* . . . 644
Van Heusden, G T, publishers 84
Van Keulen, Johannes and Gerard: *The new large shining sea-torch* 990
Van Langrens family, globe-makers 629
Van Nieuwenhuijze, C A O, *ed*: *Economic, social and political studies of the Middle East* 457
Sociology of the Middle East . . . 457, 943
Van Nostrand Company Limited 1318
van Ortroy, F: *Bibliographie sommaire de l'oeuvre mercatorienne* 935
van Raemdonck, J: *Gérard Mercator* . . . 935
Van Royen, William, *ed*: *Atlas of the world's resources* 174
and N A Bengtson: *Fundamentals of economic geography* . . . 534
van Zuylen, L: 'Production of photomaps' 901
Vance, J E, *jr*: *The merchant's world* . . . 598
Vancouver Island 300
Varenius, Bernhard 689, 1319
Descriptio regni Japoniae et Siam 1319
Geographia generalis 1319
Varenius, S Gunther 1319
Vegetation 357, 784, 827, 1380
bibliography 747
maps 120, 781, 1321
Vegetation and soils . . . 1320
La végétation de la terre 1380
Vegetation map of the Mediterranean region . . . 1321
Vegetation mapping 1321
Veis, G, *ed*: *Proceedings*, symposium on use of artificial satellites in geodesy 312
Véliz, Claudio, *ed*: *Latin America and the Caribbean* . . . 668
Venezuela 746, 850
bibliography 219
national atlas 104

Vening Meinesz Laboratorium, University of Utrecht 918
Veniss 182
Vennetier, Pierre: *Pointe-Noire et la façade maritime du Congo-Brazzaville* 1012
Vereker, C *et al*: *Urban redevelopment and social change* 354
Vermessungskunde für kartographen 312
Verner, Coolie: *The English Pilot*, note 479
Vernet, A: vegetation maps 781
Vernon, R: *The changing economic functions of the central city* 354
Vesconti, Perrinus: atlas 1080
Vestnik Moskovskogo Universiteta . . . 1214
'The V H F radio echo technique' 628
Victoria University, Social Sciences Research Centre 229
Victory Museum, Portsmouth 1195
Vidal de la Blache, Paul 54, 281, 409, 413, 535, 546, 563, 892, 1202, 1322
Atlas 112, 1322
Etats et nations de l'Europe 1322
France de l'Est 1322
Géographie universelle 535, 575, 1322
Principes de géographie humaine 1322
Tableau de la géographie de la France 1322
Vietnam 81, 449, 467
bibliography 219, 341, 1210
maps 159
Vietor, Alexander O 1267, 1323
Viewing weather from space 359
Viewpoint on Indonesia . . . 149
Vigneras, L A: *The journal of Christopher Columbus* 375
The Viking explorers 1323
Vilenskii, D G: *The Russian school of soil cartography* . . . 1252
Villages 851, 880
Villecrosse, J: geodesy bibliography 216
Les villes du tiers monde 608
Vilnay, Z, *comp*: *The new Israel atlas* . . . 989
Vince, S W E: 'Towards a national atlas' 957
Vindard *See* Richard-Vindard
Vinland 346
Vinland Map 438
The Vinland map and the Tartar Relation 1323
The Vinland map . . . (Skelton) 1185

755

759

Witwatersrand University, African Climatology Unit 362

Wöhlbier, Herbert, *ed*: *Worldwide directory of mineral industries* . . . 718

et al: *World-wide directory of mineral industries education and research* 1384

Wolde-Mariam, Mesfin: *An atlas of Ethiopia* 136

Wollin, Goesta: *The ever-changing sea* 1167

Wolman, M G: 'River channel patterns' 1137

and L B Leopold: 'Flood plains' 1137

Wolstenholme, Gordon and Maeve O'Connor, *ed*: *Man and Africa* . . . 22

Wolstenholme, M J: *An encyclopaedia of the iron and steel industry* 470

Wolter, J A: 'Source materials for the history of American cartography' 869, 908

Wonders, W C, *ed*: *Canada's changing north* 294

Wood, Alan, *ed*: *The Pre-Cambrian and Lower Palaeozoic rocks of Wales* 1335

Wood, D: *Economic aspects of pig-meat marketing* 726

Wood, H J: *An agricultural atlas of Scotland* 27

Wood, H R B: *The British Isles* 1310
Europe 1310

Wood, J G and R J Williams: *The Australian environment* 188

Wood, L J: 'Perception studies in geography' 592

Wood, M: 'Visual perception and map design' 312
Foreign maps and landscapes 525

Wood, Michael: 'Human factors in cartographic communication' 909

Wood, P D: *Essays in geography for Austin Miller* 514

Wood, Peter A: *Character of a conurbation* . . . 338

Wood, W D and R S Thoman, *ed*: *Areas of economic stress in Canada* . . . 294

Wood 527, 528
Wood 1378

Wood-Jones, F: *Corals and atolls* . . . 1016

Woodrow Wilson International Center for Scholars 480

Woods, B M: 'A continuing need: education for map librarianship' 905
'Map cataloging' 325, 357, 905

Woods, C S: *Native and introduced freshwater fishes* (New Zealand) 1113

Woods, E G: *The Baltic region* . . . 147

Woods, K S: *The development of country towns in the south-west Midlands* . . . 726

Woods Hole Oceanographic Institution 412, 970, 1348

Woods Hole Oceanographic Institutition atlas series 1348

Wool 782, 832
Wool . . . , H S Bell 782
Wool knowledge 782
Wool science review 782
The wool trade directory of the world 782

Wooldridge, S W 1094, 1349
The geographer as scientist . . . 545, 1349
ed: *Provinces of England* . . . (Fawcett) 512
and W G East: *The spirit and purpose of geography* 703, 1222, 1349
and Frederick Goldring: *The Weald* 372
and D L Linton: *Structure, surface and drainage in south-east England* 728, 865

Woolhope Naturalists' Field Club 673

Wootten *See* Greer-Wootten

Worcestershire, England, maps 1105

The Wordie Collection of Polar Exploration 1350

World Aeronautical Chart 312, 1351

World agricultural economics abstracts 377, 726, 1352

The world and the school 182

World animal review 524

World atlas of agriculture 1353

World atlas of mountaineering 1354

World beneath the oceans 1167

World bibliography of agricultural bibliographies 223

World cartography 308, 312, 905, 1355

The world cities 1356

World climatology . . . 154

World Conservation Committee, International Biological Programme 484

World Data Centres, International Geophysical Year 762

World Data Survey 47

World directory of Geographers 1357

World directory of highway officials 772

The world economic survey 1358

World fisheries abstracts 524, 1359

World fishing 1360

World Food Program 524

761